This book is to be returned on or before
the last date stamped below.

2 1 NOV 1986

1 2 NOV 1986

- 4 JAN 1989

-3 JAN 1991

1 7 DEC 1986

86/412
due 11/5/87 -

1 5 FEB 1989

1 4 NOV 1990

2 1 APR 1988

LIBREX —

The Ventilation of
South African Gold Mines

THE MINE VENTILATION SOCIETY
OF SOUTH AFRICA

EDITORIAL COMMITTEE

J. H. J. Burrows
R. Hemp
F. H. Lancaster
J. H. Quilliam

1974

ISBN: 0 620 00771 0

622.42
MIN

2nd Print by Klem-Lloyd Lithographers

Preface

R. C. J. GOODE

President, Chamber of Mines of South Africa

The effort and expertise that have gone into this long-awaited work, both by the Editorial Committee and the authors — all leaders in their various fields — deserve our thanks and our praise. Mine ventilation, with its attendant studies, is very important to the efficient operation of our mines, especially the deeper ones. This lucid publication, following on so aptly where Mr W. L. le Roux's well-received *Mine Ventilation Notes for Beginners* left off, will undoubtedly meet the demand for a readily understood reference book on a higher level. Being based on fundamentals, it has the big advantage that it will not date with the years. As I see it, this work has two main functions. It will be of educational assistance to those furthering their studies and it will be of particular value to those preparing themselves for examinations, and it will be a reference for all officials, from the Mine Manager downwards. I offer my congratulations to those concerned with the production of this useful textbook, which I am sure will be eagerly received by the industry.

Introduction

R. HEMP

Group Ventilation Engineer, Rand Mines Limited

Despite the advantages of a relatively low geothermal gradient and a temperate climate, South African gold mines are faced with considerable ventilation problems. These arise primarily because of the depth of the mines and the necessity for using water for dust suppression purposes; methane is also found on some mines, and siliceous dust is a problem on all the mines.

The magnitude of the ventilation problem faced by South African gold mines can be gauged from the following statistics.

A total air quantity of about 26 000 m³/s is circulated through 43 mines. Of this air quantity about 7 000 m³/s is filtered. More than 8 000 000 tons of rock are broken per month, and just under 280 000 persons work underground during the main working shift. In 16 of the 43 mines large underground cooling plants are used, the installed cooling capacity on individual mines varying from 1 760 kW to 38 700 kW, with a total installed cooling capacity of 160 000 kW. Despite the provision of both air and cooling the average stope wet-bulb temperature during the summer months is just over 29°C, and all men doing physical work in high temperatures are acclimatized. It is estimated that 250 000 kW of electrical power at an annual cost of R10 million is used to drive main fans and cooling plants.

Naturally this requires trained ventilation personnel, and some 500 people employed on the mines, in Group head offices, and in research organizations are concerned directly with mine ventilation. The Chamber of Mines operates a very active Ventilation Training Section which is concerned with the training of both new recruits and experienced ventilation officials.

Very few textbooks have been published dealing with mine ventilation, and there has been none dealing specifically with the ventilation of South African gold mines. It was to fill this gap that the Mine Ventilation Society decided some time ago to produce such a textbook.

Progress was slow, however, and several factors combined to change considerably the final form of the book. The first was the publication of W. L. le Roux's excellent *Mine Ventilation Notes for Beginners*. This was published shortly after the introduction of SI units in South Africa, and it was this change in the system of units which made it necessary for two Chamber of Mines publications dealing with mine ventilation to be revised and reprinted. These two publications are *Routine Mine Ventilation Measurements* (previously *Quality of Mine Air*), and A. W. T. Barenbrug's *Psychrometry and Psychrometric Charts*. It was decided that this textbook should complement these publications, and because of this the book contains, for example, no chapter on mine gases.

Sixteen authors have been responsible for twenty-one chapters in the book, and all are experts in their respective fields. They have devoted a considerable amount of their time to writing their contributions, and the Mine Ventilation Society is extremely grateful to them for all their efforts.

The Society's sincere thanks and appreciation are also due to:

Mr J. H. Quilliam, who has been chairman of the textbook committe for most of its life, and has spent so much of his time on the book.

Mr J. H. J. Burrows, who spent a great deal of time assisting with the editing of the book.

Mr F. H. Lancaster, who assisted considerably in the work of editing, and in addition, compiled the Index.

The Chamber of Mines of South Africa for their continued support and willing financial assistance.

Contents

Symbols

The following symbols are used. Where additional symbols and variations in the standard symbols are used, they are identified in the individual chapters concerned.

Symbols

A = area (m²)
a = acceleration (m/s²)
B = psychrometric constant (°C⁻¹)
C_p = thermal capacity (kj/kg °C)
C = perimeter (m)
D, d = diameter (m) or dimension (m)
E = voltage (V)
e = vapour pressure (kPa)
F = energy loss due to friction (J/kg)
g = gravitational acceleration (m/s²)
H = height (m)
H = enthalpy (kJ/kg)
h = coefficient of heat transfer (W/m² °C)
I = current (amperes)
K = friction factor (Ns²/m⁴)
k = conductivity (W/m °C)
L = length (m)
M = mass flow rate (kg/s)
m = mass (kg)
n = number
P = absolute pressure (kPa or Pa)
p_f = fan pressure loss or gain (Pa or kPa)

p = pressure loss (Pa or kPa)
Q = volume flow rate (m³/s)
q = heat transfer rate (kJ/s or kW)
R = electrical resistance (ohms)
R = gas constant (J/kg K)
R = resistance coefficient (Ns²/m⁸)
R_e = Reynolds number
r = radius (m), moisture content (g/kg or kg/kg)
S = rubbing surface (m²)
S = sigma heat (kJ/kg or J/kg)
s = entropy of fluid (J/kg K)
T = absolute temperature (K)
t = temperature (°C)
U = overall heat transfer coefficient (W/m² °C)
u = velocity (m/s)
V = velocity (m/s), volume (m³)
v = specific volume (m³/kg)
W = work (J/kg or Nm/kg)
w = density (kg/m³)
x = thickness (m)
Z = elevation (m)

Greek Letters

$\triangle$ = difference
μ = dynamic viscosity (Ns/m², kg/ms, Pa s)
η = efficiency
ϵ = emissivity

v = kinematic viscosity (m/s²)
λ = latent heat (kJ/kg)
ϕ = relative humidity

Subscripts

1, 2... = different points, phases or conditions	n = station or point
a = air	o = outside
C = convection	R = radiation
db = dry-bulb	r = refrigerant
F = friction	s = surface
f = fan	st = standard
i = inside or input	t = total or tube
L = latent	w = water
m = mean	wb = wet-bulb
	x = point

1 Duties and Organization of Ventilation Services

W. L. LE ROUX

Productivity Manager, Buffelsfontein Gold Mining Co., Ltd.

1   INTRODUCTION

The ultimate objective of mine ventilation departments is to ensure suitable environmental conditions in working places at an economic cost.

The control of dust, heat and gases and the efficient distribution of the available ventilating air together with many other services applied effectively, assist in the efficient production of gold.

Regulation 2.16.1 of the Mines and Works Regulations of the Republic of South Africa provides, *inter alia,* that:

At every controlled metalliferous mine and at every controlled diamond mine, when the total number of persons employed in the workings on any one shift exceeds 1 000, the manager shall appoint in writing one or more competent scheduled persons who shall be the holder of a certificate recognized by the Government Mining Engineer whose principal duty it shall be to examine and report to the manager on—

(*a*)   all matters relating to the mine's water supply, its quality, distribution and use,

(*b*)   the condition of the necessary appliances for using water at each working place and elsewhere,

(*c*)   the dust sampling of the mine, more particularly as regards development ends, and

1

(*d*)   the conditions of the mine relating to ventilation and health, more particularly as regards the amount of air supplied during the interval after blasting and before entry and during the working shift in all development ends and working places in which there is no through ventilation current.

The "competent person" referred to above is officially known as a Dust Inspector, and all that small and shallow mines need to do in practice is to comply with the regulation. Large and deep mines, however, go far beyond these requirements by instituting a Ventilation Department under a qualified Chief Ventilation Officer or Ventilation Superintendent, or in some cases Ventilation Engineers. Furthermore, Mining Groups employ Group Ventilation Engineers who act as consultants to the individual mines. In some instances the Group Ventilation Engineer has a staff consisting of specialized persons who are employed to carry out special investigations and experiments on the mines.

The size and importance of a ventilation department on a gold mine depends on a variety of factors such as the size and depth of the mine, the geothermic gradient, whether the mine is static or expanding, and the attitude of the management which determines whether the department should act purely in a technical advisory capacity or whether it should also have executive duties and powers.

Some idea of the magnitude of the organization required to control the ventilation of South African gold mines can be obtained from the statistics for 1952 supplied by Barcza.[1] Some comparable figures are given for 1972 to indicate how the problem grew in twenty years due to the increasing scale of mining operations and the greater depths at which these operations were being performed.

Year	1952	1972
Number of mines in survey	55	44
Total tonnage mined/month	6 130 000	8 230 000
Number of mines deeper than 2 440 m	7	12
Depth of deepest mine below surface	3 010 m	3 428 m
Highest virgin rock temperature encountered in development	47,2°C	52,4°C
Total air circulated m³/s at 1,2 kg/m³	11 700	24 550
Air quantity/1 000 tons mined/month, m³/s . . .	2,29	2,98
Air per person, m³/s	0,050 5	0,087

At present the total annual working cost of mine ventilation is probably considerably greater than R10 000 000, of which more than half is the cost of electric power. If, because of inefficient control or distribution of the available air, it should be necessary to increase all the air currents circulating through existing airways in the mines by only ten per cent, the effect of which would not be detected without the use of instruments, power costs would increase by 33 per cent or approximately R2 000 000 per annum. This figure gives some indication of the importance of efficient ventilation control.

2   STAFF REQUIREMENTS

The size of the staff required for the ventilation department of a gold mine depends on the scope of its duties and responsibilities and on the severity of the problems on the particular mine.

The minimum requirement is sufficient personnel to visit each working place once in three months in order to comply with the dust sampling demanded by the Regulations, and to do the dust counting and clerical work involved. On deep mines, however, considerably more personnel are required in order to give constant attention to air control and to investigate heat problems. On mines where occurrences of explosive gas are frequent, additional staff are also required in order to cope with gas testing and the training of mining personnel in this work. Larger mines often employ one or two assistants, usually female, specifically for the treatment and evaluation of dust samples and other office work.

On some mines the ventilation department only recommends where ventilation doors and stoppings, development fans or dust filters have to be installed, or other work has to be done by other departments. On other mines, however, the ventilation department has its own personnel of timbermen, usually in the charge of a shiftboss, to execute this kind of work.

It is also the practice on a few mines to delegate the control of compressed air to the ventilation officer, who is allowed additional personnel for this purpose.

The total white labour force of a mine ventilation department can thus consist of anything from one to twenty persons, depending on circumstances, and in addition to this there may be a Bantu labour force of between ten and two hundred employed as personal assistants, door attendants and fire patrols and in timbering, bratticing or calcium chloride gangs.

3   DISPOSITION OF VENTILATION PERSONNEL

On a smallish mine the Chief Ventilation Officer has a number of assistants of whom one is the senior assistant who acts in his place when he is away.

The efficient distribution of work and responsibilities on a large deep mine, is however, a more involved matter. A disposition of the European personnel on such a mine, which also employs specialists on dust, refrigeration and gases, is shown below.

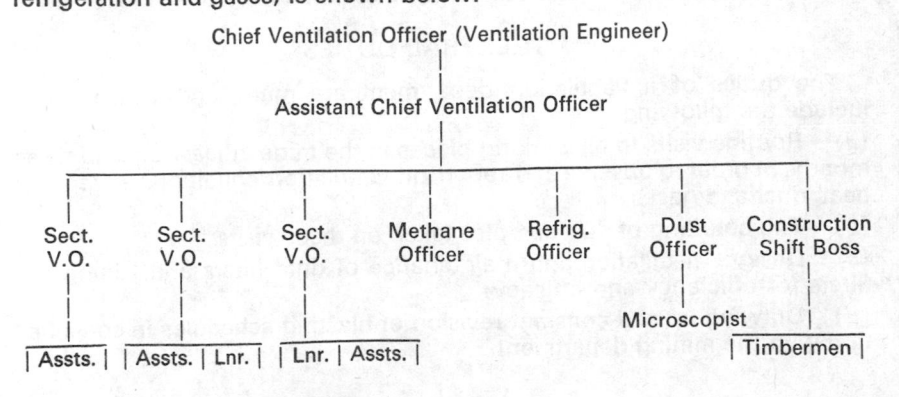

The assistants carry out regular observations of underground conditions relating to air flow, temperatures, gas, water, dust and ventilation appliances, and enter the results on suitable forms or in books before reporting to their seniors.

Each Sectional Ventilation Officer is responsible for the ventilation of a section of a mine. He studies the reports of his assistants and adds his remarks and recommendations before countersigning the reports and forwarding them to the relevant executive officials. In addition to doing as much routine observation in working places as his time allows, he also investigates all local problems occurring in his section and does a limited amount of planning. The specialists perform routine work and investigations on specific problems in their field.

The Assistant Chief Ventilation Officer organizes and controls the work of the sectionals, specialists and the timbermen. He assists the sectionals in the investigation of all difficult problems and assists the Chief with his planning. He is also responsible for the training of staff.

The Chief Ventilation Officer, apart from being in final control of everything that happens in his department, has the main duty of planning and constantly replanning the ventilation of his mine, while maintaining liaison with other departments and keeping costs down to a minimum.

4   STATUS

The status of a person or a department is a rather abstract concept which is not easily defined or measured. In everyday life the status of a person is judged largely by the remuneration he receives from his employer in relation to the remuneration paid to other employees in the same or a similar firm. However, the status of a unit in a large organization depends on its effectiveness in assisting the organization as a whole to achieve its objectives.

The status of a ventilation department depends to a very large extent on the magnitude of the ventilation problems on the mine concerned, and on the success it achieves in overcoming these problems. The latter depends not only on the capabilities and experience of the members of the staff, but also on the support the department gets from and the authority delegated to it by management, and on the co-operation of other departments.

Thus the status of a ventilation department depends on its effectiveness and its effectiveness depends to a large extent on the status conferred on it.

5   GENERAL DUTIES

The duties of a ventilation department are many and varied. They include the following:

(a)   Routine visits to all working places in the mine at least once in three months in order to observe and report on ventilation conditions as regards heat, dust and gases.

(b)   The counting of dust samples taken on these visits.

(c)   Design, installation and maintenance of dust filters and testing the filters for efficiency and efficacy.

(d)   Drawing up and constant revision of blasting schedules in consultation with the mining department.

(e)   Observation and plotting of virgin rock temperatures in order to determine the geothermic gradient in the mine, from which the rock temperatures in unexplored areas of the mine may be predicted.

(f)   Constant checking of the distribution of air flow and alteration where necessary to suit changing circumstances. A constant check must be kept on the loss of air by leakage or other causes.

(g)   In deep mines the effect of heat must be mitigated as far as possible. Where the maintenance of dry intake airways forms part of this programme, steps must be taken to keep them dry while at the same time taking measures to prevent the dust on the footwalls of these airways becoming airborne.

(h)   Constant checks of the supply of industrial water as to availability, cleanliness (silica dust content) and pressure, and as to its use in dust allaying appliances. At the same time every possible action must be taken to prevent the wastage of water.

(i)   Checking of rock drills and drill steel to see whether they conform to the requirements of mine regulations and do not produce any avoidable dust.

(j)   Periodic sampling and testing of drinking water for bacterial impurities.

(k)   Taking gas samples wherever unhealthy or dangerous conditions may exist. The sampling of diesel locomotive exhaust fumes is required by law.

(l)   Reporting verbally on unhealthy or dangerous conditions to an official who is in a position to either improve conditions, or order the removal of workers to a safe place.

(m)   Conducting pressure surveys at suitable intervals in order to determine whether restrictions to the flow of air have occurred, or to determine how the air distribution can be improved. Return airways which are not normally used as travelling ways may also have to be examined at regular intervals.

(n)   Examination of main fans to determine whether they are operating effectively as well as efficiently. Tests have to be carried out to determine how the mine ventilation is affected when any single fan or combination of fans is stopped in order that instructions may be drawn up as to what action should be taken in case of the inadvertent stoppage of any fan or fans.

(o)   Allocation, installation, maintenance and checking of auxiliary fans and control of their movements by means of an efficient system of records.

(p)   Planning of refrigeration plants and regular checking of operational efficiency.

(q)   Determination of and, where necessary, the improvement of the re-entry intervals for the mine as a whole as well as for individual development ends and tramming haulages.

(r)   Attention to the ventilation of all permanent dead ends such as orepass crosscuts and shaft-bottom loading boxes and of all large excavations such as pump chambers and hoist chambers.

(s)   The institution and control of fire patrols and drawing up of "immediate action instructions" for use in case of mine fires, based on how a fire in any part of the mine will affect the rest of the mine.

(*t*)　To give specialized assistance during mine fires in planning the fighting of the fire and in maintaining safe conditions for the fire fighters and for workers elsewhere in the mine.

(*u*)　Issue of instructions concerning the testing for explosive gas, and training of mining and other personnel in the use of the safety lamp and sometimes also in the use of other instruments.

(*v*)　Inspection of waterblasts in all development ends and auxiliary air pipes in winzes.

(*w*)　Design, installation and maintenance of extraction systems for certain surface installations such as crusher plants, assay offices, welding shops, drill-sharpening shops, carpenters' shops and lamphouses.

(*x*)　Planning the future ventilation of the mine, including the calculation of future requirements with respect to shafts, airways, fans and air cooling plants.

All these duties, and many others, can be performed effectively and economically only if the Ventilation Department is staffed by a sufficient number of capable and well-trained men who are housed in suitable offices equipped with all the necessary instruments and reference books, and only if the senior members of the department are good organizers who maintain an effective liaison with all the other departments on the mine.

6　OFFICE ACCOMMODATION

Ventilation offices can either be centralized at the main office block or at the main shaft of the mine, or dispersed to the various working shafts. There are sound arguments in favour of both methods and the final choice is affected by various factors such as the geographical distribution of the shafts, the interdependence between the shafts as far as ventilation is concerned, the complexity of the ventilation problems and whether ventilation timbermen, fire patrols and safety lamp training at the various shafts fall directly or only indirectly under the ventilation department.

Some advantages of centralization are improved training and discipline, direct control of all activities and decisions by the more capable senior members of the department, better control of instruments and of dust counting and easier access to reference books and to reports and plans. Access to the heads of other departments is also more direct.

The main advantages of decentralization are more direct liaison with the less senior executives of the mining and engineering departments and better control of the activities of ventilation timbermen, fire patrols and door attendants. The members of the department delegated to the various shaft offices gain by the experience of having to take the final responsibility for many minor decisions.

The required size of the office accommodation depends mainly on the size of the staff. It is advisable for the Chief to have his own private office, while the First Assistant could either also have his own office, or could be in an office partitioned off from the general office. The remainder of the staff can either all be housed in one general office, or separate offices can be provided for each sectional ventilation officer and his staff.

In addition there should be a laboratory and a dark room for the treatment and assessment of dust samples, and a store for instruments, tools and materials.

7   EQUIPMENT

Each member of the staff must be equipped with a set of routine instruments, preferably kept in a suitable carrying case such as the one described by Turner,[2] including the following:

High-speed anemometer
Medium-speed anemometer
Anemometer extension rod
Stopwatch
Measuring tape
Whirling hygrometer
Kata thermometer
Heating device for kata

Aluminium dust or substitute
Rod for measuring machine water
   tube gap
Konimeter
Pressure gauge with hypodermic
   needles
Portable manometer

Apart from spare items of all these instruments, the department must have at its disposal a set of specialised instruments. At least some of these must be available on the mine, while in the case of others it is quite satisfactory if they are obtainable at short notice from a Group or industry laboratory.

These specialised instruments include:

Barometers and micro-barometers
Inclined manometers and micro-
   manometers
Recording manometers
Pitot tubes
Trailing hose at least 150 m long
Assman psychrometer
Clinical thermometers and rods for
   measuring rock temperatures
Electrical devices for temperature
   measurement

Recording thermometers
Vacuum pumps and vacuum gauge
Methanometer
Chemical gas detectors
Safety lamps
Microscopes and laboratory equip-
   ment
Thermal precipitators
Nephelometers
Deep cells
Tachometers or stroboscopes.

Apart from keeping all these instruments clean and in good mechanical repair, regular steps must be taken to check their calibration. In most cases an exact calibration can be carried out only by a properly equipped laboratory or workshop, but checking different instruments against one another serves a very useful purpose by indicating when instruments are due for calibration.

It is good practice to make one member of the staff, for example the microscopist, responsible for a regular, say monthly, inspection of all the instruments. Other members of the department would be responsible for checking instruments such as anemometers, stopwatches and hygrometers against each other also at monthly intervals.

8   REFERENCE LIBRARY

It is essential that each mine ventilation office should have sufficient reference books to cover all aspects of the work and to assist in the solution of all the problems that may occur. These should include:

Several books on mine ventilation, for example:
   Roberts, A. (Ed.). *Mine Ventilation.* London, Clever Hume, 1960.
   Buffalo Forge Co. *Fan Engineering.* 6th edition, edited by R. Jorgen-
      sen. Buffalo. N.Y. 1961.

Chamber of Mines of South Africa, *Routine Mine Ventilation Measurements.* Johannesburg, 1972.

Le Roux, W. L. *Mine Ventilation Notes for Beginners.* Johannesburg, Mine Ventilation Society of S.A. 1972.

A book on exhaust ventilation systems; for example:

Alden, J. L. *Design of Industrial Exhaust Systems.* New York, Industrial Press, 1970.

One or more books on dust; for example:

Drinker and Hatch. *Industrial Dust.* New York, McGraw-Hill, 1954.

Shapiro, H. A. (Ed.). *Pneumoconiosis,* Proceedings of the International Conference, Johannesburg, 1969. Cape Town, O.U.P., 1970.

A chemistry and physics textbook; for example:

Whitaker, J. W. *Mining Physics and Chemistry*

Psychrometric tables; for example:

Barenbrug, A. W. T. *Psychrometry and Psychrometric Charts.* 2nd edition. Johannesburg, Transvaal and O.F.S. Chamber of Mines, 1965.

A general textbook; for example:

Ashrae Guide and Data Book. New York American Society of Heating, Refrigerating and Air Conditioning Engineers.

Mathematical tables.

Transactions of various Mining and Metallurgical Congresses.

British Standard Specifications B.S. 848 (methods of testing fans) and B.S. 1042 (methods for the measurement of fluid flow in pipes).

In addition, the department should receive the most important journals of ventilation and mining societies including the Mine Ventilation Society of South Africa, the South African Institute of Mining and Metallurgy and the Association of Mine Managers of South Africa, and these should be accessible to all members of the staff. Lastly, the department should have access to a more comprehensive industry library and should regularly receive its acquisition and abstract lists.

9   FILING SYSTEM

It is essential that a ventilation office should have a good filing system so as to make technical and administrative information and past records readily accessible. There are various ways of arranging a filing system, but probably the most suitable way is the arrangement of files in alphabetical groups under various collective headings such as:

(a) Airways and Ducts
(b) Development Ends
(c) Diesels
(d) Dust
(e) Educational
(f) Fans
(g) Fires
(h) Gases
(i) Heat
(j) Instruments
(k) Meetings – Societies and Committees
(l) Personnel: leave and salaries
(m) Refrigeration
(n) Stopes
(o) Tips and Filters
(p) Ventilation Methods
(q) Water.

Several relevant files are grouped under each of these headings, e.g., under the heading "Dust" there could be separate files titled:

(i)	Air Washers	(v)	Electrostatic Precipitators
(ii)	Assay Office	(vi)	Lime and Manganese Dust
(iii)	Cloth Filters	(vii)	Properties of Dust
(iv)	Cyclones	(viii)	Reduction Works.

It is essential that all important information should be readily accessible, but it is just as important that unnecessary information should not be filed and that obsolete documents should regularly be cleared out of the files before they swell the filing system to such an extent that it becomes difficult to find something which is urgently required.

10   REPORT FORMS

The purpose of any routine inspection is to determine whether conditions in the working place concerned are satisfactory. If conditions are unsatisfactory, it is necessary to find the cause in order that remedial measures may be taken.

It must be remembered that when a report is made on a routine visit, the senior official who is to receive the report is probably inundated with written reports and will give it only a cursory glance unless it makes interesting reading or has something special about it which draws his attention. Notwithstanding this, however, the report must contain all the available information in order to form a complete record. Nothing of importance may be omitted for the sake of brevity.

The best way of complying with the above requirements is to draw up a suitable report form which allows for all the relevant information to be set out compactly but also in logical sequence.

Where possible, satisfactory standards must be indicated. The results of the previous visit to the same place should always be given because they usually serve a useful purpose by indicating improvement or deterioration. In most instances a sketch is also essential because it obviates lengthy descriptions and shows at a glance what would otherwise demand much explanation. Weaknesses should be highlighted by ringing, preferably in a different colour such as red, and recommendations should be stated clearly and concisely.

Separate report forms should be used for stopes, development ends, tips and loading boxes, assay offices, reduction works, diesel locomotives, auxiliary fan census and any other type of routine inspection. As an example, a copy of a suitable development report form is shown in Fig. 1 : 1. This type of form is usually made out in triplicate. The top copy is circulated to the manager and mine overseer for their comments and signatures and is then returned to the ventilation office for filing. It takes the place of the "book" called for in Regulation 2.16.1. The second copy is circulated with the first but is retained by the mine overseer, while a third copy is kept in the ventilation office until the top copy is returned, after which it is destroyed.

There are other methods of circulating ventilation reports. On some mines it is the practice to report only those conditions which are unsatisfactory. However, if this is done it is necessary, in order to comply with Regulation 2.16.1, to keep a record of the conditions at all the

ANONYMOUS GOLD MINING COMPANY LIMITED
DEVELOPMENT VENTILATION REPORT

Mine Overseer's Section ....

Date ....

PLACE	Ref.	Time	Work	DUST			MACHINES		DISTANCES					AIR QUANTITIES				AIR TEMPERATURES						KATAS		OBSERVER'S REMARKS
				In-take	Face	Re-turn	Water Press.	Water Tube Gap	Ex-haust	Force	Water Blast	Over Lap	Drain	Exhaust		Force		For. Del.		Face		Return		Face	30 m Back	
														Int.	Del.	Int.	Del.	Wet	Dry	Wet	Dry	Wet	Dry			

REMARKS AND SIGNATURES

VENTILATION OFFICER:

SECTION MANAGER:

MINE OVERSEER:

OBSERVER:

CIRCULATION: 1 Section Manager   2 Mine Overseer   3 Ventilation Department for Filing

Figure 1 : 1

working places inspected. This record must also be signed by the production officials in charge of the various working places.

One large mine records all the ventilation measurements made in a longwall section on a special tracing. This tracing is presented to the production officials concerned at a special meeting called for this purpose.

11   TRAINING OF STAFF

Time and money spent on training are usually amply repaid. A department cannot work efficiently if each of its members does not know exactly how to carry out his allotted tasks and if he does not understand why each task has to be carried out in a specific way.

Every person has a ceiling to which he is capable of being educated, depending on his intelligence, aptitude and interest. The careful selection of staff is therefore a prerequisite to effective training. A short written test on mathematics and scientific general knowledge can give a useful indication of a candidate's suitability. Some mines use a series of scientifically evolved aptitude tests.

The induction of a new man into a department is very important. If he has had no previous mining experience it is necessary first to explain to him safety precautions and the general principles of mining. This must be followed by several underground visits with an experienced guide who should not at this stage attempt to teach him anything about ventilation. Only after this induction period should the practical and theoretical training be started.

Training courses and programmes for all the different categories of ventilation personnel are organized by the Chamber of Mines.[4]

12   LIAISON

An effective ventilation department always strives to maintain close liaison with all other departments on the mine and in particular with the mining, engineering and survey departments.

Ventilation is not an end in itself, but is a tool which has to be applied as effectively and economically as possible to assist the mining department in the efficient production of gold. Ventilation arrangements have to be reviewed from time to time in order that they may always comply as far as possible with mining requirements. Many situations occur, however, where the method or timing of mining operations can, or even have to, be altered in order to fit in with ventilation facilities. It is obvious that, to obtain such co-operation, there has to be constant liaison between these two departments at all levels.

The ventilation department decides when, where and what size of appliances such as fans, refrigeration plants and dust filters are required, but it usually falls to the engineering department to install and maintain these appliances. Close co-operation is thus also required between these two departments.

It is essential for the ventilation department to be warned of imminent holings and also to consider whether the planning of new development work can be fitted in with ventilation arrangements. For these reasons close liaison with the survey department is essential.

The task of a ventilation official is unfortunately complicated by his having to act as an inspector whose unpleasant duty it very often is to make unflattering reports on the work of persons in other departments. This tends to make him just about as popular as a traffic inspector or a tax collector. Tact, firmness and absolute honesty are the only foundations on which he can build satisfactory personnel relationships in such circumstances, and he must shun the temptation of gaining cheap popularity by turning a blind eye to that which it is his job to see.

13   DIARISING

With his many and varied duties, it is difficult for a ventilation officer to remember them all at the right time. Some duties have for example to be carried out monthly and others quarterly or annually. Diarising is a very useful means for ensuring that nothing is forgotten.

This consists of a list of recurring duties followed by a column for each month of the year. An example of a diary for sectional ventilation officers is appended. During the course of each month he uses the list as a reminder, and at the end of the month he completes it. Answers usually consist of "Yes" or "No" or a number. He then takes it to his Chief to whom he explains any omissions and anomalies.

Similar diaries can be drawn up for other persons such as the microscopist and the Chief himself, or the latter two can be combined to cover all office duties.

14   REFERENCES

1   Barcza, M. Some statistical information about the ventilation of South African gold mines. *Bull. Mine Vent. Soc. S. Afr.* Vol. 6, 1953, p. 4.
2   Turner, B. L. An improved ventilation case. *J. Mine Vent. Soc. S. Afr.* Vol. 11, 1958, p. 102.
3   Le Roux, W. L. Training of ventilation personnel. *J. Mine Vent. Soc. S. Afr.* Vol. 10, 1957, p. 186.
4   Burrows, J. The selection and training of ventilation officials. *J. Mine Vent. Soc. S. Afr.* Vol. 25, 1972, p. 225.

BIBLIOGRAPHY

Drummond, J. A., The duties and organization of a ventilation department. *Bull. Mine Vent. Soc. S. Afr.* Vol. 3, 1950, p. 106.

SECTIONAL VENTILATION OFFICER'S DIARY

	January	February	March
Instruments			
Instrument boxes in order ?	Yes	Yes	
Anemometers clean and in order ? . . .	Yes	Yes	
Checked anemometers against one another ? .	Yes	No	(x)
Hygrometers and socks clean and in order ? . .	Yes	Yes	
Kata and fingerstall clean and in order ? . . .	Yes	Yes	
Tapes in order ?.Check first 3 m	Except one	(x) Yes	
Water gauges in order ? Tubes airtight ? . . .	Yes	Yes	
Underground Work			
No. of permanent assts./Official learners . . .	2/1	2/2	
No. of U/G Shifts : Sect./P. Assts./Official learners	13/18/16	12/19/34	
No. of night shifts Sect./P. Assts./Official learners	−/ 2/ −	1/ 1/ 2	
Places working/inspected : Stope faces . .	26/10	26/8	
Rec. points . .	18/6	19/7	
Dev. ends . .	32/11	31/15	
Tips . . .	22/4	22/11	
Loading Boxes . .	8/1	8/−	(x)
No. of unsatisfactory places still to be checked .	3	1	
No. of working places *not* visited past 3 months .	9	4	
No. of heat stroke cases	—	—	
No. of filters on section/cleaned	8/2	(x) 8/8	
No. of cooling plants on section/checks . .	3/1	3/3	
Main fans and splits measured ?	Yes	Yes	
Fire patrols checked (6-monthly) ?	—	Yes	—
Speed of fans and motors checked and entered (6-monthly) ?	—	—	
Fan stoppage instructions in order ?	Yes	Yes	
Fan stoppage instructions understood by assts. ?	Yes	Yes	
Water and Gases			
No. of water samples taken	4	7	
No. of CO_2 samples (excl. diesels)	5	1	
Diesels checked (levels) ?	2 (19, 21)	3 (17, 18, 20)	
No. of methane occurrences entered in gas book .	Nil	One	
Drinking water tanks checked (3-monthly) ? .	—	—	(x)
Drinking water samples (12-monthly) ? . .	—	—	—
Airways			
Written report on all airways (6-monthly) ? . .	—	(x) Yes	—
Pressures on all doors (4-monthly) ?	—	—	(x)
Pressures entered on door plan ?	—	—	(x)
Water in intake airways reported to manager ? .	—	Yes	
Surface upcasts measured (3-monthly) ? . .	(x) Yes	—	—
Office			
Plans up-to-date (3-monthly) ?	Yes	—	—
Doors correct on plans ?	Yes	Yes	
Are all your re-entries in order ?	Not 24W	(x) Yes	
Index of small electric fans up-to-date ? . . .	Yes	Yes	
Initials of Section	ABC	ABC	
Initials of Chief	XYZ	XYZ	

NOTE: Items marked (x) have to be given urgent attention.

2 Elementary Statistics

ELIZABETH HARRIS

Formerly Statistician, Corner House Laboratories (1968) (Pty.) Ltd.

1   INTRODUCTION

In the course of their routine work mine ventilation officials record a large number of observations such as of dust concentrations, air velocities, wet kata readings and air temperatures. Unless these values are analysed and interpreted statistically, important trends might not be detected.

If full use is to be made of the data it is essential that they be analysed statistically. This is necessary for the comparison of sets of data, the analysis of the causes of certain phenomena, detection of trends and prediction of the results or effects of operations.

In general there are basically two kinds of measurements:

(a) those that are precise, e.g., the number of pages in this book, the number of children in a particular family, and

(b) those that are estimates, e.g., the fuel consumption of a car, the number of children in a typical South African family.

The first type of measurement can be made accurately, whereas the second is usually an average or other estimate of the true value. It is the second type of measurement which is of interest, and in this chapter an attempt will be made to show

(a) the variation to be expected about the average value, and

(b) the circumstances in which the result will change, and how this will happen, i.e. is the variable related to, or dependent upon, another variable, how does it change with time, and so on.

Much valuable information can be extracted from results by using statistical methods. Often this can mean that fewer readings are required and in some situations the statistician may obtain additional information without necessarily demanding more readings. The use of statistical methods means that one always has more confidence in the final results and conclusions. It has been said that there are "lies, damned lies, and statistics," so in order that acceptable methods are used to analyse the results of an experiment, the following outline is given of some useful techniques. (See Bibliography for suggestions to extend this knowledge.)

2   GRAPHICAL APPROACH

There are very few situations in which a graph cannot be used to present results. A graph often clarifies the picture that the observer has in mind, as well as providing a pictorial representation that is quickly absorbed by someone not closely connected with the experiment. Regardless of whether a graph is used in the final presentation, it is imperative that the observer should draw a graph for his own information before elaborate analysis is made.

There are numerous types of graphs and experience is the best guide as to which is the most useful in any situation. The following are some examples of commonly used graphs in ventilation departments.

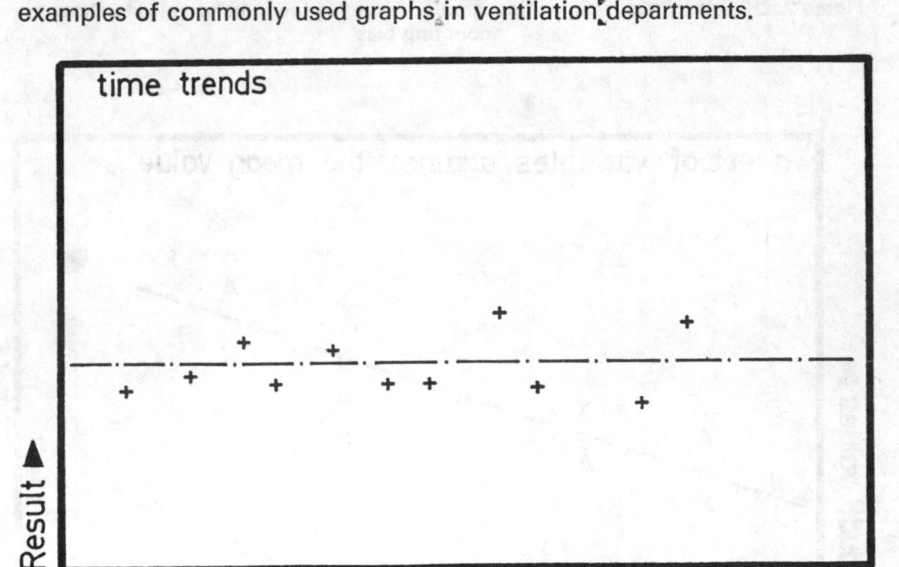

Figure 2 :1   To show quality control of temperature in an airway

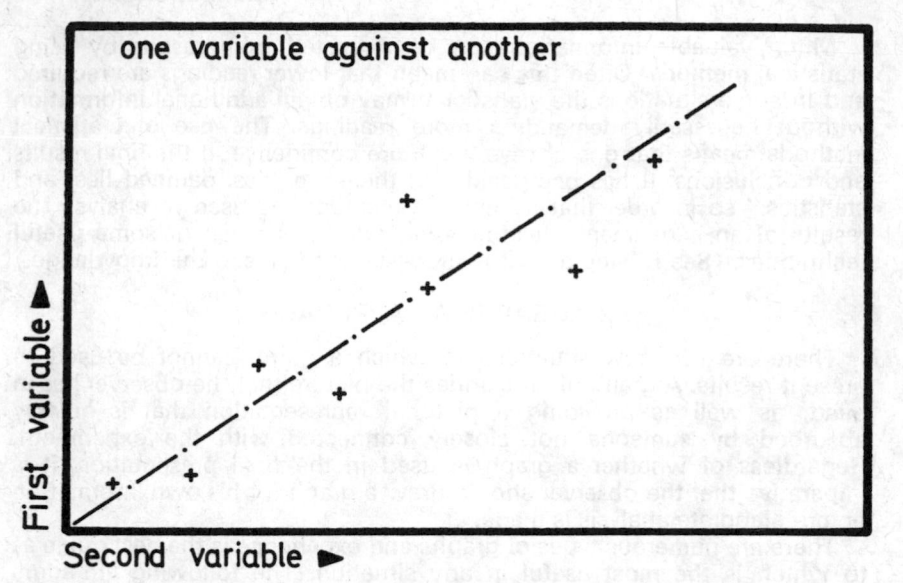

Figure 2:2   One microscopist against another counting the same samples to show any
counting bias

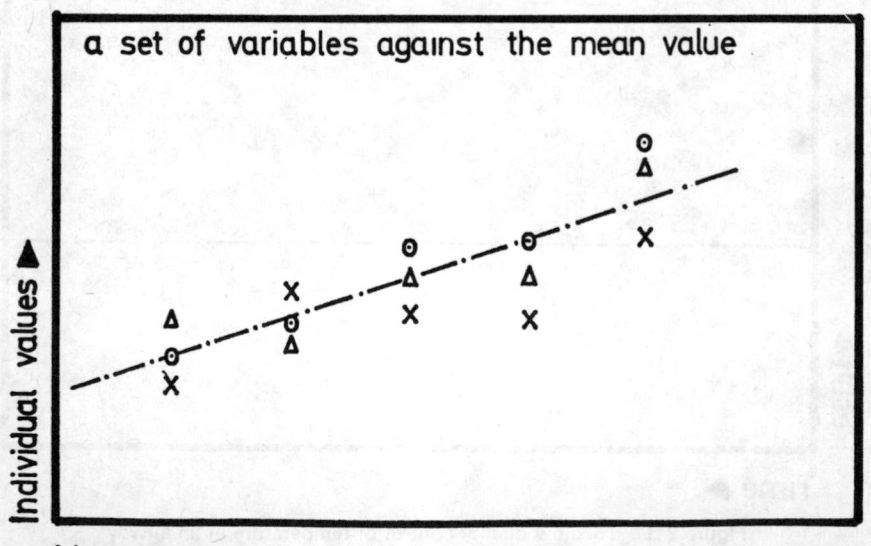

Figure 2:3   The comparison of three parallel-sampling thermal precipitators

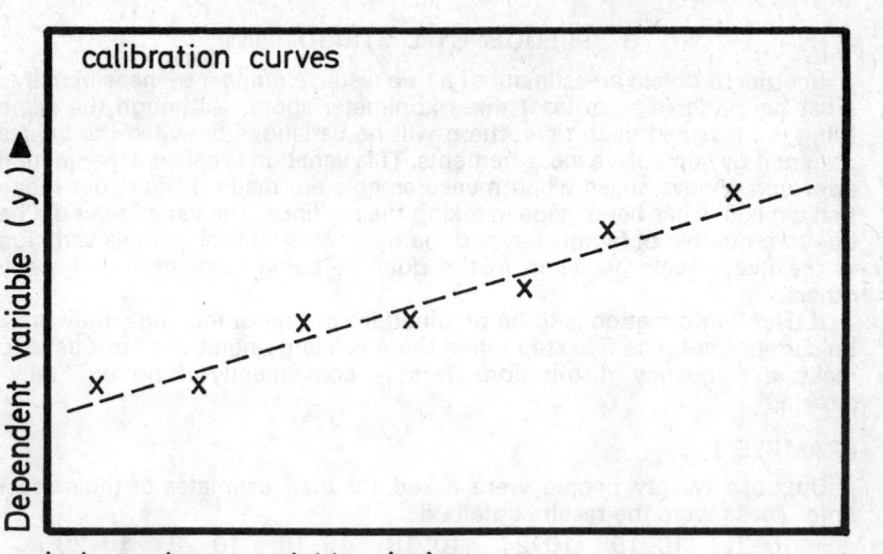

Figure 2:4   Calibrating an anemometer against an orifice plate

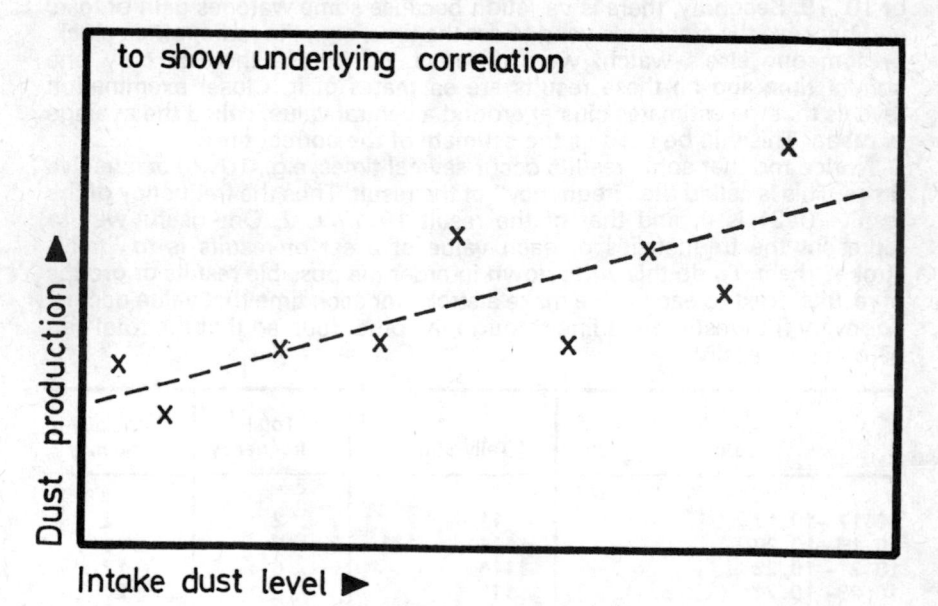

Figure 2:5   To show whether an increase in intake dust affects the dust production during a test of a dust-allaying device

3   FREQUENCY DISTRIBUTIONS

In order to obtain an estimate of a true result, a number of measurements must be made (e.g., at least three konimeter spots). Although the same thing is measured each time, there will be variations between the values obtained by successive measurements. This variation is called experimental error and always arises when measurements are made. It does not mean that a mistake has been made in taking the readings. The variation could be due to a number of factors beyond the observer's control such as variation in the instruments, variation in the quantity being measured, and many others.

If useful information is to be obtained from a set of readings, they must be summarized. The first step when there is a large number of results is to make a frequency distribution. This is conveniently done by "tally-stroking".

EXAMPLE 1

Suppose twenty people were asked for their estimates of the correct time. These were the results obtained:

10.21	10.19	10.24	10.18	10.19	10.23	10.20
10.22	10.20	10.21	10.20	10.19	10.21	10.22
10.17	10.20	10.21	10.20	10.23	10.19	

Firstly, there is a small variation because the time is given to the nearest minute. Each person had to estimate whether it was nearest to, e.g., 10.18 or 10.19. Secondly, there is variation because some watches gain or lose, and because the standards used to set the time, e.g., the radio, office clock, or someone else's watch, were different. Of course there is only one correct time and all these results are estimates of it. Closer examination reveals that the estimates cluster around a central value, called the average or mean. This will be used as the estimate of the correct time.

Notice too that some results occur several times, e.g., 10.20 occurs five times. This is called the "frequency" of the result. Thus the frequency of the result 10.21 is 4, and that of the result 10.17 is 1. One useful way to represent the frequencies of each value of a set of results is to "tally-stroke" them. To do this write down in order the possible results or groups of results. Next to each value make a stroke for each time that value occurs. For every fifth result put a line through the other four, so that the total can be obtained easily.

Value	Tally-strokes	Total frequency	Cumulative frequency
10.17—10.18	11	2	2
10.19—10.20	~~1111~~ 1111	9	11
10.21—10.22	~~1111~~ 1	6	17
10.23—10.24	111	3	20

This table represents the frequency distribution of the time estimates obtained. These results could then be plotted on the graphs below. It should be noted that

(a)   the boundaries of the histogram are midway between the class boundaries, e.g., the rectangle representing 9 has boundaries $10.18\frac{1}{2}$ and $10.20\frac{1}{2}$;

(b)   for the polygon, the frequencies are plotted at the mid-points of the class intervals.

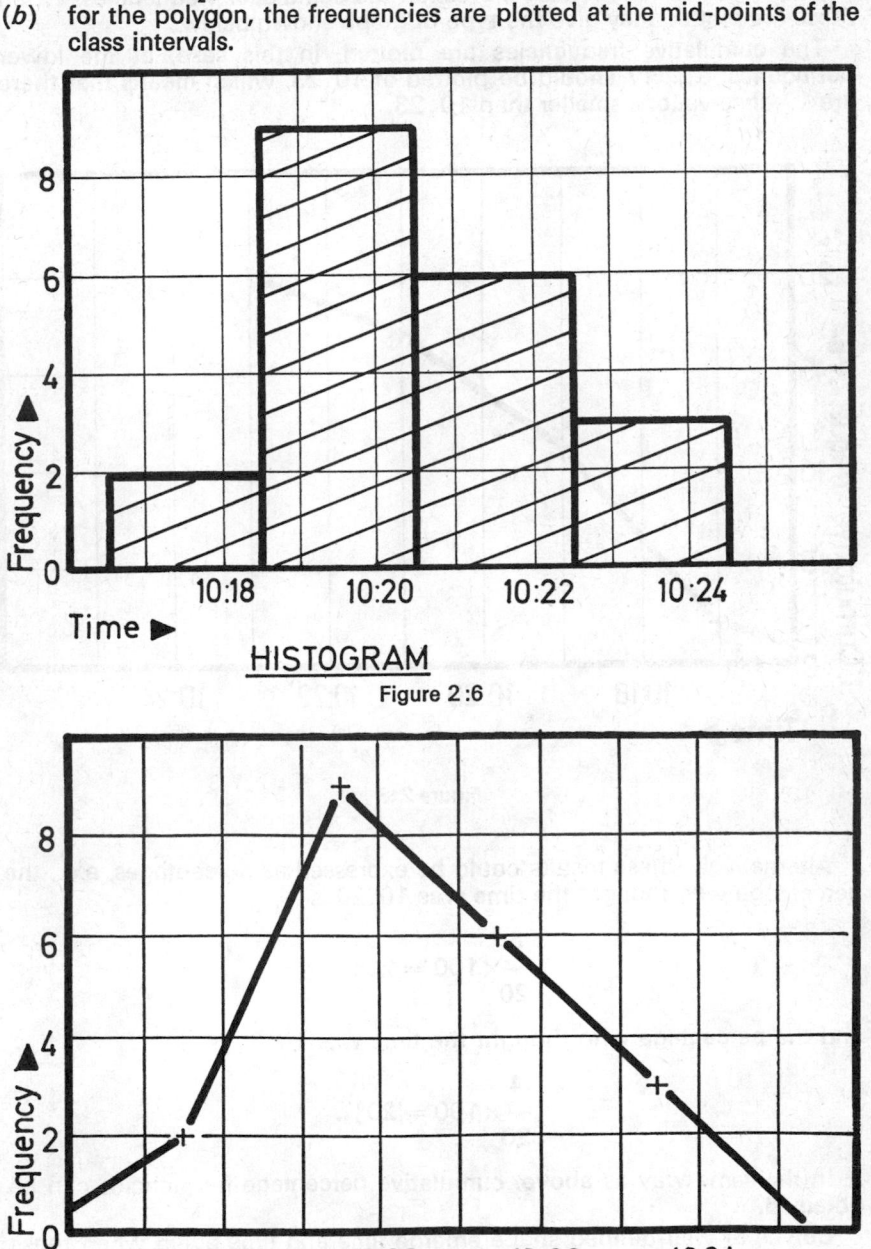

HISTOGRAM

Figure 2:6

Figure 2:7

In the last column of the table the frequencies are added together to give the number of results less than, e.g., 10.21, i.e., 11 results, and the number less than 10.23 (17). These are called the cumulative frequencies. When these are plotted they give the type of graph shown below.

The cumulative frequencies are plotted, in this case, at the lower boundaries, e.g., 17 should be plotted at 10.23, which means that there are 17 observations smaller than 10.23.

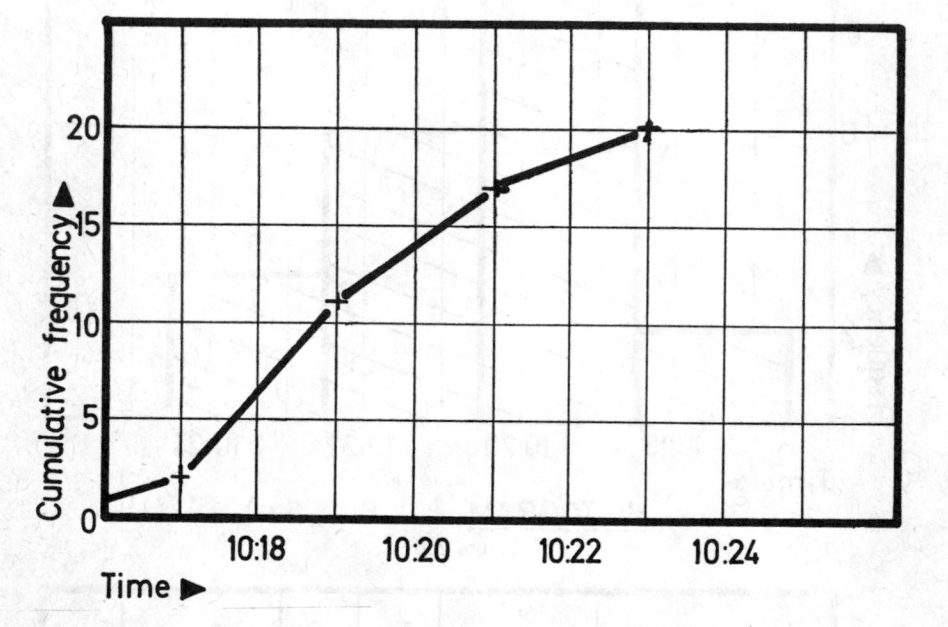

Figure 2 :8

Alternatively, these results could be expressed as percentages, e.g., the percentage who thought the time was 10.20 is

$$\frac{5}{20} \times 100 = 25\%,$$

and the percentage who thought the time was 10.21 is

$$\frac{4}{20} \times 100 = 20\%.$$

In the same way as above, cumulative percentage frequencies can be obtained.

Curves of well-defined shape emerge time and time again when these frequency distributions are made. The most usual is that which represent normal distribution.

3.1 *Normal distribution*

This is bell-shaped as shown below.

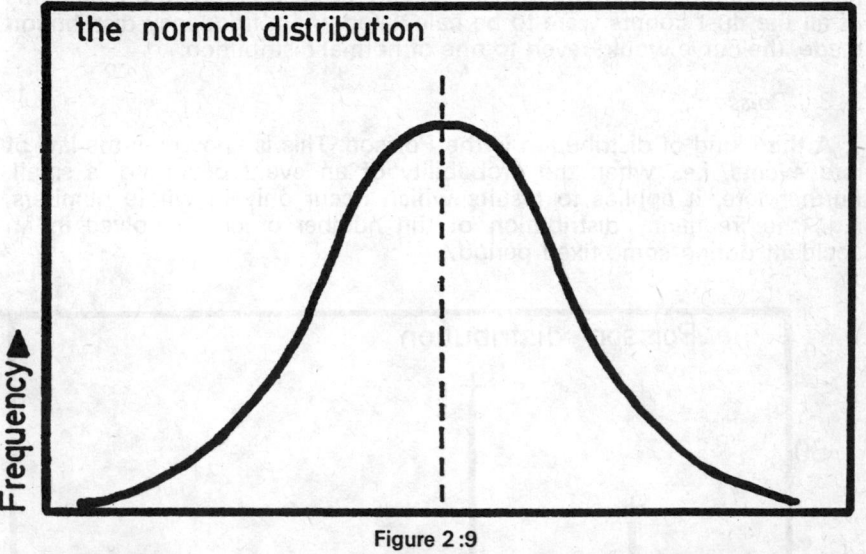

Figure 2 :9

It has a peak in the middle and tails off equally on both sides. The central value is the mean of the set of results. Notice that if the experimental variation is large, the results will be spread over a wide range; if the variation is small, the curve will have a narrow peak.

3.2 *Log-normal distribution*

One pattern that occurs in almost all dust measurements is the log-normal distribution curve shown below.

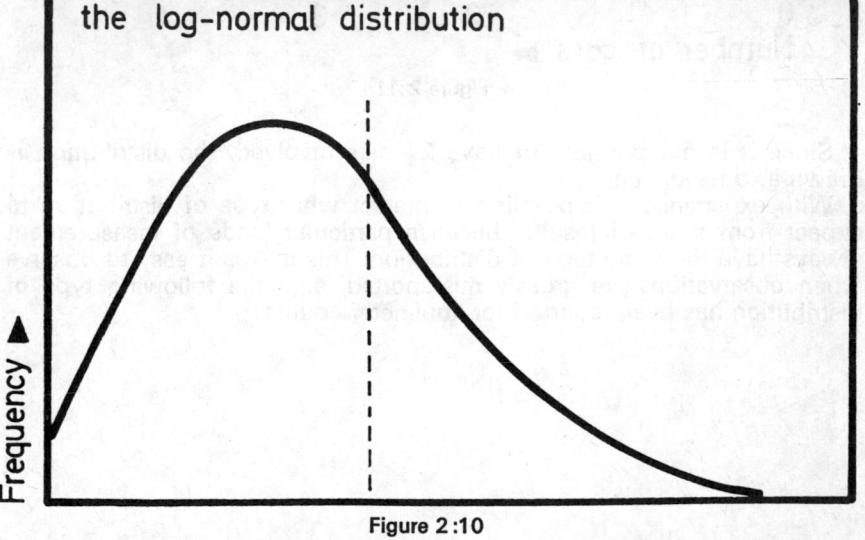

Figure 2 :10

It has a long tail on the right and the peak is not at the centre. This means, for example, that although the average dust count could be fairly low, very high counts would occasionally be recorded. If the logarithms of all the dust counts were to be calculated and a frequency distribution made, the curve would revert to one of normal distribution.

3.3 *Poisson*

A third kind of distribution is the Poisson. This is known as the law of rare events, i.e., when the probability of an event occurring is small. Furthermore, it applies to results which occur only in whole numbers, e.g., the frequency distribution of the number of cars involved in an accident during some fixed period.

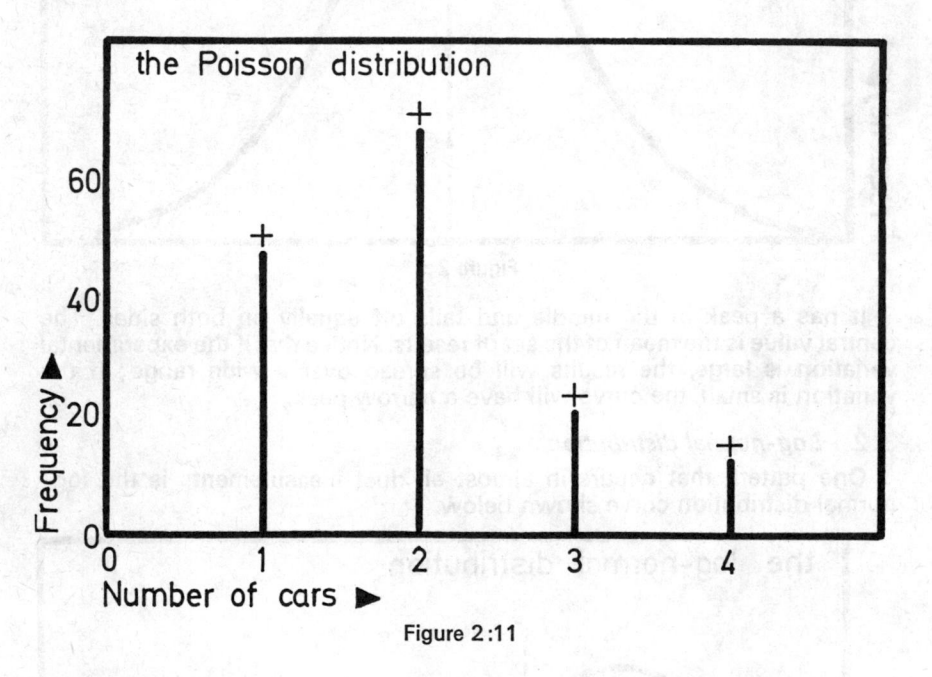

Figure 2:11

Since it is not possible to have $2\frac{1}{2}$ cars involved, the distribution is drawn as a needle chart.

With experience it is possible to predict what type of distribution to expect from a set of results, because particular kinds of measurement always have the same type of distribution. This makes it easy to observe when observations are grossly misreported, e.g., the following type of distribution has been reported for konimeter counts:

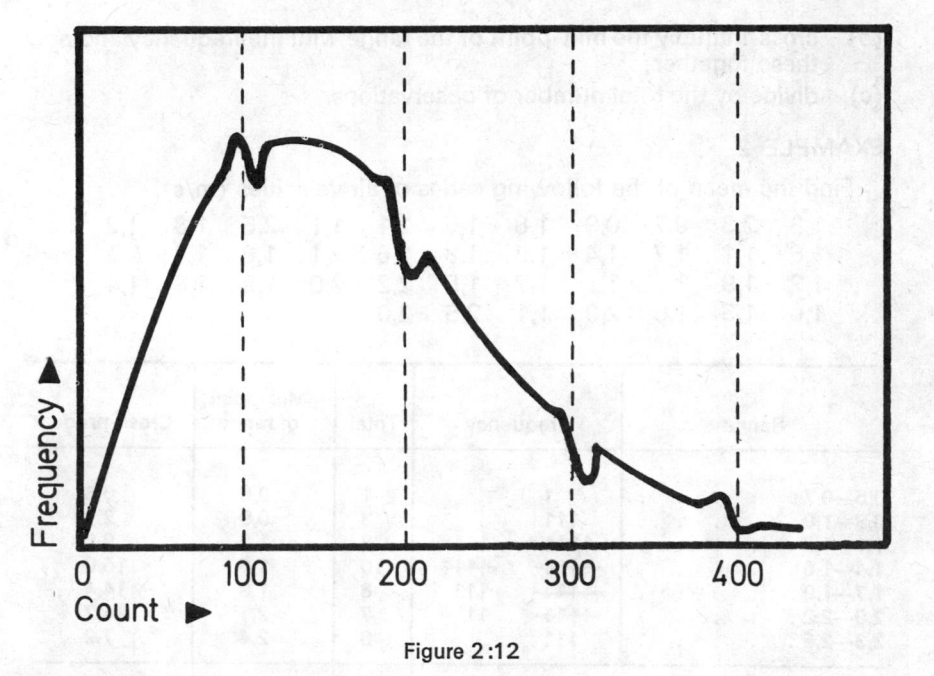

Figure 2:12

This leads one to suspect that results that should have been just greater than, say, 200 p/ml were reported as being just less than 200 p/ml.

4   THE BEST ESTIMATE OF THE CORRECT VALUE

In the estimate of the time in Example 1, it was seen that the observations clustered around the value 10.20. This will be close to the true time and so the average or mean is chosen as an estimate of the correct value. The mean is a particular "central measure".

It is defined as follows:

$$\text{Mean} = \frac{\text{sum of all observations}}{\text{total number of observations taken}}$$

If each result taken is given a symbol, $x_1, x_2 \dots$ then this formula can be represented by:

$$\bar{x} = \frac{1}{n} \sum_{i=1}^{n} x_i = \frac{1}{n} (x_1 + x_2 \dots + x_n)$$

where n is the total number of results, the Greek symbol Σ (Sigma) means "the sum of" and $\bar{x}$ stands for the mean of x_i.

If there are a large number of observations it would take too long to add them all together. In this case the observations are grouped together as follows:

(a)   tally-stroke the frequency distribution in convenient size ranges;

(b)   cross-multiply the mid-point of the range with the frequency and add these together;

(c)   divide by the total number of observations.

EXAMPLE 2

Find the mean of the following series of air velocities (m/s).

```
1,3   2,3   0,7   0,9   1,8   1,5   2,1   1,1   2,5   1,8   1,2
1,6   1,1   1,7   1,4   1,5   1,8   1,6   2,1   1,6   1,7   2,2
1,2   1,9   1,0   1,1   1,7   1,5   2,2   2,0   1,5   1,8   1,4
1,0   1,3   1,5   2,0   1,1   2,5   2,0
```

Range	Frequency		Total	Mid-point of range	Cross-product
0,5—0,7	1		1	0,6	0,6
0,8—1,0	111		3	0,9	2,7
1,1—1,3	+++++	111	8	1,2	9,6
1,4—1,6	+++++	+++++	10	1,5	15,0
1,7—1,9	+++++	111	8	1,8	14,4
2,0—2,2	+++++	11	7	2,1	14,7
2,3—2,5	111		3	2,4	7,2
Totals			40		64,2

$$\text{Mean} = \frac{64,2}{40} = 1,6 \text{ m/s}$$

It will be noticed that for the normal distribution the mean is the central value; however, for the log-normal distribution this is not so since there are a few very high values. There are other central measures which would be closer to the peak in this case. One of these is the *median*. This is defined to be the middle value when all the readings are put in order, i.e., 50 per cent of the readings will be less than the median and 50 per cent will be greater. It is easy to find the median from a cumulative percentage frequency graph as it is the value corresponding to 50 per cent.

The *mode* is the value at which most readings occur. In the example above the mean, median and mode all fall in the interval 1,4 — 1,6. For the theoretical normal distribution, all three coincide.

5   DISPERSION

Once the correct value has been estimated, the extent of the scatter around this value must be estimated. A result will obviously be more reliable when the scatter is small than when it is large. However, the amount of scatter often depends on the magnitude of the result.

For a normal distribution (or if the data can be transformed, e.g., by taking logs, to make it normal) the measure of the scatter may be given by the standard deviation, σ, which is thus a particular measure of dispersion.

This is expressed by the formula

$$\sigma = \sqrt{\frac{1}{n-1}\left[\sum_{i=1}^{n}(x_i-\bar{x})^2\right]}$$

If this formula is examined it will be seen that basically it represents the average of all the "distances" of the observations from the mean result.

If there are a small number of observations (e.g., less than 20) or if a calculator is available, the following method is most commonly used to calculate the standard deviation:

$$\sigma = \sqrt{\frac{1}{n-1}\left[\sum_{i=1}^{n}(x_i-\bar{x})^2\right]} = \sqrt{\frac{1}{n-1}\left[\sum_{i=1}^{n}x_i^2-n x^2\right]}$$

The use of this formula is illustrated in the following example.

EXAMPLE 3

Find the standard deviation of the wet kata readings:

    6,1   6,2   5,9   6,1   6,1   6,4   6,1   6,2   6,3   6,2

(a) Mean, $\bar{x}$ $= 6,16$

(b) Σx^2 $= 379,62$

(c) $n\bar{x}^2$ $= 379,456$

(d) $\Sigma x^2 - n\bar{x}^2$ $= 0,164$

(e) $\dfrac{\Sigma x^2 - n\bar{x}^2}{n-1}$ $= 0,018\ 2$

(f) $\sigma = \sqrt{\dfrac{\Sigma x^2 - n\bar{x}^2}{n-1}} = 0,13$

If there are a large number of results, the following method of calculating standard deviation should be used:

$$\sigma = \sqrt{\frac{1}{n-1}\left[\sum_{i=1}^{n}x_i^2 f_i - n\bar{x}^2\right]}$$

where x_i is the mid-point of a small range, and f_i is the frequency of observations in that range.

EXAMPLE 4

Find the standard deviation of the following:

2,3	2,1	3,1	2,6	4,2	2,9	3,9	3,2	1,2	2,0
2,1	2,4	1,7	3,1	3,5	1,9	3,2	2,5	1,8	2,3
2,7	2,8	1,9	2,7	3,8	3,3	3,0	3,5	1,9	2,9
2,7	2,0	4,5	3,7	4,1	4,4	3,3	3,0	3,7	3,6

Range	Frequency	Total (1) f_i	Mid-point (2) x_i	Square of mid-point (3) x^2_i	Cross-product (1) x (2) $x_i f_i$	Cross-product (1) x (3) $x_i^2 f_i$
1,0—1,4 . .	1	1	1,2	1,44	1,2	1,44
1,5—1,9 . .	‖‖‖	5	1,7	2,89	8,5	14,45
2,0—2,4 . .	‖‖‖ 11	7	2,2	4,84	15,4	33,88
2,5—2,9 . .	‖‖‖ 111	8	2,7	7,29	21,6	58,32
3,0—3,4 . .	‖‖‖ 111	8	3,2	10,24	25,6	81,92
3,5—3,9 . .	‖‖‖ 11	7	3,7	13,69	25,9	95,83
4,0—4,4 . .	111	3	4,2	17,64	12,6	52,92
4,5—4,9 . .	1	1	4,7	22,09	4,7	22,09
Totals . .		40			115,5	360,85

(a) Tally-stroke as above

(b) Mean, $\bar{x} = \dfrac{115,5}{40} = 2,887\ 5$

(c) $\Sigma x^2 f$ $= 360,85$

(d) $n\bar{x}^2$ $= 333,506\ 25$

(e) $\Sigma x^2 f - n\bar{x}^2$ $= 27,343\ 75$

(f) $\dfrac{1}{n-1}(\Sigma x^2 f - n\bar{x}^2) = 0,701\ 12$

(g) σ $= 0,837$

As mentioned earlier, the variation of a set of results is often dependent on the mean value, i.e., the variation is larger for a larger mean. In this case the *coefficient of variation* (C.V.) expresses the standard deviation as a percentage of the mean.

$$C.V. = \frac{standard\ deviation}{mean} \times 100$$

$$= \frac{0,837}{2,887\ 5} \times 100$$

$$= 29,0\%$$

6   LIMITS

(a)   To a set of readings

For a normally-distributed population, it is known that 66 per cent of the readings will be within $\pm$ 1 standard deviation of the mean; 95 per cent will be within $\pm$ 2 standard deviations, and 99 per cent will be within $\pm$ 3 standard deviations (These figures are close approximations).

This fact is used to put control limits on a set of results. For example, if 95 per cent limits are required, it is known that 95 in every 100 results will

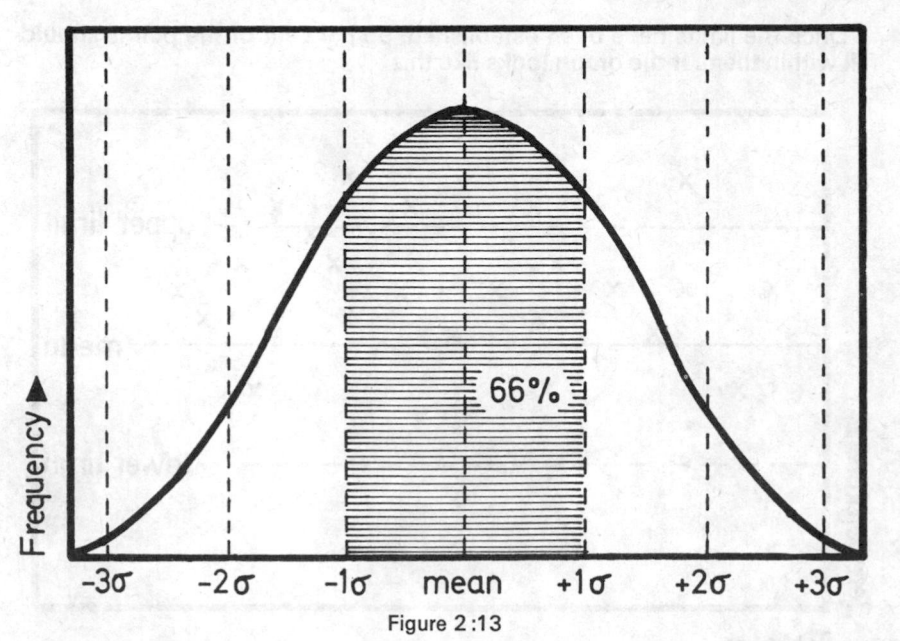

Figure 2:13

fall within these limits and 5 will fall outside. If more than 5 consistently fall outside, then these results are "out of control" and there have been changes in the experimental set-up, other than accounted for by experimental variation.

For example, suppose a set of wet-bulb temperatures were taken in an airway. The mean and standard deviation of these results were calculated, and the results were plotted on a graph (as they were taken) as follows:

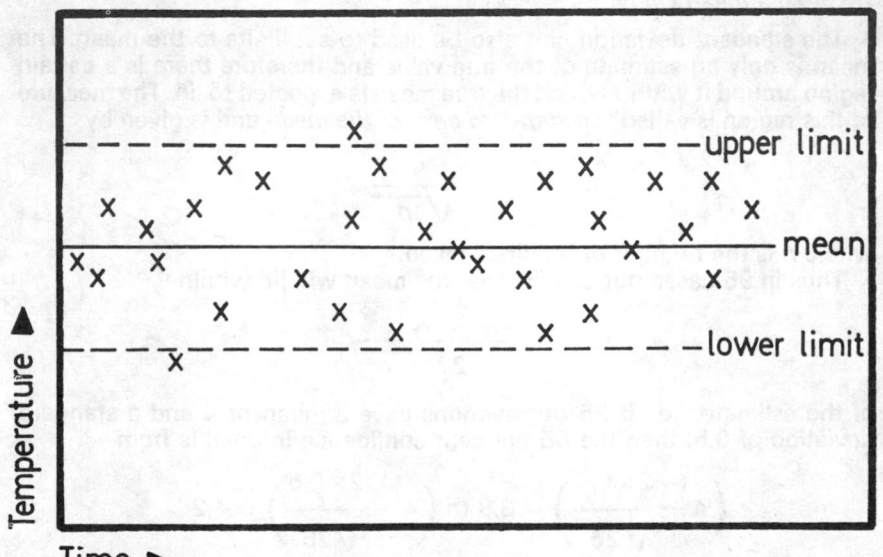

Figure 2:14

Once the limits have been established, 95 per cent of the points should fall within them. If the graph looks like this

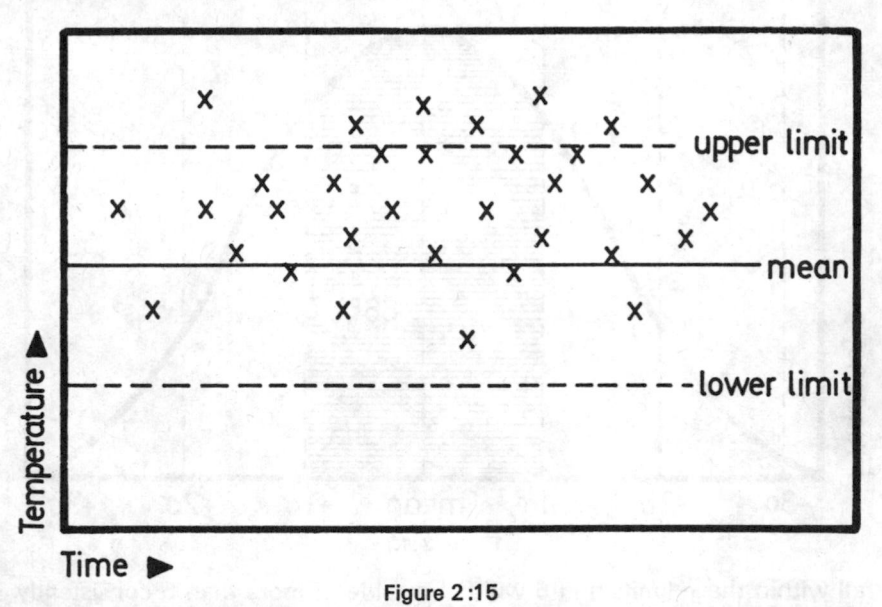

Figure 2:15

then the temperatures are higher than would be expected from normal experimental variation and the possible causes for this should be investigated. In the second example the mean was obviously not obtained from the observation chosen but was some standard laid down before.

(b) To a mean value

The standard deviation can also be used to set limits to the mean. The mean is only an estimate of the true value and therefore there is a certain region around it within which the true mean is expected to lie. The measure of this region is called the *standard error of the mean* and is given by

$$\frac{\sigma}{\sqrt{n}}$$

where n is the number of readings taken.

Thus in 95 cases out of 100, the true mean will lie within

$$\pm \frac{\sigma}{2\sqrt{n}}$$

of the estimate, i.e., if 25 observations gave a mean of 4 and a standard deviation of 0,5, then the 95 per cent confidence interval is from

$$\left(4 - \frac{2 \times 0,5}{\sqrt{25}}\right) = 3,8 \text{ to } \left(4 + \frac{2 \times 0,5}{\sqrt{25}}\right) = 4,2$$

EXAMPLE 5

Find the standard error of the mean for the results given in Example 3.

ANSWER

$$Standard\ error = \frac{0{,}13}{\sqrt{10}} = 0{,}041$$

(c) Comparison of two means

It is now possible to compare two sets of results to determine whether the one set differs significantly from the other. It is quite possible to obtain two mean results which appear to be quite different, and yet which do not show actual significant differences because of the scatter in the observations. Thus it must be stressed when comparing two results that the scatter (represented by the standard deviation) must be taken into account.

The following is a simplified test for comparing two mean results drawn from two sets of normally-distributed observations with similar scatter.

(i) Suppose the two sets of results have n_1 and n_2 readings, means $\bar{x}_1$ and $\bar{x}_2$, and standard deviations σ_1 and σ_2.

(ii) Calculate the pooled standard deviation:

$$\sigma = \sqrt{\frac{(n_1-1)\ \sigma_1^2 + (n_2-1)\ \sigma_2^2}{n_1+n_2-2}}$$

(iii) Calculate the value of

$$t = \frac{\bar{x}_1 - \bar{x}_2}{\sqrt{\left(\dfrac{1}{n_1} + \dfrac{1}{n_2}\right)}\ \sigma}$$

If this value of t is *greater than* the appropriate value of t in the table below, then the two mean results are significantly different at the 95 per cent confidence level.

n_1+n_2-2	t
8	2,301
18	2,101
38	2,026
100	1,984

Note that (n_1+n_2-2) gives the number of "degrees of freedom". "t" is calculated from the student's "t" distribution. For further details on the theory behind this test, consult the bibliography.

7 THE RELATIONSHIP BETWEEN TWO VARIABLES

Often one observation depends on the value or another (e.g., virgin rock temperature depends on depth) or two sets of measurements may be inherently related (e.g., parallel samples taken with a konimeter and a thermal precipitator). An independent variable is one which can be chosen deliberately, e.g., depth in the example above, while a dependent variable changes as the other variable changes, e.g., virgin rock temperature changes with depth of a mine.

In all but the theoretical situation, because of experimental error, if one variable is plotted against another, the observations do not all fall exactly on a curve or straight line but scatter around it. In any experiment the observations must first be plotted on a graph, from which it can be decided whether the relationship is linear or not.

If it seems reasonable to assume a straight-line relationship, a statistical technique is used to calculate the mathematical formula for the line. This is called the "least mean squares straight line" since the sum of the squares of the distances from each point to the line is a minimum.

The formula for a straight line is $y = mx + c$, where m is the slope of the line, and c is the intersection with the y-axis.

To calculate m and c for a given set of observed values of x_i and y_i, the following formulae are used:

$$m = \frac{n \sum_{i=1}^{n} x_i y_i - n^2 \bar{x} \bar{y}}{n \sum_{i=1}^{n} x_i^2 - n^2 \bar{x}^2}$$

$$c = \bar{y} - m\bar{x}$$

These formulae are not as difficult to calculate as it might seem, as the following example shows.

EXAMPLE 6

The following results were obtained for depth below surface in hundreds of metres (x) and virgin rock temperature (y).

x	y	xy	x^2	y^2*
0	20	0	0	400
3	23	69	9	529
6	25	150	36	625
9	29	261	81	841
12	31	372	144	961
15	32	480	225	1 024
18	38	684	324	1 444
21	38	798	441	1 444
24	41	984	576	1 681
27	45	1 215	729	2 025
30	48	1 440	900	2 304
$\Sigma x = 165$	$\Sigma y = 370$	$\Sigma xy = 6\,453$	$\Sigma x^2 = 3\,465$	$\Sigma y^2 = 13\,278$

*The column y^2 is needed for a later calculation (Example 7)

The calculations are shown in the table. Substituting these in the formula gives:

$$m = \frac{(11 \times 6\,453)-(165 \times 370)}{(11 \times 3\,465)-165^2} = \frac{10\,923}{10\,890} = 1,00$$

$$c = \frac{370-(1 \times 165)}{11} = 18,6$$

Thus the relationship, based on the above observations, between the rock temperature (y) and the depth (x) is:

$$y = 1,00x+18,6$$

Thus on the surface (i.e., $x = 0$) the rock temperature is 18,6 °C while at 3 000 m below surface (i.e., $x = 30$), the rock temperature is given by

$$(1,00 \times 30)+18,6 = 48,6°C$$

It must be noted that the straight line calculated above is valid only for the range over which observations have been taken. Extrapolation beyond the limits of observation is never advisable.

8   A MEASURE OF THE EXTENT OF THE CORRELATION BETWEEN TWO VARIABLES

Some variables are closely related, i.e., the one is dependent on the other, or it is another estimate of the same variable. In other cases there is no apparent trend when the one result is plotted against the other, e.g.,

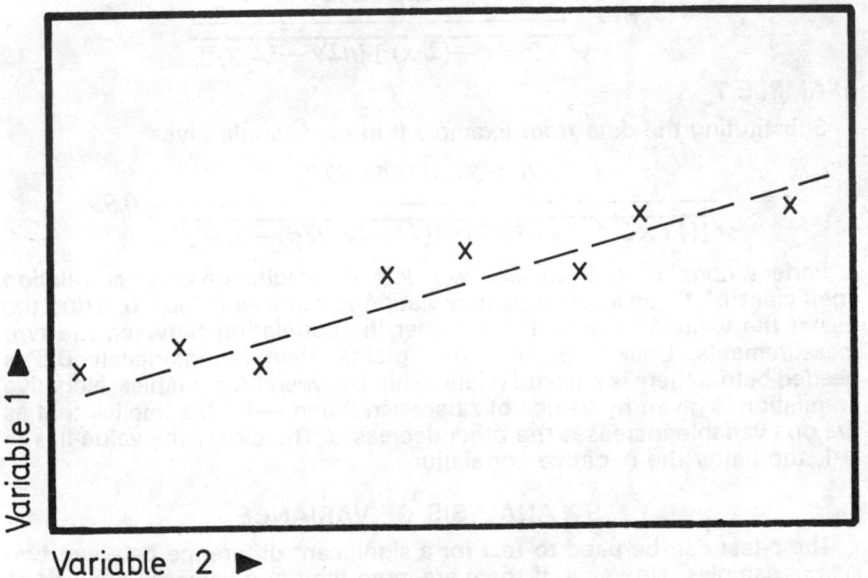

Figure 2:16

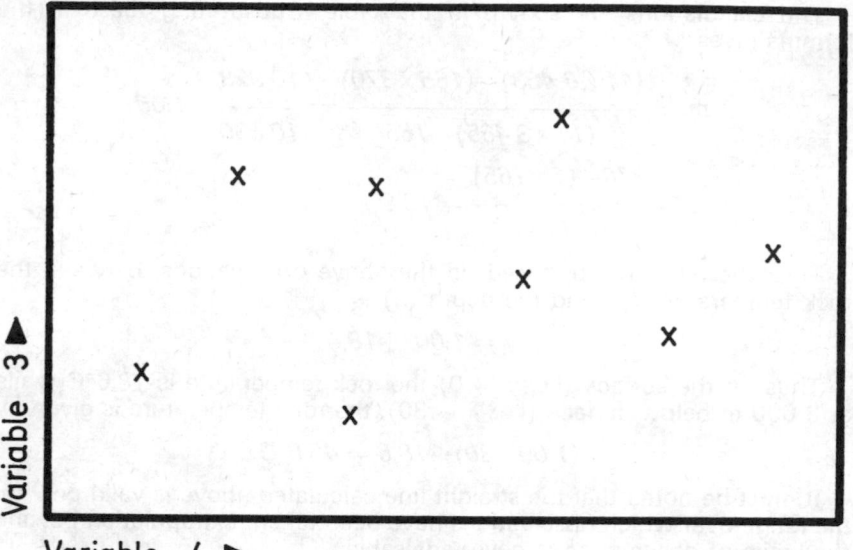

Variable 4 ▶

Figure 2:17

In comparing variable 1 with variable 2, there is obviously some relationship; this is called "high correlation". In the second case no trend is evident, i.e., there is poor correlation between variable 3 and variable 4.

The degree of correlation is given by the coefficient of correlation, r, where

$$r = \frac{n\Sigma xy - \Sigma x \Sigma y}{\sqrt{[n\Sigma x^2 - (\Sigma x)^2][n\Sigma y^2 - (\Sigma y)^2]}}$$

EXAMPLE 7

Substituting the data from Example 6 in the formula gives

$$r = \frac{(11 \times 6\ 453) - (165 \times 370)}{\sqrt{[(11 \times 3\ 465) - 165^2] \times [(11 \times 13\ 278) - 370^2]}} = 0,99$$

Perfect correlation between two sets of results gives a correlation coefficient of 1; absolutely no correlation is represented by 0. Thus the nearer the value of r is to 1, the better the correlation between the two measurements. Usually a value of r greater than approximately 0,6 is needed before there is a useful relationship between the variables. Negative correlation is given by values of r between 0 and —1; this implies that as the one variable increases the other decreases. The closer the value lies to —1, the better the negative correlation.

9   ANALYSIS OF VARIANCE

The t-test can be used to test for a significant difference between two sets of samples. However, if there are more than two sets, the analysis of variance procedure must be used.

This is based on the fact that the difference between a particular result and the overall average can be ascribed to two reasons.

(a)   the variation within a single set of observations, and

(b)   the variation between the sets.

For example, 30 consecutive side-by-side samples can be taken on several konimeters. If six konimeters are to be tested each set of thirty samples will have its own "within-set" variation, but there will also be a variation between the six sets of samples, i.e., between the six mean values.

These two variances, within-set and between-set, can be calculated and compared using the F-test. If the variation between the sets is shown to be significantly larger than the variation within the sets, then it can be concluded that the sets of samples are not all drawn from the same population, i.e., there are significant differences between some of the sets, e.g., in the konimeter example above, either one or more of the konimeters could be biased (providing the sampling positions were equivalent).

In order to calculate the within-set and between-set variances, the following formulae are used:

$$\sigma_1{}^2 = \frac{1}{N-k}\left[\Sigma x_1{}^2 + \Sigma x_2{}^2 + \ldots + \Sigma x_n{}^2 - \left\{\frac{(\Sigma x_1)^2}{n_1} + \frac{(\Sigma x_2)^2}{n_2} + \ldots + \frac{(\Sigma x_n)^2}{n_n}\right\}\right]$$

where $\sigma_1{}^2$ = within-set variance

$x_1,\ x_2, \ldots x_n$ = individual results in sets 1, 2, ... n

$n_1,\ n_2, \ldots n_n$ = number of results in sets 1, 2, ... n

N = total number of results in all sets

k = number of sets

$N-k$ = degrees of freedom for within-set variance

$$\sigma_2{}^2 = \frac{1}{k-1}\left[\frac{(\Sigma x_1)^2}{n_1} + \frac{(\Sigma x_2)^2}{n_2} + \ldots \frac{(\Sigma x_n)^2}{n_n} - \frac{(\Sigma x_t)^2}{N}\right]$$

where $\sigma_2{}^2$ = between-set variance

Σx_t = total of results in all sets

$k-1$ = degrees of freedom for between-set variance.

Note that $\sigma_t{}^2$, the total variance, can be calculated as a check on the above calculations, since

$$(N-1)\sigma_t{}^2 = (N-k)\ \sigma_1{}^2 + (k-1)\ \sigma_2{}^2$$

and $(N-1)\sigma_t{}^2 = \Sigma x^2 - \dfrac{(\Sigma\ x)^2}{N}$

The F-test for comparison of two variances is carried out as follows:

$$F = \frac{\text{larger variance}}{\text{smaller variance}}$$

If N_1 and N_2 are the degrees of freedom in each sample, the theoretical value of F can be found from tables of F values by finding the intersection of the column and row with appropriate degrees of freedom. If the calculated value of F is larger than the theoretical or critical value, then the two variances are assumed to be different.

The analysis of variance described above is the simplest form, namely, the "one-way classification".

The following is a numerical example solved by using the formula quoted:

Set

	1	2	3	4	5	
	18	12	11	13	12	
	14	13	14	8	10	
	16	8	9	5	18	
	12	13	12	5	16	
	20	10	14	9		
		10	12			

Thus

$$
\begin{aligned}
n_1 &= 5 & \Sigma x_1 &= 80 & \Sigma x_1^2 &= 1\,320 \\
n_2 &= 6 & \Sigma x_2 &= 66 & \Sigma x_2^2 &= 746 \\
n_3 &= 6 & \Sigma x_3 &= 72 & \Sigma x_3^2 &= 882 \\
n_4 &= 5 & \Sigma x_4 &= 40 & \Sigma x_4^2 &= 364 \\
n_5 &= 4 & \Sigma x_5 &= 56 & \Sigma x_5^2 &= 824 \\
N &= 26 & \Sigma x &= 314 & \Sigma x^2 &= 4\,136
\end{aligned}
$$

$$
\sigma_1^2 = \frac{1}{21}\Bigg[(1\,320+746+882+364+824) -
$$

$$
\left(\frac{6\,400}{5}+\frac{4\,356}{6}+\frac{5\,184}{6}+\frac{1\,600}{5}+\frac{3\,136}{4} \right) \Bigg]
$$

$$
= \frac{1}{21}\,(4\,136-3\,974) = 7{,}714
$$

$$
\sigma_2^2 = \frac{1}{4}\left[3\,974-\frac{(314)^2}{26} \right] = 45{,}462
$$

Check $25\ \sigma_t^2 = (21 \times 7{,}714)+4\,(45{,}462)$
$$= 343{,}842$$
$$\sigma_t^2 = 13{,}754$$

and $25\ \sigma_t^2 = \Sigma x^2 - \dfrac{(\Sigma x)^2}{N} = 4\,136 - \dfrac{(314)^2}{26} = 343{,}846$

$$\sigma_t^2 = 13{,}754$$

Testing whether σ_1^2 and σ_2^2 differ significantly.

$$
F = \frac{\sigma_2^2}{\sigma_1^2} = \frac{45{,}462}{7{,}714} = 5{,}89
$$

The numerator σ_2^2 has four degrees of freedom, and the denominator σ_1^2 has twenty-one degrees of freedom.

From the F-tables (an extract of which is shown below) the critical value corresponding to these degrees of freedom is 2,84 at a significance level of 5 per cent.

EXTRACT FROM F-TABLES[1]

95% FRACTILES OF F-DISTRIBUTION

DEGREES OF FREEDOM FOR NUMERATOR

	3	4	5
20	3,10	2,87	2,71
21	3,07	2,84	2,68
22	3,05	2,82	2,66

As 5,89 is greater than 2,84 it means that there are significant differences (at the 5 per cent level) between the means of some of the five sets. It should be noted that the analysis of variance does not pin-point which means are different.

The means of the sets are 16, 11, 12, 8 and 14 and clearly the mean for set 4 is significantly smaller than those for sets 1, 2, 3 and 5.

10   REFERENCE

1   Hald, A.   *Statistical Tables and Formulas.* New York, Wiley. 1952.

BIBLIOGRAPHY

Moroney, M. J.   *Facts from Figures.* Harmondsworth. Mddx, Penguin. 1969.

Reichmann, W. J.   *Use and Abuse of Statistics.* London, Methuen, 1961.

Hald, A.   *Statistical Theory with Engineering Applications.* New York, Wiley. 1952.

Chatfield, C.   *Statistics for Technology.* Harmondsworth. Mddx. Penguin. 1970.

3 The Properties and Effects of Dust

P. H. KITTO

Director, Physical Sciences Laboratory, Chamber of Mines Research Organisation

1 INTRODUCTION

Dust can be defined broadly as finely-divided solid matter and may, depending on its particle size, concentration and composition, be a health hazard if it is present in the environment.

The health hazard of dust produced in mining operations has been known for centuries, with the result that much time and effort have been spent on the study of the ways in which it is produced, how it behaves in the environment, how it is measured, how it is controlled and how it affects men physiologically when they are exposed to it.

The sources of dust, its measurement and its control are described elsewhere in this book. In this chapter a brief account will be given of some of the properties and effects of dust which are of significance in the mining context.

Because it is the mineral found most commonly in gold mines, particular attention will be paid to quartz dust.

2 PHYSICAL PROPERTIES OF DUST

Several parameters, or combinations of parameters, have been used for describing or defining dust and the extent to which it is present in the atmosphere. The most important of these are:

(*a*) the number of particles per unit volume;

(*b*) the size distribution of the particles;

(*c*) the mass of dust per unit volume;

(*d*) the surface area of dust per unit volume;

(*e*) the chemical composition of the dust;

(*f*) the mineralogical nature of the particles.

The first four of these parameters are dependent not only on the mode of formation of the dust but also on the physical properties of the particles themselves, particularly with the passage of time.

Factors such as rate of sedimentation and coagulation, Brownian movement, thermal and electrical forces and so on, affect the concentration of dust in the air and the magnitude of these effects is in turn dependent to some extent on the physical properties of the dust.

The property which is of most direct importance from the point of view of behaviour of dust in the mine atmosphere is the size distribution of the dust particles, because the size of particle governs the length of time for which it will remain suspended in the air and the manner in which it will settle out.

The settling rate will also be affected by the velocity of the ventilation air. In streamline flow, the particle, between certain size limits, will settle at a terminal velocity according to Stokes' Law, and these limits do, in fact, include the sizes of particle which are of most interest in underground air, that is, from 40 µm down to about 0,5 µm. In turbulent flow the motion of the particles will be largely unpredictable, and the removal of particles from such an airstream may be caused more by impingement than by settling.

2.1 *Stokes' Law*

Particles settling in a fluid soon reach a constant speed, called the *terminal velocity,* at which the gravitational force is balanced exactly by the drag of the fluid on the particle.

If the motion of the fluid round the particle is symmetrical, i.e., the particle does not have a turbulent wake behind it, we have what is called *viscous* or *streamline* flow, and the terminal velocity of a sphere under these conditions was expressed mathematically by Stokes as follows:

$$V_t = \frac{(w_s - w_f)\ d_s^2 g}{18\ \mu_f}$$

where V_t = terminal velocity
w_s = density of the sphere
w_f = density of the fluid
d_s = diameter of the sphere
g = gravitational acceleration
μ_f = viscosity of the fluid

This relationship is known as Stokes' Law, and it applies to spheres of size below that at which their velocity is such as to create a turbulent wake and above that which is of the same order as the mean free path of the fluid molecules. It applies only to dilute suspensions.

If the size of the particles is of the same order as the mean free path of the fluid molecules, the resistance to the motion of the particles becomes less and they tend to "slip" past the molecules at a greater speed than that indicated by Stokes' Law. In this case a correction due to E. Cunningham[1] may be applied to Stokes' Law, as follows:

$$V_c = V(1+A\frac{\lambda}{a})$$

where V_c = the corrected velocity
V = Stokes' velocity
λ = mean free path of the molecules
A = constant = 0,86 for air at standard conditions
a = radius of particle

The correction is important only for particles settling in a gaseous medium. The magnitude of the slip correction for spheres settling in air has been given by Davies.[2]

Table I gives the terminal velocities, according to Stokes' Law, of spheres of the density of quartz settling in air and in water over the ranges to which Stokes' Law applies with reasonable accuracy.

TABLE I

Particle diameter according to Stokes' Law μm (Error < 5%)	Terminal velocity in water cm/s	Terminal velocity in air cm/s
	For particle size greater than 76 μm Stokes' Law is not applicable because of turbulence	For particle size greater than 42 μm Stokes' Law is not applicable because of turbulence
75	0,47	
60	0,313	
50	0,218	
40	0,140	13,3
30	0,078	7,4
20	0,035	3,3
10	0,008 7	0,83
5	0.002 18	0,208
2	0,000 35	0,033
	For particle size below about 2 μm settling is too slow and errors due to convection and diffusion make Stokes' Law difficult to apply	Below 1,7 μm Cunningham's correction should be applied

Stokes' Law may also be used for calculating the settling times of particles in a centrifugal field, if centrifugal acceleration is used in the formula in place of gravitational acceleration.

2.2 Effect of shape

Particles which are not spherical in shape settle at a speed slower than that calculated from Stokes' Law. Comparisons have been made of the ratio between the mean projected area diameter of quartz particles and the

Stokes diameter, and several workers estimate this to be about 1,5. For coal it is 1,35 to 1,4.[3]

This means that quartz particles, if measured under the microscope by their projected diameters, will, on average, have a settling rate equal to that of spheres of the same density which have a diameter smaller than those measured by a factor of 1 to 1,5. Conversely, if we consider Table I above, the average quartz particle will have a projected area diameter 1,5 times that given in the table for the same settling rate.

2.3 *Brownian motion*

Particles suspended in a fluid are continuously subjected to bombardment by the molecules of the fluid, and if they are small enough these impacts result in a random jerky movement of the particles. The smaller the particles are the greater will be the movement. This movement is called Brownian motion and the average magnitude of the displacement of a particle in any direction in a given time was calculated by Einstein.[4]

For quartz particles in air the Brownian displacement in one second is appreciably larger than the distance the particle will fall in that time if the particle size is less than a quarter of a micrometre, so that Brownian motion is more important than settlement velocity for very small particles. This affects, for example, filtration efficiencies and retention of particles in the lung at sizes where it might otherwise be expected that the particles would simply be carried along by the airstream.

2.4 *Coagulation of dust particles*

When two dust particles come into contact with one another they will usually stick together, provided they are not too large, and it is not easy to separate them again. For this reason redispersed dusts or dusts which have been collected by mass methods are usually highly aggregated. The smaller the particles, the more difficult they are to separate or to remove from a surface to which they have become attached.

The cohesive forces giving rise to this type of attachment are very small and hence are much more effective for particles of size of the order of a few micrometres than for larger particles.

In very dense dust clouds, where many of the particles are likely to collide with one another due to Brownian motion or during settlement, the resultant coagulation may reduce rapidly the number of particles per unit volume.

With dust clouds of the concentrations normally existing in mines, however, reduction in the concentration by Brownian motion and settlement is slow. In turbulent air an appreciable proportion of the particles may be removed by impingement with one another and with neighbouring surfaces.

2.5 *Electrostatic effects*

Electric charges carried by dust particles may have a marked effect on their subsequent behaviour. The amount of charge carried depends on a large number of factors, particularly on the chemical composition of the particles and the humidity of the air, and in conditions of very high humidity such as exist in our gold mines, the electrostatic effect is probably negligible. In surface plants it may have an important influence on, for example, the efficiency of filtration, if this is a very dry process.

Electric charges induced on particles in an electric field are, of course, well known and applied in industrial processes such as electrostatic precipitation.

The theoretical explanation of such phenomena is beyond the scope of this book.

3   CHEMICAL PROPERTIES OF DUST

The chemical properties of a dust are the sum of the chemical properties of the individual constituents, together with any properties which may result from interaction between constituents. These obviously cannot be considered in any detail.

From the health point of view, the most important constituent of the dust found in our gold mines is quartz, a few properties of which are given below.

Quartz is the most commonly occurring crystalline form of silica, SiO_2. In its pure form it is colourless with a hexagonal crystal structure and hardness 7 on the Mohs scale. Its molecular mass is 60,06, its refractive index is 1,544 to 1,553 and its density 2,653 to 2,660. The melting point is approximately 1 470°C.

It is rather inert chemically but dissolves in hydrofluoric acid or (much more slowly) in sodium hydroxide. Small particles of quartz dissolve more rapidly (even per unit surface area) than large ones because of the imperfections in surface structure caused by the comminution process.[5]

As we are interested mainly in dusts because of their effects on the health of those exposed to them, the threshold limit values of some of the dusts encountered in metalliferous mines are given in Table II below. The chemical properties, if required, may be found in any textbook on chemistry.

The data in Table II are taken from the threshold limit values of airborne contaminants adopted by the American Conference of Governmental and Industrial Hygienists for 1972. Threshold limit values refer to time-weighted concentrations of airborne contaminants for a 7- or 8-hour work day, and a 40-hour work week to which it is believed nearly all workers may be exposed repeatedly day after day without adverse effect.

TABLE II

THRESHOLD LIMIT VALUES OF DUSTS ENCOUNTERED ON METALLIFEROUS MINES

Substance	TLV (mg/m³)
Sulphuric acid	1
Lime (calcium oxide)	5
Insoluble manganese compounds	5
Cement	10
Natural uranium compounds	0,2
Lead fume	0,2
Zinc oxide fume	5
Asbestos dust	5 fibres > 5 μm in length/ml
Coal dust	2 (respirable dust)
Quartz-containing dust	(a) $\dfrac{30}{\% \text{ quartz}+3}$ (total dust)
	(b) $\dfrac{10}{\% \text{ quartz}+2}$ (respirable* dust)
Fused silica	As for quartz
Tridymite and Cristobalite	$\frac{1}{2}$ value from quartz formula
Limestone	10
Gypsum	10
Kaolin	10
Antimony mineral dusts	0,5
Arsenic mineral dusts	0,5
Chromium mineral dusts	1
Copper mineral dusts	1
Nickel mineral dusts	1
Oil mist	5

*Both concentration and per cent quartz for the application of this limit are to be determined from the fraction passing a size-selector with the following characteristics:

Aerodynamic diameter (µm) (unit density sphere)	% passing selector
$\geq$ 2	90
2,5	75
3,5	50
5,0	25
10	0

4   PATHOLOGICAL EFFECTS

Dust is a health hazard to those exposed to it. A number of diseases can be caused by inhaling or swallowing different types of dust and certain dusts irritate the skin.

Different types of pneumoconiosis are caused by the breathing of different types of dust. For example, silicosis is caused by breathing silica from quartzite; asbestosis results from exposure to asbestos fibres, and so on. Various theories have been advanced to account for the action of silica in producing silicosis. These will be summarised following a brief description of the lungs and the respiratory tract.

The lungs are organs of unequal size, responsible for passing oxygen into the blood. They are connected to the mouth and nose by the trachea. The left lung is divided into two lobes and the right lung, which is 12 per cent larger than the left lung, into three lobes.

The lungs comprise two main functional parts. That which conducts the air to the finer parts of the lung is known as the conducting system and consists of the trachea which divides into the right and left main bronchi opposite the fourth rib. This is followed by a number of divisions after which the bronchi lose their rigidity and form bronchioles. The small bronchioles lead into the air sacs and alveoli which form the respiratory part of the lung. It is here that the oxygen is passed to the red blood cells and the carbon dioxide transferred from the blood to the alveoli.

Large dust particles are filtered out by the hairs in the nose, in the trachea or bronchi, and hardly ever reach the alveoli. The trachea down to the bronchioles is lined with cells with cilia appended to them. These cilia have a whip-like action, carrying upward any particles that touch them.

Any dust particles reaching the alveoli are taken up by the defence cells of the lower respiratory tract which are known as alveolar macrophages. The majority of these dust-laden macrophages are moved upwards to the bronchioles in a fluid lining of the lower respiratory tract assisted by movement of the muscle in the bronchioles, and from there to the cough centres from which they are coughed up. This muscle has a similar, so-called peristaltic action, to the muscle in the intestinal tract which moves the food through the different parts of the intestine.

Some of the dust-laden macrophages are not coughed out in the sputum and either remain in the alveoli or go to one of two places in the lung. They may move back into the aveolar walls and from there either pass up the lymph channels where they are trapped in the chain of lymph glands or they may aggregate around the small vessels of the lung.

In either of these two places the silica-laden macrophage produces marked scarring of the area, resulting either in lymph glands with silicotic fibrosis or in silicotic islets in the lung itself.

About sixty theories have been advanced to account for this action of silica dust. According to one group of theories based on the physical action of silica, the sharp-pointed crystals irritate the lung tissue and cause scar tissue to be formed. This explanation has been disproved by a number of workers, who have shown that non-crystalline silica can also produce fibrosis, albeit not to the same extent as crystalline silica.

The piezo-electric theory postulates the release of an electrical charge by the compression of the silica crystals. Although the experiments quoted above tend to disprove this theory it is understood that certain workers in Russia are reinvestigating it.

The chemical theories suggested that the silicic acid which is formed by quartz in a liquid medium was the cause of silicotic fibrosis. This theory was held by Professor King for many years, but it was in his own laboratories that it was disproved.

The immunological theories were introduced to explain the different effects of silica dust on people working in the same dusty occupations. In this theory it was suggested that silica so altered the alveolar macrophage that when these cells died they released a substance which was foreign to the body and which produced an allergic type of reaction in the lung which resulted in fibrosis. It is now thought that the different reactions of individuals to the inhalation of dust depend on the effectiveness of the dust-clearing mechanisms of the lung, but they may also depend on the immunological state of the individual.

This theory, which finds most support at present and on which much research work is being carried out, might well be called the macrophage theory. In this it is suggested that, although when an ordinary bacterium is taken up by the alveolar macrophage there are certain enzyme systems in the macrophage which destroy the bacterium, when a quartz particle is in the macrophage the quartz alters or destroys these enzymes and when the macrophage dies the altered enzymes which are released trigger off the formation of scar tissue. These altered enzymes attached to the membranes of the cell may be allergenic.

Based to some extent on the chemical theory of silicotic fibrosis the Canadian workers considered that aluminium oxide would prevent the toxic action of silica. Animal experiments in which monkeys were used have shown that although aluminium oxide will delay the onset of fibrosis, silicosis eventually develops especially when the animals are removed from the dust and the prophylactic aluminium oxide.[6]

More recently polyvinyl-pyridine-N-oxide has been used and it is claimed that not only does it prevent silicotic islet formation but it will dissolve the fibrous tissue. However, recent work has shown that there is no evidence of a prophylactic effect when the recommended concentrations of the aerosol are used.[7]

The International Silicosis Conference held at Johannesburg in 1930 defined silicosis as follows:

"Silicosis is a pathological condition of the lungs due to the inhalation of free silica dust. It can be produced experimentally in animals. It can be detected by clinical and radiological means which can be confirmed with the above pathological condition with sufficient accuracy to separate it from other pneumoconiosis. It also affords a fair basis for legislative measures."

As mentioned above, the larger particles hardly ever reach the alveoli. It was decided at the Pneumoconiosis Conference, Johannesburg (1959), that the following curve be adopted as an indication of particle sizes constituting a health hazard:

100% of particles of size 1 µm equivalent diameter
50% of particles of size 5 µm equivalent diameter
0% of particles of size 7 µm equivalent diameter

The equivalent diameter of a particle is the diameter of a sphere of unit density having the same settling velocity in air as the particle studied.

The figures given above have been widely accepted as the basis for the design of elutriators aimed at the elimination of all but the respirable dust in dust sampling instruments.

5   REFERENCES

1   Cunningham, E.   On the velocity of steady fall of spherical particles through fluid medium. Proc. Roy. Soc. A, Vol. 83, 1910. p.357–365.

2   Davies, C. N.   The sedimentation of small suspended particles. Symposium on particle size analysis. Trans. Instn. Chem. Eng. Vol. 25, 1947, Suppl. p.25–39.

3   Cartwright, J.   Particle shape factors. Ann. Occup. Hyg. Vol. 5, 1962. p.163–171.

4   Einstein, A.   Eine neue Bestimming der Moleküldimensionen. Ann. Physik. Vol. 19, 1906, p.289–306.

5   Kitto, P. H. *and* Patterson, H. S.   The rate of solution of particles of quartz and certain silicates. J. ind. Hyg. Toxicol. Vol. 24, 1942. p.59–74.

6   South African Medical Research Council. National Research Institute for Occupational Diseases. Annual Report 1972.

7   Webster, I.   Silicosis in South Africa. *In* Pneumoconiosis, Proceedings of the International Conference, Johannesburg, 1969, edited by H. Shapiro, Cape Town. O.U.P. 1970, p.354–361.

4 Sources and Methods of Control of Dust

J. H. QUILLIAM

*Chief, Dust Division, Physical Sciences Laboratory,
Chamber of Mines Research Organization*

1   INTRODUCTION

Dust, which is finely-divided solid matter, is produced in a number of ways. In processes in which dust is produced efforts are made to keep the concentration as low as possible and to prevent the dust from becoming airborne. If dust does get into the air steps must be taken to prevent its being inhaled by the workers or at least to reduce as far as possible the extent of the exposure of the worker to the dust.

2   GENERAL SOURCES OF DUST

The most important source of dust in mining is the rock itself. It is inevitable that large quantities of dust will be produced in mining when the rock is broken and reduced to a size which can be handled conveniently.

Only a small fraction of the dust produced from the rock actually becomes airborne if suitable dust control methods are used, but if the silica content of the rock is high, even this small amount may constitute a health hazard.

Apart from the rock and the many mining operations which produce dust there are other sources of dust in a mine, if the term dust is used in its broadest sense. The evaporation of water, for example, will leave particles of dust, and solid particles are found in the exhaust gases from diesel engines or in compressed air. Dust may also be introduced into the mine from the surface atmosphere. Some of this dust may be injurious to health, but little is known of its long-term effects, either direct or indirect, whereas it is known that inhalation of the dust from the mined rock can result in pneumoconiosis.

3   BASIC PRINCIPLES IN THE CONTROL OF DUST

In order to control dust adequately it is essential to know how, when and where it is produced and to measure that portion which becomes airborne. Methods of measurement, which are not necessarily the same as those required for estimating the health hazards associated with dust, are described in detail in Chapter 5.

Dust clouds are never static, and natural forces are constantly changing the concentration, the size distribution and the physical and chemical characteristics of dust. Factors such as sedimentation, impingement, diffusion, humidity and condensation play a considerable part in preventing the build-up of dust throughout the mine from becoming cumulative. However, these factors are usually not nearly sufficient in themselves, and it becomes necessary to employ "artificial" methods of control.

Generally, there are four rules regarding dust control which should be followed if the problem is to be tackled effectively. These are as follows, the necessity for each step after the first being a measure of the failure of the previous one:

(a)   keep dust production to a minimum and prevent it from contaminating the atmosphere by controlling it at its source;

(b)   dilute it as rapidly as possible;

(c)   filter it;

(d)   avoid it.

In most mines excessive dust production is the result of failure to take adequate steps under these four headings.

The best safeguard against over-exposure to dust is compliance with the Regulations, constant supervision and measurement of that exposure, and if undesirable concentrations exist the introduction of remedial measures as soon as possible.

4   GENERAL PREVENTATIVE MEASURES

The basic ways in which high dust exposures can be controlled or prevented are given below. It should be borne in mind, however, that "prevention is better than cure".

4.1   Removal of personnel

This is the most effective way of preventing exposure to dust. It is applied mainly after blasting by the insistence on a minimum re-entry period, by arranging a fixed blasting time for each working place so that other workers are not exposed to the blasting dust and fumes, and by ensuring that blasting takes place only at the end of the shift when most other workers have already been withdrawn. When on-shift or multiple-shift blasting is permitted, removal of personnel is impossible and the dust and fumes must either be taken directly to surface or the dust filtered out and the fumes diluted.[1]

Other ways in which workers are kept out of dusty air is by arranging that men travel in downcast shafts and by having all underground waiting places in fresh air.

4.2   Prevention of formation of dust at its source

Every effort should be made to prevent both the formation of dust at its source and its liberation into the atmosphere.

With very few exceptions, water is used for this purpose. The excessive use of water for watering-down purposes, however, can result in deterioration in temperature conditions, wastage, flooding of drains and ore passes, overloading of pumping systems and washing away of "fines" containing gold.

To prevent the excessive use of water when wetting down, a suitable spray nozzle should be used in association with a cut-off valve and a pressure-reducing valve. A spray nozzle ensures an adequate spread of water over a greater area and prevents the settled dust from being stirred up.

Laboratory experiments have indicated that a moisture content of the rock of only 1 per cent by mass produces a very significant reduction in dust production when compared with rock being transported under dry conditions.

As it is difficult to *maintain* a moisture content of 1 per cent under conditions encountered underground the optimum moisture content should be maintained at about 5 per cent for minimum dust production during transportation.

It is important that the water used for dust suppression, particularly in drilling and in water-blasts, should be as clean as possible as the evaporation of dirty water can release considerable quantities of dust.

4.3   Dilution by ventilation

This is essential when measures to suppress the dust at its source have failed. Obviously, if the quantity of air passing a given source of dust is doubled, the dust concentration from that source will be halved, and by delivering sufficient air, the dust concentration can always be reduced to below dangerous levels. To provide increased amounts of air may, however, not always be possible or economical.

4.4 *Filtration*

Airborne dust can be removed from the air by means of filters.

4.5 *Use of respirators*

In certain operations conducted on surface plants and in underground workings personnel are exposed to high concentrations of dust for only short periods of time, and fully adequate dust control measures cannot be implemented.

Such underground operations include, for example, blowing-over operations in sinking shafts, operations at shaft loading boxes and transfer points and blowing-out of electric motors. On surface plants high dust concentrations may be formed at blow-off points on rotary filters, ore grading rooms, crushing plants and in handling of dry lime. In such instances respirators should be used as a means for protection.

No known type of respirator can be worn for long periods of time without being a cause of some degree of discomfort to the wearer. Respirators must be light, easy-to-wear and be able to withstand strenuous conditions. They need not be highly efficient provided they can reduce the concentrations of dust inhaled to relatively harmless levels.

A respirator with an efficiency of, say, 90 per cent would be adequate and the possibility of making such a respirator acceptable to the miner is far greater than if a respirator of more complex design to achieve higher efficiency is used.

In 1960 Rees[2], comparing data for certification of silicosis with known dust concentrations, showed that it was not necessary to eliminate dust completely to prevent silicosis but that a moderate improvement in dust concentrations could result in the reduction in the silicosis rate to negligible proportions. The results of more recent studies of incidence rates appear to support this contention, which if correct offers substantial support to the use of low-efficiency respirators.

Possibly the greatest objection to the use of respirators is the amount of supervision necessary to ensure their regular use by workers. Their use by supervisors and officials where necessary will do much to gain the co-operation of the workers.

5 MAIN SOURCES OF DUST AND METHODS OF CONTROL IN UNDERGROUND OPERATIONS

Common sources of dust underground are:

5.1 *Blasting*

Blasting, particularly in hard rock, produces enormous quantities of dust, fumes and poisonous gases in concentrations which have been shown to be higher than those produced by any other mining process, and exposure of personnel to this dust and gas should be prevented.

This is normally done by removing men from the area before blasting and clearing the area of dust and fumes before the men return. This is comparatively easy to control in normal mining in which only one main shift is worked during twenty-four hours, but in multi-shift development there is a much greater chance of miners returning to the face before the area is properly cleared.

In development ends the amount of dust produced by the blast can be controlled to a certain extent by choice of the pattern of the round, the method of blasting, the material used for tamping and the type of explosive used.

The practical aim should, however, be the complete replacement by fresh air of the air contaminated by dust in whatever time is available before re-entry. The method of ventilation necessary to do this may depend on the time available, but normally the ordinary ventilation system operating during the rest of the shift is used.

Water-blasts are used before and after a blast in development ends. These reduce the amount of dust and noxious gases present in the air to a limited extent. The main value of the water-blast is that when subsequent watering-down is undertaken on re-entry less dust is produced.

The difficulty of enforcing the Regulations controlling re-entry into high-speed development ends after blasting is generally recognised. Procedures which will speed up the rate of reduction of dust levels during the 30-minute period after blasting (during which time re-entry is prohibited by Regulation) are very important.

The rate of decrease of dust concentrations in high-speed development ends ventilated by the exhaust-overlap system can be increased by means of the following procedures involving the use of available ventilation equipment:

1   The auxiliary booster unit should be switched off before the blast and during the re-entry period. This will reduce the throw-back of the dust fumes, permitting the end to be cleared more rapidly.

2   The rate at which air should be exhausted should not be less than 2,5 m³/s for a 3m×3m end. The use of larger exhaust volumes will increase the rate of removal of dust proportionately.

3   A 50 mm water-blast with a 10 mm diameter water outlet operated automatically by the shock wave from the blast has been found to be the most effective.

4   The maximum distance of the exhaust inlet from the face should be 25m. Results of scale model tests indicate that if this distance is reduced a greater rate of dust removal is obtained. This is not possible in practice because of possible damage to the exhaust inlet by blasting, but if the refined system, described below, is adopted, such a reduction can be attained.

According to this system, a compressed air-operated fan is fitted to a smaller pipe inserted into the mouth of the standard exhaust column and extending to within a metre of the face. The inlet of the smaller pipe is fitted with a protective screen and an additional short length of expendable pipe to protect it from the blast. The auxiliary force unit must be switched off before the blast and during the re-entry period. Any reduction in the diameter of the small inlet pipe has no effect on the clearing time. By increasing the exhaust volumes used, the clearing times can be reduced still further.

A similar method of reducing dust levels rapidly during the re-entry interval is the extended exhaust system.[3]

5.2   Mechanical loading

During mechanical loading after blasting in development ends high dust levels can be encountered. When the conventional exhaust overlap system is used this dust is inhaled by all personnel working between the face and the exhaust inlet i.e., the majority of the development labour force.

When the extended exhaust system is used with the force fan off during loading, only the personnel working ahead of the loader are exposed.

It is recommended, therefore, to switch off the auxiliary unit during the mechanical loading operations as well as during the blast if the extended exhaust system is used.

The production of dust by mechanical loaders can also be partially controlled by directing the exhausts of the loaders away from the footwall and maintaining the hoppers in a clean condition.

Water spray equipment should comprise an integral part of mechanical loaders and should operate automatically when the loader moves forward. Water control valves should be interconnected with the mechanism operating the loader movement.

5.3   *Drilling*

A large quantity of rock is pulverised to form dust during the drilling process and if this dust becomes airborne it constitutes a major dust hazard of underground mining. This occurs where mining methods are out-of-date and supervision is poor, but this dust is not a necessary evil. Potentially, the rotary-percussive type of machine-drill in general use in South African gold mines presents a much greater dust hazard than, say, a rotary diamond drill, because with the former type of drill all the rock from the hole is pulverised, whereas with the latter a solid core is formed; nevertheless, the modern rotary-percussive machine, if maintained in good condition and properly used, has been shown to produce very little airborne dust from the rock except during the comparatively short period of "collaring".

The most important means for preventing entry into the atmosphere of dust which is produced by drilling is the use of adequate quantities of water. The water must be at such a pressure that a sufficient quantity is provided to keep the rock surface wet all the time, so that the rock is actually broken under a film of water. Breaking rock under water is a highly efficient way of preventing the dust produced from becoming airborne, but an inadequate film of water, or the presence of air bubbles, will permit the dust to enter the atmosphere. Most modern drilling machines therefore, are so designed that an air-free flow of water is provided at the bottom of the hole being drilled.

This does not, however, prevent dust from entering the air during the initial collaring period when the water is not confined to the hole and the dust cannot be so easily trapped. Various means have been tried to prevent the escape of dust during collaring, ranging from simple hand-held sprays to elaborate types of suction traps round the end of the drill steel, but no single method has been found to be very efficient.

If some of the compressed air operating the drill leaks into the front head of the drill and escapes down the drill steel, it will cause dry drilling and carry out of the hole the dust thus created.

Also some of this compressed air will escape through the front head release ports and in doing so will atomise some of the water also in the front head. This atomised water, which forms a fog at the front head release ports of many rock-drills, evaporates rapidly and if the water is dirty, as it often is, many dust particles will remain in the air.

The use of a sealed-spline rock-drill reduces the amount of dust produced at this source considerably. The piston of such a rock-drill is designed so that the splines on the back portion of the piston are not exposed while the air adjacent to it is under pressure. This forms a seal which prevents excessive leakage of compressed air into the front head of the machine.

Apart from producing dust from rock, machine-drills pollute the atmosphere in other ways. If, for example, the water used contains mineral particles and if this water is atomised by being mixed with the compressed air, dangerous quantities of dust can be produced. This however can be largely prevented by good machine design and by the use of clean water. Finally, the machine exhaust itself should be checked to see that it does not contain contaminants from the compressed air and the lubrication system of the drill.

A machine which complies with the Regulations, and which is checked regularly and maintained in good condition will produce very little dust. What dust is produced can be diluted by the supply of adequate quantities of ventilating air.

5.4   *Transportation of rock*

Increased mechanisation in the handling of rock has become a major source of dust. In South African gold mines at present there are almost as many scrapers used as there are rock-drills, and a large number of mechanical loaders are also in common use. Control of the dust produced by these devices is difficult. Good ventilation is of course essential, unless exposure to the dust can be avoided, and the controlled use of water has been shown to help considerably.

Scraping in particular is a major cause of dust generation underground. Dust is generated mainly by the abrasion of the footwall and/or rock on the footwall by the scraper blades.

It has been shown that dust concentrations produced by gully scraping could be reduced considerably by

(i)   using high-capacity shovels of as light a construction as possible, consistent with operating requirements,

(ii)   reducing scraper speeds to approximately 0,6 m/s or less, and

(iii) using scraper shovels in tandem as required for the desired tonnage.

As air which flows along scraper gullies often finds its way to nearby working faces, it is essential to reduce the amount of dust produced during scraping operations. Broken rock should be wet down thoroughly before being moved and *maintained* in a wet condition.

High-pressure water jets directed onto dry broken rock cause dust to be released from the rockpile and, as previously suggested, spray-nozzles should be used. In addition, a certain amount of atomisation will occur when water is discharged at high pressures. This can result in the liberation of dust into the ventilating air if the water contains dust.

To overcome these shortcomings of conventional methods of dust prevention in scraper gullies, a device known as a "drip-feed" has been used. It consists of a length of hose, of either rubber or plastic, with holes or slots at approximately 150 mm intervals along its length. The length of hose should be sufficient to cover the width of the scraper gullies. One end of the hose is sealed and the other connected to a water supply.

The *drip-feed* is mounted across the scraper gully in such a position that it is clear of the scraper rope and is situated at points at which the broken rock normally accumulates during scraping operations, that is, near the top of the scraper gully and at points at which the rock is transferred from one scraper shovel to another. In a long gully there should be drip-feeds at, say, 45 to 70 m intervals.

Access to stope faces which have been blasted is usually limited due to the accumulation of broken rock, making effective wetting-down a difficult task. Consequently, wetting-down is often inadequate. High dust concentrations are, therefore, frequently generated when the scrapers start operating.

Off-shift wetting-down by means of fog nozzles located at the bottom of each stope panel or located in series along the face results in considerable saving in time at the beginning of the shift. It is as effective in controlling dust as is the conventional method of wetting-down with a hose at the beginning of the shift, provided the water pressure and the air velocity are high enough to cause the fog to be carried over the whole length of the panel.

Fog nozzles are recommended for off-shift wetting-down because of the time saved in the wetting-down period on re-entry. Satisfactory nozzles are nozzles with a 2,5 mm spraying orifice, as this size hole will not clog easily.

Dispersion of the fog is affected by a number of factors and each mine should determine for itself the most suitable arrangements for its particular stoping conditions. As packs and other equipment tend to produce dry "shadows" in certain areas, a check should be made on re-entry, and all dry patches watered down well by means of a hand hose fitted with a spray head.

Although large quantities of rock are still moved by shovelling, energy considerations make it obvious that this cannot be considered a serious source of dust in comparison with other more intensive mining operations. It can, however, result in a certain amount of dispersion in the air of dust unless the material is kept damp.

5.5   *Falling rock*

When rock is handled underground, it often falls either over rock surfaces or through the air. The greater the impact, the greater the amount of dust produced, and in certain situations such as at large tips, very high dust concentrations may be generated in spite of the measures taken to keep the rock wet.

For this reason it is usual to ventilate such tips by downcasting the air and then filtering this air before it rejoins the main air current. Many types of filter are used, but by far the most common is the flannel bag filter. During 1971, out of a total of 1 330 filter units used underground in 44 South African gold mines, 90 per cent were of the fabric filter bag type, with a total capacity of over 6 800 m³/s. Most of these filters were installed at tips.

A high air velocity over the mouths of tips (either with or without filters) combined with the upsurge of dust-laden air during tipping can produce undesirably high dust concentrations which are released into the main air stream and self-closing swing doors have been used to reduce this leakage. In new mines, consideration should be given to the establishment of main tips in by-passes and not in the main airways.

Excessive quantities of dust are produced at stope tips and as conventional flannel bag filters cannot be used at such points, fog nozzles should be used. If, in particular instances, the use of fog nozzles is not possible, for example, if they increase humidity and sludging problems seriously, a box-filter constructed of polyurethane foam can be used to remove the dust. The end of the exhaust duct should extend at least one metre below the grizzly of the tip. The filter should operate continuously throughout the shift as stopping and starting the fan causes dust to be released from the filter. The fan (compressed air or electric) drawing air through the filter must be switched off at blasting time to avoid overloading the filter with dust. The filter should be hosed down thoroughly at the end of each shift.

5.6 *Miscellaneous operations*

There are several other processes which produce high dust concentrations but, generally speaking, they affect only a limited number of workers or they are of short duration. Examples are blowing-over in sinking shafts and the blowing-out of drill-holes. The best protection against short-period exposure to high dust concentrations, if exposure is unavoidable, is a respirator. The dust in question should be checked for concentration, size distribution and composition, and, if shown to be potentially hazardous, respirators should be worn.

The examples given above, and others such as the moving of men and material, the cleaning of cars, watering-down, the changing of flannel filter bags, sweeping, evaporation of dirty water falling from bottom discharge skips pick-up of dry dust by high-speed air and so on, are not primary sources of dust in that the dust is not produced directly from the rock but is redispersed dust which was originally produced by some other operation.

Dusts produced underground from sources other than the rock may be important from the point of view of general health, but, as already mentioned, little is known of their long-term effects on either general health or their role in the development of pneumoconiosis. Examples are the dusts from diesel exhausts, welding, guniting, and the handling of cement, lime or other finely-divided material.

The charging of drill-holes with blasting agents such as ANBA and ANFEX which are in prill form is done with specially designed loading equipment in which compressed air is used to inject the explosive into the hole. This operation may produce dust by the ejection of disintegrated material with the air coming from the hole. This disintegrated material may not only become an irritant when it comes into contact with the skin but may also contaminate the ventilation air.

The disintegrated material ejected from the hole by the compressed air can be controlled by two types of suppressors, namely,

(i)   the filter-type suppressor :
(ii) the deflector-type suppressor.

The filter-type suppressor which is produced in various sizes, consists of a perforated rubber cup filled with "Resilair" filter medium through which the loading tube is inserted and which, during loading, is pressed up against the collar of the hole. The perforations permit the passage of air from the blow-back while the dust is collected by the filter medium which can be cleaned from time to time by rinsing in water.

The deflector-type suppressor is a device which is fitted onto the loading tube and comprises a funnel-shaped collecting hood joined to a sweep bend and an expanding tail cone at right angles to the axis of the tube. A "fishtail"-shaped discharge in place of the cone improves the performance of this suppressor and provides a pressure recovery of about 25 per cent.

The deflector is made to slide over the loading tube so that the inlet cone covers the drill-hole. Compressed air and dust ejected from the drill-hole are blown back into the inlet cone and around the sweep bend by the residual pressure of the air and are directed downwards through the tail cone at a moderate velocity so that some of the material settles on the footwall.

Precautions which should be taken to reduce blow-back are:

(i)   the compressed air supply to the loader if not automatic, should be turned off as soon as the hole has been filled with the required amount of explosive, and

(ii) the loading tube should be aligned centrally because if it is tilted upwards or downwards, increased blow-back will result.

Because compressed air produces dust when it is used to clear drill-holes, its use for this purpose is prohibited by Regulation (10.21.5). It is, however, permitted to use compressed air to blow out a hole if the compressed air is applied together with water through a blowpipe approved for that purpose.

Desludgers have been developed for cleaning out drill-holes without the use of compressed air, preparatory to charging up with ANBA or any other explosive.

With such devices water is injected through a tube or probe inserted into the hole to wash it out and the water remaining in the hole is then removed by merely turning a two-way stop-cock which causes the water to create a suction as it flows through the T-piece.

6   MAIN DUST-PRODUCING OPERATIONS ON SURFACE PLANTS AND METHODS OF CONTROL

After being conveyed to the surface, the broken rock must be transported to the crushing and milling plant where it is reduced to a finely-divided state in order that the gold and other associated metals may be extracted.

During these processes, large quantities of dust are produced—virtually all the gold bearing rock is, in fact, reduced to the size of dust—and special efforts are made to prevent this dust from becoming airborne.

The sources of dust production on surface may be classified into four main headings—transfer points, screens, crushers, and miscellaneous operations.

6.1   Transfer points

The number of transfer points varies considerably from mine to mine. Generally speaking, the rock is tipped from the skips at the shaft into storage bins from which it is taken by conveyor belts to and from the different types of crusher, the screens and the mills. Storage bins are used at several points in the circuit, and these constitute still further transfer points.

The amount of dust produced at transfer points is not usually large as long as the material is wet, but if it is allowed to dry, large clouds of dust may be produced. This is liable to happen if the rock travels long distances in the open or when the plant is started if the operation is not continuous. Particular care must be taken at the transfer points in the vicinity of down-cast shafts to ensure that the dust produced does not contaminate the intake air to the mine.

In addition to water, exhaust ventilation is also used at transfer points to reduce dust production.

6.2 Screens

Stationery or vibrating screens are in common use for size classification of the broken ore. Large amounts of dust are released from the screen if the material is allowed to dry, but as long as it is wet, screening does not present much of a hazard. Nevertheless, many screens are equipped with exhaust ventilation.

6.3 Crushers

The crushing process is a source of large quantities of dust. Most crushers are, in fact, supplied with exhaust ventilation, the exact method of application depending on the type of crusher being used and on its situation. The dusty air is, in some cases, blown directly into the atmosphere, but the modern practice is to pass it first through some type of wet scrubber.

6.4 Miscellaneous operations

Milling: Once the rock has been crushed to the required degree of fineness it passes to the mills, but, as they are totally enclosed and because milling is carried out in the wet state, they do not produce large quantities of dust.

Rotary filters: A point in the circuit where dust can be a problem is at the blow-off points of the rotary filters. Here the pulp is filtered from the solution containing the gold, and the "cake" of finely-divided rock is blown off the filter by means of compressed air. This can produce high dust concentrations especially if the air pressures used are too high, but the dust can be controlled easily by exhaust ventilation.

Observations of the blow-off have indicated that while the cake is dislodged within less than a second, compressed air continues to pass through the interstices of the cloth and to atomise the sludge. During the initial dislodging period, the cake loosens and, before dropping away, actually acts as a protective blanket preventing atomised sludge from being blown from the cloth into the atmosphere. The blow-off period can be reduced and confined to the net time required for dislodging the cake and the amount of dust produced reduced by means of automatic cut-off valves attached to the compressed air supply at each filter.

Workshops: Dust conditions in workshops have been found to vary widely. The presence of forge fires, open hearth fires, compressed air hammers, cutting machines, oxy-acetylene torches, electric arc welding plants and the conducting of a number of operations not only cause local contamination but also give the general atmosphere a very mixed dust and smoke content. Oxy-acetylene torches and electric arc welding result in contamination of the air by metal fumes which often produce high dust concentrations.

The silica content of the dust is generally low except where work on salvage of underground equipment is the major operation.

Welding fumes are invariably present in most workshops, and fixed or adjustable exhaust hoods fitted over the workshop benches, as well as flexible exhaust hoods with magnetic collars, should be used to draw fumes away from the operators. As helmets must be worn by welders for protection of the eyes, a small volume of air at a positive pressure can be supplied to the inside of the helmet by means of a tube encircling the lens holder. This protects the wearer from fumes, and also provides relief from the radiant heat produced by oxy-acetylene or arc welding units.

Grading rooms: Samples of crushed ore in the form of sludge are taken at regular intervals for grading in order to check on milling efficiencies.

These samples are dried, mixed, weighed and graded. As the grading is done in sealed Tyler screen units no dust is released. The mixing process can release high concentrations of dust which can be controlled if the operations are done in a ventilated fume cabinet.

Assay crushers: Rock samples for assay purposes have to be crushed and pulverized and this produces high dust levels. Such dust must be controlled as near as possible to the point at which it is produced and before being dispersed into the atmosphere. In practice the source of dust should be totally enclosed and placed under a negative air pressure or alternatively, an exhaust hood installed near the source of the dust. The emphasis on the design of such dust control systems should be placed on exhausting sufficient air to create velocities in the zone to be ventilated that will control the dust-bearing air currents before the breathing zone of the operators is reached.

7   UNDERGROUND DUST EXTRACTION PLANTS

7.1   *Flannel bag and sawdust filters*

Underground air can be filtered through fabrics such as flannel bags and blankets, through granulated material, mainly sawdust, and by means of electrostatic precipitators.

Flannel bags are by far the most widely used because they are easy to install and maintain. The most recent type of installation consists of a bank of 100 mm diameter vertical bags about 2 m long, attached to an overhead frame with rocker arm manipulator to remove the dust from the bags with the fan stopped.

Sawdust filters are not as popular because they are more difficult to install, require a larger excavation, more maintenance and are less efficient.

Nearly all underground air filtration units are installed at tips and loading boxes. One exception is the filtration of blasting fumes from development ends on multi-shift blasting. In such cases the air is filtered usually in two stages, first through blanket or coir matting and then through flannel bags or electrostatic precipitators, because of the extremely high dust load. These filters are installed in series with a filter to remove nitrous fumes. This latter filter consists of a bed of vermiculite treated with a solution of sodium carbonate and potassium permanganate.[1]

7.2   Polyurethane filters

High concentrations of dust can be generated in longwall stoping systems, that is, where the same air ventilates several levels. One method of reducing such dust levels is to introduce intermediate filtration of the air at convenient points.

It is not practicable to filter all the air passing through a stope, but if a substantial proportion of the air at the face is filtered and reintroduced into the main airstream, the concentration of dust in the air can be reduced. The extent of the reduction will depend on the proportion of air filtered and on the efficiency of filtration. It is obviously essential that the filter system must be suitable for use in stopes and must be able to withstand the shock of blasting.

Porous polyurethane foam, green in colour and referred to as "Vitaprene", 25 mm thick with a density of 20 kg/m³ and with an open-cell structure, allows air to flow through it and acts as a filter of moderate efficiency.

The filtering velocity is approximately 0,5 m/s for a pressure drop of 1,25 kPa when dust has collected on the polyurethane foam. This high filtering velocity reduces the size of the filter required to handle a given volume of air to only one-fifth of the size of a flannel bag installation. The foam is readily cleaned by hosing it down with water.

The use of a polyurethane foam filter either in cylindrical form or attached to mat packs can bring about reduced dust levels in stopes, particularly near the filter return. However, in situations where the intake dust levels and dust production are both high, i.e., where dust control is most needed, the use of intermediate filters seldom creates a safe condition from an unsafe condition. This will probably prejudice the acceptance of these filters.

When cooling coils are used in stopes it is possible to design a system in which a polyurethane foam filter is mounted before the cooling coils but in which the same fan is used. The resultant filtration of the dust before it passes over the cooling coils will prevent settlement of the dust. This can cause choking of the coils and a reduction of the effective heat exchange efficiency.

7.3   Electrostatic precipitation

Electrostatic precipitators, although more expensive to install, require much less fan power because of their low resistance, and consequently are cheaper over a long period. They can be very efficient if properly maintained and can be installed in a reasonably small space. However, they require regular attention by the electrical staff and are not well suited to the moist conditions usually prevailing underground. For these reasons they are not favoured and are recommended only for installations where large air quantities have to be filtered and where maintenance is commonly carried out.

Generally, two-stage units are used comprising an ionizing and a collecting section.

8   SURFACE EXTRACTION PLANTS

In South African gold mines the surface dust filtration plants deal mainly with the disposal of the large quantities of dust emitted into the air in the course of the crushing, sorting and milling processes.

The nature of the dust is the same as that produced underground as it is derived from the same rock, but the crushing and sorting are generally done under fairly dry conditions. The quantities and the sizes of the dust particles produced are very different from those of dust produced underground and large amounts have to be trapped and separated from the air. This dust is much coarser than that which becomes airborne underground, but still contains a small proportion of the dangerous 0 to 5 micrometre size range mixed with the coarser dust.

This explains why, although the principles of filtration are fundamentally the same on surface as underground, the problems to be faced are vastly different.

An advantage is that the filtered air is not recirculated but is emitted into the atmosphere where it is immediately diluted further and dispersed. The filtering efficiency of surface plants therefore need not be as high as that required underground; nevertheless, the emission of large quantities of dust into the atmosphere is not permitted. The quantities of dust to be separated and collected are so large that sampling methods to determine the efficiency of surface dust filtration plants must be different, and gravimetric sampling is used instead of number concentration methods.

Filtration plants of the strainer type, such as those in which the filter medium is cloth, cannot be used as the pressure build-up is too rapid, requiring immediate removal of the dust caught in the filter.

Although the efficiency of the filter need not be as high as that of filters underground, the quantity of dust emitted, even at the top of a high stack, should not be excessive in our modern industrial areas where large quantities of smoke and dust released into the atmosphere give cause for considerable concern.

The fundamental operation in dust filtration on surface is:

(a) conveying the dust and air to the point of filtration;

(b) separating the dust from the air; and

(c) removing the dust which has been separated.

The main object is to ensure that dust released by the crushing and sorting operations does not contaminate the air breathed by the operators, and exhaust points must be installed so that the airborne dust is carried to the filter plant. Since the size and cost of the extraction plant will be proportional to the amount of air to be handled, this should be as low as possible. In order to do this and still control the emission of dust, all sources of dust should be enclosed as much as possible. The velocity of the dust and air exhausted should be about 15 m/s.

Dust is separated from the air inside the extraction plant by

(a) settling the dust;

(b) impinging the dust particles on dry or wet surfaces; and

(c) centrifugally separating the dust from the air.

8.1   *Settling*

This method is used only when very coarse dust has to be removed from air. A chamber 2 m high would have to be 30 m long and the air velocity 0,5 m/s to settle all particles of 10 μm. If necessary, the air can thereafter pass through another dust extraction plant to separate the finer dust from the air. The size of dust particles encountered in reduction works does not warrant the installation of settling chambers.

8.2   *Impingement*

In this case the action depends upon the inertial effect on the particles as the air stream is suddenly diverted (similar in principle to centrifugal action). Because of their inertia, the large dust particles do not follow the deflected air-stream but are thrown out of their course towards regions of low air velocity where they settle out with the smaller dust particles remaining in the deflected air current. To ensure a good separation a sharp deflection and a high air velocity are required. Cross-sectional areas have to be kept low, otherwise secondary eddies are set up which prevent the settling of the dust particles. Wet impingement may comprise use of water sprays, water surfaces where the particles of dust are "wetted" by the liquid used, or the adherence of dust to a viscous (adhesive or sticky) surface. Also, finely-atomised water may be included in the air stream when the air is passing through a spray chamber. Air washers are generally used for dust removal and cooling, and can also be used as humidifiers.

8.3   *Centrifugal separation*

Centrifugal action as applied to large rotating bodies of air can be depended upon to remove only the heavier particles from the air stream. Usually dust particles of 10 micrometres and more can be extracted from the air when dry centrifugal dust extraction plants are used. Where dusts are finer, wet centrifugal extraction methods must be used and the particles which can be separated are 3 to 5 μm in size.

8.4   *Electrostatic precipitation*

Electrostatic precipitators used on the mines consist of two-stage units, each unit or cell being about 1,5 m² in frontal area. Each cell is made up of two sections, the ionising section and the dust collection section. In the ionising section the dust particles pass through an ionising field where the dust particles receive an electrostatic charge. This ionising field is maintained electrically by means of a high voltage. The ioniser consists of a row of alternate vertical wires and cylinders equally spaced across the entrance. The wires are maintained at a positive potential of about 13 kilovolts, while the cylinders are earthed.

The charged dust particles pass into the collector section, which consists of closely-spaced plates alternately earthed and charged at about 6 kilovolts. The electrostatic field between the collector plates drives the positively-charged particles to the earthed plates, where they accumulate and are removed by periodical washing. Electrostatic precipitators should not be used in fiery mines or in any explosive atmosphere, since they are liable to arc, especially under conditions of high humidity.

9   CLASSIFICATION OF DUST EXTRACTION PLANTS

A wide variety of dust extraction plants are available and it is not the intention in this chapter to describe them in detail. Reference can be made to manufacturers' specifications for this purpose. The table below is offered as a guide for the selection of any type of plant and the principle of operation is indicated by the diagrammatic sketches in Figs. 4:1, 4:2, and 4:3.

Type of plant	Size range μm		Efficiency %	Air velocity m/s	Dust load	Resistance kPa	
Scrubber	3	to 100+	70	2	Low	0,025 to 1,25	
Flannel bags	0,1	to 100+	95	0,025 to 0,125	Low	0,25 to 0,75	
Cyclones	3	to 100+	70	20	High	0,75 to 1,25	
Venturi scrubbers	0,01 to 100+		90+	60 to 120	High	2,5 to 5,0	
Electrostatic precipitators	0,01 to 100+		90 to 95	1 to 2	High	0,05 to 0,125	

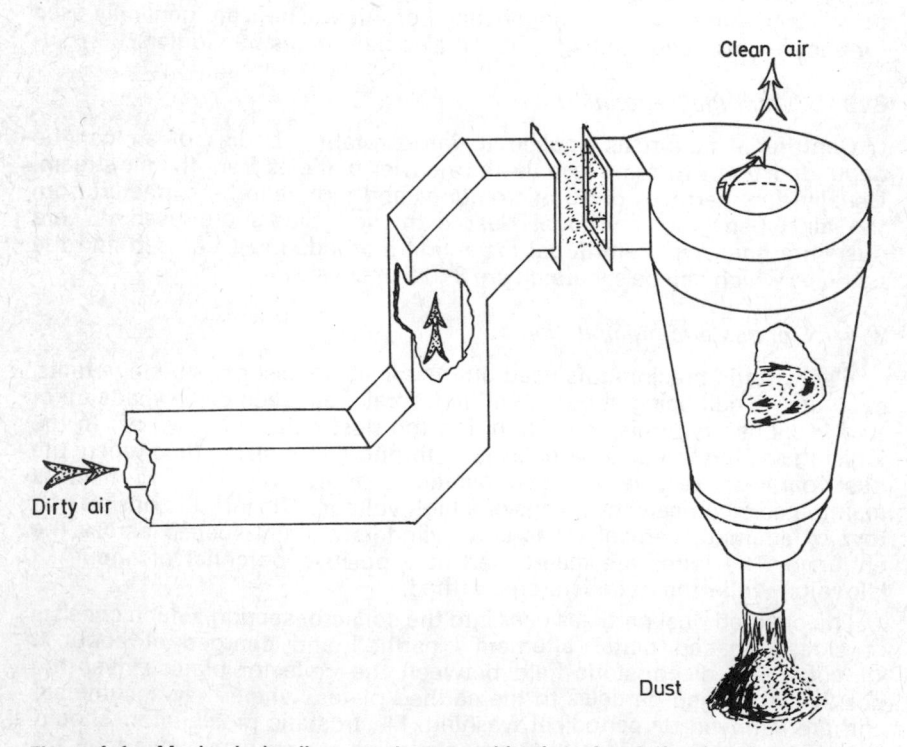

Clean air

Dirty air

Dust

Figure 4:1   Mechanical collector, using a combination of centrifugal and gravitational forces

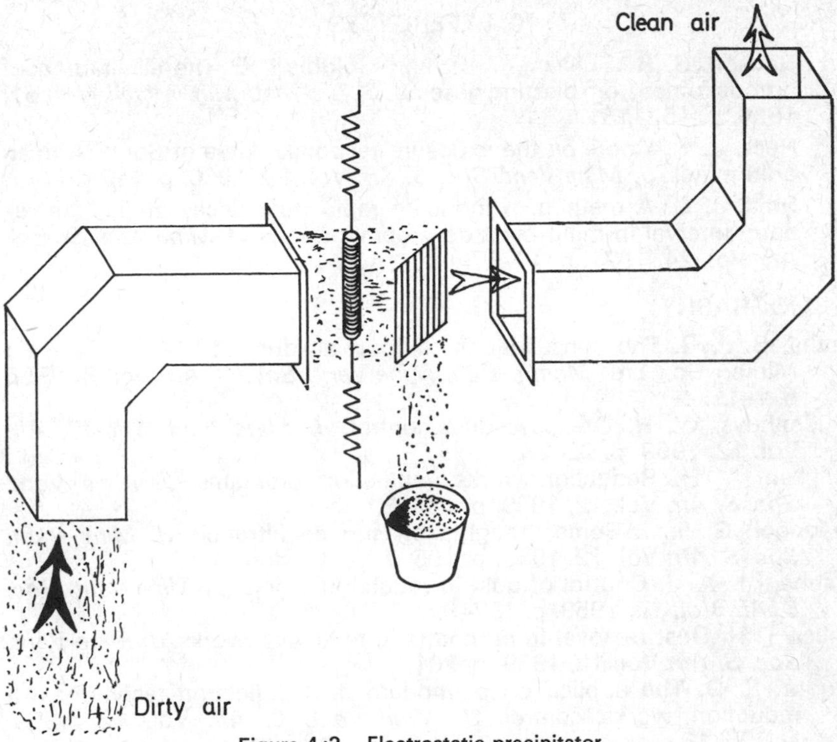

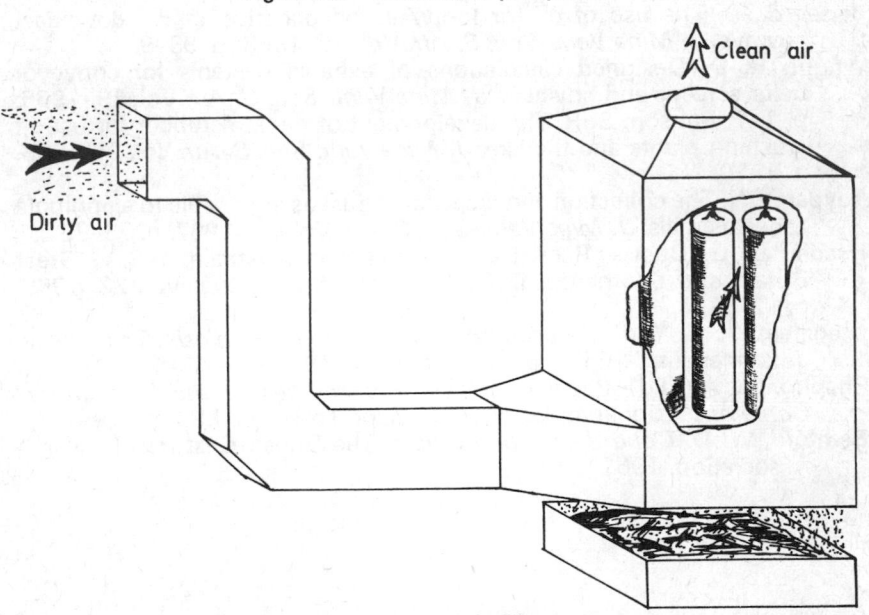

Clean air

Dirty air

Figure 4:2   Electrostatic precipitator

Clean air

Dirty air

Figure 4:3   Fabric Filters

10 REFERENCES

1   Rabson, S. R. Quilliam, J. H. and Goldblatt, E. The elimination of nitrous fumes from blasting gases. *J. S. Afr. Inst. Min. Metall.* Vol. 61, 1960. p. 152–181.

2   Rees, J. P. A note on the exposure-response curve of South African gold mines. *J. Mine Vent. Soc. S. Afr.* Vol. 13, 1960. p. 145–147.

3   Smit, J. G. A method of inducing rapid dust decay during the re-entry interval in multi-blast development ends. *J. Mine Vent. Soc. S. Afr.* Vol. 24, 1971. p. 46–57.

BIBLIOGRAPHY

Botha, B. J. R. The consolidation of footwall dust at Vlakfontein Gold Mining Co., Ltd. *Month. Bull. Mine Vent. Soc. S. Afr.* Vol. 8, 1955 p. 1–11.

Geldenhuys, W. H. Ore pass dust control. *J. Mine Vent. Soc. S. Afr.* Vol. 12, 1959. p. 22–23.

Mokken, A. H. Reduction works ventilation problems. *J. Mine Vent. Soc. S. Afr.* Vol. 12, 1959. p. 185–8.

Braunger, G. F. J. Some thoughts on surface filtration. *J. Mine Vent. Soc. S. Afr.* Vol. 12, 1959. p. 195–7.

Slabbert, L. A. J. Control of dust in reduction works. *J. Mine Vent. Soc. S. Afr.* Vol. 12, 1959. p. 197–9.

Miller, T. H. Dust removal from motors in reduction works. *J. Mine Vent. Soc. S. Afr.* Vol. 12, 1959. p. 201.

Wright, R. D. The application of modern dust collection techniques in reduction works control. *J. Mine Vent. S. Afr.* Vol. 12, 1959. p. 205–16.

Visser, B. C. The use of oil for footwall consolidation in dry downcast airways. *J. Mine Vent. Soc. S. Afr.* Vol. 16, 1963. p. 98–9.

Wright, R. D. Designed calculations of exhaust systems for conveyor belts, screens and crushers. *J. Mine Vent. Soc. S. Afr.* Vol. 19, 1966. p. 1–7. Rabson, S. R. The development of a wet scrubber for use at crushing plants and the like. *J. Mine Vent. Soc. S. Afr.* Vol. 21, 1968. p. 1–10.

Kuyper, L. N. The collection and disposal of dust as applicable to amphibole asbestos mills. *J. Mine Vent. Soc. S. Afr.* Vol. 20, 1967. p. 73–96

Beadle, D. G. Dust – Recent developments in Australia, U.S.A., Great Britain and South Africa. *J. Mine Vent. Soc. S. Afr.* Vol. 22, 1969. p. 17–51.

Orenstein, A. J. (Ed) *Proceedings of the Pneumoconiosis Conference*, Johannesburg, 1959. London, Churchill, 1960.

Shapiro, H. A. (Ed) Pneumoconiosis. *Proceedings of the International Conference*, Johannesburg, 1969. Cape Town, O.U.P. 1970.

Bamford, W. D. *Control of airborne dust.* The British Cast Iron Research Association, 1961.

5 Methods of Dust Sampling and Assessment

J. H. QUILLIAM

Chief, Dust Division, Physical Sciences Laboratory, Chamber of Mines Research Organization.

1   INTRODUCTION

The presence of dust in mine air is caused by almost every mining operation. Examples are blasting, scraping, drilling, tipping and shovelling. The inhalation of dust may cause pneumoconiosis which is a general term for a large group of diseases of the respiratory organs including all the specific forms of diseases caused by dust, such as silicosis, asbestosis and anthracosis.

The importance of controlling dust has long been recognised and dust levels have been measured in South African gold mines for over half a century.

The method of sampling used in mines in the early days was the "sugar tube" method which was abandoned in 1938. A prototype konimeter was developed by Sir Robert Kotze in 1916 and brought into general use in 1922; improved forms of this instrument are still being used for routine sampling on mines. The thermal precipitator with microscopic assessment of samples was introduced in 1933. Several instruments incorporating variations of the basic principles which have proved to be of value in research work have been developed.

An important recent development is the automatic assessment of thermal precipitator slides by means of a diffraction size frequency analyser and in recent years much attention has been given to the development of instruments and methods for the gravimetric sampling of dust.

It is generally accepted that any parameters measured in the sampling of dust should relate reasonably closely to the health hazard of the dust.

In addition, one overall integrated measurement of the dust should be obtained, and the nearer this is related to the health hazard of the dust the more meaningful it will be.

The International Pneumoconiosis Conference held in Johannesburg in 1959, examined carefully all the relevant information then available, and recommended that:

(a)   Measurements of dust in pneumoconiosis studies should relate to the "respirable fraction" of the dust. The recommended sampling curve was defined as effectively 100 per cent for particle sizes of one micrometre and less; 50 per cent for particle sizes of 5 micrometres and 0 per cent for particle sizes of 7 micrometres and greater. All these sizes refer to the equivalent diameter of unit density particles but because of shape factors and the tendency of particles to be deposited on slides with their maximum cross-sectional areas parallel to the slide, the same curve is applied without a density correction in South Africa to quartz particles.

(b)   In the light of present knowledge, dust levels should be expressed as the average level of dustiness over an appropriate period of sampling, such as one shift.

(c)   In the light of present available evidence, the best single descriptive parameter to measure is considered, in the case of quartz, to be the surface area of the respirable dust, and in the case of coal dust, the mass of the respirable dust.

If dust sampling is to be placed on a sound scientific basis, the questions of what should be measured and what can be measured must be considered.

2   OBJECTS OF DUST SAMPLING

The Mines and Works Act and Regulations stipulates that sampling must be undertaken not less than once in three months, in metal mines at all working places where harmful dust can be created.

The main object of dust sampling is to obtain a measurement of the amount of dust in the air in order to locate the sources of undesirably high dust concentrations, so that control or remedial measures can be introduced.

There are many subsidiary objects and the choice of instrument, strategy employed and methods of assessment should be based on the particular object in view. The objects of routine dust sampling are:

(a)   to detect working places in which dust concentrations are high,

(b)   to determine the cause of such conditions,

(c)   to obtain an indication of what control measures are necessary,

(d)   to determine the effectiveness of dust suppression methods or equipment,

(e)   to determine whether satisfactory conditions have been obtained after remedial action has been taken, and to ensure that they remain satisfactory,

(f)   to provide records of dust conditions so that trends can be assessed.

For research purposes, dust is sampled for many reasons, for example, the correlation of dust exposures with the incidence of disease (epidemiological studies), air pollution control, the development of methods for the provision of dust indices, the prevention of formation of dust in specific operations, and generally for controlling the dust situation in mines.

3   PARAMETERS DETERMINED BY DUST SAMPLING

The following parameters are determined from dust samples:

3.1   *Number concentration in particles per millilitre* (p/mℓ)

The thermal precipitator is the most generally accepted standard instrument used for determining the number concentration of dust particles in the respirable range, and is used mainly in research. The konimeter, the samples of which are assessed at a much lower magnification, also provides a record of the number concentration and is used in routine work on mines. The samples taken by both instruments are assessed by microscope.

3.2   *Mass concentration in milligrams per cubic metre* (mg/m³)

Several types of portable instruments are used to collect bulk samples on membrane filters. The mass of the dust collected is obtained after ashing with subsequent analysis of the constituents by X-ray diffraction. The mass size distributions are usually carried out by the Andreasen sedimentation tube method.

3.3   *Surface area in square micrometres per millilitre* (μm²/mℓ)

Samples for surface area measurements are collected either by the thermal precipitator or some form of bulk (gravimetric) method.

Thermal precipitator samples can be assessed by means of the optical microscope and/or the electron microscope, photoelectrically or by means of a diffraction size frequency analyser.

It is usual, when counting by means of a microscope, to measure only the projected surface area by comparison with a series of circles within an eye-piece graticule.

The photoelectric method of assessment for thermal precipitator samples is used as a matter of routine for colliery dust control. As the scope of this chapter is confined to dust in gold mines, this method is not described.

The surface area per unit volume is obtained from gravimetric samples by an air permeability method.

3.4 *Composition*

Samples are taken as described in Section 3.2. Chemical and X-ray methods of analysis, the latter applicable to crystalline solids, can be used, with differential thermal analysis as a good alternative for measurements on quartz.

4   DUST SAMPLING INSTRUMENTS

4.1 *The konimeter*[1]

The instrument in general routine use is the new Witwatersrand konimeter. The instrument is used to take 5 mℓ snap samples of air containing dust which are caused to pass through a tapered jet and to impinge on a glass slide coated with adhesive. The dust is deposited on the slide in the form of a "spot"; a number of such spots can be taken on one glass slide.

The standard instrument is fitted with a size selector which removes from the air sample dust aggregates and water droplets of a size outside the respirable range, which normally cause overestimation of the dust concentrations by their partial or complete disintegration on the slide.[2]

4.2 *Thermal precipitator*

This instrument is used to provide a measure of the average dustiness of air over various periods of time. The standard thermal precipitator was introduced in the gold mining industry in 1933, but it has not been adopted as a routine sampling instrument.[3]

Thermal precipitators in various forms have been developed and used for research investigations where greater accuracy is required than can be obtained with the konimeter and where it is desired to obtain the size distribution of the dust; the surface area of the particles is obtained by calculation from the number count in the various size groups or directly by means of a diffraction size frequency analyser.[4]

The precipitating action of the thermal precipitator depends on the phenomenon that if air is drawn past a heated body, the fine dust particles in the air will be deflected and deposited on relatively cold surfaces in the near vicinity of the heated body. This is caused by the greater intensity of molecular bombardment on the side of the dust particles nearest to the heated body. (See Chapter 3 on "Properties and effects of dust".)

Various types of thermal precipitators have been used, such as the standard types with water aspirators or with mechanical aspirators. Modified thermal precipitators have either bellows-type aspirators or mechanical aspirators, and in long-sampling thermal precipitators the slides are moved continuously by clockwork so as to obtain a record of changes in dust concentrations over periods of up to 24 hours.

4.3 *Accuracy of thermal precipitator and konimeter sampling*

The accuracy of the konimeter depends on the properties of the dust being sampled. If the dust is aggregated and contains water droplets, impingement of the dust on the slides is likely to cause break-up of the aggregates which will result in an abnormally high count. The use of a size selector greatly reduces this effect. If the dust is fine, the count will be low, as the collecting efficiency is less for fine particles.

Although not a precise instrument, the konimeter is useful for routine sampling and for the rapid detection of high concentrations.

Where the dust concentration varies in time and space the volume sampled is too small and the time of sampling, one quarter of a second, is too short to give an accurate value of the dust concentration. The magnitude of these errors can be reduced by taking a larger number of samples over a longer period of time.

The accuracy of results obtained by means of the thermal precipitator depends far less on the accuracy of the instrument itself than on the variations in dust concentrations expected in airborne dust and on the accuracy of assessment of the samples.

The efficiency of deposition of the dust sample depends on a number of factors, such as the rate of airflow, the temperature of the wire, and the size, shape and density of the particles. For all practical purposes the slight loss of the larger particles within the pneumoconiosis-producing size range is probably not significant when the other errors in sampling and assessment are taken into account.

Experiments with thermal precipitators sampling side by side have shown that the coefficient of variation of a single sample is about 13 per cent if based on a number count.

It has also been shown that the average coefficient of variation between samples taken underground may be about 40 per cent for samples taken over a period of one to two hours. These coefficients of variation can of course be reduced in the usual manner by increasing the number of samples taken.

4.4 *Gravimetric samplers*

Gravimetric sampling, as the term implies, is carried out for the assessment of dust concentration by mass.

Gravimetric sampling consists basically of two steps, first, the collection of a representative portion of the dust from the air, and, second, the assessment of the collected material by determination of its mass and analysis by X-ray diffraction or chemical means.

One method of sampling is to deposit the dust by drawing the air through a suitable filter. A commonly used type of gravimetric sampler with filter holder is shown in Fig. 5:1 (*a*) and (*b*). Gravimetric samples can also be taken by means of an electrostatic precipitator, a small cyclone or other apparatus operating on the centrifugal principle, or by bubbling the air through a suitable liquid.

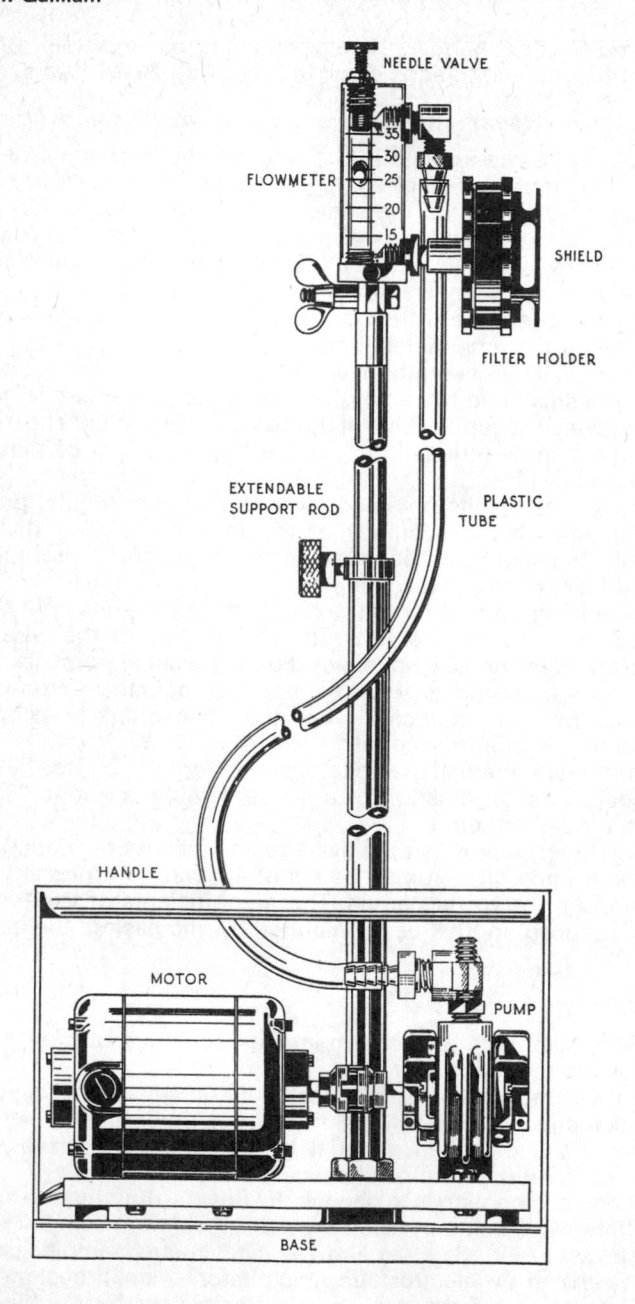

GRAVIMETRIC SAMPLER

Figure 5:1 (a)

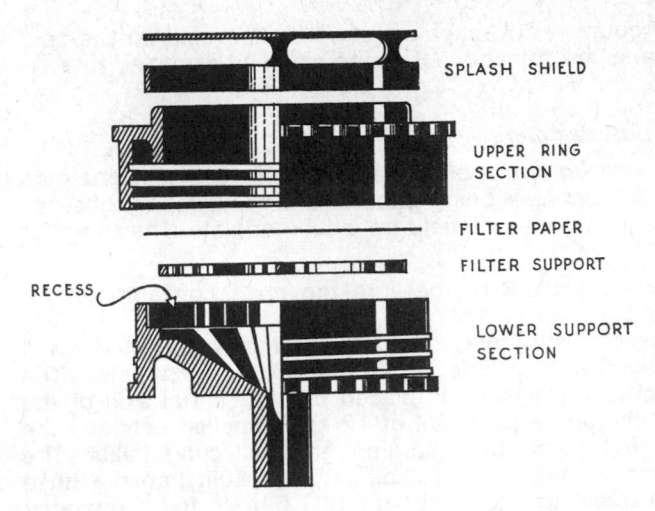

SPLASH SHIELD

UPPER RING
SECTION

FILTER PAPER
FILTER SUPPORT

RECESS

LOWER SUPPORT
SECTION

EXPLODED VIEW
(PART SECTION)

ISOMETRIC VIEW
(WITHOUT SHIELD OR FILTER PAPER)

DETAILS OF FILTER HOLDER

Figure 5:1 (b)

4.5 *Stack sampling unit*

This unit is used to determine the rate of mass flow of solids in stacks and ventilation systems. The main features are a probe and nozzles generally of stainless steel with cooling fins if necessary, rotameter, vacuum gauge, thermometer, Pitot tube and pump. Suitable filter papers, such as membrane filters or glass fibre filters can be used where high temperatures are encountered. Graphs are available for rapid on-the-spot velocity estimates and the selection of probe size and sampling rate for isokinetic sampling.

4.6 Electrostatic dust samplers

The electrostatic sampler works on the principle of electrically charging the dust particles in the air or gas being sampled and collecting the charged dust particles in an intense electric field on a tube or plate. The samplers are of two types, namely:

(1) Those which are used to measure the mass concentration of dust in a gas.

In this type of instrument, the dust is usually collected on a tubular collecting electrode, as in the MSA air sampler. The corona discharge electrode is placed on the central axis of the collecting tube and a potential of 12 kV is applied between the electrodes to provide the charging and collecting fields. The MSA instrument has a small aspirating fan built into the head providing a sampling rate of about 0,001 5 m^3/s and is operated from a mains power supply.

As this instrument is too small for sampling gases in ducts or stacks, a task for which the electrostatic sampler is well suited, a special sampler has been designed for this application. It can be coupled to a sampling tube in a duct or stack and air is drawn through it by an external aspirator, and a potential of 18 kV is supplied to the electrodes. The insulating body of the unit supporting the electrodes is heated electrically to prevent condensation of vapours which might cause electrical failure. This sampler is operated from a mains power supply or a compact battery supply.

(2) Those which are used to collect bulk quantities of airborne dust for chemical or physical analysis.

The small tube samplers described above are not able to collect a large sample in a practical length of time in a low dust concentration area, and a parallel-plate sampler with a large collecting surface area capable of processing larger volumes of air has been developed for this purpose.

4.7 General purpose air mover

This unit is used for general gravimetric sampling purposes, particularly where large volumes of air are involved.

The volume sampled is regulated by using a variable transformer and measured by means of calibrated orifice plates from 3 mm to 40 mm in diameter. The maximum vacuum at the pump is 10 kPa.

5   UNDERGROUND DUST SAMPLING STRATEGY

If adequate dust control is to be achieved in a mine four requirements for dust sampling must be met. It is necessary:

(a) to determine the true overall dust level in a mine, and to determine whether this is varying or remaining static, that is, to indicate trends in dust levels (Positional or personnel sampling.);

(b)   to determine fluctuations in the dust levels, or the maximum dust levels during a period of one shift;

(c)   to determine the amounts of dust produced by various operations such as scraping, drilling, shovelling, tipping, which will indicate whether any new dust control methods should be investigated; (Operational sampling.);

(d)   to pinpoint individual causes of dust production so that remedial action may be taken as soon as possible. (Trouble shooting.)

The following two methods have been used to determine overall dust levels or dust indices in mines:

5.1   *Positional sampling using the thermal precipitator*[7]

By careful selection of sampling points an adequately broad picture can be obtained from relatively few sampling points.

It is essential to include sampling points which will show clearly the build-up of dust concentrations in the air from the point at which the air leaves the downcast shafts up to the beginning of the return airway systems. Usually 40 to 50 sampling points along this route are enough to make such an investigation in an average-sized gold mine.

Typical sampling points include the following:

(a)   main stations on downcast shafts;

(b)   positions beyond main tips;

(c)   deliveries of intake airways;

(d)   the bottoms, centres, and tops of the main stoping sections;

(e)   the faces of randomly-selected development ends;

(f)   return air from randomly-selected development ends;

(g)   the intake of main return airways;

(h)   randomly-selected isolated workings.

The number of sampling points of each type should take into account the relative number of workers in each type of working place; that is, many more sampling points should be selected in stopes than in, say, haulages.

Each sample is taken over a period of one to two hours and the slides assessed using the diffraction size frequency analyser to determine respirable surface area, or under the microscope to determine number concentration.

Samples should be taken at each point during at least three different shifts, preferably some days apart, so that any variations in working conditions are likely to be accounted for. The average of the values for each sampling point is plotted on a sequential sampling chart.[8] From this plot it can be determined whether average dust conditions at each point are above or below the "acceptance" level or whether they are borderline.

In order to provide guidance to a mine manager, it is desirable that some definite "limit of acceptability" be set. There is no legal limit, or even an agreed value, for this criterion in South African gold mines. If the parameter of respirable surface area is used, a value of 300 $\mu m^2/m\ell$ is suggested as a limit in order to indicate whether conditions in working places are acceptable.

5.2   *Konimeter sampling near personnel*

A second method whereby the overall dust picture in a mine can be obtained is by taking a sample at every person, or at every second or third person in all working places or in a representative number of working places on a predetermined route. The sampler takes the dust samples regardless of what task the person is doing. To obtain valid results the sampling should be distributed evenly over the whole of the shift.

This method involves taking a large number of samples each of relatively short duration, and the disadvantages of this are :

(*a*)   the lack of accuracy of the konimeter, particularly for high dust levels, as well as the underestimation of fine dust ; and

(*b*)   the need to count the konimeter samples under the microscope, which is laborious, time-consuming and subject to human error.

5.3   *Occupational sampling*

To measure the dust levels to which workers in various job categories are exposed, and to be able to ascertain fluctuations or maximum dust levels within a shift period.

The dust risk associated with specific occupations can be measured satisfactorily by "personnel sampling" during the course of a shift.

This is possibly the least useful method for dust control purposes because the dust level at any given man may not be due primarily to work he is doing. The dust at his working place may come from work being performed some distance away in the air stream reaching him. It is, however, very useful for research purposes and has been used in epidemiological studies to determine the relationship between the amount of dust breathed and the development of silicosis, which has led to the derivation of curves showing the probability of a man contracting silicosis after he has worked a specified number of shifts at specific dust levels. [9]

5.4   *Operational dust sampling*

This method is designed to measure the amount of dust produced by the various operations in a mine e.g., by scraping, drilling, tipping, etc.

It comprises taking simultaneous samples of the intake and return air from the specific operation and determining, by difference, the amount of dust produced.

5.5   *Trouble shooting*

Samples are taken with the konimeters at various points in the working places. If dust levels are high, remedial action is taken.

This method does not give a valid overall picture of dust levels in the mine. It does not provide information on the specific operations causing the dust, and does not give a measure of how much dust men breathe throughout the shift.

It does, however, play a very important part in dust control as it indicates where dust levels are unsatisfactory. It is often possible to identify the causes and suggest what action is needed for improvement.

Before selecting any one of the above methods, the objects of the sampling should be defined clearly and only then should the strategy be selected.

6 GRAVIMETRIC DUST-SAMPLING TECHNIQUES[10]

6.1 *Exposure or environmental sampling*

The purpose of this type of sampling is to assess the dust concentrations in the air to which personnel are exposed, in other words, to measure the dust hazard.

Gravimetric methods as distinct from particle number estimates are used particularly where the dust is toxic. In such cases, it is the dose or mass of dust absorbed in the system that decides the extent of the danger. Mass determination rather than number of particles is also indicated in all cases where the material is relatively soluble and would therefore soon be completely dissolved in the human system. Gravimetric methods are used in the mining industry for sampling uranium, manganese, lime and lead dusts, and fumes. Gravimetric methods can also be used to sample siliceous dust to supplement the results of number determinations.

The characteristic features are the relatively small quantities of dust present, ranging from less than 0,1 mg/m³ to 100 mg/m³, the normal temperature and pressure and the relatively static nature of the air where velocities are generally less than 0,5 m/s.

Sampling is comparatively simple as ordinary filter materials may be used. No difficulties arise from undue increase in resistance as the dust collects on the filter, and no complications result from kinetic effects due to high air velocities.

A suitable method of sampling is to draw air at a measured rate of 0,4 ℓ/s through a filter paper 55 mm in diameter by means of a pump. The sampling period may vary from 20 minutes to an hour or more.

6.2 *Stack sampling*

This method of sampling is used to assess the amount of dust produced by a process, or leaving a process or plant through a stack, or to determine the efficiency of a dust collector by measuring the amount of dust entering and leaving it. In all cases, the emphasis is on the recovery or the loss of dust in terms of mass of material. In these circumstances number determinations have no significance.

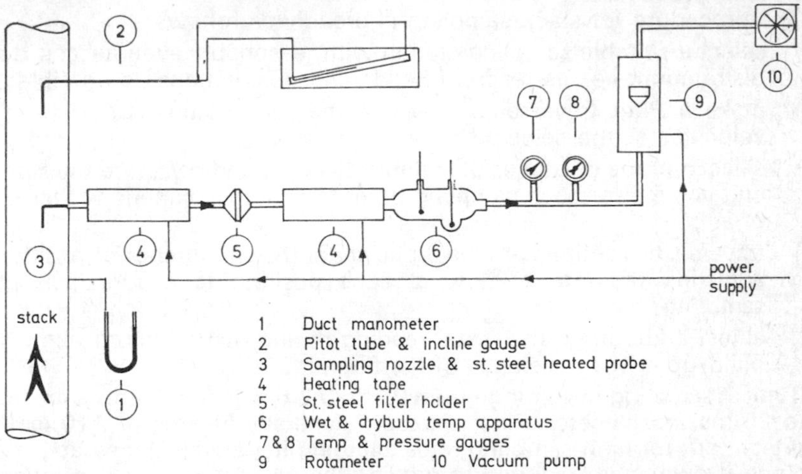

1	Duct manometer	
2	Pitot tube & incline gauge	
3	Sampling nozzle & st. steel heated probe	
4	Heating tape	
5	St. steel filter holder	
6	Wet & drybulb temp apparatus	
7 & 8	Temp & pressure gauges	
9	Rotameter	10 Vacuum pump

Figure 5:2   Stack sampling apparatus

The characteristic features are the high concentrations of dust, the high velocities of the dust-laden air in the duct or stack, and the frequently severe temperature and corrosive conditions. These conditions often make stack sampling a complicated matter and place it in a different category from exposure sampling. High dust concentrations cause high resistance to be built up rapidly on the collecting filter, with resulting decrease in flow rate necessitating frequent adjustment and extensive correction for density at the measuring apparatus.

Isokinetic sampling is necessary because of the high air stream velocities (typically 5 to 15 m/s) and the resultant inertial effects of the dust.

When the gas is drawn into the nozzle with a velocity *greater* than the velocity existing in the stack at the sampling point, a number of streamlines *converge* and crowd into the nozzle. The fine particles follow the deflected streamlines but the coarser particles continue along their original paths and miss the nozzle completely. Hence the volume of gas extracted will contain fewer coarse particles than actually exist in the same volume in the flue. As a result the calculated mass concentrations would be too low and the particle size distribution would be false.

Similarly, if the gas enters the nozzle with a velocity *less* than the velocity existing in the flue, a number of the streamlines *diverge* so that they do not enter the nozzle.

The fine particles are transported along these deflected streamlines, but the coarse particles, because of their greater inertia, leave the streamlines and enter the nozzle. Hence, the volume of gas extracted will contain *more* coarse particles than this same volume contains in the flue. As a result, the calculated mass concentration would be *higher* than that actually existing in the flue at the sampling point.

Failure to sample isokinetically gives inaccurate results which may vary from as low as a half of the correct results, if sampling is too rapid, to as high as two or three times the correct result if sampling is too slow.[11] The position is complicated further because the dust concentration profile is seldom uniform across the sampling cross-section. The duct or stack must therefore be traversed at a sufficient number of positions to obtain representative results.

The procedure for stack sampling is broadly as follows:

(*a*)   select a suitable sampling station with reasonably even air and dust distribution, i.e., as far from bends and obstructions as possible;

(*b*)   make a Pitot traverse to establish the total volume flow and the velocities at the selected sampling position;

(*c*)   select a probe or probes of suitable diameter and *calculate* the sampling volume for each sampling point to ensure isokinetic withdrawal of air;

(*d*)   traverse the section with the probe at a sufficient number of positions, adjusting the rate of flow at each position to ensure isokinetic sampling;

(*e*)   adjust and correct the meter reading during operations to allow for build-up in the resistance of the filter.

Typical sampling rates range from 0,1 to 0,2 ℓ/s. Normal probes are from 5 to 25 mm in diameter. Filter sizes are generally 55 mm or 110 mm in diameter, but for high sampling rates a larger filter area is necessary.

Special pumps are required to provide the necessary duty and to cope with the increase in pressure, which may reach up to 25 kPa as the dust is deposited on the filter.

The procedure is complicated further if the air is at a high temperature. For high temperatures, as with air from furnaces (flue gases), corrections must be made for the cooling of the air before it passes through the metering apparatus.

For high temperatures, and when corrosive gases are encountered, the sampling equipment should be constructed of special material, and suitable heat-resistant filtering material must be used. The gas should not cool below the dew point.

Electrostatic sampling can be used instead of the filter methods. It has the advantage that there is no increase in resistance so that sampling rate adjustments are easier to make and maintain.

To estimate the efficiency of a dust collector, samples are taken simultaneously at the inlet and outlet over reasonable periods of time to ensure representative conditions. The amount of dust removed is assessed on a mass basis, reference being made to operating data, e.g., main volume flow, manometer reading, and so on. In efficiency tests and also where stack sampling is conducted for the purpose of determining the specifications required for a suitable dust collector, samples are, in addition to mass evaluation, generally subjected to size analysis on a mass basis.

7   SAMPLING ON SURFACE PLANTS AND IN WORKSHOPS

Routine dust sampling on surface reduction plants and workshops is done by means of the konimeter.

Independent annual surveys are done by the Chamber of Mines Research Laboratories in surface plants of uranium producing mines as follows:

(a)   acid mist at rotary filters using a gravimetric sampler. Insoluble material and acidity (as sulphuric acid) are reported in mg/m^3;

(b)   siliceous dust at rotary filter and precipitation plants using konimeters (p/mℓ) and thermal precipitators (respirable surface area expressed as μm^2/mℓ);

(c)   manganese and lime in reagent sections using gravimetric samplers. Concentrations of manganese as Mn and lime as CaO in mg/m^3;

(d)   uranium content at rotary filter sections and precipitation plants, gravimetrically, with results reported in μg/m^3.

8   DUST ASSESSMENT METHODS

8.1   *Optical microscope*

The microscope has been of the greatest value in assessing the relative dangers due to dust in working places.[12]

In the examination of dust samples one is concerned more with the actual sizes of the particles than with the actual magnification of the particle.

To measure these, a *graticule* is focussed in the same plane as the enlarged images of the particles. The particles are sized by comparison with circles of known size.

The graticule may be ruled suitably and its apparent dimensions measured by examining an object of known size, usually a micrometer gauge with lines ruled 10 micrometres (0,01 mm) apart.

8.2 *Assessment of konimeter samples*

The slide carrying the samples is mounted on the microscope stage and the eyepiece graticule adjusted until the two 18° sectors cover a representative section of the spot. The particles are counted, the area covered by the two 18° sectors being one tenth of the whole spot. As each spot is obtained from 5 ml of air, the count represents the dust counted in $5 \times 0,1$ mℓ, i.e,. 0,5 mℓ. Therefore, concentration in p/mℓ equals $2 \times$ actual count. For counts greater than 1 000 p/mℓ estimates are made in steps of 500 p/mℓ.[1]

Specifications which are recommended for the konimeter microscope are provided in "Routine Mine Ventilation Measurements."[1]

8.3 *Assessment of thermal precipitator samples under the optical microscope*

Various methods are available for counting and the one which is chosen will depend on the degree of accuracy required.

Usually the dust particles are sized at the same time as they are counted. Two commonly used methods of counting are given below:

(i)   Multiple-traverse counting

The dust strip mounted in a vertical position is passed across the field of view of the microscope and a traverse made across the width of the strip. A single traverse will only provide limited accuracy, and hence greater accuracy can be obtained by counting the particles in a number of traverses of the sample. The number of traverses to be made depends on the accuracy required but at least three traverses at widely separated intervals in the strip, i.e., at 0,25, 0,5 and 0,75 along its length, are made.

(ii)   Truncated multiple-traverse counting

The greater the number of traverses made the more representative the results will be. Multiple-traverse counting becomes very laborious if there are many traverses.

The details of truncated multiple-traverse counting are:

(a)   three traverses are counted on each slide, the first in the middle of the dust strip, the other two half-way between the middle and the ends of the dust strip;

(b)   if less than 20 particles have been counted in the smallest size range, counts are made on more traverses until a total of 20 particles of this size or 20 traverses have been counted;

(c)   if 20 particles have been counted after a number of traverses in the smallest range, this size range may be ignored in further traverses;

(d)   counting is continued until either 20 particles have been counted or 20 traverses have been made in each size range;

(e)   if, in any traverse, 20 or more particles are counted in any of the bigger size ranges and not in a smaller size range, more traverses are made, all sizes being counted from the smaller size range upwards, until 20 particles have been counted in this range. Only then can this size range be ignored in future traverses;

(f)   the traverses must be evenly distributed along the length of the strip.

The recommended specifications for the thermal precipitator micro-scope are:

Eyepiece	Approximately 10 to 15 × compensating
Objectives	(i) 16 mm Achromatic N.A. not less than 0,25
	(ii) 2 mm of high quality, having a N.A. of approx. 1,30
Condenser	Abbe. N.A. approx. 1,2
Dark field stop	As found suitable
Eyepiece graticule	A commonly used eyepiece graticule is shown in Fig. 5:3
Lamp	Built into the body of the miscoscope
Stage	Mechanical with vernier scales

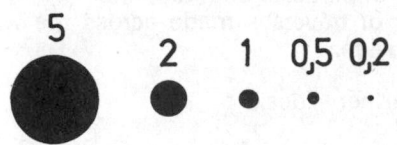

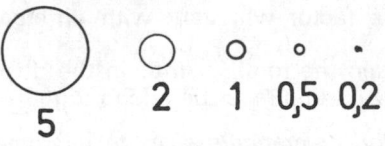

Figure 5:3   Five-spot graticule

8.3.1   *Methods of sizing*

The sizing of particles is done at the same time as the particles are counted, using a suitable graticule. The particles are sized by comparing the area of each particle and assigning the particle to the appropriate size group between two adjacent circles on the graticule. Each particle must be sharply in focus for the matching process. For the sizing of small particles, the intensity of the particle is used as a guide to its size. The more intense the particle, the larger it is.

The number of size groups into which the particles are to be assigned will depend on the requirements of the investigation. There are several sizing graticules, the most commonly used being the 5-spot type (Figure

5 : 3). The choice of graticule depends on the accuracy with which it is desired to know the size grading. For many purposes, grading into only four size groups is sufficiently accurate.

8.3.2 *Calculation of results*

Calculation of particles per millilitre (p/mℓ):

(*a*)   In the standard thermal precipitator, two microscope slides known as partner slides are obtained from each sample.

(*b*)   For each slide, calculate $\dfrac{n}{t}$ for each size group, where

   n = number of particles counted, and
   t = number of traverses made across the width of the dust strip on *one* slide.

(*c*)   Add $\dfrac{n}{t}$ for partner slides.

(*d*)   Concentration of dust in p/mℓ $= \dfrac{n}{t} \times \dfrac{F}{V}$

   where
   F = microscope factor, and
   V = volume of air sampled in millilitres.

Note :   The microscope factor is obtained by dividing the length of the dust sample by the width of the graticule used to count the dust particles. For example, if the average sample length is 9,7 mm and the apparent width of a 5-spot graticule is 0,009 mm for the objective used, then the microscope factor would be

$$F = \frac{9,7}{0,009}$$

$$F = 1\,070$$

The microscope factor will vary with different types of lenses and tube lengths.

In order to obtain the total "p/mℓ" in the dust sample, the values of "p/mℓ" in each size group must be added together.

8.3.3 *Conversion of graticule sizes to micrometres*

The diameter, in μm, of the graticule circles must be known in order to give the actual sizes of the particle ranges measured. Their apparent sizes will depend on the magnification used and are determined by means of a micrometer.

8.3.4 *Calculation of respirable surface area and total surface area*

It is possible to calculate the respirable surface area (RSA) from counts under the microscope of thermal precipitator slides. In most cases, it is sufficiently accurate to do this from the counts divided into four particle size groups. The method of making this calculation was developed by Joffe and Sichel.[13] It is also possible, in the same calculation, to determine the "total surface area" (TSA) of the particles on the slide.

8.4 *Automatic assessment of thermal precipitator samples by means of a diffraction size frequency analyser*[4]

In the past the surface area of the respirable fraction of the dust has been determined by counting the number of dust particles of each size under a microscope. This technique is time- and labour-consuming and the reproducibility and accuracy are limited by the human element.

The Diffraction Size-Frequency Analyser (DISA) is a new instrument in which the diffraction of light is used as a basis for measuring particle size and determining respirable surface areas. Because it is a simple instrument which requires no high-precision work and no critical adjustment, it lends itself particularly well to automation. Reproducibility of the results is of a high order and theoretically the accuracy should also be very good.

8.5 *Assessment of gravimetric samples*[10]

8.5.1 *Chemical analysis*

The methods of assessment of the collected dust vary according to the type of dust and other conditions. The simplest method is to collect the dust on a filter, the mass of which is determined before and after sampling, but in actual practice this cannot be done with small quantities of dust since it is difficult to bring filter paper to constant mass because it absorbs moisture and loses mass during drying. For the determination of siliceous and other incombustible dusts, the filter paper is ignited and the mass of the residue obtained.

For determination of dust containing substances such as lead, which tend to volatilize only at high temperatures, the filter paper is burnt off by heating it at a controlled temperature, of, say 500°C, without material loss of the substance.

Various types of filters are available. "Membrane" or "Millipore" filters are highly efficient and are more constant in mass than cellulose filters, but cannot be heated as high as 100°C without loss of mass. "Microsorban" filters are effective, but cannot be heated to temperatures above 50°C. Glass fibre filters, which have been found to be constant in mass and to withstand temperatures up to 500°C, are used frequently.

For the determination of uranium, lead and other toxic dusts, e.g., manganese and lime, the collected material is dissolved in a suitable reagent, usually either after removing the filter material by combustion, or directly from the paper, and the contaminant determined by chemical analysis.

8.5.2 *X-ray diffraction*[14]

This method can be applied only to crystalline solids, a distinguishing feature of which is the regular arrangement of their atoms in what can be regarded as planes. There will be many such planes in a single crystal and the distances between parallel planes (i.e., the lattice spacings) constitute a fundamental property of any particular crystalline substance, which can be identified if the lattice spacings can be measured. Most of the X-rays pass right through the crystal, but a small fraction are reflected by each plane.

If the wave-length of the X-ray is of the same order as the spacing between the planes, interference occurs. This is caused by the second reflected ray following a longer path to the detector and either cancelling out or reinforcing the first reflected ray. The effect of this is that the X-rays are concentrated into certain directions by such multiple reflections.

In this method the sample pulverised to a fine powder is used, hence the term "X-ray powder analysis." This powder is packed into a suitable sample holder, which, together with the detector, is rotated and the X-rays reflected by the powder are scanned. Fragments are usually 5 to 10 micrometres in diameter and would have approximately 5 000 planes. The intensity of the reflected X-rays is recorded on a chart against the angle of the detector. The trace obtained is characteristic of the substance being tested, each peak representing the spacing between a particular set of planes.

9   FUTURE TRENDS

It seems that in the sampling of dust only the respirable dust should be measured, that is, only the dust which will reach and remain in the lungs where it will react to cause fibrosis. In the present state of knowledge the choice of respirable mass as a measure of coal dust appears to be sound and is enjoying increasing support in many countries. The choice between respirable surface area (RSA) and respirable mass as parameters for dust in metal mines is uncertain. The practical difficulties in measuring respirable mass in South African gold mines are considerable, because of the very low mass concentrations of dust in the mine air.

Dust samplers driven by self-contained power supplies, (e.g., batteries) have such a low sampling rate (2 to 10 litres per minute) that sampling must be continued for many hours if a sufficiently large sample is to be obtained. Because of the small mass of dust collected on the filter, the determination of mass is time-consuming and may be of limited accuracy due to effects of humidity on the filter. (To avoid this, "constant-mass" membrane filters can be used for such work.) Respirable mass measure-ments appear to be practicable when the period of sampling extends over, say, a full shift or longer. A constant monitoring device using compressed air as the power source has been developed for this purpose.

If it is desired to convert from sampling on a number concentration basis to a respirable mass basis on local metal mines, it must be appreciated that there will be no direct relationship between the old parameter and the new. Thus, places or processes in which there are high concentrations of very fine dust (samples are often obtained in which more than 90 per cent of the particles visible under the high power optical microscope are less than half a micrometre in diameter) will, on the number concentration basis, be regarded as "dusty" while on the respirable surface area or respirable mass basis they will probably give a "low" measurement. Conversely, samples in which a significant number of particles in the size range of 2 to 5 μm are present may give a low result on the number concentration parameter, but will give a high value when assessed in terms of respirable surface area. After dust sampling based on a new parameter is introduced, it may take time to become accustomed to judging dust conditions in terms of the new basis.

Another important factor is the composition of the airborne dust which frequently has properties significantly different from those of the parent rock from which it is produced. Only a small fraction of the total airborne dust in South African gold mines consists of quartz — commonly less than 30 per cent — although quartz forms 60 to 70 per cent of the original rock.

10   REFERENCES

1   Chamber of Mines of South Africa. *Routine mine ventilation measurements,* Johannesburg, 1972.

2   Quilliam, J. H. and Kruss, J. A. L. The performance of konimeters fitted with size selectors. *J. Mine Vent. Soc. S. Afr.,* Vol. 25, 1972. p. 60–67.

3   Quilliam, J. H., Kruss, J. A. L. and Blignaut, P. J. The results of the field trials of the modified thermal precipitator. *Chamber of Mines Research Report* No. 5/70, 1970.

4   Talbot, J. H. Automatic dust measurement; diffraction size frequency analyser. *J. Mine Vent. Soc. S. Afr.,* vol. 20, 1967. p. 21–30.
    Diffraction apparatus for assessing dust samples. *J. Mine Vent. Soc. S. Afr.,* Vol. 18, 1965. p. 8–10.

5   Buckley-Jones, P. Instruments for gravimetric sampling. *J. Mine Vent. Soc. S. Afr.,* vol. 18, 1965. p. 23–4.

6   Blignaut, P. J. Electrostatic dust samplers. *J. Mine Vent. Soc. S. Afr.,* Vol. 18, 1965. p. 25–6.

7   Quilliam, J. H. and Beadle, D. G. A critical review of the relative merits of the Rand Mines method and the Chamber of Mines method of undertaking dust surveys on mines. *Chamber of Mines Research Report* No. 69/68, 1968.

8   Beadle, D. G. Sequential control charts. *J. Mine Vent. Soc. S. Afr.,* Vol. 18, 1965. p. 19–21.

9   Beadle, D. G. The relationship between the amount of dust breathed and the development of radiological signs of silicosis; an epidemiological study in South African gold mines. Walton, W. H. *ed.,* — Inhaled particles III, Proceedings of an International Symposium organized by the British Occupational Hygiene Society, in London. Old Woking, Surrey, Unwin, 1971, Vol. 2. p. 953–66.

10   Rabson, S. R. Gravimetric sampling. *J. Mine Vent. Soc. S. Afr.,* Vol. 18, 1965. p. 21–3.

11   *Control of particulates and gaseous pollutants.* U.S. Dept. of Health, Education and Welfare. Public Health Service, Oct., 1961.

12   Kitto, P. H. The microscope as an aid to dust control. *Bull. Mine Vent. Soc. S. Afr.,* Vol. 4, 1951. p. 207–19.

13   Joffe, A. D. and Sichel, H. S. Estimation of the surface area of dust sample from three-spot graticule counts. *J. Mine Vent. Soc. S. Afr.,* Vol. 18, 1965. p. 99–108.

14   Bradley, A. Determination of the composition of dust by X-ray diffraction. *J. Mine Vent. Soc. S. Afr.,* Vol. 18, 1965. p. 26–7.

6 Sources of Heat in Mines

J. H. QUILLIAM

Chief, Dust Division, Physical Sciences Laboratory, Chamber of Mines Research Organization

1 INTRODUCTION

The object of mine ventilation is to provide suitable environmental conditions in working places at an economic cost.

The continuation of mining activities normally involves operating at ever-greater depths, and one of the serious problems which arises in deep-level mining is the high temperature of the environment.

The high temperatures in deep-level mines produce atmospheres which have an adverse effect on the comfort and efficiency of underground personnel and to some extent on safety and health. These adverse effects are aggravated by the increased humidity caused by the evaporation of moisture, relative humidities being above 85 per cent in most hot working places.

The degree of wetness of mine airways and working areas has a profound influence on heat flow. This constitutes an additional problem in that wet mining has to be practised to settle dust and reduce the pneumoconiosis risk.

Heat is one of the major limiting factors which determines the depth to which mining can be carried out economically. Productivity decreases with increase in wet-bulb temperatures, for a given air velocity, and unless temperatures can be kept below the critical limits, work becomes either impossible or so inefficient as to be uneconomical.

In planning new deep-level mines or the deepening of existing mines certain basic problems have to be considered. It is important to be able to estimate or predict what the wet- and dry-bulb temperatures will be in the airways and working areas, how conditions will affect the efficiency of the labour force and what methods will be required, and at what cost, to make the environment acceptable.

A detailed knowledge of the sources from which heat enters the mine air is essential in the estimation of the air volumes and refrigeration required to provide tolerable environmental conditions underground, and is the obvious starting point in the study of the complex subject of heat in mine air.

It must be emphasized that the quantities of heat introduced into the mine air current from these different sources vary considerably from one mine to another and from one situation in a given mine to another.

2   HEAT FROM ROCK

The determination of the amount of the heat transferred from the rock under specific mining conditions requires a knowledge of the thermal properties of the rock and the ventilating air.

From the examination of cores obtained from boreholes it is possible to determine the nature of the strata which will be encountered in mining operations.

Borehole surveys can provide, in addition, data on the temperature of the natural rock (virgin rock temperature) in places where it has not been affected by heating or cooling from any artificial source.

The temperature of the rocks comprising the earth's crust increases with increase in depth, and it is known that the temperature gradient varies according to the type of rock formations and is inversely proportional to the thermal conductivity of the rock.

The geothermal flow of heat from the hot core of the earth is about 0,05 W/m² and is practically constant over most of the earth's surface. Where rocks of low conductivity such as lavas overlie mining areas the temperatures underground are high. This is particularly so in the Orange Free State gold fields.

Figures 6:1 and 6:2 illustrate the approximate virgin rock temperatures at various depths on both local and other mining fields.

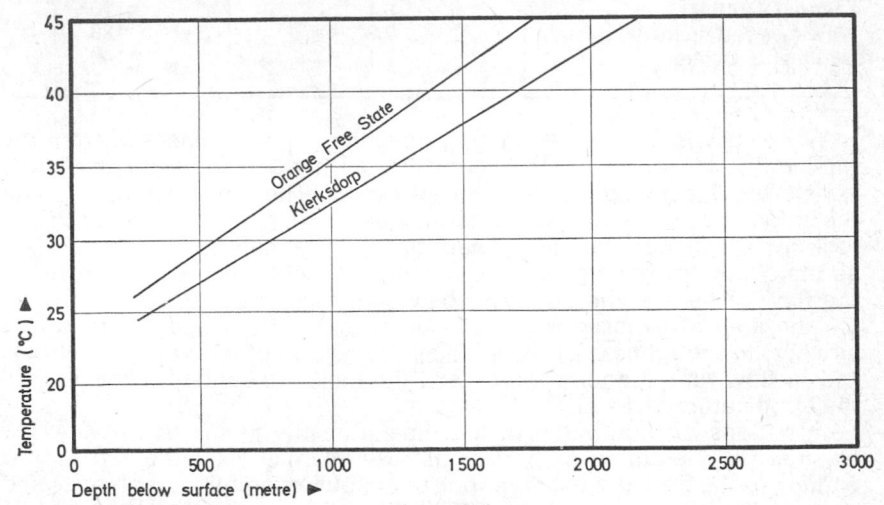

Figure 6:1

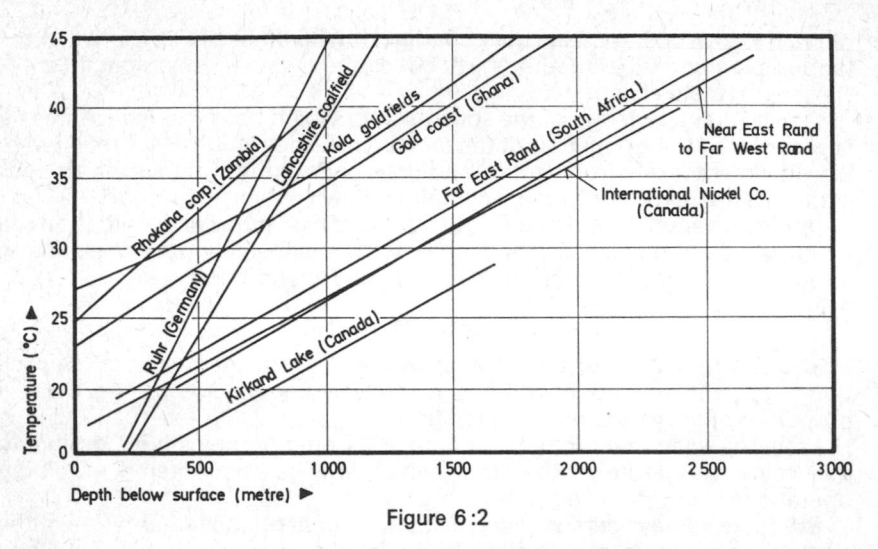

Figure 6:2

Rock temperatures can be estimated fairly accurately, or can be measured. From a knowledge of the depths at which these temperatures are observed the increase in temperature per 1 000 m of vertical depth, that is, the temperature gradient for a specific geological formation, can be calculated.

Formation	Temperature gradient °C/1 000 m	Geothermal step m/°C
Dolerite series	27,6	36
Karroo series	25,5	39
Upper Ventersdorp lava. . .	15,7	64
Witwatersrand sediments . .	13,7	73
Karroo dolerite	9,1	110
Witwatersrand quartzite . .	7,8	128
OFS reef quartzite	7,1	140

When rock is exposed by mining operations, heat is liberated from the rock and is picked up by the ventilation air current, the amount of heat transferred depending on a number of factors. The variables which affect the flow of heat within the strata include the physical properties of the rock such as its density, thermal capacity and thermal conductivity, as well as the degree of homogeneity of the strata. The parameters which affect the flow of heat at the boundary between the strata and the passing air are the area of exposed rock surface, the size, shape and length of the airways, the roughness of the surface, the degree of wetness of the rock, the air flow rate, the temperature and the moisture content of the air, and the temperature of the rock.

In regions of high virgin rock temperature the increases in wet- and dry-bulb temperatures in horizontal airways may be attributed almost entirely to the flow of heat from rock to air, but locomotives, hot pipes and open drains can also contribute a significant amount of heat to the air.

There is little doubt that in deep-level mines natural heat from exposed strata is a major cause of high temperatures. In all large mines the total ventilating air in its passage through shafts, haulages, stopes, and so on, is exposed to many millions of square metres of rock surface. In a typical large and deep mine the heat energy added to the total ventilating air by the rock is equivalent to somewhere between 20 000 and 30 000 kW. This is apart from the heat due to autocompression and from other sources.

Estimates of the amount of heat picked up by the air from the rock in a Witwatersrand mine (mining 100 000 tons/month) have been made by Barenburg[1] and are shown in the table below.

Depth m	Heat pick-up kJ/s (kW)
600	3 500
1 200	5 300
1 800	8 800
2 400	17 600
3 000	31 700

3   HEAT GENERATED BY THE AUTOCOMPRESSION OF AIR

It is known that the temperature of air can change with change in pressure. The expansion of air while it performs work will produce cooling just as compression will produce heating.

When air descends in a mine shaft it is compressed at the rate of approximately 1,1 kPa per 100 m of vertical depth because of the column of air in the shaft. The potential energy possessed by air at the top of the shaft is converted into heat energy by the time the air reaches the bottom of the shaft.

The increase in heat content due to autocompression of 1 kg of air passing 100 m vertically down a shaft is calculated as follows:

$$\frac{\text{Gravitational acceleration} \times \text{mass} \times \text{distance}}{1\ 000}$$

$$= \frac{9,79 \times 1 \times 100}{1\ 000} = 0,979 \text{ kJ/kg}$$

hence the increase in dry-bulb temperature $= \dfrac{0,979}{C_{pa}}$

$$= \frac{0,979}{1,02} = 0,96\ ^{\circ}\text{C (no moisture evaporated)}$$

The increase in wet-bulb temperature is variable and depends upon the initial pressure and temperature of the air and is best obtained from psychrometric charts.

4   WASTE HEAT FROM POWER-OPERATED MACHINERY

The usual sources of power underground are electricity and compressed air.

Apart from the type of power used, the amount of heat generated varies according to the type of work done. In horizontal workings all the energy supplied to machinery is absorbed in overcoming frictional loads and therefore ultimately enters the air in the form of heat.

Work done against gravity, however, as when pumps deliver water to the surface, or when rock is hoisted, increases the potential energy of the material being raised and this portion of the energy does not appear as heat.

4.1   Fans, mechanical scrapers, hoists

Mechanical ventilation produced by power-operated fans increases the amount of air which flows through a mine. The energy loss in the motors, the aerodynamic losses in the fans as well as the energy of compression of the air by the fans all cause the temperature of the air to rise.

The heat given to air by fans is equal to the thermal equivalent of the electrical energy put into the fan motor.

In most mines the underground fans are a major consumer of power and every effort should, where possible, be made to keep them in the return airways.

The amount of heat generated by the electric motors of mechanical loaders, scrapers and hoists is considerable, especially by the motors and controlling resistances of the hoists on vertical and inclined shafts. In a stope the heat from scraper motors provides a very large fraction of the total heat gain. This heat may increase air temperature considerably if the ventilation is not adequate.

The magnitude of increases in air temperature in mines from these sources is, however, small compared with that produced by auto-compression of the air and by the natural heat from the strata. In localized places such as hoist chambers the effect could, however, be considerable.

4.2   Compressed air power

Compressed air leaving a compressor at the surface of a mine is usually at a temperature higher than that of the atmospheric air, and when delivered down a shaft there is a transfer of heat from the pipe to the ventilating air.

It is usual to pre-cool the compressed air before it enters the mine in order to remove some of the heat, thus reducing the amount of heat transferred to the ventilating air in the shaft. Pre-cooling has an additional benefit as it removes moisture from the compressed air.

The temperature of the compressed air going down a mine shaft increases due to auto-compression in exactly the same way as the ventilation air. Because of the greater density of the compressed air, the pressure rise per 100m is much more than the average rate of 1,1 kPa/100m for ventilation air, and is between 5 and 7 kPa/100m depending on the pressure.

Compressed air working by expansion does so at the expense of its own content of pressure energy which is reduced by an amount equal to the amount of work done. If all of the work is done against friction the amount of heat produced is equal to the loss of heat due to expansion and the two cancel out.

4.3 Locomotives

Since locomotives are operated on near-horizontal gradients no work is done against gravity. The amount of heat produced by battery and trolley locomotives is equivalent to the energy consumed. In the case of diesel locomotives the amount of heat produced is equivalent to the calorific value of the total amount of fuel consumed, the average value of which is approximately 44 000 kJ/kg. Thus, if the specific gravity of the fuel is known and the quantity consumed measured, the total amount of heat produced can be calculated.

On an average, a diesel locomotive consumes about 0,24 kg of fuel per kWh. Given that the calorific value of the fuel is 44 000 kJ/kg, the total energy in the quantity of fuel used can be calculated, that is,

$$\begin{aligned}
\text{Total energy} \ &= 0,24 \times 44\ 000 \\
&= 10\ 560 \text{ kJ/h per kW} \\
&= 176 \text{ kJ/min per kW} = \text{approx. 3 kJ/s/kW} \\
&= \text{approx. 3kW/kW}
\end{aligned}$$

Of this energy 1 kW is converted into mechanical energy, with the remaining portion appearing as heat in the exhaust gas and in the engine itself.

Heat may thus be released into the mine air at a maximum rate of 3 kW/kW, but on average the rate of production of heat is approximately 1 kW per rated kW because of the intermittent operations of the locomotive.

In general, the amount of heat from diesel locomotives is relatively small, but in limited areas where ventilation is poor it could be significant.

5   HEAT FROM PERSONS

The amount of heat produced by the human body varies according to the amount of work performed. Wyndham[2] has provided the following data:

At rest	: 90 to 115 W
Light rate of work	: 200 W
Moderate rate of work	: 275 W
Hard rate of work (intermittent)	: 470 W

For example, 6 000 men in a mine working at a rate which produces an average rate of heat dissipation of 275 W cause a gain in heat by the ventilation air of 1 650 000 W or 1 650 kW. If the mass flow of the air in the mine is 500 kg/s the heat increase of the air is 3,30 kJ/kg.

This corresponds to an increase of approximately 0,7 °C in the wet-bulb temperature.

6   OTHER SOURCES OF HEAT

6.1 Oxidation of timber and other materials

The oxidation of minerals such as pyrite, sulphide ores and coal is another source of heat. In the South African gold mines the decomposition of iron sulphide, and to a smaller extent, of marcasite and pyrrhotite found in the reef, as well as the decay of timber used for roof support, generate small amounts of heat, but this is not a serious factor.

6.2   *Electric lights*

Electric lighting generates only a very small amount of heat which depends on the wattage of the lamp. All the electrical energy supplied to a light globe appears as heat.

6.3   *Blasting explosives*

Practically all the heat that is released by explosives is removed from the mine by the ventilation air during the re-entry period, so that heat generated in the detonation of explosives is not an important factor.

The amount of explosive used per ton of rock mined varies considerably. For example, in stoping operations, approximately 1 kg of explosive is used per ton of rock blasted, and for development ends approximately 2,5 kg of explosive is used per ton of rock blasted. The theoretical amount of heat released by the detonation of the commonly used explosives is as follows:

Ammon gelignite (60 per cent) = 4 650 kJ/kg
Ammon dynamite (60 per cent) = 4 030 kJ/kg
Anfex   = 3 820 kJ/kg.

Using a reasonable average value of heat generated, the approximate amount of heat produced in stoping operations is 4 000 kJ/ton of rock and for development 10 000 kJ/ton of rock.

Assuming that in a typical mine the rock broken per month (25 days) is 100 000 tons, that is, 4 000 tons/day of which 3 200 tons is obtained from stoping and 800 tons from development, the amount of heat generated by blasting explosives in stopes is equal to 3 200 × 4 000 = 12,8 million kJ and, from development is equal to 800 × 10 000 = 8 million kJ. This provides a total of 20,8 million kJ.

The extent to which this heat increases the temperature of ventilating air is difficult to calculate because the heat is dissipated intermittently during the blasting period. However, since this heat is removed rapidly by the ventilating air when no personnel are on the return-air side, the effect is of no consequence as a source of heat in mines during the subsequent working shift.

6.4   *Heat due to movement of rock masses*

Gravitational forces acting above excavations produced by mining operations cause subsidence which results in crushing, fracturing and grinding within the rock mass. This movement performs work against friction and all the work appears as heat which remains inside the rock. The quantity of heat generated, however, is small enough to be ignored completely in relation to the heat transferred from the rock.

7   HEAT BALANCE IN AN ACTUAL DEEP-LEVEL GOLD MINE

In a study[3] in 1966 a heat balance was obtained for a deep-level mine to provide some idea of the magnitude of the problem. The following basic data were used:

Rock hoisted   : 190 000 tons/month
Sludge pumped   : 204 000 ℓ/day
Water sent down   : 635 500 ℓ/day
Water pumped out   : 4,91 Mℓ/day

Compressed air	: 13,7 m³/s over 24 hours
Explosives	: 180 000 kg/month
Electric power sent down mine	: 200 000 kWh/day
Surface ventilation fans	: 4 176 kW
Underground fans	: 3 281 kW
Ventilation air (upcast)	: 524 m³/s at 1,2 kg/m³ (72 per cent to deepest stoping areas)
Personnel underground per day	: 5 760 (83 per cent in dayshift—63 per cent in deepest stoping areas)
Underground refrigeration (for deepest stopes only)	: 3 517 kW

Heat balance (all quantities in millions of kJ/day).

Heat removed

By ventilation air	2 470
By Rand Water Board water	30
Total heat removed	2 500 million kJ/day
	= 29 000 kJ/s (kW)

Heat picked up

Category	Detail	Daily heat Quantity	Category Total	Category Percentage
Stopes	People Stopes, airways, worked-out areas	30 1 300*	1 330	53
Ore and water	Rock Sludge Water	59 9 231	299	12
Machinery	Explosives Electrical mining machinery Compressed air and diesel fuel	7 90 negligible	97	4
Feed-back	Power for fans Power for refrigeration	637 142	779	31
				100

*Obtained by difference

Total heat pick-up = 2 500 million kJ/day
= 29 000 kJ/s (kW).

Barcza[4] in 1953 estimated that the heat gain between downcast and upcast shafts in fifty-five South African gold mines amounted to approximately 420 000 kW (kJ/s). This is approximately 7 600 kW per mine.

8   PREDICTION OF UNDERGROUND CONDITIONS

The ventilation engineer has a choice of methods available for the prediction of underground conditions. He will have some idea of the prevailing conditions on surface in the case of a completely new mine in the planning stage, or, where a new mining area has to be entered from an existing section, the conditions at the start of the new section will be familiar to him. In order to obtain a value for the heat pick-up or temperature increase which can be expected, the first approach would be to assess the effects of auto-compression, machinery, etc. Then the process of heat flow from the rock must be examined.

The analysis of the heat conduction process within the rock has been tackled by several people. Goch and Patterson[5] have analysed the heat flow in the region surrounding a cylindrical excavation in homogeneous iso-tropic rock when the surface temperature remains constant. Concer[6] has carried out a similar analysis for both cylindrical and elliptical excavations which advance uniformly into the rock in a direction perpendicular to their axes. Starfield[7] extended Goch and Patterson's work to the case where a convective heat transfer coefficient exists at the surface of the excavation and where the air temperature remains constant with time. Starfield also considered the case of the rectangular stope advancing in step fashion into the rock. In all these models, the effects of time variations in air temperature could be allowed for by the use of comparatively simple calculations.

The work mentioned in the preceding paragraph provided the basic information necessary for predicting air temperatures. Wiles[8] used Goch and Patterson's work together with a most detailed model of heat and mass transfer processes at the surface of the excavation to predict wet-bulb temperature increases in airways. Wiles' work was handicapped by the lack of suitable computing facilities at that time and was never used to any great extent. Starfield, using a similar approach to that of Wiles, but without such a detailed analysis of the heat and mass transfer processes at the surface of the excavation, produced computer programs for the prediction of temperature increases in both airways and stopes. In this work, Starfield assumed that any moisture present was uniformly distributed around the excavation. Starfield and Dickson[9] took full advantage of the powerful computer techniques then available to carry out a very detailed study of heat flow into an airway. They assumed a square excavation with only the footwall being wet, and used a numerical analysis technique to calculate the heat conduction in the rock. This method required very long computing times and Starfield then produced a program which used the results of this work to obtain very quick answers to problems concerning air temperature increases in airways. This work highlighted the effect of drains upon heat flow in airways.

Whillier[10] has provided a simplified method for calculating the heat pick-up underground and hence for calculating refrigeration requirements in stoping areas. It is applicable to a wide range of mining conditions with only a few overall mining parameters required to be specified. In particular, the rate of heat pick-up from the rock is considered to be independent of the ventilation rate within the range of airflow rates usually encountered in South African mining practice. The method of calculation is applicable particularly to situations in hot deep mines in which refrigeration is used.

This method permits an estimate to be made of the rate of heat pick-up in any given stoping zone. The influence of this heat on the ventilating air can then be evaluated with any assumed ventilation rate, condition of incoming ventilation air and maximum permitted wet-bulb temperature of the ventilating air. The method also permits a rapid estimate to be made of the refrigeration requirements for the stoping zone.

As far as the empirical approach is concerned, all work in this field has been done by Lambrechts. His work covered the investigation of temperature increases in stopes, airways and shafts and in three separate papers he has produced some very useful results.[11,12,13] The empirical approach has the obvious disadvantage of applying only to the conditions under which the observations were made, and this, together with the inevitable scatter in the observations, has formed the most common objection made to his work. It must be admitted, however, that underground temperatures do fluctuate with time, sometimes fairly considerably, and it is doubtful whether the theoretical approach could ever predict this fluctuation other than in a statistical manner. Lambrechts' work did provide some answers to heat flow problems, where only experience and intuition provided them before, and it also provided a very convenient set of data for comparison with the results of the theoretical work. Indeed, it was this which led Starfield and Dickson to investigate the effects of drains.

9   REFERENCES

1   Barenbrug, A. W. T. Air conditioning in the mining industry. *Bull. Mine Vent. Soc. S. Afr.,* Vol. 3, 1950. p. 164–74.

2   Wyndham, C. H., *et al.* Practical aspects of recent physiological studies in Witwatersrand Gold Mines. *J. chem. metall. Min. Soc. S. Afr.,* Vol. 53, 1953. p. 287–313.

3   Cook, N. G. W. and Whillier, A. A study of the optimization of the refrigeration and ventilation on mines. Part 1—overall heat balance on a deep mine, *Chamber of Mines of South Africa Research Report,* no. 54/66 (Rev.), 1966.

4   Barcza, M. Some statistical information about the ventilation of South African gold mines. *Bull. Mine Vent. Soc. S. Afr.,* Vol. 6, no. 9, 1953. p. 4–18.

5   Goch, D. C. and Patterson, H. S. The heat flow into tunnels. *J. chem. metall. Min. Soc. S. Afr.,* Vol. 41, 1940. p. 117–28.

6   Concer, D. B. Heat flow towards a moving cavity. *Quarterly Jnl. of Mechanics and Applied Mathematics.,* Vol. 12, 1959. p. 222–31.

7   Starfield, A. M. A rapid method of calculating temperature increases along mine airways. *J. S. Afr. Inst. Min. Metall.,* Vol. 70, 1969. p. 77–83.

8   Wiles, G. G. Wet bulb temperature gradients in horizontal airways. *J. S. Afr. Inst. Min. Metall.,* Vol. 59, 1959. p. 339–59.

9   Starfield, A. M. and Dickson, A. J. A fundamental study of heat transfer and moisture pick-up in mine airways. *J. S. Afr. Inst. Min. Metall.,* Vol. 68, 1967. p. 211–34.

10   Whillier, A. Estimation of heat pick-up by ventilation air in stopes. *Chamber of Mines of South Africa Research Report* No. 2/73, 1973.

11   Lambrechts, J. de V. Prediction of wet-bulb temperature gradients in mine airways. *J. S. Afr. Inst. Min. Metall.,* Vol. 67, 1967. p. 595–610.

12   Lambrechts, J. de V. The estimation of ventilation air temperatures in deep mines. *J. chem. metall. Min. Soc. S. Afr.,* Vol. 50, 1950. p. 125–30.
13   Lambrechts, J. de V. An empirical study of heat flow in stopes in South African gold mines. *J. S. Afr. Inst. Min. Metall.,* Vol. 59, 1959. p. 285–316.

BIBLIOGRAPHY

Lambrechts, J. de V. The determination of heat losses from underground machinery. *Bull. Mine Vent. Soc. S. Afr.,* Vol. 4, 1951. p. 143–6.

Wiles, G. G. Theory underlying temperatures in horizontal airways. *J. chem. metall. Min. Soc. S. Afr.,* Vol. 55, 1954. p. 255–7.

Bromilow, John G. Conditioning of the ventilation air in coal mining. *Trans. Instn. Min. Engrs.* Vol. 116, 1957. p. 538–60.

Wiles, G. G. and Quilliam, J. H. Some temperature gradients observed in specially selected underground airways. *J. S. Afr. Inst. Min. Metall.,* Vol. 59, 1959. p. 360–8.

Wiles, G. G., Quilliam, J. H. Murray, N. M. Two methods of measuring the rate of evaporation of water into an airstream. *J. Mine Vent. Soc. S. Afr.,* Vol. 12, 1959. p. 120–8.

Starfield, A. M. The computation of temperature increases in wet and dry airways. *J. Mine Vent. Soc. S. Afr.,* Vol. 19, 1966. p. 157–65.

Starfield, A. M. The computation of air temperature increases in advancing stopes. *J. Mine Vent. Soc. S. Afr.,* Vol. 19, 1966. p. 189–99.

Whillier, A. Heat—A challenge in deep-level mining. *J. Mine Vent. Soc. S. Afr.,* Vol. 25, 1972. p. 205–13.

7 The Physiological and Psychological Effects of Heat

C. H. WYNDHAM

Director, Human Sciences Laboratory, Chamber of Mines Research Organization

1 INTRODUCTION

High temperatures and humidity in the gold mines of South Africa are major health hazards and are causes of reduced productivity. The reasons for this are:

(a) The high virgin rock temperatures at the great depths at which gold is mined.

(b) The legal requirement that the rock should be watered down to settle the silica-containing dust. This causes an atmosphere saturated with water vapour in working places.

(c) The human energy costs of the drilling of holes for the blast, the shovelling of broken rock out of the stopes and tramming it to the tip are high because these mining operations are, in general, only partially mechanised.

93

(*d*)   The high rate of turnover of the Bantu labour force (almost 100 per cent per annum) which results each year in the recruitment of about 300 000 new labourers who are not adapted to physical work in hot conditions.

The fact that in these circumstances this health hazard has been contained is due largely to the efforts of the ventilation engineer and the medical physiologist. This chapter deals with the contributions made by the medical physiologist.

2   HISTORICAL BACKGROUND

By the 1920's mines in the central Witwatersrand had reached depths at which the wet-bulb temperatures in some working places, because of the high virgin rock temperatures, exceeded 30°C (86°F). The first fatal case of heat stroke was reported in 1924.

In Figure 7.1 are given the numbers of fatal heat stroke cases and the total numbers of Bantu males working underground for each year of the period 1924 to 1970. The numbers of fatal heat stroke cases were taken from the Government Mining Engineer's records and, because all fatal cases are notifiable and an enquiry is held, the numbers are probably a reasonably accurate record of the annual rate of fatal cases of heat stroke over this period. Non-fatal cases of heat stroke are not included in Figure 7:1 because for many years no distinction was made in the Government

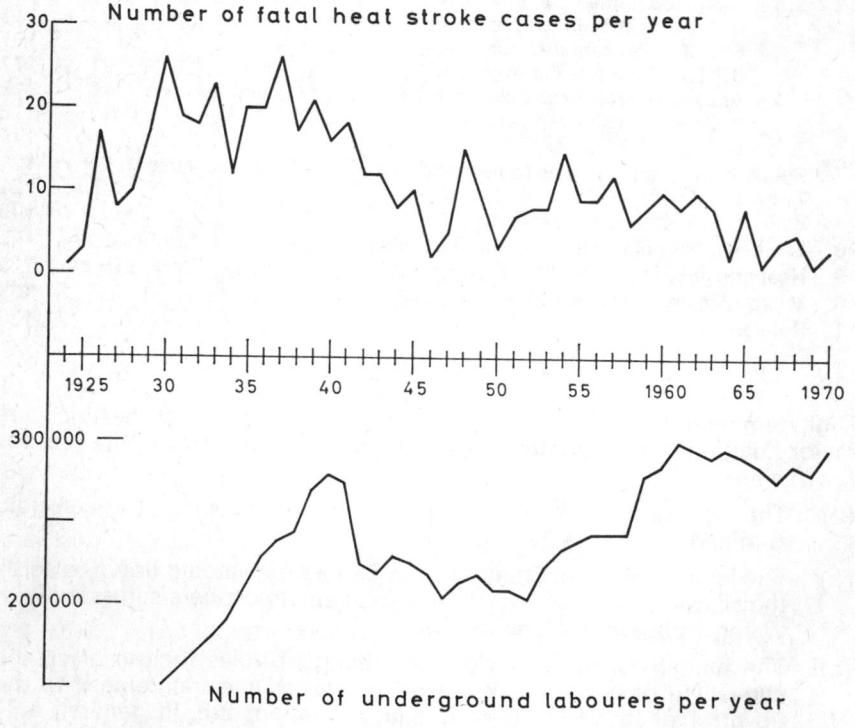

Figure 7:1

Mining Engineer's records between cases of non-fatal heat stroke and heat exhaustion and the diagnosis of the latter cases was not based upon sound criteria. The numbers of Bantu males working underground were obtained from Chamber of Mines records.

From Figure 7:1 it is clear that between 1924 and 1930 there was a sharp increase in the annual death rate from heat stroke. With a view to discovering the main causes of heat stroke Dr E. H. Cluver, then Secretary of Public Health, carried out the first systematic study of the incidence of heat stroke in the gold mining industry and published his results in 1932.[1] He found that ninety-two deaths from heat stroke had occurred in the seven-year period, 1924 to 1931. Sixty-nine of the deaths occurred in two mines which, by 1930, had reached a depth of 1 700 m below the surface. Sixty-seven of the ninety-two fatal cases occurred in working places in which the wet-bulb temperatures were over 30°C. It was estimated that the population of Bantu males at risk at such temperatures was 14 000.

The two mines concerned immediately took steps to combat heat stroke by introducing a form of acclimatization to heat. The procedure introduced by Village Deep G.M. Co. Ltd., in 1925 and by City Deep Ltd., in 1926 comprised the placing of new recruits on light work in hot conditions underground for the first ten days of their contracts. Men with previous mining experience were treated in this way for five days. No similar provision was made for men who had been in hospital; they returned immediately to normal work. These measures were ineffective. The death rate continued to increase and, in 1930, twenty-six fatal cases of heat stroke occurred. The alarm which this high death rate from heat stroke occasioned in the gold mining industry at that time is described in a paper by Dreosti in 1935.[2] "Heat stroke was becoming a serious menace at City Deep mine, especially as still greater depths were contemplated. Further, during the period of acclimatization the average amount of work output per labourer per shift was equivalent to only one-third of the normal shift. The financial position of the mine was such as to be profoundly affected by the loss of efficiency".

Dr Dreosti, the Senior Medical Officer of the City Deep mine hospital, carried out a series of investigations into the heat tolerance of Bantu mine workers[2]. He showed that Bantu recruits to the mine varied greatly in their tolerance to work in heat. The heat tolerance test was severe. The men were made to shovel rock along a trough in the floor of a hot room in which the wet-bulb temperature was maintained at 35°C (the air was saturated with water vapour). In a sample of 20 000 men, 15 per cent were judged to be "heat-intolerant" in that their oral temperatures rose to over 39°C (102°F) after an hour of shovelling rock in the hot room. 25 per cent were "heat-tolerant" in that their oral temperatures did not rise above 38°C (100°F), and the remaining 60 per cent were regarded as "normal" reactors to work in heat.

In a further investigation on a small sample of heat-intolerant recruits, the oral temperature responses of 17 per cent did not improve after seven days of a daily exposure to one hour of work in the hot room. The remaining 83 per cent improved rapidly and by the fourth day showed a "heat-tolerant" response. As a result of these studies the method of acclimatization in City Deep mine was altered in March 1932 in the following way:

Heat-intolerant recruits were acclimatized for fourteen days.

Heat-tolerant men were acclimatized for four days.

Normal reactors were acclimatized for seven days.

The success of the new procedures was such that in the eight-year period, 1932 to 1940, there were only four further deaths from heat stroke in City Deep gold mine. This achievement must be seen in the light of eight deaths from heat stroke in that mine in a single year, 1930.

A major part of the credit for the improvement in the heat stroke position must go to the ventilation engineer. The condition of the air in the working places in the mines was improved by increasing markedly, by means of powerful fans, the volumes of air circulated through the mines and the planned direction of air in the working places. The effect of these steps was considerable, and by 1939 City Deep Ltd., for example, was able to dispense with the heat tolerance test and to acclimatize its recruits in stopes in the mine.

The effect of these two steps to improve the heat stroke position in the gold mines, that is, better ventilation and improved acclimatization, was such that, as shown in Figure 7:1 in spite of an increase in the numbers of Bantu working underground to reach the unprecedented total of 280 000 by 1940, the numbers of deaths per annum from heat stroke did not rise above twenty in the latter part of the 1930's. A further demonstration of the ameliorative effect of these two steps is seen in the fact that in the early 1940's when, due to the competition for Bantu labour from the war industries, the labour force in the mines decreased to about 200 000 men, the annual death rate from heat stroke fell to about eight per annum.

In the 1950's radical changes occurred in the risk factors associated with heat stroke. In the central Witwatersrand shafts were sunk to depths of over 3 000 m and mines were opened up in the Free State where the geothermal gradient is higher than on the Witwatersrand. These new circumstances led to more and more working places with wet-bulb temperatures above 30°C and some even exceeding 32°C. Also after 1957 there was a sharp increase in the recruitment of Bantu to the mines so that by 1960 there were again 300 000 Bantu males working underground in the mines.

In the 1960's these two factors led to a steady increase of the number of Bantu males working physically at high wet-bulb temperatures. This is indicated in Figure 7:2 which shows estimates of the numbers of Bantu males in different ranges of wet-bulb temperatures for the period 1957 to 1968, together with the annual rate of fatal heat stroke cases. The estimates of the former are based on the numbers of stopes and development ends in these ranges of wet-bulb temperature in the Chamber's annual ventilation returns from mines and upon an estimate of the average gang strengths in these working places over the period.

Figure 7:2 shows that since 1957 there has been a steady decrease in the numbers of men working at wet-bulb temperatures less than 27°C, the decrease being about 30 per cent between 1957 and 1968. By contrast, there has been a marked increase in the numbers of men working at the higher, and more dangerous wet-bulb temperatures. It has been estimated that the total population working at wet-bulb temperatures higher than 27°C increased from 77 000 in 1957 to 105 000 in 1961 and to 130 000 in 1968, an increase over the whole period of about 70 per cent. Had no drastic measures been taken to meet this large increase in the numbers of workmen at risk from heat stroke it could have been expected that there

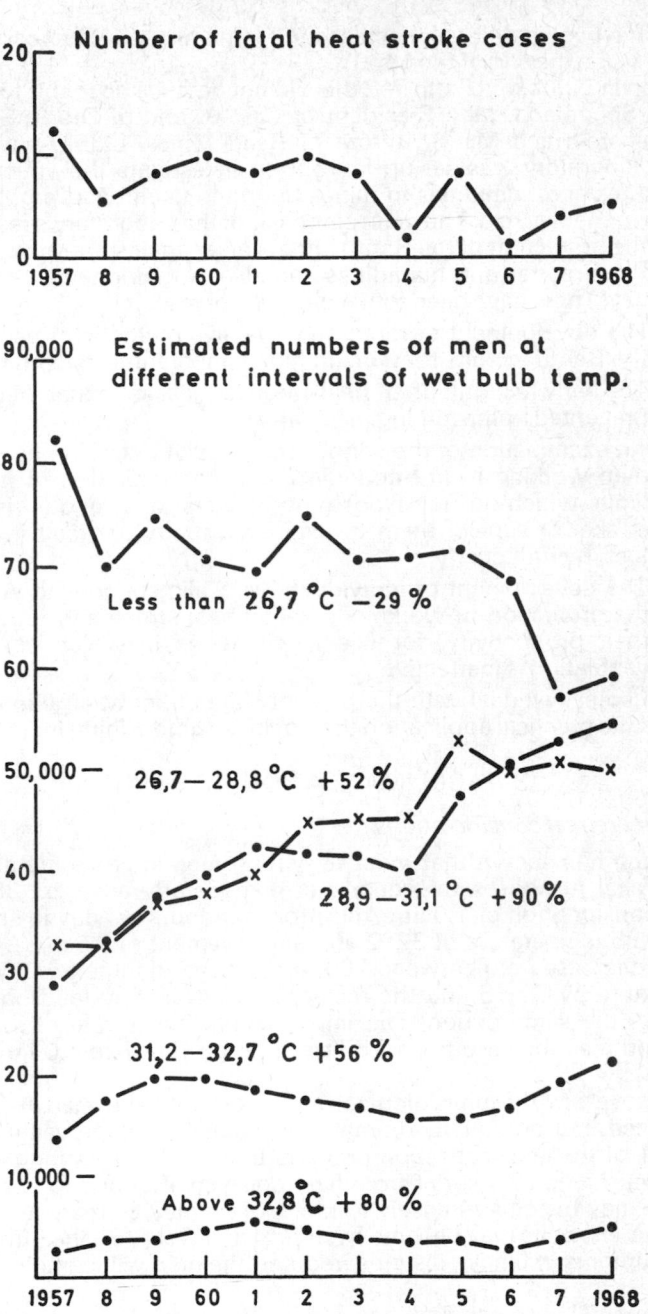

Figure 7:2

would have been a dramatic increase in the numbers of fatal cases of heat stroke towards the end of the 1960's.

As seen in Figures 7 :1 and 7 :2 this did not occur. Due to the foresight of Sir Basil Schonland, then President of C.S.I.R. and of Drs F. G. Hill and A. J. Orenstein and Mr M. Barcza of Rand Mines, Ltd., a physiological research laboratory was set up in 1950 to investigate the effects of high temperatures and humidities in mines upon the health and productivity of the Bantu mine workers. The main emphasis of the Laboratory's research has been on the protection of the Bantu mine worker against the adverse effects of high temperatures and humidities and also of their effects upon human productivity. There have been four main areas of research :

(*a*)   The development of rapid and effective methods of acclimatizing the Bantu recruits for work in high temperatures and humidities.

(*b*)   The early recognition of heat-intolerant cases so that they could be prevented from working in hot areas.

(*c*)   An examination of the various methods of assessing heat stress of men working in hot conditions and the definition of heat stress limits which do not expose the workers to an undue risk of heat stroke, or subject them to excessive strain, or result in a serious loss in productivity.

(*d*)   The development of individual micro-climate cooling systems for the protection of workmen against heat stroke and for increasing their productivity, for use in situations in which conventional ventilation is ineffective.

This chapter will deal with the present state of knowledge in the above fields and the practical application thereof in the gold mining industry.

3   ACCLIMATIZATION TO HEAT

3.1   *Theoretical considerations*

Research has shown that most fit, young men improve rapidly in their physiological responses to working at a moderate rate (i.e., 35W or an oxygen consumption of 1,0 litre/min) for four hours per day in severe heat (a wet-bulb temperature of 32°C and air movement of 0,5 m/s). The heart rate may decrease from between 160 to 180 beats/minute on Day 1 to 120 beats/minute by Day 5 and the rectal temperature may fall from 40°C to 38°C over the same period. The improvement in the rate of sweating is slower and may increase from 0,5 litre/hour on Day 1 to 1,0 litre/hour by Day 10.

The above are the physiological indicators that the man has become acclimatized, but an equally dramatic psychological improvement occurs. On Day 1 of the acclimatization procedure the man may struggle to complete the task and may suffer from heat collapse after one to two hours of work. He may become intensely irritable, or he may be morose and refuse to obey orders, or he may become hysterical and weep. By the fifth day all of these symptoms will have disappeared and the man will complete the task with ease.

Fundamental research,[3 − 7] has thrown light on the physiological adjustments which are mainly responsible for the improvement in the ability of a man to work in heat. On the first day of work in heat his blood vessels in the skin open wide but, due to the loss of fluid from the circulatory system through the sweat, the volume of fluid in the circulatory system is inadequate, i.e., the capacity of the system is greater than the contained volume. In consequence the flow of blood back to the heart is insufficient and the stroke volume of the heart diminishes.

The body compensates for the fall in stroke volume by increasing the heart rate and, temporarily, the cardiac output is maintained. However, the increase in heart rate to 160 to 180 beats/min is an indication that the circulatory system is in a very unstable state. If there is any further reduction in the volume of the circulating blood, for example, due to the pooling of blood in the veins of the legs when men stand erect in heat, then the stroke volume will decrease even further. Because the heart rate is at its maximum, cardiac output cannot be maintained in these circumstances. The blood pressure falls dramatically and the man collapses. The diminished blood volume also leads to a temporary shutting-down of blood vessels beneath the skin and this decreases the flow of heat to the skin, by convection in the blood, from muscles where it is produced. In this way the temperature in the "core" of the body where the vital organs such as the brain, liver, kidneys, heart, etc., are located rises excessively and may even reach heat stroke levels.

After two or three days of acclimatization the state of the circulatory system changes dramatically. The volume of blood within the circulatory system increases. This improves the return of blood to the heart, the stroke volume increases, and the heart rate may fall to 120 beats/min.

The physiological mechanism by which the blood volume expands is not altogether clear. For some time it was thought to be due to increase in the secretion of aldosterone from the suprarenal glands, which acts on the kidney tubule causing it to retain NaCl. The increased retention of salt causes an isotonic expansion of fluid volume in the entire extra-cellular spaces, i.e., both within and without the circulatory system.

Recent research [8] indicates, however, that it is a shift of protein into the vascular space which is more important in expanding the blood volume during acclimatization. There is also some evidence that the tone of the blood vessels beneath the skin, particularly the veins, increases and this aids further the return of blood to the heart [9]. Whatever the cause of the increase in stroke volume, the general effect is to improve the circulation of blood in and also the transfer of heat to the skin.

With acclimatization, sweating begins sooner and the rate of sweating increases. Evaporation of water from the skin is more effective and skin temperature falls in consequence. Therefore not only is heat brought more readily to the skin but it is also transferred more effectively from the skin to the surrounding air. Body temperature therefore falls. The mechanisms whereby the sweat gland increases its rate of sweating and starts to sweat earlier when the man is acclimatized are not known.

3.2   Practical applications

One of the first problems to which the Human Sciences Laboratory addressed itself was the acclimatization of Bantu recruits for work in heat. Investigations showed that the procedures then in operation had several serious shortcomings.

A production stope was nominated as the acclimatization centre, but no systematic training was given to the men placed in charge of the procedures. New recruits were put into a hot stope under the direct supervision of a

Bantu supervisor who was supposed to increase, gradually, the amount of work the men did over a 14-day period so that at the end of the period the men would be shovelling rock at the normal rate for the mine. In practice the new recruits worked in a place where they did not interfere with production and, being out of contact with the European supervisor, it was rare that the men ever achieved the normal rate of work. In fact, the Bantu supervisors, being fearful of having a heat stroke case develop under their control, took the easy way out and made sure that the men did not achieve the normal rate of work. In consequence, the men were not acclimatized when they had completed the fourteen days of acclimatization. This was shown by the fact that most heat stroke cases occurred *just after* the men had completed the procedure, and in the production figures which showed that the recruits were producing at only one-fifth of the normal rate for that area of the mine, for the entire period of fourteen days.

The mines' method of dealing with the heat stroke problem after acclimatization was to extend the period during which the men were protected from moderately hard work by having the recent acclimatizees wear a "red armlet" for a further period of seven to fourteen days. This meant that the total period of acclimatization in most hot mines was twenty-eight days during which the men were only one-fifth productive.

As this system of acclimatization was neither safe nor efficient, a new method was introduced and was tried out in the stopes of City Deep Ltd. Co. in 1953 for a period of three months under direct, scientific supervision[10]. The main innovation was to have the new recruits shovel rock in production stopes at the normal rate for a period of twelve days under close supervision. Work during the first six days was in relatively cool stopes and in the second six days in the hottest conditions the men were likely to experience subsequent to acclimatization. Thus the men, while under direct supervision, were first conditioned to physical work in mild heat and then adapted, in the second week, to the most severe heat condition they would experience subsequently.

The acclimatization trial in City Deep Ltd. showed that Bantu recruits could be properly acclimatized by this new procedure and that they were fully productive during the whole period of fourteen days of acclimatization. Thus two important objectives were realized. First, the men were fully protected, being carefully supervised during acclimatization, and by being properly acclimatized when they left the centre. Secondly, mine managements achieved full production and there was soon competition between miners to have the acclimatization centre in their stopes.

In order to maintain a high standard of supervision in the acclimatization centres when the new procedures were introduced more widely into the gold mining industry, European supervisors were specially trained in their various duties and responsibilities. These included the use of clinical thermometers and the oral temperatures of *all* acclimatizees were measured before each acclimatization shift and also during work on the first two days of the cool and hot stages in order to detect any man who might be developing an abnormal temperature. The European supervisor was instructed, further, to measure immediately the oral temperature of any recruit under his care who behaved strangely as well as those feeling unwell and those who felt too hot.

By 1960 nearly all of the hot mines had adopted this new method of acclimatization on a voluntary basis, and some 200 000 Bantu (new recruits and reacclimatizees) were being acclimatized by these new methods each year. There were 125 European supervisors and nearly 1 000 Bantu supervisors engaged in the supervisory duties. It had been hoped to eliminate heat stroke from the gold mining industry once these new acclimatization procedures were in general use. By 1960, as shown in Figure 7.1 this was not the case. A study was therefore made of each heat stroke case that occurred in the five-year period, 1956–1961, with the object of discovering the main causal factors and of dealing with them[11].

One of the factors revealed by the study was that the training of the European supervisors of acclimatization was inadequate in certain respects and this was put right. Another was that the European and Bantu supervisors in production areas, where most of the heat stroke cases had occurred, had little knowledge of the causes and prevention of heat stroke. The Chamber of Mines therefore accepted a recommendation that *all* underground officials and Bantu supervisors be trained in the prevention of heat stroke, i.e., be aware of the factors which could lead to heat stroke, in the early recognition of the signs and symptoms of heat stroke and in the cooling underground of suspected cases.

Another factor brought to light by the study was that when heat stroke cases were transported immediately to the surface without being cooled, which was the general medical instruction in such cases at that time, they were usually admitted to hospital with very high body temperatures (often greater than 41°C) and with severe involvement of the central nervous system[12]. The mortality rate in such cases exceeded 50 per cent. These findings gave strong support to the proposal that all cases of suspected heat stroke should be cooled underground until the rectal temperature was reduced to below 39°C.

In 1965 a radical innovation in the acclimatization of Bantu recruits was introduced[13]. This came about because it was increasingly difficult to produce the correct combinations of continuous work (the shovelling of rock in stopes) and atmospheric heat. This was due to the greater use of mechanical aids, such as scrapers, in the removal of rock from stopes. In the new procedure the recruits worked for four hours each day in a climatic room in which the temperature and humidity of the air could be controlled within narrow limits. The work comprised stepping on and off benches which were adjusted in height according to the men's weights in order to standardize the work rate. The men stepped at specified rates controlled by a metronome. This method of work was chosen because although it would have been more desirable to have the men shovelling rock the size of air-conditioned space required for shovelling rock would have made the climatic room prohibitively expensive. The procedure occupies eight days during which the work rate is increased gradually to a level on the final day which is equivalent to the most strenuous underground tasks, i.e., shovelling rock and tramming it (oxygen consumption of 1,4 ℓ/min)[14]. The optimum air condition for acclimatizing men for this work rate is 32°C wet-bulb temperature (saturated air) with a low air speed of 0,5 m/s.

Although this new procedure was started only in 1965 in one mine it has now been adopted by 32 mines using 28 climatic chambers each holding between 60 and 200 men. It is estimated that some 280 000 Bantu mine workers are acclimatized by this means each year. The rapid switch-over to this new method of acclimatization is due to the many advantages it offers over the underground procedures. Some of these are :

(a)   It is safer because every man who completes the full period can be regarded as having been properly acclimatized for hard work in moderate heat and as conditioned for hard physical work.

(b)   Supervision is more effective and easier because the men are in a confined space under bright light and can all be seen by the supervisors who walk between the rows of benches. It has therefore been possible to measure the oral temperature of the men during work *each day* of acclimatization, which means that every man who develops too high a body temperature can be detected, and this adds greatly to the safety of the procedure. It has thus been possible to reduce drastically the numbers of supervisors.

(c)   If a man should develop hyperpyrexia, or any other form of heat illness, he can be sent to hospital within minutes as compared with the minimum period of one hour required to move him from underground acclimatization centres.

(d)   The procedure requires only four hours each day and the rest of the shift can be used for instruction in Fanakalo or in job or safety instruction.

(e)   The load on the shaft is reduced at a critical period as these men are not sent underground.

(f)   The reduction in the period of acclimatization from twelve to eight days makes available to the mine four fully productive shifts.

(g)   In times of heavy influxes of labour to the mine the climatic rooms can be used for four or five shifts and thus up to 1 000 men can be processed each day; this has eliminated the shifts previously lost while the men waited on surface to be admitted to the underground acclimatization centres.

It has been estimated that the gain of four shifts per recruit and the reduction in the number of supervisors means an annual saving of between 1 and 2 million rand to the gold mining industry. In addition, the procedure has been made safer and the men are better acclimatized.

The general effect of these various measures on the heat stroke position is illustrated in Figure 7.3 by considering together the increase in the numbers of men working physically in wet-bulb temperatures above 29°C and the incidence of fatal heat stroke per annum between 1957 and 1968. This shows that in spite of the fact that the numbers of men at risk almost doubled during this period, the incidence of fatal heat stroke decreased five-fold, that is, from 0,25 per 1 000 in 1957 to 0,05 per 1 000 in 1968. It would not be unreasonable to consider that the marked improvement in the heat stroke position over this period is due mainly to such measures as the proper acclimatization of all Bantu recruits, the training of all underground officials in the prevention and recognition of heat stroke cases, and the immediate cooling underground of suspected cases of heat stroke.

However, Figure 7.3 also indicates that there has been an alarming trend in recent years for more and more Bantu to be working at dangerously high wet-bulb temperatures. This trend is apparently due to the cost of conventional ventilation increasing non-linearly with increase in depth. This makes it increasingly difficult for mine managements to keep wet-bulb temperatures in working places below 32°C as mines go deeper. Because of this it is important for mine managements to know the maximum rates of work

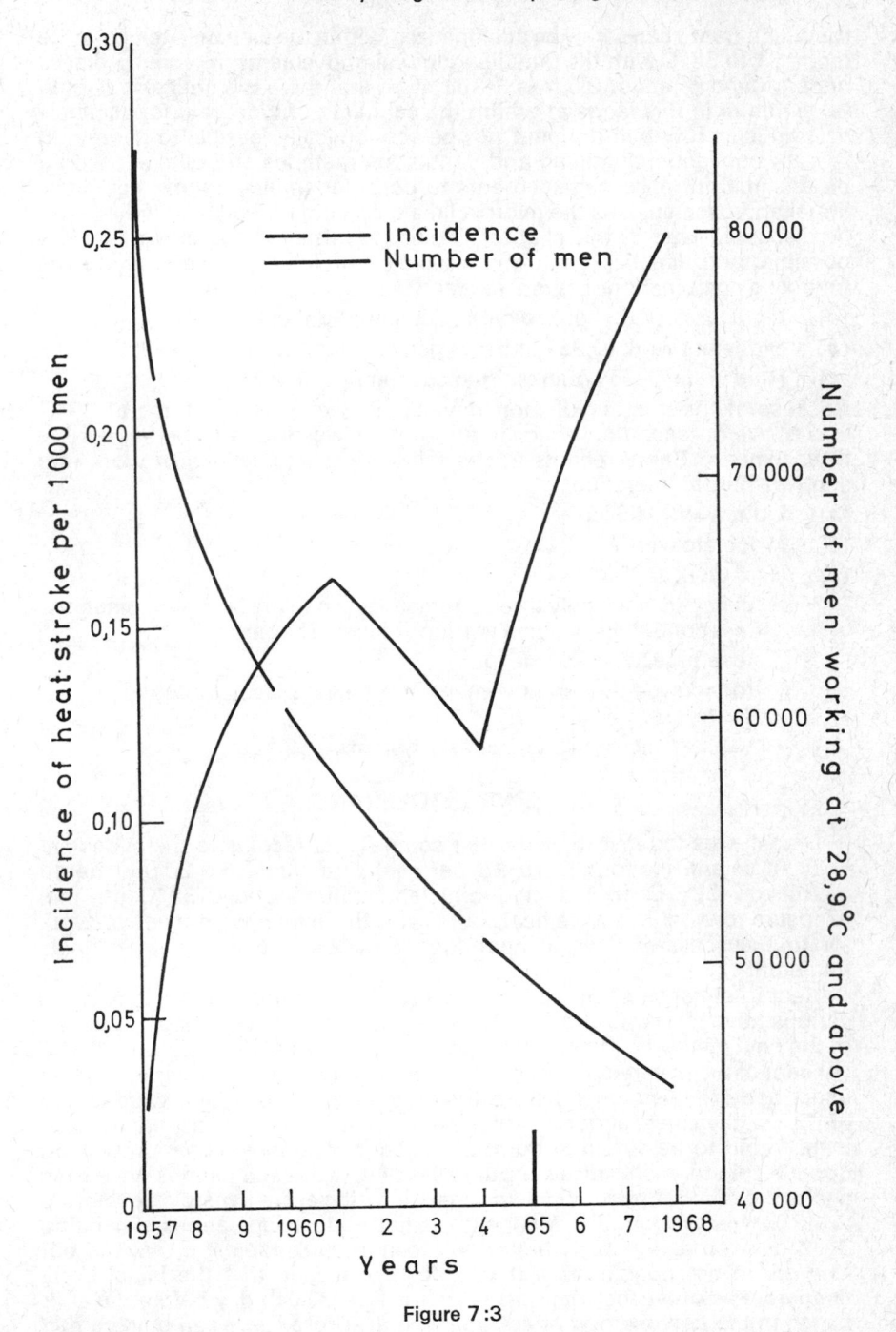

Figure 7:3

for which Bantu can safely be acclimatized within the wet-bulb temperature range 31 to 36°C with the prevailing low air movements in working places underground of about 0,5 m/s. It might be that there is a critical wet-bulb temperature in this range at which the safe limit of work rate for acclimatization is so low that it would not be economically feasible to mine with present conventional mining and ventilation methods and where it would be essential for mine managements to consider employing an unconventional approach such as the micro-climate cooling of workmen, which will be discussed later in this chapter. Studies to this end have shown that it is possible to acclimatize Bantu mine recruits safely and successfully to the following combinations of work rate and wet-bulb temperature:

(a)   Light work (0,65 ℓ/min oxygen consumption) at 34°C
(b)   Moderate work (0,95 ℓ/min oxygen consumption) at 32°C
(c)   Hard work (1,45 ℓ/min oxygen consumption) at 31°C

Because of the number of men developing rectal temperatures of 40°C and above on each day of acclimatization, it was found to be impossible to acclimatize Bantu recruits at the following combinations of work rate and wet-bulb temperature:

(a)   Light work at 36°C
(b)   Moderate work at 34°C
(c)   Hard work at 32°C

Mine managers have only three alternatives when the latter combinations of heat stress conditions occur in working places. They are:

(i)   to reduce the work rate, or
(ii)   to increase the air movement in working places to between 1,0–1,5 m/s, or
(iii) to use a micro-climate cooling system.

4   HEAT INTOLERANCE

Dreosti was the first to show that some Bantu recruits to the mines are heat-intolerant. He found that 15 per cent of a sample of 20 000 Bantu recruits to City Deep Ltd. had oral temperatures above 39°C on first exposure to work in severe heat, but that if these men were made to work for four successive days in heat then only 2 per cent remained heat-intolerant[2].

Heat intolerance of Bantu mine recruits has also been a problem in the various new acclimatization procedures. An unexpected finding in the trial of the new method of acclimatization in City Deep Ltd. in 1953 was that 6 per cent of the new recruits, in their first two or three days underground, had initial body temperatures, before they began to work, which were above 38°C, i.e., they were abnormal. Many of these men on being sent to hospital were found to be suffering from an infection. The most common was an upper respiratory virus disease, but cases of measles and mumps were seen and cases of lobar pneumonia and malaria with severe hyperpyrexias of up to 42°C were reported[15]. Men with initial body temperatures exceeding 38°C develop dangerously high body temperatures rapidly if they are put to work in hot conditions[16]. It was for this reason that the initial body temperatures of *all* acclimatizees were measured each day before the shift began in the new method of acclimatization. These cases can be regarded as being temporarily heat-intolerant because the majority acclimatized satisfactorily after they were discharged from hospital.

Another form of temporary heat intolerance which has come into prominence lately is that due to dehydration. Dehydration occurs when men fail to drink more than a fraction of the fluid they lose in sweat. Studies have shown that men who are working moderately hard in hot conditions and are completely deprived of water, may develop a water deficit of about three litres of water after four hours of work. The body temperatures of such men are much higher than those of men who drink water *ad libitum* but, what is more serious, is the fact that some men who are severely dehydrated are liable to develop heat stroke levels of body temperature (i.e., above 41 °C). It has been estimated that the risks of men who work moderately hard at a wet-bulb temperature of 33,9°C, developing heat stroke levels of body temperature, are five times as great in men deprived of water than in men drinking water *ad libitum.* No advantage was shown in forcing men to drink as much as they lost in sweat compared with drinking water *ad libitum* (when they generally finished the shift about one litre in water deficit). Nor was there any advantage in giving men 0,3 per cent saline to drink instead of plain water. Other studies have shown that as a safe general rule, acclimatized Bantu working at wet-bulb temperatures of about 32°C should be provided with at least three litres of drinking water over the shift in order to prevent serious dehydration. In this context it is, in Israel, a court martial offence if under operational conditions, each soldier is not provided with one litre of drinking water per hour. By this means heat stroke was virtually eliminated from the Israeli forces in their recent desert campaigns.

In addition to cases of "temporary" heat intolerance, it was observed during the initial trial of the new method of acclimatization in City Deep Ltd. that some men consistently developed high body temperatures during work each day. Such men were sent to hospital after three successive days of hyperpyrexia, but in the majority of cases the medical officers were unable to find any cause for the abnormal body temperature responses during work. These men were regarded as being heat-intolerant and were discharged to surface work. In climatic room acclimatization it was found that up to 20 per cent of recruits ran consistently high body temperatures over the first five days of the procedure but that if they were re-cycled, starting from day one, the percentage with consistently high temperatures fell to about 2 per cent. This is the same figure that Dreosti found for permanent heat intolerance among Bantu mine recruits.

Considerable research has gone into the identification of the causes of permanent heat-intolerance, because if the causes are known then it should be possible to recognize the recruits who are potentially heat-intolerant and prevent them from working in hot areas. Research in South Africa and overseas[17,18] has shown that one of the greatest causes of heat-intolerance is a low capacity for physical work of an endurance nature (measured by the physiologist in terms of the individual's maximum oxygen intake). Another important factor is a low body weight. Bantu recruits of less than 50 kg in weight are more liable to high body temperatures when doing moderately hard work than men of average body weight. A low body weight and low capacity for endurance work often go together in the same individual because these two factors are significantly correlated in the Bantu population of the mines. Because of the higher risks of heat stroke of recruits with low work capacities or low body weights, mines have been advised not to acclimatize such men. To assist mine managements in classifying men who are not suitable for acclimatization because of low work capacity, a physical selection test has been introduced and is now used by most mines.

Another cause of heat intolerance is advanced age. Bantu of over 45 years of age are much more liable to heat stroke than younger men when they work hard under hot conditions[19]. More than 50 per cent of the heat stroke deaths in one period were found to be in men of over 45 years of age. Another cause of heat intolerance is the combination of gross over-weight

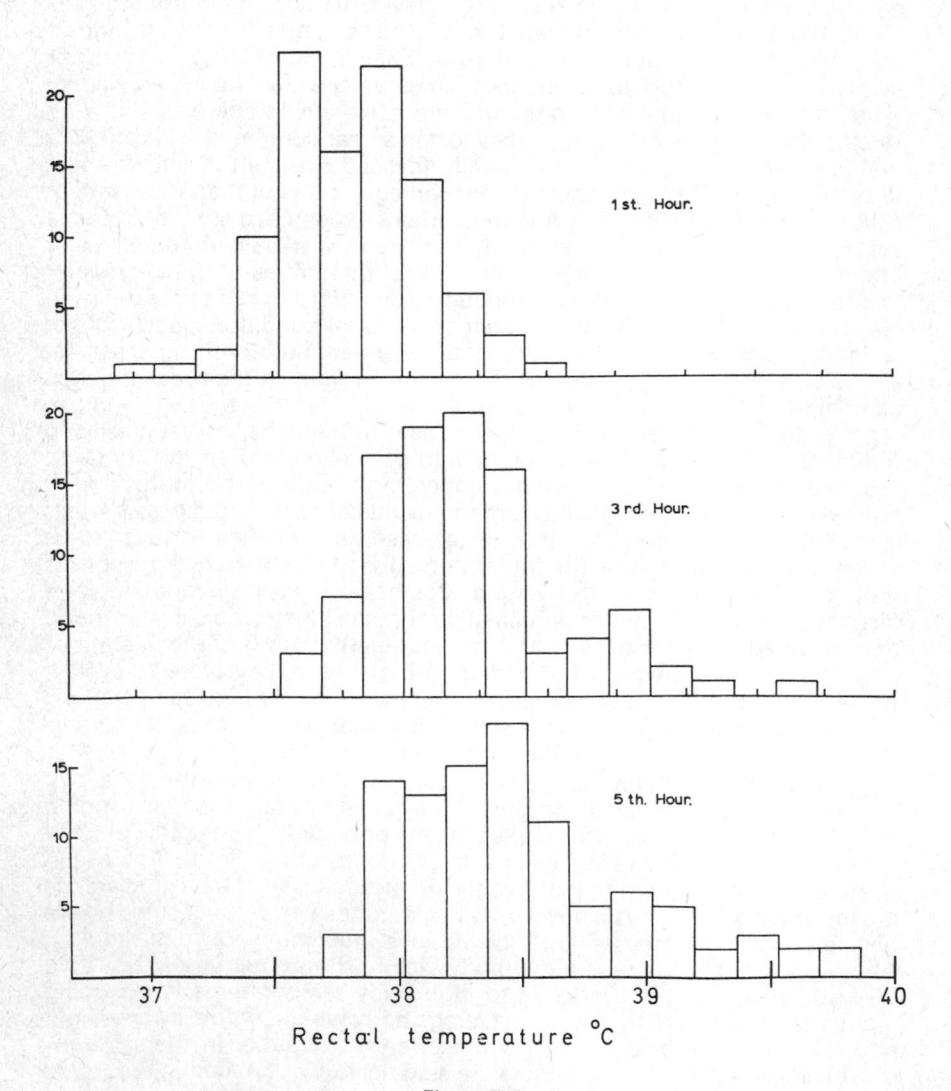

Figure 7:4

and low work capacity. This factor is more important in European members of Proto teams than in Bantu mine workers in whom obesity occurs rarely. Although research has high-lighted a number of causal factors in heat intolerance which have led to steps being taken to exclude men with a high risk, cases are still being reported of heat intolerance for which no causal factors have yet been found.

Another aspect of heat intolerance is that heat-intolerant individuals tend to give histograms of the distribution of body temperatures showing a skewness towards the right, that is, indicating a higher and more dangerous body temperature. This is well illustrated in the histograms, Figure 7:4, of 99 acclimatized Bantu men after 1, 3 and 5 hours of work at an oxygen consumption of 1 ℓ/min, an air temperature of 32°C (with the air saturated with water vapour) and 0,5 m/s air speed. It will be noted that the distribution of body temperatures after one hour of work is normal, but by the end of the third hour the distribution is skewed to the right and by the end of the fifth hour the skewness to the right is even more marked. In the next section we shall discuss the need to be able to estimate the probability of men, in a specific combination of work rate, wet-bulb temperature and air movement, reaching heat stroke levels of body temperature, from data of the type given in Figure 7:4. With information of this nature for a wide range of heat stress conditions, mine managements would be in a position to decide under what heat stress conditions it would be safe for their men to work and what conditions are too dangerous because of a high probability of the men under such conditions reaching heat stroke levels of body temperature.

Finding a mathematical model which would fit, satisfactorily, the skew distributions which develop after 2 to 3 hours of work in heat and which could be used to estimate the probability of reaching heat stroke levels of body temperature, proved to be a formidable and challenging task[20,21,22]. The solution to the problem was the use of the three-parameter, log-normal distribution[22].

The log-normal distribution has proved to be sufficiently flexible to fit all of the experimental data upon which it has been tried so far. An example of the excellent fit to experimental data is given in Figure 7:5 which contains the log-normal distributions fitted to the data on the ninety-nine men given in Figure 7:4; it also gives the means ($\bar{x}$), the standard deviations (s) and the skewness parameters (σ).

Munro *et al.*[23] subsequently estimated these parameters by applying the log-normal distribution to the fourth-hour rectal temperatures obtained on samples of acclimatized and unacclimatized men exposed to the same 45 different combinations of wet-bulb temperatures, air speed and work rate. The results obtained for the acclimatized and unacclimatized men are given in Figure 7:6. This Figure shows that the mean body temperature is higher, the standard deviation is wider and the skewness is greater, as the heat stress is increased in both acclimatized and unacclimatized men and that all of these parameters are less satisfactory for the unacclimatized men. This indicates, of course, that at a particular heat stress level unacclimatized men have a much higher probability of reaching heat stroke levels of body temperature than the acclimatized men.

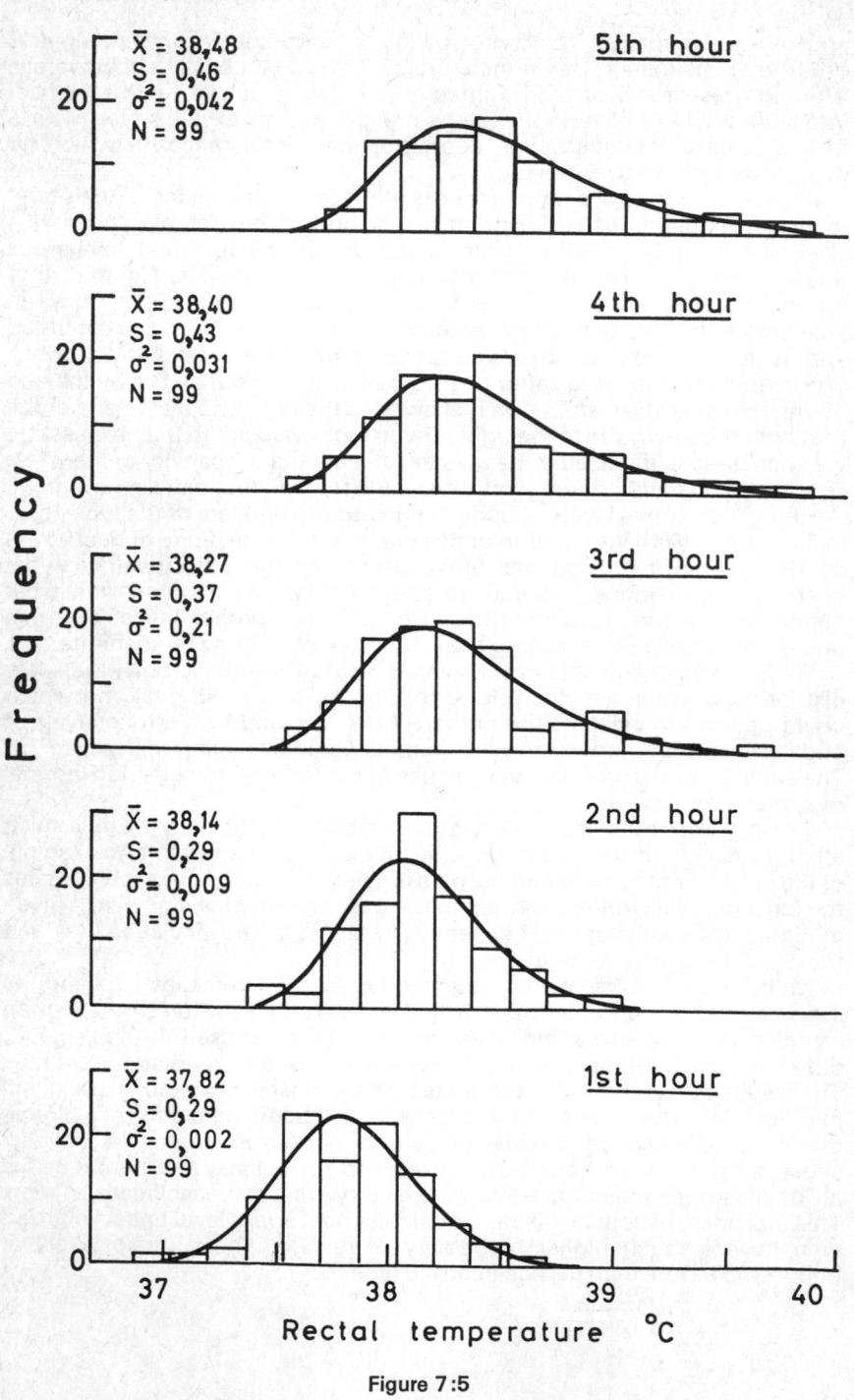

Figure 7:5

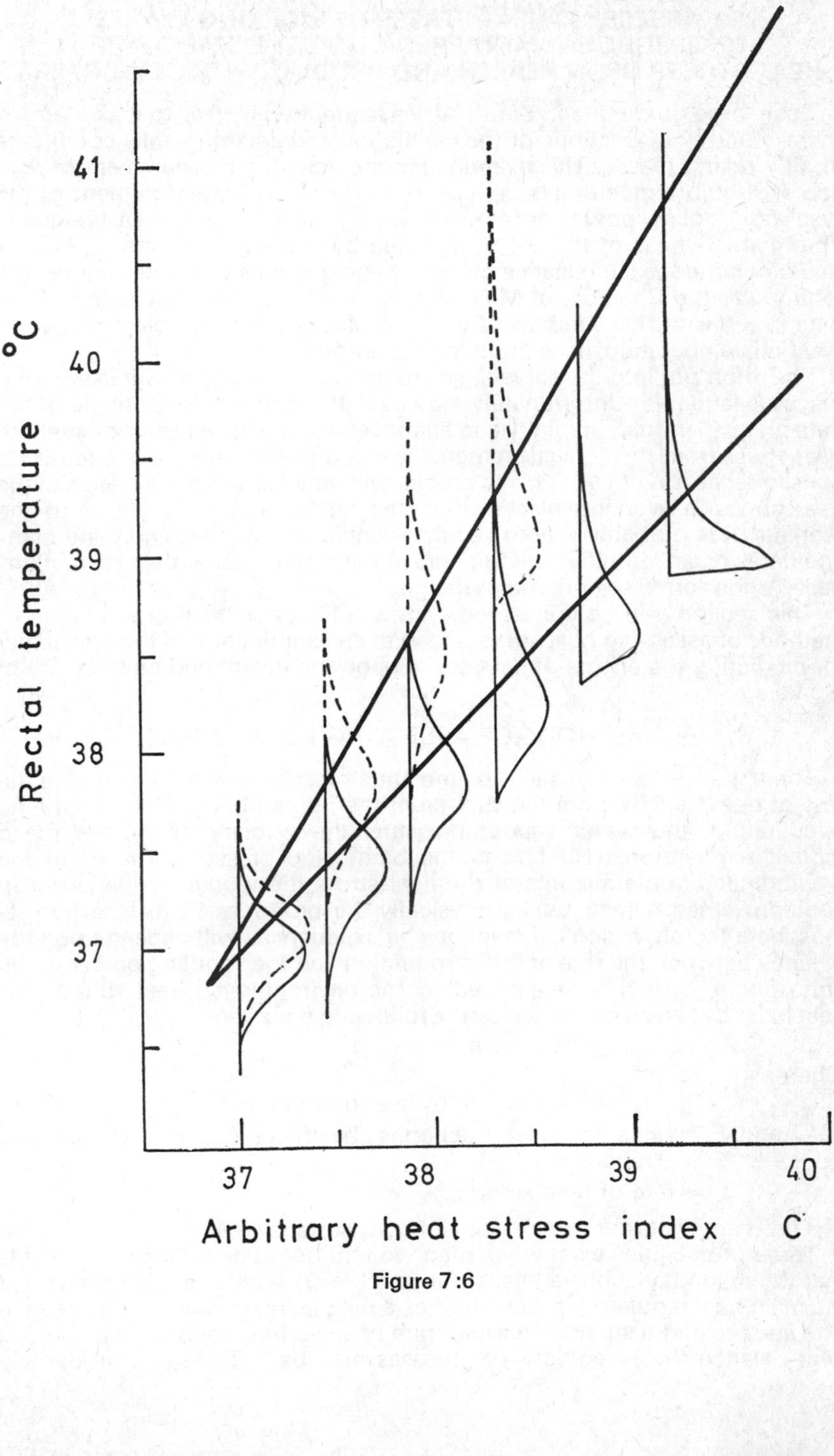
Rectal temperature °C
41
40
39
38
37
37
38
39
40
Arbitrary heat stress index C

Figure 7:6

5   ASSESSING HEAT STRESS OF WORKING PLACES UNDERGROUND AND PREDICTING THE EFFECTS OF HEAT STRESS UPON HEALTH AND PRODUCTIVITY OF WORKERS

Each large gold mine in South Africa is required by law to make regular three-monthly inspections of the ventilation and environmental conditions in all working places. This examination includes the measurement of dry- and wet-bulb temperatures, air speed and either the measurement of the wet kata cooling power or its calculation from the other measurements. The thermal stress of the air, as reflected by these measurements, is kept under continuous surveillance by mine managements and these figures are returned to the Chamber of Mines which issues an annual collation of the data in terms of the numbers of working places at various class ranges of wet bulb temperature, in addition to other information.

The effort put into the surveillance of the heat stress of the air in working places is laudable. Unfortunately, however, the best use is not made of the data on temperature, humidity and air movement because the assessment of heat stress from these measurements is made in only the crudest terms. In consequence it is not possible to predict with any accuracy the effects of the heat stress in working places upon the health and productivity of the workers. It is probably true to say that ventilation officials and mine managements make "intuitive" judgments in this regard rather than predictions based upon sound scientific knowledge.

This section will be concerned with a critical appraisal of a number of methods of assessing heat stress and with an examination of their reliability for predicting the effects of heat stress upon the health and productivity of workers.

6   METHODS OF ASSESSING HEAT STRESS

There are five elements in the ambient atmosphere which determine the rate of heat transfer from the surface of the human body. They are the air temperature, the water vapour pressure, the velocity of air, the mean radiant temperature (MRT) and the barometric pressure. These are the environmental determinants of the heat stress the workers experience. In addition, when a man works physically, he produces heat. In a hot atmosphere the physiological reactions he experiences will depend upon the balance between the rate of heat production and the "cooling power of the atmosphere" which is determined by the environmental heat stress. This heat balance can be expressed by the following equation:

$$M \pm C \pm R - E = S$$

where

$$M = \text{the rate of heat production,}$$

R, C and $E = $ rates of heat exchange by radiation, convection and evaporation,

$$S = \text{rate of heat storage.}$$

The units are watts per square metre of body surface area.

Three possibilities exist when men work in hot atmospheres. The first is that the men may achieve heat balance ($S = 0$) with only a mild strain of the main heat regulatory processes, i.e., a mild increase in blood flow to the skin surface and a small increase in rate of sweating. Second, in achieving heat balance these regulatory processes may be put under considerable strain which may result in discomfort, circulatory instability and heat collapse and a loss in efficiency. Third, if the capacities of the regulatory systems are insufficient for the establishment of heat balance ($S > 0$), then the body will gain heat, resulting in hyperpyrexia and possible heat stroke.

Physiological strain, as indicated by sweat rate, heart rate and body temperature, has been studied in relation to certain heat stress parameters, singly or in combination. The relative effects of the various heat stress parameters differ in different circumstances and their interaction upon physiological and psychological reactions is complex. It is for this reason that so many different solutions have been proposed to give quantitative expression to the heat stress/human strain relationship.

MacPherson[24] lists 19 different methods of assessing heat stress and his list is not exhaustive. The present section will be confined to those methods which are relevant to the gold mining industry.

6.1 Direct assessments of environmental heat stress

6.1.1. Wet-bulb temperature

Haldane, as a result of his experiences in the Cornish tin mines and his studies in a hot room in Oxford, stated in 1908[25] that the wet-bulb temperature was the best single measure of environmental heat stress. He went on to give the limiting wet-bulb temperature for men stripped to the waist in still air as 31°C; for an air speed of about 1 m/s the limit was raised to 34,5°, and for physical work such as climbing steps at 4 m/min, the limit was lowered to 25,5°C.

There is no doubt that in the conditions of still air and high relative humidities of the Cornish tin mines at that time, wet-bulb temperature was a good measure of environmental heat stress, but it is, of course, of limited value in conditions of high air speed and high mean radiant temperature.

6.1.2 The kata thermometer

Hill *et al.* in 1916[26] introduced the kata thermometer as "a method of measuring the relative rate of heat loss to which the skin is exposed by convection, radiation and evaporation with varying atmospheric conditions". The kata thermometer is an advance over the wet-bulb temperature as a means for measuring the heat stress of the ambient atmosphere because it takes account of more of the environmental heat stress parameters, but the small size of the kata thermometer compared with that of man means that the "cooling power" of a hot and humid atmosphere is about twice as great for the kata thermometer as it is for man.

Although Hill and his colleagues went to great pains to give exact quantitative expression to the heat transfer from the kata thermometer, only three papers were written on the relationship between the heat stress of atmospheres, as measured by kata cooling power, and physiological reactions of man. In the last of these Vernon and Warner[27] stated that wet-kata readings had no advantage over wet-bulb temperatures in the particular conditions they examined, a range of dry-bulb temperatures, moist and dry air, and a single work rate and air movement.

Orenstein introduced the wet-kata thermometer into the gold mining industry in South Africa in 1919 and Orenstein and Ireland in 1922[28] summarized the relationship between kata cooling powers and man's reactions as follows:

Physiological reactions of men at different kata cooling powers

| Cooling power | | Physiological reactions of men stripped to the waist |
Wet-kata	Dry-kata	
5	1,5	Extremely oppressive; profuse sweating; rise in body temperature and heart rate especially when work performed.
10	3,5	Distinctly oppressive; body temperature can be kept normal only by profuse sweating; skin flushed and wet; pulse rate high.
15	5,5	Lower limit for comfort.
20	8,0	Quite comfortable for work.
25	10,0	Cool and refreshing for work.

Vernon[29] agreed with Orenstein and Ireland that the endurable limit was a wet-kata cooling power of 5. However, he noted that as he became acclimatized he could work in moist and still air at a wet-bulb temperature of 32°C compared with Haldane's limit of 25°C. Vernon was aware that the relationship between the heat stress of the environment, as measured with the wet-kata thermometer and the resultant human reactions, is not a simple one. He stated, "As the cooling power of the wet-kata depends only upon the wet-bulb temperature and air velocity it might be assumed that the wet-kata cooling power would offer a convenient index of comfort under moist conditions. Unfortunately, this is not so". However, it was not until 1936 that the kata thermometer appears to have been finally dismissed in the United Kingdom as a means of measuring environmental heat stress from which one could predict accurately man's reactions to work in heat. Lawton[30] as a result of his experience in deep mines, criticized the use of the wet-kata cooling power and Bedford, in his contribution to Lawton's paper, states, "it by no means follows that because in two places we have the same kata cooling power we shall feel equally warm in both". Bedford considered that the reason for this discrepancy is that the kata thermometer, being much smaller than man, is more sensitive in its response to low air speeds than is man.

The wet-kata thermometer has continued to be used in the gold mines of the Witwatersrand as a means for measuring the heat stress of the atmosphere in working places. In recent years the heat stress has increasingly been judged by taking the wet-bulb temperature and air speed into account, in conjunction with wet-kata cooling powers, in deciding whether the heat stress of the atmosphere in a working place is excessive. No standards have been laid down for this purpose.

6.1.3   *Heat transfer from man*

(a)   *Heat stress index of Belding and Hatch*

Haines and Hatch[31] in an engineering approach to the problem of heat stress, proposed that the rate of evaporative cooling required to maintain heat balance (E_{req}) and the potential of the atmosphere for evaporative cooling (E_{max}) could be determined with sufficient accuracy for man in most industrial situations. They used the coefficients of heat transfer for radiation, convection and evaporation for nude men reported by the research group at Fort Knox during World War II and certain simplifying assumptions and approximations. They suggested that a consideration of E_{req} and E_{max} would indicate whether an atmosphere had sufficient cooling power for a man to be able to maintain heat balance and also, whether E_{req} would exceed the limit of sweat-rate a man could maintain for an eight-hour shift.

They proposed the following assumptions and simplifying approximations for the calculation of heat transfer by radiation and convection:

(i)   That the surface area should be 1,86 m² for the so-called 70 kg "standard" man.

(ii) That the skin temperature should be 35°C, irrespective of the environmental heat stress.

(iii) That the calculations be based upon the Fort Knox equations for nude men because, unfortunately, the equations for clothed men were unacceptable.

(iv) That the heat losses from the respiratory tract be neglected because they are negligible under hot conditions.

(v)   That heat storage be neglected because it would be important only under conditions above the limiting conditions where E_{req} exceeds E_{max}.

E_{req} was calculated from the heat balance equation:

$$E_{req} = M \pm R \pm C$$

where

$$M = \text{the rate of metabolism}$$

and

$$R \text{ and } C = \text{rates of heat exchange by convection and radiation in watts per square metre (W/m}^2).$$

The equations they use for calculating R and C are:

$$R = 7(T_r - 35)$$
$$C = 1{,}8V^{0,6}(T_a - 35)$$

where rates of heat exchange are in W/m², T_r and T_a in °C and V in m/s.

T_r can be estimated with sufficient accuracy from the measurement of the temperature of a standard black globe (T_g), air temperature (T_a) and wind velocity (V) and the following equation:

$$T_r = T_g + 0{,}24V^{0,5}(T_g - T_a)$$

They claim that this equation is reasonably accurate for globe temperatures in the range 35–55°C.

E_{max}, the potential of the atmosphere for evaporative heat loss, is given by the equation:

$$E_{max} = 28V^{0,6}(5{,}6 - P_{wa})$$

where

$P_{wa} =$ the saturated water-vapour pressure (kPa) at air temperature.

They suggested, as a quantitative index of heat stress (HSI), the following equation:

$$HSI = E_{req}/E_{max} \times 100$$

If E_{req} equalled E_{max}, or E_{req} exceeded 1 500 W/m², then HSI was assigned a value of 100 and it was proposed that a "standard" man would find such a condition of heat stress "physiologically" impossible for work for any length of time without a rise in temperature.

When Belding and his colleagues attempted to use this approach to assess the heat stress of industrial situations, they ran into a num-number of snags[32,33]. One was that the E_{req}, which they calculated from the equation, was much greater than the rates they measured. They attributed this discrepancy to the fact that the men in industry were wearing clothes, whereas the coefficients of heat transfer used were obtained on nude men. They therefore suggested that the values calculated for R and C be reduced by one-third, but this proposal was entirely without experimental support. They also found that in conditions of extreme heat, the assumption of a skin temperature of 35°C was incorrect and for such conditions, where the body stored heat, the mean skin temperature was probably closer to 38°C.

There is little doubt that the determination of E_{req}, the rate of evaporative heat exchange needed to maintain thermal equilibrium, and of E_{max}, the evaporative heat potential of the atmosphere, has considerable merit. E_{req} establishes the total heat load and also the main source of heat stress in the environment; it also allows one to determine whether the amount of sweat required to maintain thermal equilibrium is within the sweat capacity of the average workman. E_{max} indicates whether the atmosphere is able to evaporate the amount of sweat the man must produce in order to remain in thermal equilibrium. Whether the calculations of HSI contributes anything to the understanding of the thermal stress/human strain relationship is doubtful. Belding and Hatch[34] acknowledge this in the statement that "the critical strain in heat is usually circulatory". It is not possible to make any estimate of the circulatory strain from HSI. Because of doubts about the validity of the coefficients of heat transfer they used and the problem of predicting human strain reactions, this approach has not been used in the gold mining industry, even as an experimental approach for the assessment of heat stroke.

(b)   Specific cooling power

The approach adopted by Haines, Belding and Hatch has the virtue that it is based on the sound principles of engineering heat transfer whereas most heat stress indices are purely empirical. At the Human Sciences Laboratory attempts have been made to use the heat transfer approach in a manner which avoids the shortcomings of the HSI[35]. Using the sophisticated instrumentation of a wind tunnel, equations have been derived for human heat transfer which are more accurate than those derived by the Fort Knox group. Care has been taken to ensure that the equations will be valid in underground environments. Heat transfer equations have been used to assess heat stress in a way which has meaning both in terms of the physiological reactions of men and of the performance of ventilation and refrigeration systems.

The instrumentation of the wind tunnel allows direct measurement of human heat transfer by radiation, convection and evaporation. Men clad in shorts have been exposed to environments covering the entire ranges of temperature, humidity and wind speed experienced underground. On the basis of about 1 000 measurements of radiation and convection, the following predictive equations have been derived:

$$R = 17 \times 10^{-8}(T_r/2 + 290,7)^3(\overline{T}_s - T_r)$$
$$C = 8,3(P_a/101,3)^{0,6}V^{0,6}(\overline{T}_s - T_a)$$

where

$\overline{T}_s$ = mean skin temperature (°C)
T_r = mean radiant temperature (°C)
P_a = barometric pressure (kPa)
T_a = mean air temperature (°C).

The fraction of the total body area participating in radiant heat transfer is taken to be 0,75.

The equation for maximum evaporative heat transfer is based on a theoretical analysis of the relationship between convective and evaporative heat transfer[36]. Accordingly:

$$E_{max} = (15\ 100/Pa)(Pa/101,3)^{0,6}V^{0,6}(\varphi P_{wa} - P_{ws})$$

where

φ = the relative humidity

and

P_{wa} and P_{ws} = the saturated water vapour pressure (kPa) at air temperature and skin temperature, respectively.

The vapour pressure gradient ($\varphi P_{wa} - P_{ws}$) can be expressed in terms of wet-bulb temperature (T_w), skin temperature and barometric pressure.

The cooling power of the environment, or the maximum rate of heat transfer between man and environment, is given by

$$Q_{max} = R + C + E_{max}$$

Q_{max} has been calculated as a function of skin temperature and the five environmental parameters T_a, T_w, T_r, V and P_a for the entire range of underground environments. In comparison with wet-bulb temperature (T_w) and wind speed (V), the parameters T_a, T_r and P_a have a minor effect on Q_{max}. Average values of T_r, P_a and wet-bulb depression can be employed without introducing appreciable error in the calculation of Q_{max} for most underground environments. The following typical values can be used:

$$P_a = 100 \text{ kPa}$$
$$T_a = T_r = T_w + 2°C.$$

The calculation of Q_{max} requires a knowledge of skin temperature. However, the studies in the wind tunnel have shown that in hot environments, acclimatized men, in equilibrium, exhibiting only mild strain, have mean skin temperatures close to 35°C, irrespective of air temperature, humidity, wind speed or work rate. One can therefore define the *specific cooling power* of an underground environment referred to a skin temperature of 35°C and assuming $P_a = 100$ kPa,

$$T_a = T_r = T_w + 2°C.$$

Figure 7:7 shows specific cooling power as a function of wet-bulb temperature with wind speed as parameter. Horizontal lines on Figure 7:7 are lines of equal cooling power and therefore define equivalent combinations of wet-bulb temperature and wind speed.

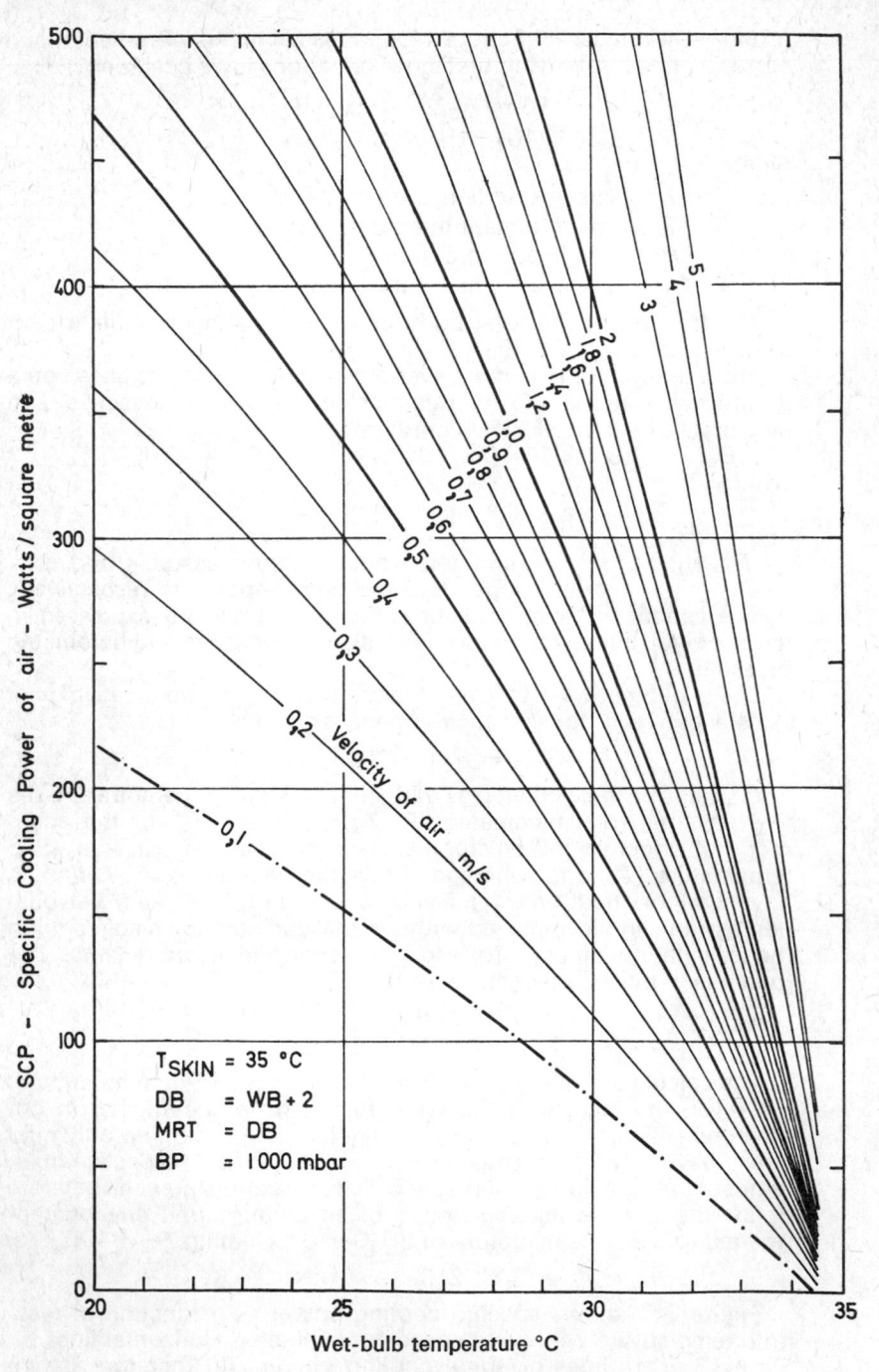

Figure 7:7

The ventilation engineer can use calculations of specific cooling power to determine the combinations of temperatures and wind speed which provide particular cooling rates most economically. In most working places underground wind speeds are low, and at low wind speeds higher cooling powers are attained more easily by increasing the wind speed than by decreasing the wet-bulb temperature.

Values of cooling power can also be used in conjunction with estimates of metabolic rate to assess the environmental conditions necessary for a man performing a specific task to attain equilibrium. Figure 7:8 based on measurements of the oxygen intakes of underground tasks[36], shows the metabolic rates associated with various tasks. Neglecting the energy leaving the body in forms other than heat, a working man will be able to attain equilibrium in a particular environment if the cooling power of that environment equals or exceeds the metabolic rate associated with his task. An acclimatized man will be able to attain equilibrium with a skin temperature of 35°C, and exhibit only mild strain if the *specific* cooling power equals or exceeds the metabolic rate. Metabolic rates of 90, 180 and 270 W/m² are typical of light work (e.g., winch driving), moderate work (e.g., sweeping, machine) and hard work (tramming and shovelling), respectively.

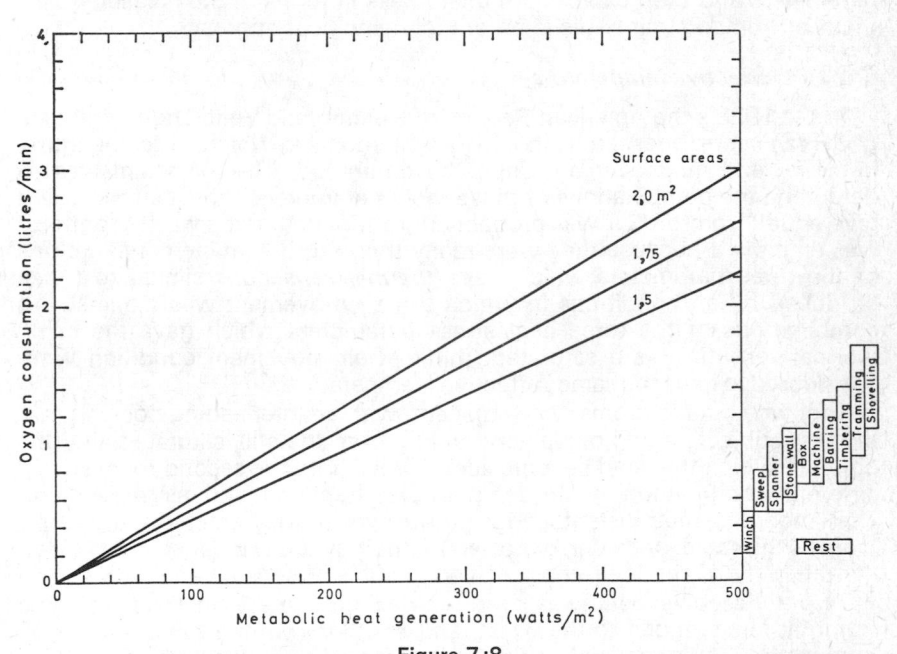

Figure 7:8

It will be apparent to those familiar with underground environments that many men work in environments where, according to Figures 7:7 and 7:8, they cannot be in equilibrium with the environment. A man not in equilibrium in a hot environment accumulates heat and his body temperature rises. Evaporative heat transfer rises very rapidly with increasing skin temperature. When equilibrium is not possible with a skin temperature of 35°C, skin temperature will rise until evaporation is sufficient to allow equilbrium. The extent of skin temperature rise required may be so great in severe heat that body temperature rises to heat stroke levels. The heat transfer equations above can then be used to predict the skin temperature at which equilibrium will be possible, that is, the skin temperature at which cooling power equals metabolic rate.

Increases of skin temperature above 35°C are associated with increased body core temperatures and increased circulatory strain, indicating physiological strain which, if excessive, may lead to heat stroke. Preliminary analysis has shown that *predicted equilibrium skin temperature* might be a good index of heat stress in conditions where metabolic rate exceeds specific cooling power.

6.2   Assessing heat stress from measurements of human reactions

As indicated in the previous section there was, until very recently, no satisfactory way of determining the total heat stress of environment and metabolism on man. The alternative was to measure *one* element of human strain under a wide range of different combinations of different heat stress parameters and then express the heat stress in terms of the measured element of human strain. This is an entirely empirical approach.

6.2.1   Effective temperature

In the 1920's the American Society of Heating and Ventilation Engineers (ASHVE) set up a research laboratory with rooms in which air temperature, humidity and air movement could be controlled. The main aim was to determine the combinations of these three parameters of heat stress which give equal "comfort". It was probably unfortunate that the word "comfort" was employed because they were really trying to determine combinations of the three parameters which gave *thermal sensations* similar to those produced by air conditions in which the air movement was minimal. All combinations of the three heat stress parameters which gave the same thermal sensation as a saturated, minimal air movement condition were considered to have the same "effective" temperature[37,38,39].

The two climatic rooms were adjacent, with an interleading door, so that the test subjects could move very rapidly from the still, saturated air condition to which they had become accustomed, into the second room with a different combination of air temperature, humidity and air movement. They recorded their instantaneous *sensations* as they entered the second room as the same, or colder, or hotter. In this way the experimenters avoided the difficulty of the well-known phenomenon of sensory adaption.

Two series of experiments were carried out, one with three subjects sitting at rest stripped to the waist, and another with the same three subjects clothed in light-weight suits. The relationship between the three heat stress parameters and effective temperatures were expressed in simple nomogram form. For any combination of air temperature, wet-bulb temperature and air speed, it was possible from these charts to read off directly the effective temperature. There were two charts. One was for men at rest stripped to the waist, the "basic" effective temperature chart, and the other for men sitting in light suits, the "normal" effective temperature hcart[40,41].

The influence on temperature sensation of radiant heat was not investigated in ASHVE's original programme, but Bedford[42] proposed that the effect of radiant heat on temperature sensation could be taken into account by substituting for air temperature in the effective temperature chart, the measurement of the temperature inside a 150 mm blackened copper sphere (Globe temperature). This was called the "corrected" effective temperature. It should be appreciated that Bedford's proposal was purely tentative and no subsequent studies have been made to determine whether this proposal is valid for thermal sensation.

The effective temperature charts were used extensively in the 1920's and 1930's to determine the zone, and limits, of thermal comfort for populations in different climates and in different occupations[43,44,45]. This information was invaluable to ventilation engineers in designing air conditioning equipment for human habitations. However, in the last ten years the effective temperature has come under heavy criticism from the reconstituted ASHRAE laboratory at Kansas State University. Using a different experimental approach, i.e., the thermal sensation after the subjects had adjusted to the new air conditions (taking sensation votes up to three hours after entering a particular environment) it was found that the original effective temperature experiments exaggerated the effect on thermal sensation of high relative humidities.[46,47] The effective temperature charts should therefore be employed with some caution for determining comfort limits.

Effective temperature was also used for another purpose. Studies in ASHVE had shown, surprisingly, in an index based upon thermal sensation, that the heart rates and rectal temperatures of men under different conditions of heat stress were more closely correlated with effective temperature than with wet-bulb temperature[48,49]. There was a need in hot industries to be able to set limits of heat stress which would not expose the men to severe strain. Effective temperature was used extensively in industry and elsewhere for this purpose. As late as 1944 Bedford recommended to the Royal Navy Personnel Research Committee in the United Kingdom that the "corrected effective temperature scale should be adopted by the Royal Navy as the official scale of environmental warmth" and at one of its meetings in that year the Committee recommended that "a corrected effective temperature of 26,7°C is the upper desirable limit for the compartments of ships which is compatible with efficiency; the Committee is prepared to accept a corrected effective temperature of 30°C as the upper tolerable limit".

However, use of the effective temperature by physiologists brought to light a number of shortcomings as an index of heat stress for the prediction of physiological strain:

(a) It does not give sufficient weight to the deleterious effect of low rates of air movement below 0,5 m/s, when men work in hot and humid environments[50,53].

(b) It exaggerates the stress of high dry-bulb temperatures when men work in severe heat with air movements in the range 0,5 to 1,5 m/s[50,51,52].

(c) It gives insufficient weight to the harmful effects of high air movements (above 1,5 m/s) at air temperatures in excess of 49°C[52].

(d)   Climates of similar physiological severity, assessed by rectal temperature, heart rate, sweat rate and tolerance time, do not have the same effective temperatures, especially in severe heat stress[51, 54, 55, 56].

Another shortcoming of effective temperature is that it assesses only the environmental heat stress and it is essential to take account of the metabolic heat load when determining limits of heat stress at which excessive physiological reactions occur. Thus one has either to have a separate effective temperature limit for each work rate or to modify the effective temperature along the lines first proposed by Smith[57] or later by Wyndham et al.[58] to take metabolism into account.

6.2.2 P_4 SR index

During World War II the Medical Research Council in the United Kingdom set up a research group to study the physiological reactions of men to heat. One of the results of its earlier studies was that effective temperature, as indicated above, is highly inaccurate in conditions of high heat stress. In consequence the research group proposed that "there would appear to be the need for a simple index or method of assessing the physiological effects of any combinations of temperature, humidity, radiation and air movement of men working at different levels of activity and wearing different types of clothing".[59]

The team used the rate of sweating as their physiological measure of heat stress because they had noted that a small change in heat stress caused a substantial change in the rate of sweating. In order to develop the index they measured the amount of sweat produced by four highly acclimatized young naval ratings exposed for four hours of intermittent rest and work to a large number of different combinations of the following heat stress factors:

(a)   Air temperatures from 27 to 55°C

(b)   Wet-bulb temperatures from 27 to 36°C

(c)   Air movements from 0,05 to 4 m/s

(d)   Metabolic rates of 60 to 200 W/m²

(e)   White drill shorts or dark cotton twill overalls

(f)   Mean radiant temperatures elevated between 2° and 10°C above air temperature (only 8 experiments).

From the measurements of sweat rates over 1 000 experiments McArdle et al.[60] produced a complicated nomogram by means of which the "predicted four-hourly sweat rate" could be calculated for any combination of the above heat stress parameters. It must be appreciated that although the nomogram was expressed in sweat rate units, the use of this measure of physiological strain was merely a convenient method of expressing the total heat stress of environmental, metabolic and clothing heat loads. Thus all of the combinations of the above heat stress parameters which give a P_4SR of 1,0 can be said to impose the same heat stress upon the individual and because of the close correlation shown between sweat rates, rectal temperatures and P_4SR values, all combinations of heat stress parameters giving a P_4SR of 1,0 could be expected to produce the same sweat rates and rectal temperatures, within the limits of experimental error.

Arguing in the same way, a fall in wet-bulb temperature or an increase in air movement which reduces P_4SR by 1,0 could be expected to relieve the total heat stress by equal amounts. Another of McArdle et al.'s aims was to establish an upper tolerable limit of heat stress as measured by the P_4SR index. They found in their experiments that at P_4SR values of 4,5 and above, "one or more subjects were unable to complete the experiment" They recognized that this limit applied to highly acclimatized and physically fit men and might not be valid for men who were less well acclimatized and less fit.

Large-scale validation trials of the P_4SR index were carried out in the M.R.C.'s Tropical Research Unit at Singapore in the period 1948 to 1953. The main conclusion was that, in spite of differences between the London and Singapore results in some details, the original P_4SR nomogram takes account of the various heat stress parameters with sufficient accuracy for it to be used for assessing heat stress and predicting physiological reactions in practical situations.[60] One important difference from the London findings was that the upper tolerable limit of P_4SR on men accustomed to living in the tropics was 3,5. The lower limit of men in Singapore probably reflects the fact that they were not as well acclimatized as the highly acclimatized men in the London studies.

In spite of the sound physiological basis for this index of heat stress and the costly and extensive validation at Singapore, it has not caught on as a means for assessing heat stress in industrial situations. As far as is known, the only place in which it is being used in daily practice is at Mt Isa Mine in Australia and even there it is being used only in a very modified form to establish the climatic conditions underground in the mine at which either the shift should be reduced to six hours or work stopped entirely. Possibly the main reason for industry being reluctant to use the index is the complicated method of calculating P_4SR values, which makes it difficult for ventilation engineers to make a spot check on the heat stress in a working place underground.

7   PREDICTING HUMAN REACTIONS TO HEAT AND DEFINING LIMITS OF HEAT STRESS

For convenience, the human reactions to heat of discomfort, loss of efficiency and decrease in productivity, excessive physiological reactions and heat stroke are dealt with separately in this section, but, of course, the body reacts as a whole to heat stress. For example, men who experience excessive physiological reactions are also, generally, very uncomfortable and suffer a loss in efficiency and their productivity falls.

7.1   Comfort

Yaglou and Drinker[45] of the original ASHVE team gave the following comfort limits for men and women clad in light clothing and engaged upon sedentary occupations:

Season	Effective Temperature °C		
	Lower limit	Optimum	Upper limit
Summer	18	21	26
Winter	15	19	23

50 per cent of their sample was comfortable between 17 and 22°C in winter and between 19 and 24°C in summer. Comfort limits were much lower in the United Kingdom, probably due to heavier clothing, with 70 per cent being comfortable at between 14 and 17°C in winter. However, as pointed out earlier, recent research in the ASHRAE laboratory[40,47] has shown that effective temperature gives too much weight to relative humidity. The optimum air temperature for comfort of North Americans is 25°C, irrespective of relative humidity[47]. Other studies by the same laboratory give optimum temperatures as 22, 18 and 16°C respectively, for light, moderate and hard work[62].

The above findings are on unacclimatized individuals. White men living in the hot, humid tropics of Australia have been found to have an optimum effective temperature for comfort of 27°C[63]. No studies have been made of the optimum comfort conditions for miners accustomed to work in high temperatures and humidities, but from the Australian study one would expect the optimum effective temperature for comfort to be about 27°C.

7.2   Efficiency and productivity

Orenstein and Ireland,[28] Bedford and Warner[64] and Caplan and Lindsay[65] investigated the effects of heat and humidity upon productivity of miners, but none of these studies is above criticism. The first thoroughly scientific studies of the effects of heat on human performance were made by Mackworth in the M.R.C.'s Applied Psychology Unit at Cambridge during World War II and by Pepler of the same Unit in Singapore[66,67]. The experimental apparatus used by these two researchers varied greatly in the amount of mental and physical effort required from the subjects. They expressed their results in terms of effective temperature although no systematic studies have ever been carried out to determine whether effective temperature gives the correct relative weighting to the effects upon human performance of different combinations of heat stress parameters. The upshot of Mackworth and Pepler's studies is that human performance, irrespective of the complexity of the task, falls off significantly between 27 and 30°C effective temperature.

There have been some doubts about the general applicability of these results to industrial work situations because

(a)   the social context in which men work in industry is entirely different from that of the experiments;

(b)   the routine of rest and work in the experiments bears little relationship to that obtaining in industry, and

(c)   the state of acclimatization of the subjects was not known but probably varied over the period of the experiments.

Because of the importance of having accurate information upon the effects of heat, humidity and air movement on human productivity of *acclimatized* Bantu workers in the gold mines in South Africa, an extensive study of the subject was embarked upon in the late 1950's[68]. The site used was a development end adjacent to an underground refrigeration plant from which either cool or hot saturated air could be drawn into the development end through separate ventilation ducts. By judicious mixing of the two streams of air, the wet-bulb temperature could be controlled at any temperature between 27 and 35°C. By means of an auxiliary fan, air speeds of from 0,5 to 4 m/s could be obtained at these air temperatures.

Under supervision pairs of newly acclimatized men shovelled as much rock as they were able from an unlimited supply at the end of the development end, into 1-ton mine cars for a period of five hours. A new team was used each day at each wet-bulb temperature and air speed combination. Five to seven teams were studied. The wet-bulb temperatures were 27, 29, 30, 32 and 35°C, and air movements were 0,5, 2,0 and 4,0 m/s. The mean outputs of the teams in tons per shift were plotted against wet-bulb temperatures for each air speed, and the curves were fitted to the plots. From these curves, the percentage fall in production with increase in wet-bulb temperatures was calculated, taking the production figure at 27°C as 100 per cent. The curves of percentage decrease in production with increase in wet-bulb temperature are presented for pairs of air movements, together with 78 per cent confidence limits, in Figures 7:9, 7:10 and 7:11. They show the percentage decrease in production with increase in wet-bulb temperature; the beneficial effects of an increase in air movement from 0,5 to 2,0 m/s and the relatively small increase in benefit with further increase in air movement above 2,0 m/s.

These results are also given in terms of effective temperature in Figure 7:12 which, in agreement with Mackworth and Pepler, shows a significant decrease in production as effective temperature increases from 27 to 30°C; at an effective temperature of 34,5°C production falls to 25 per cent of that at 27°C.

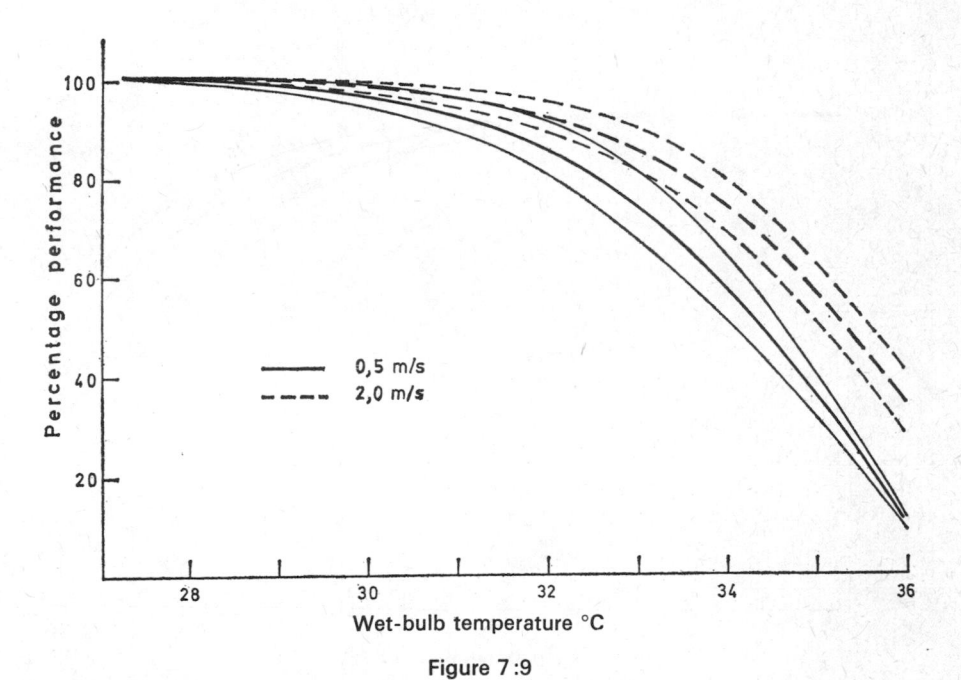

Figure 7:9

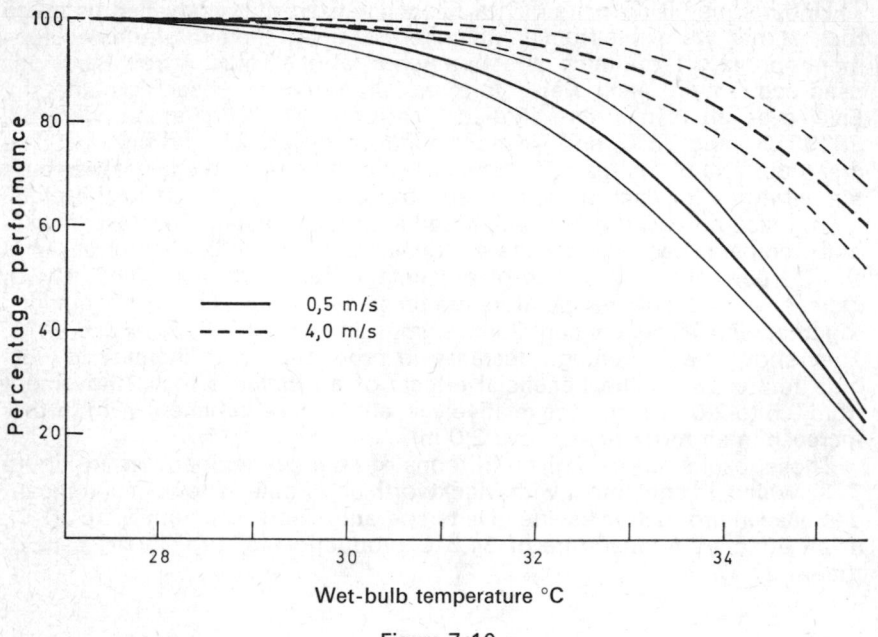

Figure 7:10

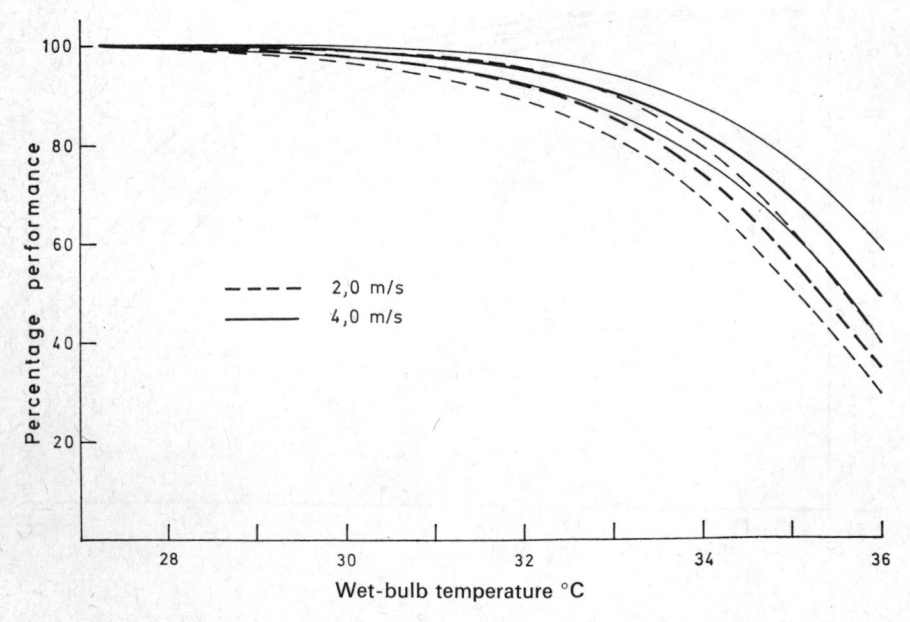

Figure 7:11

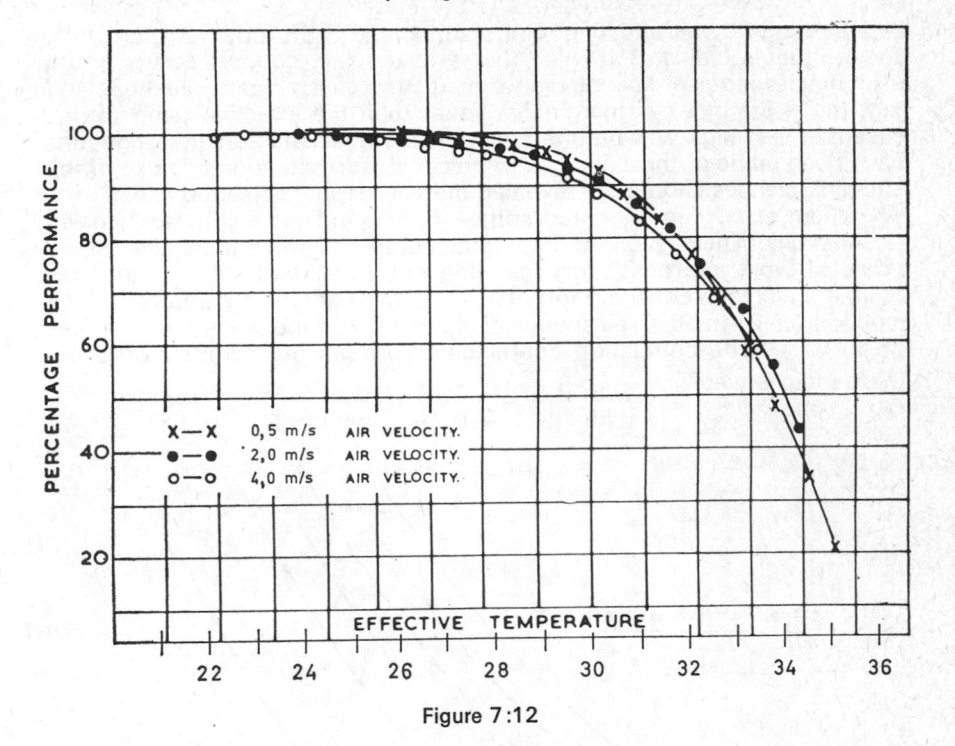

Figure 7:12

8   EXCESSIVE PHYSIOLOGICAL STRAIN AND HEAT INCAPACITATION

Physiologists do not agree upon the physiological criteria which should be used to characterize "excessive" strain; nor upon the index of heat stress which should be employed for determining this limit, nor upon the method of expressing this limit.

One reason for the lack of agreement upon the physiological criteria for excessive strain may be because of the influence of acclimatization. Bruner[68], for example, reported that German coal miners had difficulty in completing the shift if their heart rates and rectal temperatures exceeded 115 beats/min and 38°C, respectively. These miners were not acclimatized. British physiologists noted that some "acclimatized" naval ratings found conditions "unendurable" when sweat rates exceeded 1 litre/hour and rectal temperature 38,6°C. By contrast Eichna et al.[51] and Wyndham et al.[70] on highly acclimatized U.S. service men and Bantu mine workers, respectively, did not find that any of their subjects were incapacitated until their rectal temperatures exceeded 39°C and heart rates were 130 to 140 beats/min. Thus for acclimatized men it appears logical to take as criteria of excessive strain a rectal temperature of 39°C and/or a heart rate of 130 to 140 beats/min.

Another point of contention is which index of heat stress is the best predictor of physiological strain. Extensive comparisons have been made in climatic rooms of the relationships between such physiological reactions as sweat rate, heart rate and rectal temperature on one hand, and wet-kata cooling power, effective temperatures and P_4SR index on the other. These studies indicate[29,31,56,71] that the wet-kata cooling power is the least precise index of heat stress for predicting physiological reactions and that the P_4SR index is marginally better than the effective temperature, except at very high wet-bulb temperatures. Few satisfactory investigations have been made of these indices in practical work situations. Those of the Human Sciences Laboratory revealed the serious snags referred to earlier[71]. Wyndham *et al.*[72] investigated some of these indices at Mt Isa Mine in N. Australia. They recorded oral temperatures of 86 miners after three hours of work and of 29 men carrying out a standard step-routine (requiring an oxygen consumption of 1,0 litre/min) at air temperatures which ranged from 21 to 56°C, air speeds of 0,5 to 2,0 m/s and globe temperatures up to 57°C. The correlation coefficients between oral temperatures and these indices were:

with P_4SR — 0,75   with E.T.   — 0,64
with HSI   — 0,71   with W.B.   — 0,51

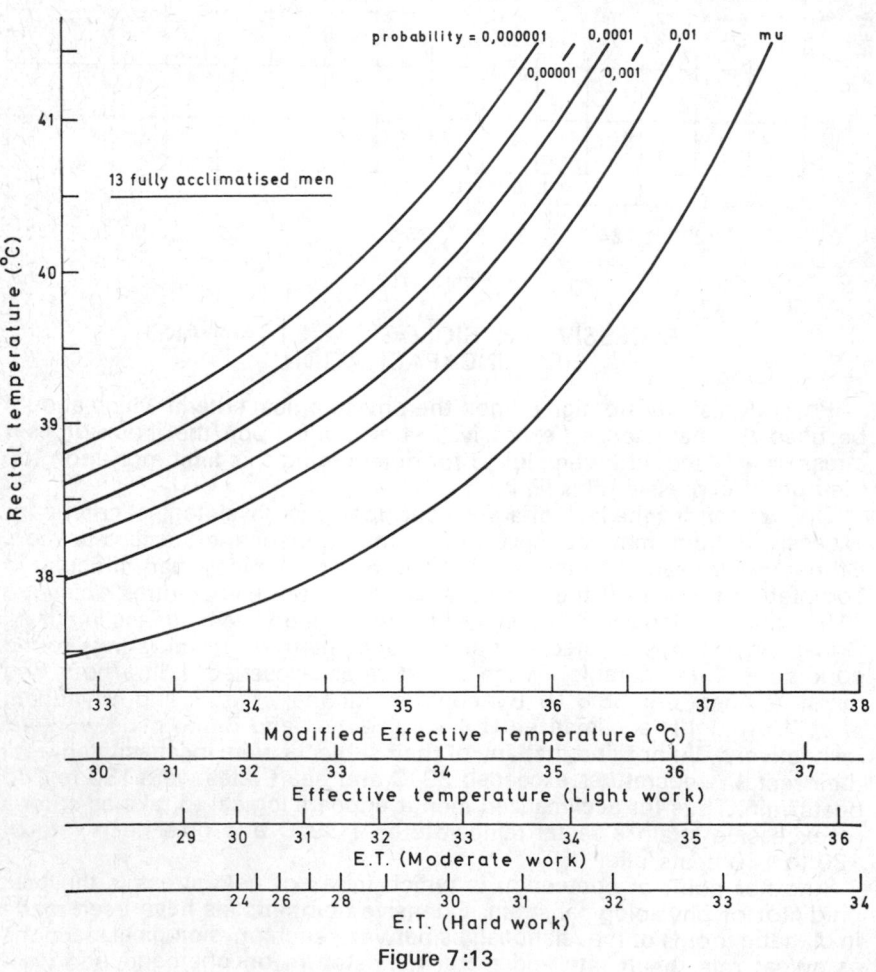

Figure 7:13

Another point of disagreement among physiologists is the method of expressing the limits of heat stress at which excessive physiological reactions and/or heat incapacitation occur. Physiologists have been very loose in their thinking in this regard. For example, the British physiologists define the limit as the P_4SR level which "one or more subjects find unendurable". This is unacceptable to industrial management because they wish to know the probabilities of excessive reactions and/or incapacitation at different levels of heat stress in precise statistical terms. For example, the probability of heat incapacitation might be 1/10 at 32°C, but only 1/million at 30,5°C effective temperature and this information, in conjunction with climatic data, would be of great importance. Wyndham et al.[58] tackled this problem by calculating the statistical probabilities of acclimatized and unacclimatized men reaching different fourth-hour rectal temperatures over a wide range of heat stress conditions as expressed by the "modified"

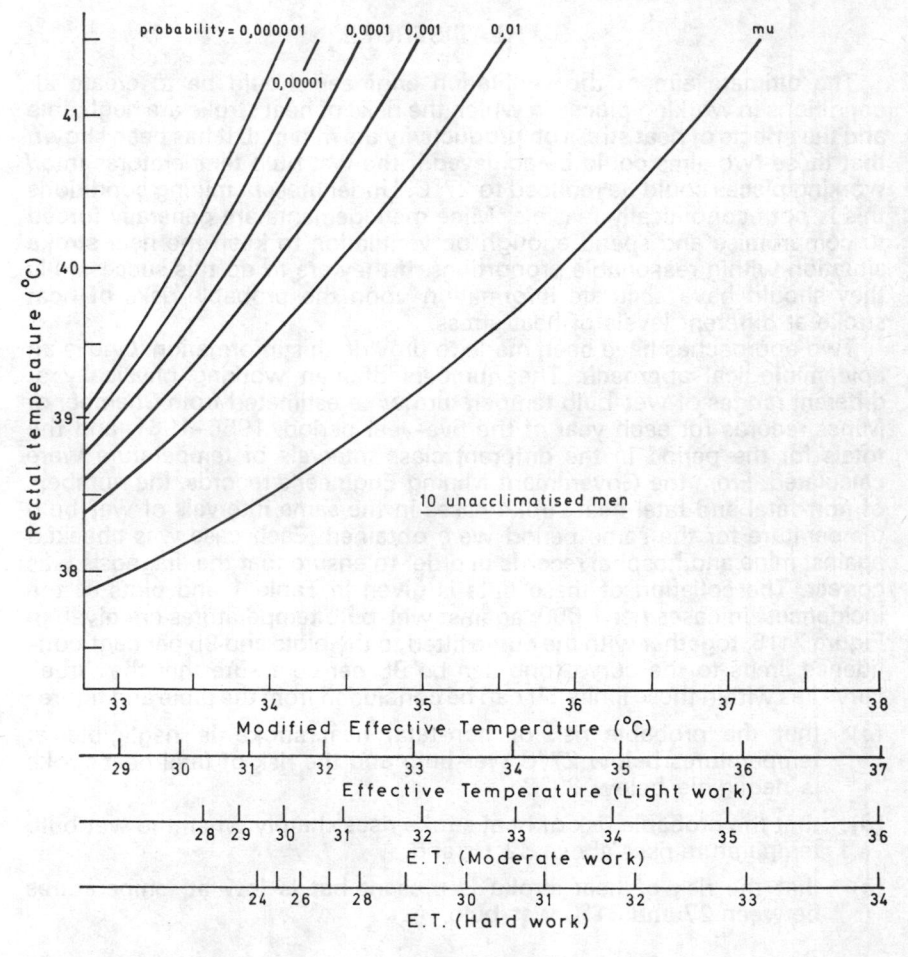

Figure 7:14

effective temperature. The difficulties involved in estimating these probabilities are dealt with under the section on heat intolerance. It suffices to say
here that because of the skewness which develops in the distribution of
body temperature after an hour of work in heat, log-normal distributions
had to be fitted to the data and probabilites of reaching different body
temperatures calculated from these log-normal distributions. The results are
given in Figures 7:13 and 7:14 for acclimatized and unacclimatized men,
respectively. In practice a ventilation official would estimate the "basic"
effective temperature from his measurements of dry- and wet-bulb temperatures and air speed and the "basic" effective temperature chart. He would
then on the appropriate graph determine the probability of reaching a
fourth-hour rectal temperature of 39°C for the different work rates. On the
basis of these probabilities he could advise mine management about the
level of work which the men could carry out without too high a probability
of excessive reactions or of heat incapacitation.

9   HEAT STROKE

The ultimate aim of the ventilation engineer should be to create air
conditions in working places in which the risks of heat stroke are negligible
and the effects of heat stress on productivity are minimal. It has been shown
that these two aims could be achieved if the wet bulb temperatures in *all*
working places could be reduced to 27°C. Under present mining conditions
this is not economically feasible. Mine managements are generally forced
to compromise and spend enough on ventilation to keep the heat stroke
situation within reasonable proportions. If they are to do this successfully
they should have accurate information upon the probable risks of heat
stroke at different levels of heat stress.

Two approaches have been made to provide this information. One is an
epidemiological approach. The numbers of men working physically at
different ranges of wet-bulb temperature were estimated from Chamber of
Mines records for each year of the five-year period, 1956–1961, and the
totals for the period in the different class intervals of temperature were
calculated. From the Government Mining Engineer's records, the numbers
of non-fatal and fatal heat stroke cases in the same intervals of wet-bulb
temperature for the same period were obtained. Each case was checked
against mine and hospital records in order to ensure that the diagnosis was
correct. The collation of these data is given in Table 1 and plots of the
incidences, in cases per 1 000, against wet-bulb temperatures are given in
Figure 7:15, together with the curve fitted to the plots and 95 per cent confidence limits to the curve (one can be 95 per cent sure that the "true"
curve lies within these limits). It can be concluded from the table and figure:

(a)   that the probable risk of non-fatal heat stroke is negligible at
       temperatures below 27°C wet-bulb and the risk of fatal heat stroke
       is negligible below 29°C;

(b)   that the probable risk of heat stroke rises sharply when the wet bulb
       temperature rises above 32°C; and

(c)   that the risk of heat stroke is present but is low at temperatures
       between 27 and 31°C wet-bulb.

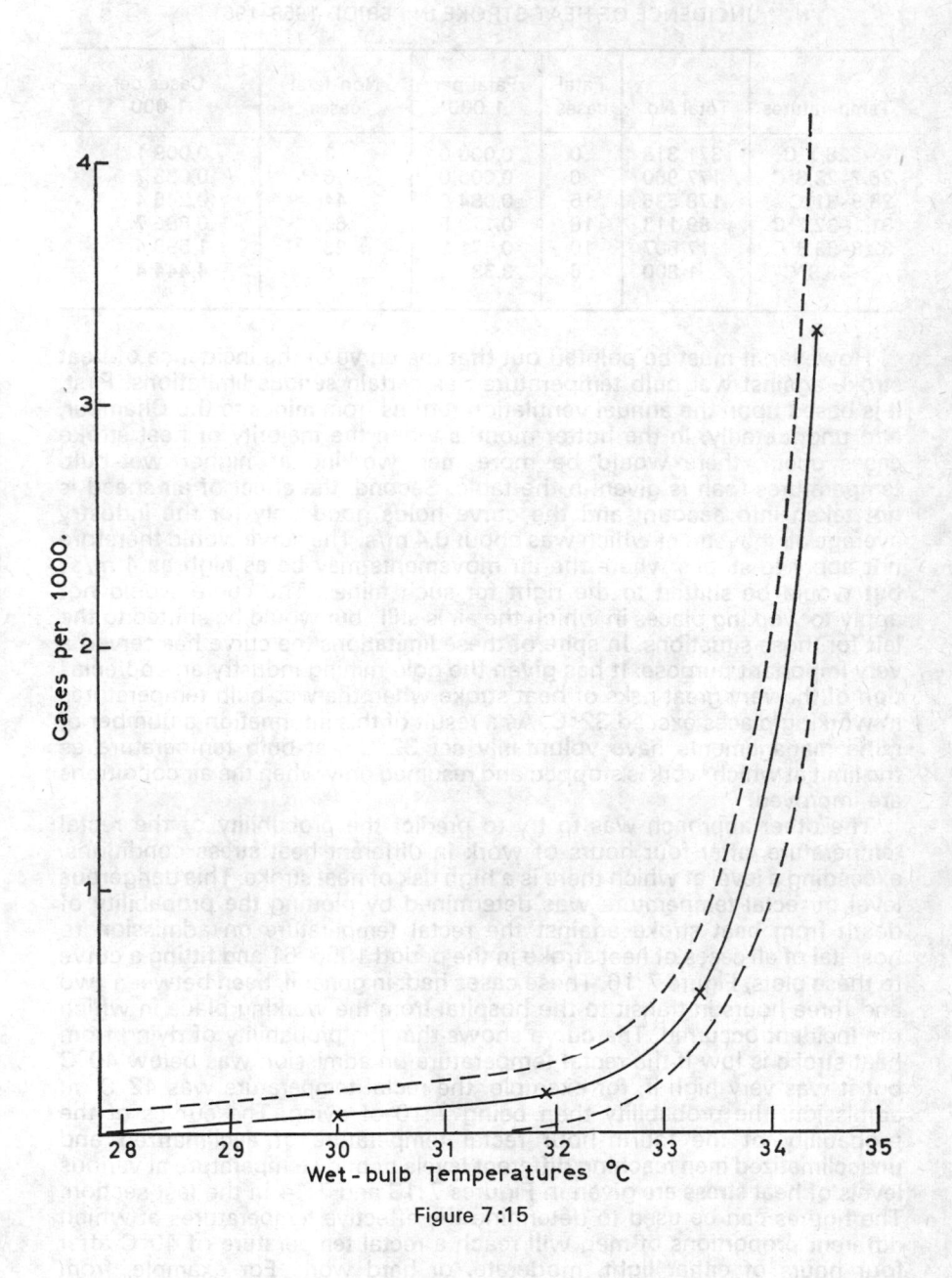

Figure 7:15

INCIDENCE OF HEAT STROKE IN PERIOD 1956–1961

Temperatures	Total No.	Fatal cases	Fatal per 1 000	Non-fatal cases	Cases per 1 000
<26,7°C	371 318	0	0,000 0	3	0,008 1
26,7–28,8°C	177 960	0	0,000 0	6	0,033 7
28,9–31°C	178 536	15	0,084 0	44	0,246 4
31,1–32,7°C	89 113	16	0,179 5	62	0,695 7
32,8–33,8°C	17 507	10	0,571 2	28	1,599 4
>33,9°C	1 800	6	3,333 3	8	4,444 4

However, it must be pointed out that the curve of the incidence of heat stroke against wet bulb temperature has certain serious limitations. First, it is based upon the annual ventilation returns from mines to the Chamber, and undoubtedly, in the hotter months when the majority of heat stroke cases occur, there would be more men working at higher wet-bulb temperatures than is given in the table. Second, the effect of air speed is not taken into account and the curve holds good only for the industry average air movement which was about 0,4 m/s. The curve would therefore not apply to stopes where the air movements may be as high as 4 m/s; but would be shifted to the right for such mines. The curve would not apply to working places in which the air is still; but would be shifted to the left for those situations. In spite of these limitations the curve has served a very important purpose. It has given the gold mining industry an appreciation of the very great risks of heat stroke when the wet-bulb temperatures in working places exceed 32°C. As a result of this information a number of mine managements have voluntarily set 32°C wet-bulb temperature as the limit at which work is stopped and resumed only when the air conditions are improved.

The other approach was to try to predict the probability of the rectal temperature, after four hours of work in different heat stress conditions, exceeding a level at which there is a high risk of heat stroke. This dangerous level of rectal temperature was determined by plotting the probability of death from heat stroke against the rectal temperature on admission to hospital of all cases of heat stroke in the period 1956–61 and fitting a curve to these plots, Figure 7:16. These cases had, in general, been between two and three hours in transit to the hospital from the working place in which the incident occurred. The curve shows that the probability of dying from heat stroke is low if the rectal temperature on admission was below 40°C but it was very high if, for example, the rectal temperature was 42°C on admission, the probability then being 7:10 of dying. The curves of the probability of the fourth-hour rectal temperature of acclimatized and unacclimatized men reaching different levels of body temperature at various levels of heat stress are given in Figures 7:13 and 7:14 in the last section. The figures can be used to determine the effective temperatures at which different proportions of men will reach a rectal temperature of 40°C after four hours of either light, moderate, or hard work. For example, from Fig. 7:13 one can determine that only 1 in a million acclimatized men would reach a rectal temperature of 40°C after four hours of moderate work at an effective temperature of about 32°C. This agrees very well with the

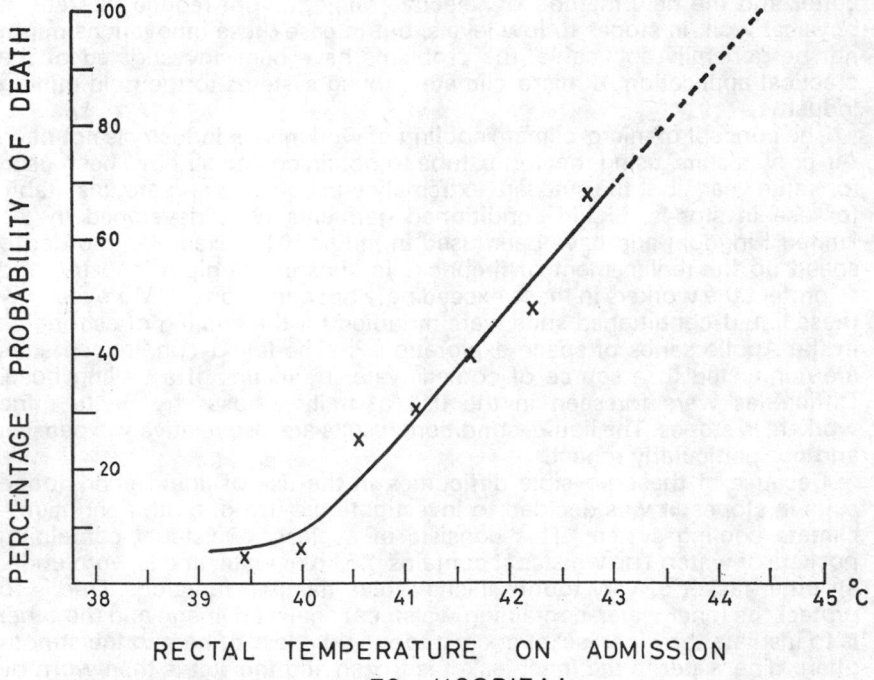

RECTAL TEMPERATURE ON ADMISSION
TO HOSPITAL

Figure 7:16

maximum wet-bulb temperature to which we can acclimatize Bantu workers, given earlier.

These curves could be used by ventilation engineers to determine the effective temperatures for different work rates at which there is a very low risk of heat stroke (i.e., a rectal temperature of 40°C after four hours of work). This would be the safe limit of environmental heat stress at which to aim in working places. They could also use the figures to determine the risks of heat stroke to which men are exposed in effective temperatures which exceed these limits and could employ these risks as a powerful argument with mine managements to improve ventilation in working places.

10   MICRO-CLIMATE COOLING SYSTEMS

It is predicted that as the gold mines go deeper they will eventually reach a depth at which, even with greatly increased expenditure on conventional ventilation, it will be impossible to keep the wet-bulb temperature in working places below 32°C. It may even rise to 34 or 36°C. It was shown in the section on acclimatization that it is impossible to acclimatize Bantu recruits to the mines for anything more than light work at these last two wet-bulb temperatures. Mine managements will therefore have to face the fact that either they must change the method of mining to one which eliminates all but light work, or they must adopt an unconventional method of cooling mine workers. The introduction of the rock-cutter and the new method of selective mining might reduce the rate of physical work in stopes to low levels, but in case these innovations might not be generally applicable, the problems have been investigated of the practical application of micro-climate cooling systems to the gold mining industry.

The concept of micro-climate cooling of workmen in industry is not new. Air-cooled suits, using the vortex tube to obtain cooled air have been used for some years, but the suits are extremely cumbersome and are unsuitable for use in stopes. Liquid-conditioned garments were developed in the United Kingdom and have been used in industry, for example, in order to speed up the replacement of firebricks in kilns in the glass industry, and to protect the workers in these exceedingly hot conditions[73]. More recently these liquid-conditioned suits were modified for the cooling of astronauts in the Apollo series of space explorations[74]. The liquid-conditioned suits are connected to a source of cooled water by means of a trailing hose. Difficulties were foreseen in the use of trailing hoses by Bantu mine workers in stopes. The liquid-conditioned suits are also relatively expensive and not particularly robust.

Because of these possible difficulties in the use of liquid-conditioned suits in stopes, it was decided to investigate the use of a different micro-climate cooling system. This consists of a plastic waistcoat containing pockets of water. The waistcoat contains 4,5 kg of water and is worn under an outer jacket of very tough plastic which has two functions. One is to protect the inner water-containing waistcoat against damage and the other is to insulate the inner jacket against too rapid a loss of heat to the atmosphere. The water in the inner jacket is frozen and the suit is then worn by the workmen over a woollen vest. The water in the waistcoat acts as a heat-sink and the phase-change of 4,5 kg from ice to water provides considerable cooling. Calculations indicate that 4,5 kg of water would protect a man working moderately hard for about four hours in severe heat and humidity. The advantages of this system are that the workmen are completely mobile and the costs of the waistcoats are low.

However, before they could be recommended to the gold mining industry it was important to establish, by laboratory trials, whether these pre-frozen waistcoats would be effective and also compare their effectiveness with that of the liquid-conditioned suits. The latter were obtained from the manufacturer of the Apollo astronaut garments and are commercially available. The garment is a sleeveless waistcoat made of elastic fibre. To the inside of the garment is attached 47 m of small-bore plastic tubing. Chilled water is circulated through the tubing at a rate of 50 litres/hour. In both the liquid-conditioned garment and the pre-frozen waistcoat, the trunk is covered to just below the rib margin and the arms and legs are left unencumbered. Thus the garments interfere minimally with men when they move about or shovel rock in stopes.

In the laboratory tests the subjects worked at a moderate rate for either four or six hours in two very hot and humid conditions, both with and without the garments, and their reactions were compared with those observed at the same work rate in comfortable air conditions. The two hot conditions were 32 and 34°C and a few trials were made at 36°C wet-bulb temperatures. The results showed that the liquid-conditioned garment protected the workmen completely against temperatures of up to 34°C in that their body temperatures and heart rates were the same as those measured when they worked under the comfortable air conditions. The pre-frozen jackets gave good protection at 32°C and considerable protection at 34°C, but the protection was not quite as good as that provided by the liquid-conditioned garment. Two pre-frozen jackets were needed for a six-hour shift. The preliminary trial at 36°C wet-bulb temperature indicated that these systems give good protection to the workmen even in these severe, hot and humid conditions.

The psychological benefit of these cooling systems was even more dramatic than the physiological benefits. The men were highly co-operative and in good humour even at the end of the shift. This contrasted markedly with the exhaustion and bad temper of the men after the shift without micro-climate cooling at 34°C wet-bulb temperature.

Preliminary field trials of the pre-frozen jackets in the stopes of a hot mine have led to some minor modifications of the jackets, but no major snags were brought to light and large-scale trials are being carried out on a mine at the time of writing. The pre-frozen jacket is also being tried out in extremely hot and humid conditions in a copper mine in Zambia where men drive mechanical loaders in wet-bulb temperatures as high as 38°C.

From these preliminary trials it is clear that the micro-climate cooling systems have an important role in the gold mining industry in protecting workmen who have to work in extreme heat and humidity and in increasing productivities in the very hot and deep mines of the future.

11   REFERENCES

1   Cluver, E. H. An analysis of ninety-two fatal heat stress cases on Witwatersrand gold mines. *S. Afr. Med. J.* Vol. 6, 1932. p. 15–23.

2   Dreosti, A. O. Problems arising out of temperature and humidity in deep mines of the Witwatersrand. *J. chem. metall. Min. Soc. S. Afr.,* Vol. 36, 1935, p. 102–29.

3   Wyndham, C. H. The rôle of acclimatization on the sweat rate/rectal temperature relationship. *J. Appl. Physiol.* Vol. 22(1), 1967, p. 27–30.

4   Wyndham, C. H. Benade, A. J. S. Williams, C. G. Strydom, N. B. Goldin, A. and Heyns, A. J. Changes in central circulation and body fluid spaces during acclimatization to heat. *J. Appl. Physiol.* Vol. 25(5), 1968, p. 586–93.

5   Rowell, L. B. Kraningll, K. K. Kennedy, J. W. and Evans, T. O. Central circulatory responses to work in dry heat before and after acclimatization. *J. Appl. Physiol.* Vol. 25(5), 1968, p. 509–18.

6   Rowell. L. B. Brengelmann, G. L. Detry, J. M. R. and Wyss, C. Venomotor responses to remote and level thermal stimuli to skin in exercising men. *J. Appl. Physiol.* Vol. 38(1), 1971, p. 72–7.

7   Bass, D. E. Kleinman, C. R. Quinn, M. Henschel, A. and Hegnaur, A. Mechanisms of acclimatization to heat. *Medicine.* Vol. 34, 1955, p. 323–80.

8   Senay, L. C. *et al.* Protein and fluid shifts during acclimatization. *J. Phys.* Vol. 224, 1972, p. 61–68.

9   Wood, J. E. and Bass, D. E. Responses of veins and arterioles of the forearm to working during acclimatization to heat in man. *J. Clin. Invest.* Vol. 39, 1960, p. 825–33.

10   Wyndham, C. H. Strydom, N. B. Morrison, J. F. du Toit, F. D. and Kraan, J. G. A new method of acclimatization to heat. *Int. Z. angew. Physiol.* Vol. 15, 1964, p. 373–83.

11   Wyndham, C. H. A survey of causal factors in heat stroke and their prevention in the gold mining industry. *J. S. Afr. Inst. Min. Metall.* Vol. 66(4), 1965, p. 125–55.

12   Wyndham, C. H. A survey of research initiated by the Chamber of Mines into clinical aspects of heat stroke. *Proc. Min. Med. Officers Assoc.* Vol. 45, 1966, p. 68–80.

13   Wyndham, C. H. and Strydom, N. B. Acclimatizing men to heat in climatic rooms in mines. *J. S. Afr. Inst. Min. Metall.* Vol. 70, 1969, p. 60–4.

14   Morrison, J. F. Wyndham, C. H. Mienie, B. and Strydom, N. B. Energy expenditure of mining tasks and the need for the selection of labourers. *J. S. Afr. Inst. Min. Metall.* Vol. 69, 1968, p. 185–91.

15   Strydom, N. B. Morrison, J. F. Booysens, J. and Peter, J. A six-monthly survey of the 2-stage method of acclimatization as applied at Simmer and Jack G.M. *S. Afr. J. Med. Sci.* Vol. 20, 1955, p. 37.

16   Wyndham, C. H. Strydom, N. B. Morrison, J. F. du Toit, F. D. and Kraan, J. G. Thermal responses of men with high initial temperatures to the stress of work in heat. *J. Appl. Physiol.* Vol. 6, 1954, p. 687–90.

17   Wyndham, C. H. Strydom, N. B. Williams, C. G. and Heyns, A. J. An examination of certain individual factors effecting the heat tolerance of workmen. *J. S. Afr. Inst. Min. Metall.* Vol. 68, 1967, p. 79–91.

18   Hausman, A. Belayew, D. and Patigny, J. Criteria for the selection of rescuers called to work at high temperatures. *Rev. de L'Instituet d'Hyg. des Mines.* Vol. 21, 1966, p. 36–47.

19   Strydom, N. B. Age as a causal factor in heat stroke. *J. S. Afr. Inst. Min. Metall.* Vol. 72, 1971, p. 112–14.

20   Winer, P. Maritz, J. S. and Wyndham, C. H. Estimation of heat stroke risks. *Nature.* Vol. 193, March 3, 1962, p. 848–49.

21   Maritz, J. S. Estimation of heat stroke risks using extreme value distribution. Research Report 12/65, Chamber of Mines of South Africa.

22   Sichel, H. S. A mathematical model, heat stress and heat risks for highly acclimatized mine workers during 4 hours of work. Reports Nos. 1 and 2, from Operations Research Bureau, Johannesburg, December 1966 and March 1967.

23   Munro, A. H. Sichel, H. S. and Wyndham, C. H. Effect of heat stress and acclimatization in body temperature response of men at work. *Life Sciences.* Vol. 6, 1967, p. 749–54.

24   Macpherson, R. K. The assessment of the thermal environments; a review. *Brit. J. Ind. Med.* Vol. 19, 1962, p. 151–63.

25   Haldane, J. S. The influence of high temperatures. *J. Hyg.* Vol. 5, 1905, p. 494–513.

26   Hill, L. Griffith, O. W. and Flack, M. The measurement of the rate of heat loss on body temperature by convection, radiation and evap-

oration. *Phil. Trans. Roy. Soc.* Section B (London) Vol. 207, 1916, p. 183–220.

27 Vernon, H. M. and Warner, C. G. The influence of the humidity of air on capacity to work at high temperatures. *J. Hyg.* Vol. 32, 1932, p. 431–63.

28 Orenstein, A. J. and Ireland, H. J. Experimental observations upon the relation between atmospheric conditions and the prevention of fatigue in mine labourers. *J. Ind. Hyg.* Vol. 4(1), p. 30–46 and Vol. 4(2), 1922, p. 70–91.

29 Vernon, H. M. The index of comfort at high atmospheric temperatures, p. 116–144 in The Kata thermometer in studies of body heat and efficiency. *Med. Res. Counc. Spec. Rep.* Series 73 (London), 1923.

30 Lawton, B. R. Atmospheric conditions in deep mines. 25th Report in The control of atmospheric conditions in hot and deep mines. *Trans. Inst. Mining Eng.* Vol. XCIII, 1936–1937, p. 37–53.

31 Haines, G. F. and Hatch, T. F. Industrial heat exposure and evaluation and control. *Heat and Ventilation*, Vol. 49, 1952, p. 93–105.

32 Belding, H. S. and Hatch, T. E. Index for evaluating heat stress in terms of physiological strain. *Heating, Piping and Air Conditioning*, Vol. 27, 1958, p. 129–36.

33 Belding, H. S., Hertig, B. A. and Riedel, M. Z. Laboratory simulation of hot industrial jobs to find effective heat stress and resulting physiological strain. *Am. Ind. Hyg. Assoc. J.* Vol. 21, 1960, p. 25–31.

34 Belding, H. S. and Hatch, T. F. Problems relating severity of exposure to heat, Report No. 3, Division of Occup. Health, Graduate School of Public Health, University of Pittsburg, 1960.

35 Mitchell, D. and Whillier, A. Cooling power of underground environments. *J. S. Afr. Inst. Min. Metall.* Vol. 72, 1971, p. 93–9.

36 Whillier, A. The calculation of heat exchange between air and wet surfaces. *J. S. Afr. Inst. Min. Metall.* Vol. 67, 1967, p. 396–402.

37 Houghton, F. C. and Yaglou, C. P. Determining lines of equal comfort. *ASHVE Trans.* Vol. 29, 1923, p. 163–76 and 361–84.

38 Houghton, F. C. and Yaglou, C. P. Cooling effects on human body produced by various air velocities. *ASHVE Trans.* Vol. 30, 1924, p. 193–211.

39 Houghton, F. C., Teague, W. W. and Miller, W. E. Effective temperature for persons lightly clothed and working in still air. *ASHVE Trans.* Vol. 32, 1926, p. 315–20.

40 Yaglou, C. P. and Miller, W. F. Effective temperatures with clothing. *ASHVE Trans.* Vol. 31, 1925, p. 89–99.

41 Yaglou, C. P. The thermal index of atmospheric conditions and its application to sedentary and industrial life. *J. Ind. Hyg.* Vol. 8, 1926, p. 5–19.

42 Bedford, T. Environmental warmth and its measurement. *Med. Res. Council.* War Memo No. 17 (London) 1946.

43 Houghton, F. C. and Yaglou, C. P. Determinations of comfort zone. *ASHVE Trans.* Vol. 29, 1923, p. 361–84.

44   Yaglou, C. P. The comfort zone for men at rest and stripped to the waist. *ASHVE Trans.* Vol. 33, 1927, p. 285–98.

45   Yaglou, C. P. and Drinker, P. The summer comfort zone: climate and clothing. *ASHVE Trans.* Vol. 35, 1929, p. 269–86.

46   Koch, W., Jenning, B. H. and Humphreys, C. M. Sensation responses to temperature and humidity under still air conditions in the comfort zone. *ASHRAE Trans.* Vol. 66, 1960, p. 264–73.

47   Nevins, R. G., Roles, F. H., Springer, W. and Feyerkem, A. M. Temperature-humidity chart for thermal comfort of selected persons. *ASHRAE Trans.* Vol. 72, 1960, p. 283–91.

48   McConnell, W. J., Houghton, F. C. and Phillips, F. M. Further studies of physiological reactions. *ASHVE Trans.* Vol. 29, 1923, p. 353–60.

49   McConnell, W. J. and Yaglou, C. P. Work tests in atmospheres of high temperatures and various humidities in still and moving air. *ASHVE Trans.* Vol. 31, 1928, p. 101–22.

50   Benson, R. S., Colver, T., Ladell, W. S. S., McArdle, B. and Scott, J. W. The ability to work in severe heat. *Med. Res. Council. R.N.P.R.C.* No. 45/205 (London) 1945.

51   Eichna, L. W., Ashe, W. F., Bean, W. B. and Shelley, W. B. The upper limits of environmental heat and humidity tolerated by acclimatized men working in hot environments. *J. Ind. Hyg.* Vol. 27, 1945, p. 59–84.

52   Robinson, S., Turrell, E. J. and Gerking, S. D. Physiologically equivalent conditions of air temperature and humidity. *Am. J. Physiol.* Vol. 143, 1948, p. 21–31.

53   Dunham, W., Holling, H. E., Ladell, W. S. S., McArdle, B., Scott, J. W., Thomson, M. L. and Weiner, J. S. The effects of air movement in severe heat. *Med. Res. Council. R.N.P.R.C.* No. 43/316, 1946.

54   Brebner, D. F. MacKerslake, D. and Waddell, J. L. The effect of atmospheric humidities on the skin temperature and sweat rates of resting men at two ambient temperatures. *J. Physiol.* Vol. 144, 1958, p. 299–306.

55   Ellis, F. P., Ferres, H. M., Lind, A. R. and Newling, S. B. The tolerable upper levels of warmth for acclimatized Europeans working in the tropics. *Med. Res. Council. R.N.P.R.C.* 53/759 (London) 1953.

56   Lind, A. R. and Hellon, R. F. Assessment of physiological severity of hot climates. *J. Appl. Physiol.* Vol. 11, 1959, p. 35–40.

57   Smith, F. Indices of heat stress. *Med. Res. Council.* Memo No. 29 (London) 1955.

58   Wyndham, C. H. and Heyns, A. J. A. The assessment of heat stress in working places underground in mines. Part 8. Estimating the probability of reaching heat stroke levels of body temperature at different levels of heat stress. C.O.M. Research Report 35/71, Johannesburg, 1971.

59   McPherson, R. K. Physiological responses to hot environments. *Med. Res. Council. Spec. Rep.* No. 268 (London) 1960.

60   McArdle, B., Denham, W., Holling, H. E., Ladell, W. S. S., Scott, J. W., Thomson, M. L. and Weiner, J. S. The prediction of the physiological

effects of warm and hot environments. *Med. Res. Council. R.N.P.R.C.* 47/391, (London) 1947.

61   Bedford, T. Basic principles of ventilation and heating. Lewis, London, 1948, p. 88–9.

62   McNall, P. E., Joax, J., Rohles, F. H., Nevins, R. G. and Spring, W. Thermal comfort (thermally neutral) conditions for three levels of activity. *ASHRAE Trans.* Vol. 73, 1967, p. 131–4.

63   Wyndham, C. H. Thermal comfort in the hot, humid tropics of Australia. *Brit. J. Ind. Med.* Vol. 20, 1963, p. 110–17.

64   Bedford, J. and Warner, G. G. Observations on the working capacity of coal miners in relation to atmospheric conditions. *J. Ind. Hyg.* Vol. 13, 1931, p. 252–60.

65   Caplan, J. and Lindsay, A. J. An experimental investigation of the effects of high temperatures on the efficiency of workers in deep mines. *Bull. Inst. Mining Metall.* (U.K.) Vol. 480, 1946, p. 1–30.

66   Mackworth, N. H. Researches on the measurement of human performance. *Med. Res. Council. Spec. Rep. Ser.* No. 268 (London) 1950.

67   Pepler, R. D. Warmth and performance: an investigation in the tropics. *Ergonomics.* Vol. 2, 1958, p. 63–88.

68   Cooke, H. M., Wyndham, C. H., Strydom, N. B., Maritz, J. S., Bredell, G. A. G., Morrison, J. F., Peter J. and Williams, C. G. The effects of heat on the performance of work underground. *J. Mine Vent. Soc. S. Afr.* Vol. 14, 1961, p. 177–88.

69   Bruner, H. Arbeitsmöglichkeiten unter Tage bei erschwerten klimatischen Bedingungen. *Int. Z. angew. Physiol.* Vol. 144, 1958, p. 295–306.

70   Wyndham, C. H., Strydom, N. B., Morrison, J. F., Williams, C. G., Bredell, G. A. G., von Rahden, M. J. E. and Munro, A. Heat reactions of Caucasians and Bantu in Southern Africa. *J. Appl. Physiol.* Vol. 19(4), 1964, p. 598–606.

71   Wyndham, C. H., v.d. Bouwer, W., Patterson, H. E. and Devine, M. G. Examination of heat stress indices. *Arch. Ind. Hyg. & Occup. Med.* Vol. 7, 1953, p. 221–33.

72   Wyndham, C. H., Allen, McD. A. Bredell, G. A. G. Andrew, R. Assessing the heat stress and establishing the limits for work in a hot mine. *Brit. J. Ind. Med.* Vol. 24, 1967, p. 255–71.

73   London, R. C. A review of work in United Kingdom on water cooled suits. Proc. Symposium on Individual Cooling. ed. S. Konz. p. 138–69, Kansas State University, Manhattan, Kansas, 1969.

74   Richardson, D. L. Portable life-support systems for extra-vehicular activity. Ibidem p. 51–77.

8   Introduction to Steady-State Heat Transfer

A. WHILLIER

*Assistant Director, Mining Research,
Chamber of Mines Research Organization*

Symbols

A	=	area, m^2	I	=	current, amperes
b	=	thickness, m	k	=	thermal conductivity, W/m °C
B	=	psychrometric constant, °C^{-1}	L	=	length, m
C_p	=	thermal capacity, J/kg °C or kJ/kg °C (also known as the specific heat)	$LMTD$	=	log mean temperature difference, °C
d	=	diameter, m	m	=	mass, kg
e	=	vapour pressure, kPa	M	=	mass flow rate, kg/s
F_{ev}	=	emissivity and view factor	P	=	absolute pressure, kPa
h	=	coefficient of heat transfer, W/m^2 °C	q	=	rate of heat transfer, W
			r	=	radius, m
			R	=	electrical resistance, ohms

R_e	= Reynolds Number	U	= overall heat transfer coefficient, W/m² °C
t	= temperature, °C		
T	= absolute temperature, K	V	= velocity, m/s
	= (273,15 + t)		

Greek letters

Δ	= difference			
ϵ	= emissivity			
λ	= latent heat, kJ/kg			
ϕ	= relative humidity			
μ	= viscosity, Ns/m²			

Subscripts

a	= air
C	= convection
db	= dry-bulb
F	= fouling
L	= latent
m	= mean
R	= radiation
s	= surface
wb	= wet-bulb

1   INTRODUCTION

Ventilation personnel in the South African gold mining industry are frequently called upon to do calculations concerning such diverse phenomena as the rate of heat gain by chilled water in pipes in humid airways underground, and the prediction of air conditioning loads in office buildings or acclimatization chambers. While a large number of good reference books on heat transfer are available, these are almost without exception written as specialist texts for use at university level. Ventilation personnel on mines can generally not be expected to be expert in the field of heat transfer, since they have a wide range of responsibilities in which heat transfer plays only a small part.

The present chapter is therefore intended to meet the need for a concise presentation of the fundamentals of heat transfer processes, and for simplified methods for solving rapidly the various heat transfer problems that arise in mining. This presentation should sacrifice precision for simplicity with the thought that in most instances what is needed is an indication of the magnitude of the amount of heat being transferred and not a prediction of its exact value. In this chapter only steady-state heat transfer is treated.

1.1   *The nature of heat transfer*

Heat transfer can be regarded as being a flow of thermal energy *resulting from a temperature difference.* Thus, the temperature of air passing over an electric heater will rise as a result of heat flowing into the air from the hot element. The rate of heat transfer from the heater in watts is equal to I^2R where I is the electric current in amperes flowing through the electrical resistor wire of resistance R ohms. If the heat cannot escape anywhere else, in other words if there are no losses, then all of this heat must enter the air stream. If the rate of flow of the air is M kg/s, then the law of conservation of energy requires that:

$$I^2R = \text{rate of heat transfer (watts)}$$
$$= M \times \text{increase in enthalpy of the air}$$
$$= MC_{pa}(t_2 - t_1)$$

In this instance the increase in enthalpy is equal to the product of the thermal capacity of the air, C_{pa} and the temperature rise $(t_2 - t_1)$ since there is no change in moisture content of the air. C_{pa} is commonly called the specific heat at constant pressure.

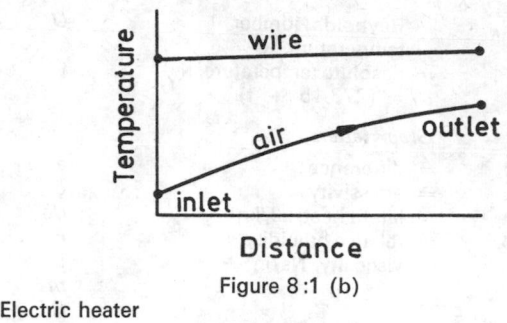

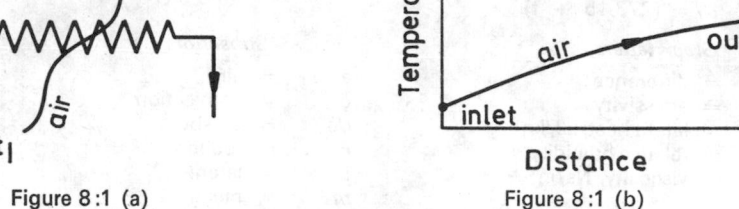

Figure 8:1 (a)

Figure 8:1 (b)

Electric heater

EXAMPLE 1

In a fan-type electric heater, air at 15°C is blown at the rate of 0,2 m³/s over an electric heater element. A current of 8 amperes passes through the element, which has a resistance of 28 ohms. Determine the temperature of the air leaving the heater. Assume that the density of the air is 1,1 kg/m³, and that its thermal capacity, C_{pa} is 1,015 kJ/kg °C.

ANSWER

Rate of heat transfer $= I^2 R = 8 \times 8 \times 28 = 1\,792\,W$
Temperature rise $= 1\,792/(0,2 \times 1,1 \times 1,015 \times 1\,000)$
$= 8,02\,°C$
∴ Leaving air temperature $= 15 + 8,02 = 23,02\,°C$.

So far in this calculation we have been concerned only with the conservation of energy. If we were now to set ourselves the task of finding the temperature of the electric resistor wire (see Problem No. 7), then we will have to make an analysis of the *heat transfer* of the system. This chapter will provide a basis for carrying out such heat transfer analyses.

As another illustration, consider the case of hot water in a pipe that passes through an airway, say, 100 metres long. This might be water going from the condenser of an underground refrigeration plant to the cooling tower. Figure 8.2 illustrates the situation where both the air and the water are flowing in the same direction.

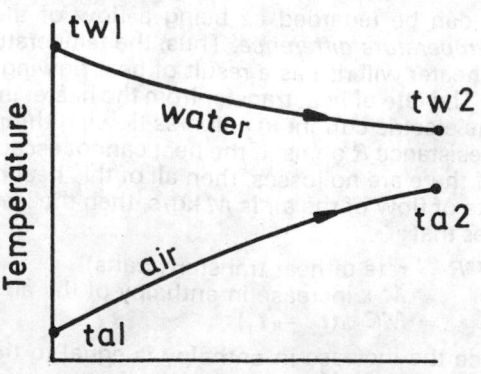

Figure 8:2   Heat exchange in an airway

If the water temperature changes from t_{w1} to t_{w2} then we know from the law of conservation of energy that the air will change its temperature from t_{a1} to t_{a2} according to the relation:

Heat flow rate $= M_w C_{pw}(t_{w1} - t_{w2}) = M_a C_{pa}(t_{a2} - t_{a1})$, where M_w, M_a are the mass flow rates of the water and air and C_{pw}, C_{pa} are the thermal capacities (specific heats), respectively.

$$C_{pw} = 4,187 \text{ kJ/kg}°C \quad \text{for water and}$$
$$C_{pa} = 1,015 \text{ kJ/kg}°C \quad \text{for ambient air.}$$

The question now is, if the mass flow rates and only the entering temperatures t_{w1} and t_{a1} are known, how can we predict the final temperatures t_{w2} and t_{a2}? Or, in other words, how can we predict the rate at which heat will flow from the water into the air? In order to do this we must apply heat transfer analysis to the system.

In conducting any heat transfer analysis, detailed attention must be given to the path followed by the heat in going from the hot to the cold zone. Thus the heat passes through solid bodies by *conduction.* It passes from solid surfaces to adjacent fluids by *convection,* and across an air space from one solid surface to another by *radiation.* In the event of evaporation or condensation taking place at a surface that is in contact with air, there is in addition a *latent heat transfer* that is proportional to the rate of evaporation or condensation. Several of these processes can occur simultaneously without influencing each other.

In the sections that follow, each of these modes of heat transfer will be considered in turn, and methods will be presented for doing the calculations simply and accurately.

While the processes of heat transfer in themselves are quite straightforward and relatively easy to understand, the greatest complication arises in the variety of geometric arrangements that can occur in practice. Thus, while the transfer of heat from a hot pipe to the surrounding air appears at first sight to be a straightforward matter, one is soon faced with such questions as what is the influence of the pipe flanges, of the pipe hangers or supports, of the direction of flow of the air relative to the pipe, and of nearby randomly-occurring obstructions to air flow. Clearly, no universal answer can be given to such questions. Two courses of action are possible. One is to claim that the problem is so complicated that it is impossible to calculate anything that will be meaningful. This is the negative approach of a defeatist. The other approach, and the one advocated in this chapter, is to ignore the complications until the preliminary calculations have been done, and then to ask the question: "What *percentage* effect would the complications be likely to have on the answer obtained from the idealized calculations?" It is quite amazing how often answers to extremely complicated problems can be obtained in this way by using greatly simplified models of the real situation for purposes of calculation.

1.2   *Procedure followed*

In this chapter the methods of calculation that are given refer to somewhat idealized situations, and they have been presented in the simplest possible way in order to encourage the reader to use them. Wherever possible "typical average values" of coefficients applicable in mining situations have been quoted so as to speed the initial calculation. Only when greater precision is needed in the answer need the user resort to more exact methods of calculation, or, if justified, consult more detailed references. As the reader develops through his own experience a feel for the subject and an appreciation of the relative significance of different aspects, so he will develop short-cuts in his calculations that lead rapidly to the required answers.

The perfectionist or specialist will, in this chapter, often encounter statements that he considers to be of doubtful validity. In each such case he is urged to add at a convenient place the phrase "under the conditions usually encountered in deep-level mining". Hopefully this will make him more sympathetic to the approach adopted.

The reader is presumed to have an understanding of the meaning of such terms as temperature, heat and humidity, and the use of psychrometric charts[1,2]. Where doubt exists he should immediately consult the relevant chapters in this book or some other suitable reference.

Perhaps the most suitable general-purpose reference for mine ventilation is the ASHRAE *Handbook of Fundamentals*[3] which contains a vast amount of information on many aspects of heat transfer, ventilation, air conditioning and refrigeration. In fact, no ventilation official should be without this reference book.

2   HEAT TRANSFER BY CONDUCTION

2.1   *Fundamental heat conduction equation* (steady state)

Heat passes through solid bodies (and through still fluids and fluids in laminar flow) by a process called *heat conduction*. Consider the case of a plane wall, Figure 8.3a, of thickness b and cross-sectional area A, with one surface maintained at temperature t_1 and the other at t_2. Under steady-state conditions, that is, when all temperatures remain constant with time, the rate of heat flow from the hot side to the cold side will be:

$$q = kA(t_1 - t_2)/b \qquad \ldots 1$$

where

q = heat flux rate, watts
k = thermal conductivity of material, W/m °C
A = cross-sectional area, m²
b = thickness, m.

2.2   *Thermal conductivity, k*

The ability of different materials to conduct heat varies widely. Typical k values (in W/m °C) are:

Metals		Minerals		Fluids	
Copper	380	Quartzite	6	Still water	0,62
Aluminium	190	Concrete	1,7	Still air	0,028
Brass	97	Wood	0,17		
Steel	45	Insulation	0,034		
Stainless steel	16				

Still air has the lowest conductivity. Thermal insulation materials serve to maintain a layer of air surrounding the surface in the form of a large number of tiny pockets, thus preventing movement of the air. The k values of insulation materials, hence, tend to approach but never quite attain the k value for still air. (An exception to this is where the permanently sealed cavities are made to contain some gas of high molecular mass, such as CO_2, or refrigerant 12 during manufacture.)

2.3   Effect of shape

The above equation for calculating heat conduction is for the simplest case of one-dimensional heat flow across a wall of constant cross-sectional area. The solution of problems of two- and three-dimensional heat flow requires the use of calculus and hence will not be considered in this chapter. However, of frequent occurrence in engineering are cases of radially-symmetrical (cylindrical) heat flow, for which the same equation can be used but with the area term A being taken as a suitable mean area.

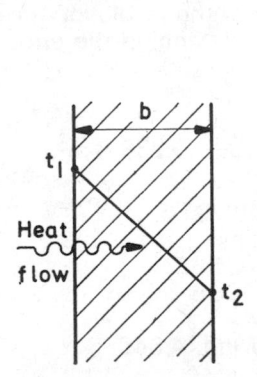

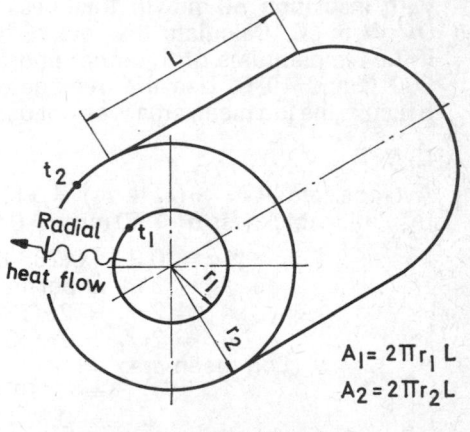

$A_1 = 2\pi r_1 L$

$A_2 = 2\pi r_2 L$

Figure 8:3 (a) Plane wall   Figure 8:3 (b) Cylinder

Conduction of Heat

2.4   Cylindrical shapes

A common situation in engineering involves the conduction of heat from the inside to the outside, or *vice versa*, of pipes. Examples are the conduction of heat through insulation on pipes, through the walls of chimneys, etc. In such cases the same conduction equation given above is used, but the question arises as to which area to use for the term A in this equation. Clearly it can be neither the inside area nor the outside area, but some intermediate value must be used. An exact mathematical analysis of the problem indicates that the correct area to be used is the logarithmic mean area, defined as:

$$A_m = \frac{(A_2 - A_1)}{\log_e A_2/A_1} = \frac{(A_2 - A_1)}{2,303 \log_{10} A_2/A_1} \qquad \ldots 2$$

However, in practically all situations encountered in engineering it is perfectly adequate to use the arithmetic mean, or average area:

$$A_{av} = (A_1 + A_2)/2$$

The reason is that the error involved is invariably less than the uncertainty in the k value that is assumed for the material. Using the average value also considerably simplifies the calculations.

The error involved in using the average in place of the log mean depends on the radius ratio of the outer to the inner surface, and hence on the area ratio. As the table below shows, even if the one radius is twice the other, the error will still be only 4 per cent. The logarithmic mean is always slightly less than the arithmetic mean.

Ratio A_2/A_1 . .	1,1	1,2	1,5	2	3	5
Error using A_{av}, % .	0,1	0,27	1,36	4,0	9,9	20,7

EXAMPLE 2

A steam pipe in a uranium plant is 26 mm in diameter and is covered with insulation 50 mm in thickness. The k–value of the insulation is 0,2 W/m °C. Calculate the rate of heat loss per metre length of pipe if the temperatures of the inner and outer surfaces of the insulation are 300°C and 40°C. Use the average area, and also determine the error because the log mean area was not used.

ANSWER

Average area $A_{av} = \pi(r_1 + r_2) = \pi(13 + 63)/1\,000 = 0,238\,8$ m^2
Insulation thickness $b = 50$ mm $= 0,05$ m

$$\therefore q = 0,2 \times 0,238\,8 \times (300 - 40)/0,05$$
$$= 344 \text{ W per metre length of pipe}$$
$$A_1 = 2\pi r_1 = 2\pi(13/1\,000) = 0,081\,65$$
$$A_2 = 2\pi r_2 = 2\pi(63/1\,000) = 0,395\,8$$
$$\text{Log mean area} = (A_2 - A_1)/\log_e A_2/A_1$$
$$= 0,395\,8 - 0,081\,65/\log_e 4,846$$
$$= 0,314\,1/1,58$$
$$= 0,198 \text{ m}^2 \text{ per m length.}$$

The error is hence $[(0,238\,8/0,198) - 1)] = 0,2$ or 20 per cent. (Note that in this instance the ratio of outer to inner area is $63/13 = 4,846$, so that the error is unacceptably large.)

3 HEAT TRANSFER BY RADIATION

All surfaces radiate heat energy at a rate depending on the fourth power of their absolute temperature. Thus the net heat transfer between two surfaces that can "see" each other will be the difference between the amounts of energy radiated by each:

$$q_R = 5,67[(T_1/100)^4 - (T_2/100)^4] \times A_1 \times F_{ev} \qquad \ldots 3$$

where

$q_R =$ net radiant heat flux, watts
$T =$ absolute temperature $K(T = 273,15 + t°C)$
$A_1 =$ smaller of the two areas, m^2
$F_{ev} =$ emissivity and view factor.

In the above equation, the number 5,67 is the Stefan-Boltzmann constant.

3.1   *Emissivity and view factor, F_{ev}*

View factors (geometric factors) are used to specify how much of the radiation that is emitted by each surface is "seen" by the other. In addition, shiny metallic surfaces radiate less energy than dull or non-metallic surfaces. In other words, they have a low emissivity, ϵ. Most materials encountered in engineering, however, have very high emissivities, usually more than 95 per cent.

In general, the determination of emissivity and view factors is a very complicated process, and when in doubt, suitable text books[3,4] on radiant heat transfer should be consulted. However, in practically all situations which arise in mining the combined emissivity and view factor may be calculated from the following equation:

$$F_{ev} = \frac{1}{\dfrac{1}{\epsilon_1} + \dfrac{A_1}{A_2}\left(\dfrac{1}{\epsilon_2} - 1\right)} \qquad \ldots 4$$

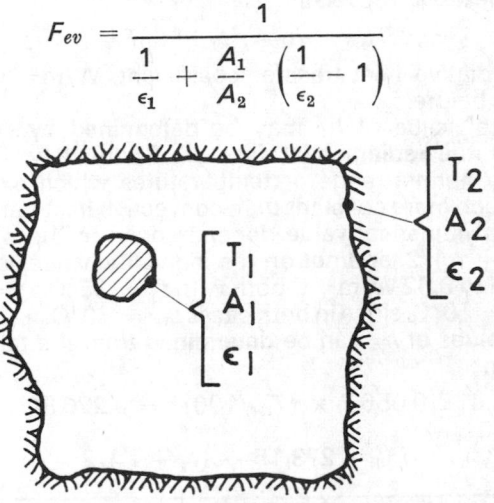

Figure 8:4   Radiation example

EXAMPLE 3

A galvanized steel pipe 70 mm in diameter carrying hot water at 70°C passes through an office 5 m × 4 m × 3 m high. The pipe passes along the long side of the office. Determine the emissivity and view factor, F_{ev}, and hence the rate of heat transfer by radiation into the office. Assume that all surfaces in the office have an emissivity of 0,95, and that the emissivity of the galvanized pipe is 0,8. The office has an average temperature of 24°C.

ANSWER

$$A_1 = \pi \times (70/1\,000) \times 5 = 1,1 \text{ m}^2$$
$$A_2 = 2[(5 \times 4) + (4 \times 3) + (3 \times 5)] = 94 \text{ m}^2$$
$$F_{ev} = \frac{1}{(1/0,8) + (1,1/94)(1/0,95 - 1)} = 0,8$$
$$T_1 = 273,15 + 70 = 343,15 \text{ } K$$
$$T_2 = 273,15 + 24 = 297,15 \text{ } K$$
$$(T_1/100)^4 = 138,66$$
$$(T_2/100)^4 = 77,97$$

Radiant heat flux:

$$q_R = 5{,}67(138{,}66 - 77{,}97) \times 1{,}1 \times 0{,}8$$
$$= 303 \text{ watts (over 5m length)}$$

It should be noted that in addition to this radiant heat flux, there will be *convection* of heat to the air. The calculation of the convective heat flux will be considered later.

3.2 *Radiative heat transfer coefficient,* h_R

Because of the computational difficulties that arise from the use of fourth powers of temperature, a linearized form of the radiation flux equation is often used. It is as accurate as the Stefan-Boltzmann equation given above. The linearized relation is:

$$q_R = h_R A_1(t_1 - t_2)F_{ev} \qquad \ldots 5$$

where h_R = radiative heat transfer coefficient, W/m^2 °C, and the other terms remain as before.

The numerical value of h_R may be determined by equating the two expressions for the radiant heat flux q_R. Fortunately, h_R remains fairly constant in the normal range of temperatures which exist in mining. In fact it is very much more constant than convective heat transfer coefficients. Furthermore, its numerical value depends only on the average temperature, $t_{av} = (t_1 + t_2)/2$, and not on the individual values of t_1 and t_2. Thus h_R will be equal to 6,32 W/m^2 °C both with $t_1 = 35$°C, $t_2 = 25$°C and with $t_1 = 50$°C $t_2 = 10$°C, since in both cases $t_{av} = 30$°C.

Numerical values of h_R can be determined from the table or calculated from the relation:

$$h_R = 4 \times 0{,}056\,7 \times (T_{av}/100)^3 = 0{,}226\,8(T_{av}/100)^3$$

where

$$T_{av} = 273{,}15 + (t_1 + t_2)/2$$

t_{av} °C . . .	10	20	30	40	50	60
h_R W/m^2 °C. . .	5,15	5,71	6,32	6,97	7,65	8,39

The error involved in using these values of h_R is usually very small; it depends on the ratio of the two absolute temperatures and not on their individual or average values as shown in the next table. When h_R is used the value of the energy flux is always slightly lower than the exact value (equation 3) by the percentage shown in the table.

Ratio T_2/T_1 . . .	1	0,95	0,9	0,8	0,7	0,6
Error in h_R, % . .	0	0,066	0,28	1,23	3,1	6,2

In mining situations the ratio T_2/T_1 is invariably higher than 0,95, so that errors in using h_R will be much less than 0,1 per cent.

EXAMPLE 4

Repeat example 3, using the radiative coefficient, h_R.

ANSWER

$t_{av} = (70 + 24)/2 = 47°C$

Interpolating from the table above:

$h_R = 7,44$ W/m² °C
$q_R = 7,44 × 1,1 × (70 - 24) × 0,8 = 301$ watts

(The exact value using equation 3 was 303 watts).

3.3 Visible and thermal radiation

Confusion often arises because radiation is known to cover a wide range of wavelengths, and the wavelength does influence emissivity or reflectivity.

In the interests of simplicity radiation will be regarded here as being of two broad types, defined somewhat loosely as "visible" or short-wave radiation, and "thermal" or long-wave radiation. "Visible" radiation is of short wavelength to which the eye responds (0,4 to 0,7 micrometres), and also of invisible wavelengths to as great as 2 or 3 micrometres. "Thermal" radiation includes all radiation of wavelength greater than 2 or 3 micrometres, and more particularly radiation of wavelength in the range 5 to 20 micrometres. The latter includes essentially all radiation emitted by bodies cooler than about 200°C. Hence, in mines it is only the thermal, or long-wave radiation that is of importance.

Radiation emitted by any body covers a very wide range of wavelengths. The table below indicates how the median and quartile wavelength varies with temperature. (Half of the energy radiated by a body at a given temperature will have a wavelength less than the median wavelength; a quarter of the energy will have a wavelength less than the quartile wavelength.)

Temperature °C	50	100	200	400	800
Median wavelength micrometres	12,7	11	8,7	6,1	3,8
Quartile wavelength micrometres	9	7,8	6,1	4,3	2,7

By plotting these wavelengths against absolute temperature on log-log paper the reader will be able to derive the simple (but exact) relationship that was used in preparing the table.

Visible (short-wave) radiation behaves in a manner quite different from that of thermal (long-wave) radiation in several respects. For example, visible radiation is transmitted by water; one can, for example, see the bottom of a swimming pool. Similarly, one can see through glass. Again, the colour of a surface plays a large part in determining how much visible radiation is reflected. Hence, light-coloured surfaces are cooler than dark-coloured surfaces when exposed to the sun. Thermal (long-wave) radiation, however, is absorbed in water and by glass within a fraction of a millimetre below the surface, and colour has no influence on the reflective properties of surfaces for thermal radiation. Thus, one should not be confused by visible characteristics of surfaces when doing calculations involving heat transfer by radiation.

The emissivity and absorptivity of a surface are equal, *for radiation of the same wavelength*. Thus, a white-painted surface having an emissivity of 0,95 will also have an absorptivity for thermal (long-wave) radiation of 0,95 even though its absorptivity for solar radiation (all short-wave) will be only about 0,2.

3.4   Passage of radiation through air

Thermal radiation passes freely through *dry* air with no effect on the air at all. In such cases no effect is noticeable until the radiation is absorbed on some solid or liquid surface. The reason is that the radiation does not react with the nitrogen and oxygen molecules of the air.

The large number of water molecules present in *humid* air, however, intercept some of the radiation thus reducing the amount that is transmitted. Radiation absorbed in this way causes direct heating of the air. In humid stoping conditions such as exist in deep mines (wet-bulb temperature exceeding about 30°C) practically all thermal radiation will be absorbed by the vapour molecules within a few metres. Hence, thermal radiation will not travel far in humid underground environments.

4   HEAT TRANSFER BY CONVECTION

Convection is the name given to the process by which heat is transferred between a moving fluid and an adjoining solid surface that is at a different temperature. An example is the transfer of heat from a hot rock surface into the ventilation air in a mine.

4.1   The boundary layer

Consider the case of still air adjoining a hot vertical surface. This might, for example, be the air in an electric substation adjoining a hot surface of a transformer. If a very small thermometer, such as a thermocouple, were to be moved slowly away from the hot surface into the air, the temperature that it would indicate would be as illustrated in the top sketch in Figure 8:5a. After the thermometer has been moved away from the surface for a distance of a few millimetres, no further change in temperature of the air would be detected.

Similarly, if a very small anemometer, such as a hot-wire anemometer were to be moved slowly away from the surface, it would indicate a variation in velocity similar to that illustrated. The air would have zero velocity at the surface, and zero velocity at a distance further than a few millimetres from the surface, but in between these two positions the air would be moving upwards.

This narrow zone of movement adjoining the surface is called the *boundary layer,* and it is the boundary layer that exerts a dominating influence in convective heat flow. Very careful measurements have shown that for air the thickness of the boundary layer as determined by temperature measurements is almost identical to the thickness as determined by velocity measurements.

The above example is an illustration of a process of *natural* convection, in which the movement of the air is caused by buoyancy effects, the hot air adjoining the surface rising because of its lower density. There are many situations, however, where the fluid is forced to move along the surface by a fan or pump. The illustration in Figure 8:5b shows the temperature and

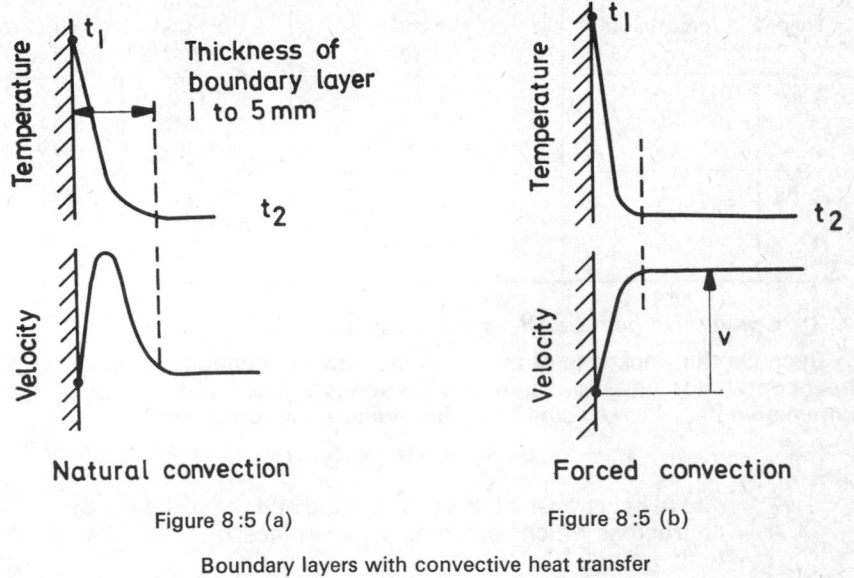

Natural convection

Figure 8:5 (a)

Forced convection

Figure 8:5 (b)

Boundary layers with convective heat transfer

velocity profiles that would be found in such a situation. A very important difference is that the thickness of the boundary layer has been reduced, and this brings out another important factor in convection.

It is common experience that the faster the velocity of the flowing fluid, the easier is the heat transfer. This is because the heat has to be conducted across the boundary layer, the thickness of which gets less as the velocity increases. In the section on heat conduction it was shown that the conductivity of water and air are both small, so that the need to conduct the heat across the slow-moving portion of the boundary layer is the major cause of resistance to the transfer of heat. Clearly, therefore, it is desirable to keep the boundary layer as thin as possible, in order to achieve a low restriction to heat transfer.

The thickness of the boundary layer at any position depends mainly on three factors. These are the shape of the surface relative to the flowing fluid, the velocity and turbulence of the flowing fluid and the distance along the surface in the direction of flow for which the boundary layer has been able to grow.

The Reynolds number (R_e) of the flow is a dimensionless parameter that characterizes the velocity and turbulence of the flow, and the size of the body. Experience has shown that the Reynolds number is by far the most important parameter in specifying the thickness of the boundary layer and hence the resistance to heat flow.

The Reynolds number is calculated as follows:

$$R_e = \text{Velocity} \times \text{size} \times \text{density/viscosity}.$$

Typical values for density and viscosity of water and air are as follows:

Fluid	Temperature °C	Viscosity Ns/m²	Density kg/m³	Prandtl No. $C_p\mu/k$
Water	0	$1{,}792 \times 10^{-3}$	1 000	4,3
	20	$1{,}005 \times 10^{-3}$	998	2,44
	40	$0{,}656 \times 10^{-3}$	993	1,59
Air	0	$17{,}0 \times 10^{-6}$	Density	0,71
	20	$17{,}9 \times 10^{-6}$	depends on	0,71
	40	$18{,}8 \times 10^{-6}$	pressure	0,71

4.2   Convective heat transfer coefficient, h_C

Because the thickness of the boundary layer is generally unknown, the heat conduction equation, equation 1, cannot be used in the calculation of convective heat flow. Instead, the following equation is used:

$$q_C = h_C A(t_1 - t_2) \qquad \qquad ...6$$

where

q_C = rate of heat transfer between the fluid and the surface, watts
A = area across which heat transfer takes place, m^2
t = temperature, °C
h_C = convective heat transfer coefficient, W/m² °C

The calculation of convective heat transfer, therefore, resolves into a prediction of the coefficient, h_C, for the particular flow situation involved.

4.3   Prediction of h_C

As mentioned above, the resistance to heat transfer by convection depends largely on the thickness of the boundary layer, which in turn depends primarily on the Reynolds number for a given configuration. Generally speaking, the relationship between heat transfer coefficient and Reynolds number is expressed in the form:

$$h_C D/k = \text{(coefficient)} \times \text{(Reynolds number)}^n$$

where the exponent n depends on the configuration, and the coefficient depends on both the configuration and the fluid. In this expression, k is the thermal conductivity of the fluid, while D is a convenient size parameter such as the diameter of the pipe.

An extensive list of relations of this type for a wide variety of flow situations is given in Chapter 2 of the ASHRAE *Handbook of Fundamentals* (1972), Reference 3.

In mine ventilation practice the most common heat transfer situations involve the flow of water or air inside pipes and of air over the outside surfaces of pipes or along tunnels. Heat transfer coefficients for these situations may be deduced from the three graphs, Figures 8:6, 8:7, 8:8.

The curves for air refer to a standard density of 1,2 kg/m³. For air at other densities, and particularly for compressed air, the coefficient should be multiplied by the correction factor obtained from Figure 8.7. It should be noted that the heat transfer coefficients for water are several hundred times larger than those for air.

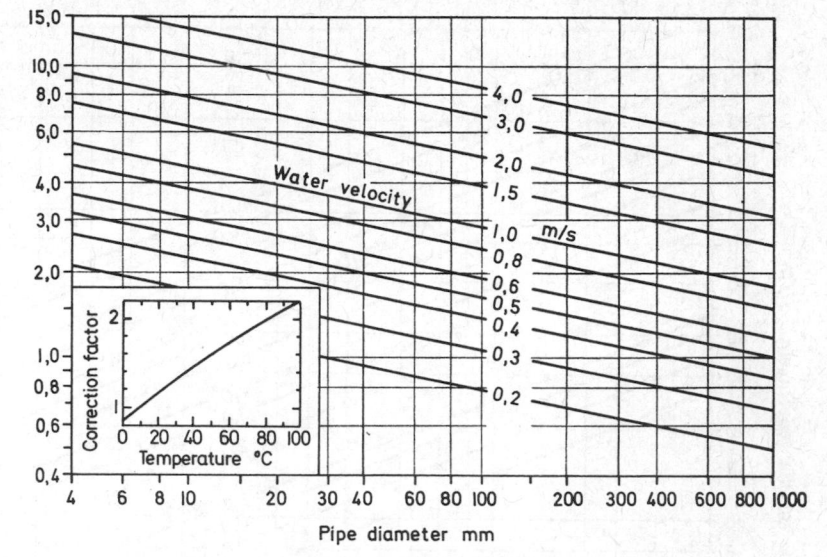

Figure 8:6   Water flow inside pipes

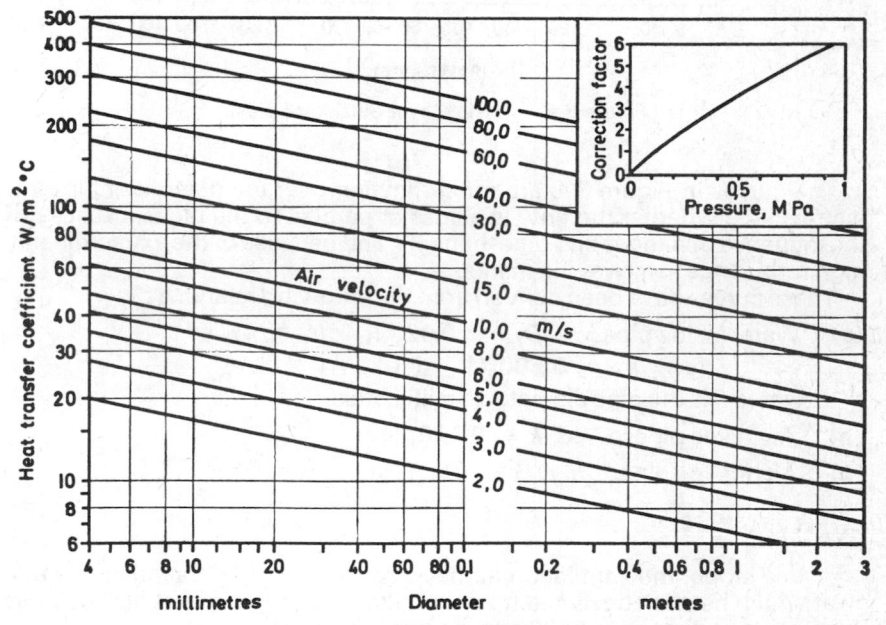

Figure 8:7   Air flow inside pipes

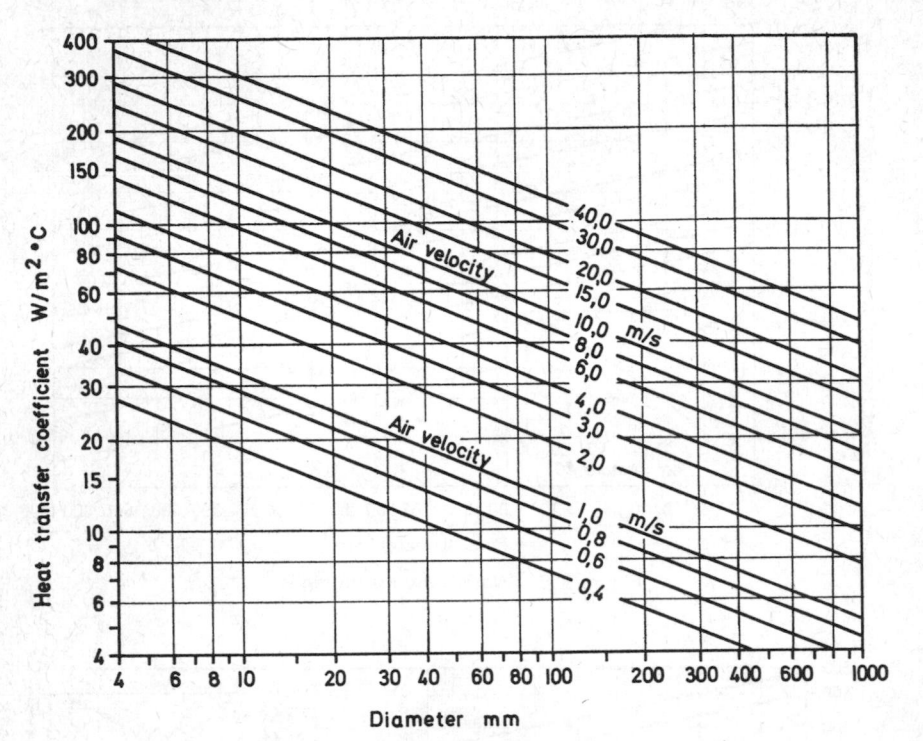

Figure 8:8   Air flow over outside of pipes

The curves in Figure 8:8 are for air flowing over the outside of pipes. It matters little whether the flow is across or parallel to the pipes, because of the influence of flanges and pipe-hangers, and because of the extraordinarily high turbulence in airways in mines.

These curves have been derived from the following relations:

(a)   Water inside pipes: $h_C D/k = 0,023\ R_e{}^{0,8}(C_p\mu/k)_w{}^{0,4}$

or $h_C \cong 5\ 680\ (1 + 0,015\ t)V^{0,8}/d^{0,2}$

where d is the pipe diameter in millimetres.

(b)   Air inside pipes: $h_C D/k = 0,02R_e{}^{0,8}$

(c)   Air outside pipes: $h_C D/k = 0,2\ R_e{}^{0,6}$

EXAMPLE 5

In a stope, the ventilation air has a speed of 1 m/s. Calculate the rate at which heat is convected from a workman, assuming that his body has an average diameter of 200 mm. Assume, further, that

(a)   The workman has a skin area of 1,5 m², and an average skin temperature of 35 °C.

(b)   The condition of the air is 29 °C wet-bulb, 31 °C dry-bulb, and 100 kPa pressure.

ANSWER

The convective heat transfer coefficient of the air passing over the workman is found from Figure 8:8 (diameter 200 mm, air speed 1 m/s) as $h_C = 9{,}5$ W/m² °C.

The rate at which heat is convected away from the man is

$$q_C = h_C A(t_{skin} - t_{dry\ bulb})$$
$$= 9{,}5 \times 1{,}5 \times (35 - 31)$$
$$= 57\text{W}$$

This is of the order of a fifth of the total metabolic heat generated by the man (see Chapter 7).

4.4   Coefficients for natural convection

The above discussion concerned coefficients for forced convection, that is, for situations in which the velocity of the fluid is known. Occasionally situations involving natural convection arise, in which case the following equations may be used to estimate the convective heat transfer coefficient:

For air

$$h_C = 1{,}4(\Delta t)^{1/3} \qquad \qquad \dots 7$$

For water

$$h_C = 190(1 + 0{,}012t_w)(\Delta t)^{1/3} \qquad \dots 8$$

where Δt is the difference between the temperatures of the fluid and surface in °C, and, in equation 8, t_w is the temperature of the water.

Equations 7 and 8 are valid only for natural convection occurring in places which are large compared with the dimensions of the heat transfer surface. In small enclosures such as in annular spaces, the coefficients will be very much less than the values calculated from the equations.

EXAMPLE 6

Determine the rate at which heat is convected to the air from the pipe in the situation described in example 3. How does this compare in magnitude with the heat that is radiated from the pipe?

ANSWER

The difference in temperature between the pipe and the air is 46°C. Assuming that the air in the room is not being circulated by a fan, equation 7 yields the convective heat transfer coefficient as:

$$h_C = 1{,}4(46)^{1/3} = 5{,}02 \text{ W/m}^2 \text{ °C}$$

The heat transfer by convection for the 5 m-long pipe is:

$$q_C = 5{,}02 \times 1{,}1 \times 46 = 254\text{W}$$

This is a little less than the heat radiated from the pipe, $q_R = 303\text{W}$, as was calculated in Example 3. The total amount of heat transferred is, of course, the sum of these two.

5. OVERALL COEFFICIENT OF HEAT TRANSFER

In most practical situations the rate of heat transfer is governed by all three of the processes of conduction, radiation and convection, depending on the particular configuration of the equipment involved. In order to illustrate the method of calculation to be used in such situations, the case will be considered of hot water flowing inside an insulated steel pipe, as illustrated in Figure 8 :9. The calculations will be done for a pipe of length *L*. It could equally be done on the basis of unit length of the pipe, since the total rate at which heat is transferred is proportional to the total length of pipe.

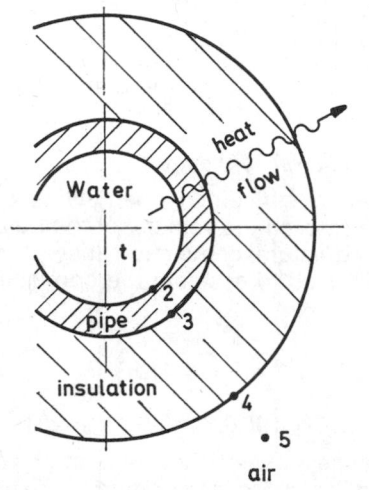

Figure 8 :9   An insulated pipe

The method of calculation follows directly from the fact that the same amount of heat that is convected from the water to the pipe wall must in turn be conducted radially outwards through the steel pipe and through the insulation until it reaches the outer surface of the insulation. From this point it passes outwards by the joint processes of convection to the air, and radiation to the surroundings.

The appropriate equation for each portion of the heat-flow path must be written. Usually, however, the only temperatures that are known are those of the water, t_1, and the air, t_5. The other temperatures at the interfaces must be assumed, and then subsequently eliminated from the equations by algebraic manipulation.

In calculations involving pipes the complication of using the log mean area in place of the arithmetic mean area is almost never justified. The errors involved are much less than the uncertainties in the individual coefficients. This is the reason why the arithmetic mean areas A_{23} and A_{34} are used.

Thus :

convection from water to pipe wall $q = h_2 A_2(t_1 - t_2)$

conduction through pipe wall $q = k_{pipe}A_{23}(t_2 - t_3)/(r_3 - r_2)$

conduction through insulation $q = k_{ins}A_{34}(t_3 - t_4)/(r_4 - r_3)$

convection and radiation at outer surface $q = (h_4 + 0{,}95h_R)A_4(t_4 - t_5)$

where

$$r = \text{radius}\,;A_2 = 2\pi r_2 L\,;A_3 = 2\pi r_3 L\,;A_4 = 2\pi r_4 L$$

$A_{23} = (A_2 + A_3)/2 \,; A_{34} = (A_3 + A_4)/2$

k_{ins} = thermal conductivity of the insulation material.

k_{pipe} = thermal conductivity of the pipe.

h_2 = convective heat transfer coefficient between the water and the inside pipe surface.

L = length of pipe.

h_4 = convective heat transfer coefficient between the ambient air and the outside surface of the insulation.

h_R = radiative heat transfer coefficient. The number 0,95 is an assumed value for the emissivity and view factor, F_{ev}.

The unknown temperatures, t_2, t_3 and t_4 can be eliminated from the above equations because the heat quantity q is the same in each case, to give the generalized formula:

$$q = UA(t_1 - t_5) \qquad \text{(watts)} \qquad \dots 9$$

where

$$UA = \cfrac{1}{\dfrac{1}{h_2 A_2} + \dfrac{r_3 - r_2}{k_{pipe} A_{23}} + \dfrac{r_4 - r_3}{k_{ins} A_{34}} + \dfrac{1}{(h_4 + 0{,}95 h_R) A_4}} \qquad \dots 10$$

In the case of heat exchangers the UA factor has an added importance. When it is desired to transfer heat from one fluid to another under specified temperature conditions, suitable equipment must be purchased. In effect, it is the UA which is being purchased. Thus, a cost comparison of different designs of heat exchanger must be done on the basis of the UA factors.

In calculations involving overall heat transfer coefficients, it is always easier to calculate the UA product and not to calculate the U value itself. The reason is that this avoids the need for an arbitrary decision on which area to use and it greatly simplifies the selection of mean areas for the cylindrical portions. Another advantage of using the UA formula in the form given is that it is equally applicable to plane walls, cylinders, or any other shape, provided that suitable average areas are used for A_{23} and A_{34}. For plane walls, all areas are obviously equal and in this case it is usual to cancel all A terms from the UA expression and, hence, to calculate U by itself.

EXAMPLE 7

A steel pipe 150 mm inside diameter and 160 mm outside diameter carries cold water (10°C) at 0,5 m/s along a mine airway. The air in this airway is at 24°C wet-bulb, 27°C dry-bulb and 100 kPa pressure, and has a velocity of 3 m/s. The pipe is covered with insulation material 30 mm thick, having a thermal conductivity of 0,035 W/m °C. Determine:

(a)   The UA factor for a 1-metre length of insulated pipe.

(b)   The rate of heat gain by the water, per metre length of pipe.

(c)   The temperature of the inner and outer surfaces of the pipe, and of the outer surface of the insulation.

ANSWER

(a) In order to determine the UA factor from equation 10 it is first of all necessary to evaluate the various r, A and h terms. Thus:

$$r_2 = 0{,}075 \text{ m}; r_3 = 0{,}08 \text{ m}; r_4 = 0{,}11 \text{ m}$$
$$(r_3 - r_2) = 0{,}005 \text{ m}; (r_4 - r_3) = 0{,}03 \text{ m}$$
$$A_2 = 0{,}471 \text{ m}^2; A_3 = 0{,}503 \text{ m}^2; A_4 = 0{,}691 \text{ m}^2$$
$$A_{23} = (0{,}471 + 0{,}503)/2 = 0{,}487 \text{ m}^2; A_{34} = 0{,}597 \text{ m}^2$$
$$k_{pipe} = 45 \text{ W/m °C (from table on page 142, for steel)}$$
$$h_2 = 1\,400 \text{ W/m}^2 \text{ °C (from Figure 8:6)}$$
$$h_4 = 18 \text{ W/m}^2 \text{ °C (from Figure 8:8)}$$
$$h_R = 6{,}1 \text{ W/m}^2 \text{ °C (from table on page 146, at 27°C)}$$

The four denominator terms in equation 10 can now be evaluated:

$$1/(1\,400 \times 0{,}471) = 0{,}001\,515$$
$$0{,}005/(45 \times 0{,}487) = 0{,}000\,228$$
$$0{,}03/(0{,}035 \times 0{,}597) = 1{,}435$$
$$1/(18 + 0{,}95 \times 6{,}1)0{,}691 = 0{,}060\,8$$

Total of denominator terms $= 1{,}497\,543$

Thus $UA = 1/1{,}497\,5 = 0{,}668$ W/°C.

(b) The rate of heat gain by the water per metre of pipe length is
$$q = 0{,}668 \times (27 - 10) = 11{,}35\text{W}$$

(c) The intermediate temperatures can be calculated from the equations immediately preceding equation 9. Note that the temperature terms in each case must be reversed since the flow of heat in this example is inwards.

$$(t_2 - t_1) = q/h_2A_2 = 0{,}001\,515\,q = 0{,}017\,2°C$$
$$\therefore t_2 = 10 + 0{,}017\,2 = 10{,}017°C$$
$$(t_3 - t_2) = q(r_3 - r_2)/k_{pipe}A_{23} = 0{,}000\,228\,q = 0{,}002\,59°C$$
$$\therefore t_3 = 10{,}017 + 0{,}002\,59 = 10{,}02°C$$
$$(t_5 - t_4) = q/(h_4 + 0{,}95h_R)A_4 = 0{,}060\,8\,q = 0{,}69°C$$
$$\therefore t_4 = 27 - 0{,}69 = 26{,}31°C.$$

Several important features of this calculation should be noted.

(i) The UA factor is for a one-metre length of insulated pipe.

(ii) The dominant term in the UA factor is the resistance to heat flow that is provided by the insulation. Of the total temperature drop of $(27 - 10) = 17°C$, as much as $16{,}29°C$ occurs across the insulation.

(iii) The water-side coefficient, and the pipe wall have so little effect that they could have been neglected. Neglecting these terms would be equivalent to assuming that the outside of the pipe was at the same temperature as the water. The temperature calculations show that the outside of the pipe is at a temperature (t_3), only $0{,}02°C$ above that of the water.

(iv) The air-side resistance is not small enough to be neglected.

(v) The outside temperature of the insulation ($26{,}31°C$) is well above the dew-point temperature of the air ($23°C$) so that no condensation will take place on the insulation cover.

5.1   Fouling factor $1/h_F$

Equation 10 for calculating the UA factor is a completely general equation for any kind of heat transfer situation. providing the terms are suitably modified. For example, in heat exchangers where it is necessary to take into effect scale deposits on the inside of the tubes, such as in condenser tubes, a further term $1/h_F A_2$ is added in the bottom of the UA equation. The term $1/h_F$ is called the *fouling factor,* the numerical values of which vary considerably, a typical value in mine refrigeration plant calculations being $1/h_F = 0,000\ 3$ m^2 °C/W. Of course, in heat exchangers there would be no insulation around the pipe, so that the insulation term would fall away. Also, if the outer fluid were a liquid instead of air, the radiation term h_R in equation 10 would fall away. A more detailed discussion of the significance of the fouling factor is given in the chapter on refrigeration.

5.2   Relative orders of magnitude of the different terms

It will usually be found in the expression for UA that certain terms exert a dominating influence in the determination of the numerical value of UA, and, therefore, in determining the heat flow rate. In such cases certain of the other terms may be neglected. A knowledge as to which to neglect can be obtained only by experience or by calculation, such as was illustrated in the above example.

5.3   Log mean temperature difference

In equation 9 for calculating the rate of heat transfer, the temperature difference is between that of one fluid inside the pipe and that of the other outside the pipe at any position along the pipeline. Obviously, if the amount of heat transfer is large, the temperatures will vary quite significantly along the length of the pipe, and the question then arises as to which values of the temperatures to use. The same problem arises in all heat exchangers. Obviously, some average temperature difference must be used.

Consider a heat exchanger through which a hot fluid and a cold fluid are flowing, Figure 8:10. For convenience let these two fluids be water and air, designated by subscripts w and a, respectively. Assume that at one end of the heat exchanger the temperatures are t_{w1} and t_{a1}, while at the other end they are t_{w2} and t_{a2}, respectively.

The difference in temperature between the two fluids at the two ends will be:

$$\Delta t_1 = t_{w1} - t_{a1}, \text{ and } \Delta t_2 = t_{w2} - t_{a2}$$

In equation 9 for calculating the heat flow q, clearly some average of these two temperature differences must be used in place of $(t_1 - t_5)$. In fact, it is the logarithmic mean of Δt_1 and Δt_2 that must be used. This is denoted by the letters $LMTD$, and is calculated as follows:

$$LMTD = \frac{\Delta t_1 - \Delta t_2}{\log_e \Delta t_1/\Delta t_2} = \frac{\Delta t_1 - \Delta t_2}{2,3 \ \log_{10} \ \Delta t_1/\Delta t_2}$$

In order to avoid difficulties with negative numbers, it is advisable to choose Δt_1 as the larger of the two numbers when calculating the log mean temperature difference.

It must be emphasized that the temperature differences Δt_1 and Δt_2 are determined at the two ends of the heat exchanger. It does not matter in

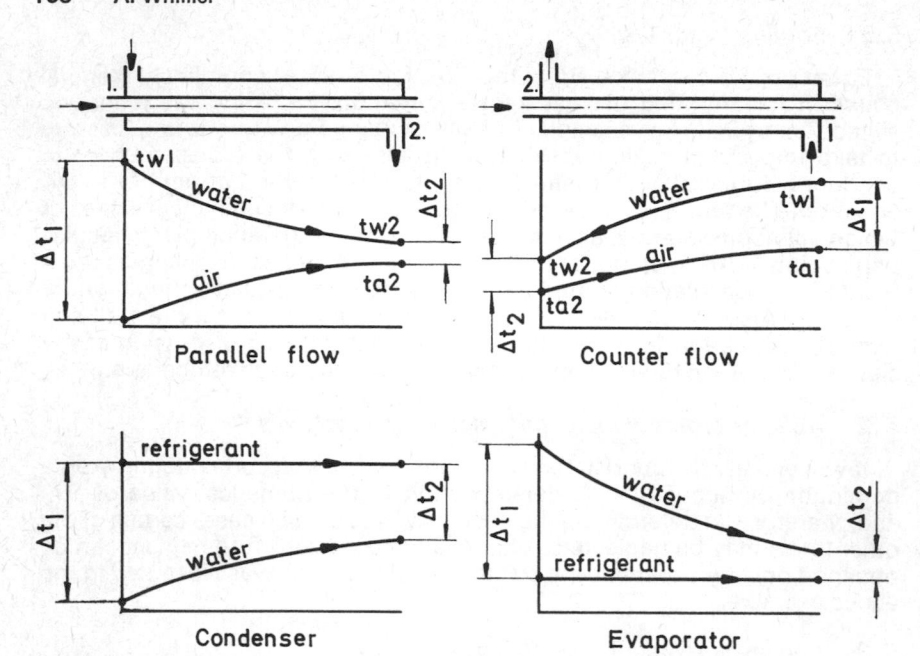

Figure 8:10   Temperature differences in heat exchangers

which direction the fluids are flowing at the measuring points, or whether the flow is counter-current or parallel.

5.4   Use of arithmetic mean in place of log mean

In an earlier section when discussing the mean areas to be used in calculating the heat flow by conduction through cylindrical bodies it was mentioned that arithmetic means, or averages could always be used in place of logarithmic means. This is also true in the case of temperature differences, provided that the temperature difference at one end, Δt_1, is not too much larger than the temperature difference at the other end, Δt_2. Using arithmetic means has the advantage of speeding up the calculations.

The error involved when using the arithmetic mean temperature difference $(\Delta t_1 + \Delta t_2)/2$ in place of the logarithmic mean, $LMTD$, may be estimated from the following table. The logarithmic mean is always less than the arithmetic mean and the error is defined as

[(arithmetic mean)/(logarithmic mean) $-$ 1]

Ratio $\Delta t_1 / \Delta t_2$	1,1	1,2	1,5	2	3
Error, per cent	0,1	0,3	1,3	4	10

EXAMPLE 8

Water enters the condenser of a refrigeration plant at 35°C and leaves at 41°C. The condensing temperature of the refrigerant is 45°C. Determine the log mean temperature difference and the arithmetic mean (or average) temperature difference.

ANSWER

$\Delta t_1 = 45 - 35 = 10°C; \Delta t_2 = 45 - 41 = 4°C$
$LMTD = (10 - 4)/\log_e (10/4) = 6/0,916\ 3 = 6,545°C$
Average difference $= (10 + 4)/2 = 7°C$
Ratio $= 7/6,545 = 1,07;$ (7 per cent difference).

EXAMPLE 9

In order to provide cool drinking water in a mine an 8,84 m long water jacket is provided around a 160 mm o.d. chilled-water pipe. The flow is counter-current. Measurements give the following results:

chilled water temperatures   : in 18,0°C; out 18,15°C
drinking water temperatures: in 31,94°C; out 20,5°C
drinking water flow rate   : 0,047 kg/s

Determine the *UA* factor for the heat exchanger, and the *U* factor based on the outside area of the pipe.

ANSWER

Rate of heat transfer $= 0,047 \times 4\ 187 \times (31,94 - 20,5)$
$= 2\ 250$ watts
$\Delta t_1 = (31,94 - 18,15) = 13,79°C$
$\Delta t_2 = (20,5 - 18,0) = 2,5°C$
$LMTD = (13,79 - 2,5)/\log_e (13,79/2,5) = 6,61°C$
$\therefore UA = 2\ 250/6,61 = 340,4\ W/°C$
$A = \pi d L = \pi \times 0,16 \times 8,84 = 4,44\ m^2$
$\therefore U = 340,4/4,44 = 76,6\ W/m^2\ °C$

If in this calculation the average temperature difference $(13,79 + 2,5)/2 = 8,15°C$ had been used instead of the logarithmic mean, the value of *U* would have been 62,1 W/m² °C, which is low by 19 per cent.

6   HEAT TRANSFER AT WET SURFACES

6.1   *Simultaneous convective, radiative and latent heat transfer*

When a surface in contact with air is colder than its surroundings, there will be a transfer of heat into the surface by convection from the air and by radiation from the surrounding surfaces. If, in addition, the temperature of the surface is lower than the dew-point temperature of the air, then condensation will also take place. Thus, in addition to the convective and radiative heat transfer there will be a so-called *latent heat transfer*, since in condensing the water vapour will release its latent heat.

Thus

$$q = q_C + q_R + q_L$$

When a wet surface is hotter than the dew-point temperature of the air, evaporation will take place so that the latent heat transfer will be away from the surface.

Situations can arise in which the latent heat transfer is away from the surface while the convective and radiative heat transfer are towards the surface. An example of this is the wet-bulb thermometer.

6.2   *Condensation*

When condensation occurs the latent heat flow into the surface is equal to the product of the rate of condensation and the latent heat of condensation. The latent heat of condensation of water vapour is about 2 430 kJ/kg and it varies only slightly with temperature. Its value may be calculated from equation 11 below:

$$\lambda = 2\,501 - 2{,}378t \qquad \qquad \ldots 11$$

where t is the temperature in °C at which the evaporation or condensation takes place.

The rate of condensation is dictated by the same boundary layer considerations as in the case of convection. If very careful measurements are made of the moisture content of the air at different distances from the surface at which evaporation or condensation is taking place, and the vapour pressure determined from these measurements, the variation of vapour pressure with distance from the surface will be as indicated in Figure 8:11.

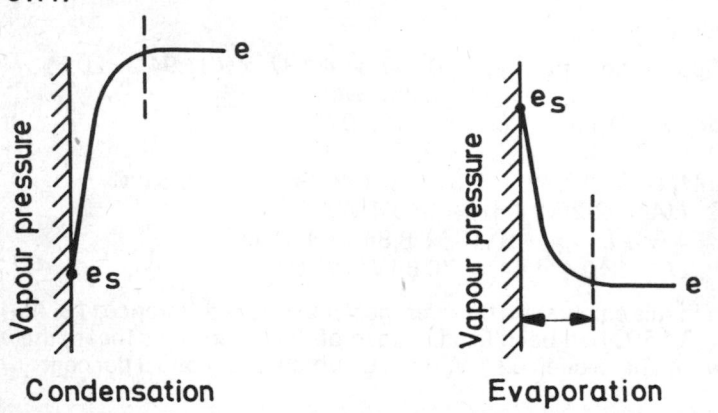

C ondensation   Evaporation

Figure 8:11   Variation of vapour pressure (compare with Figure 8:5)

The thickness of the boundary layer as determined by these measurements is practically identical to the thickness of the thermal boundary layer (see Figure 8:5). In addition, it has been verified experimentally that the rate of condensation is directly proportional to the convective heat transfer coefficient h_C. The "driving force" causing condensation is the vapour pressure, just as temperature is the driving force that causes heat flow. Thus:

$$\text{Rate of condensation (g/s)} = h_C A[0{,}7(\phi e_{db} - e_s)/P] \qquad \ldots 12$$

where

P = barometric pressure, kPa

e_s = saturated vapour pressure at the temperature of the surface, t_s, kPa

e_{db} = saturated vapour pressure at the dry-bulb temperature, kPa

ϕ = relative humidity.

Multiplying by the latent heat (λ, kJ/kg), gives the rate of heat transfer due to condensation (W). Thus:

$$q_L = A h_C \lambda[0{,}7(\phi e_{db} - e_s)/P] \qquad \ldots 13$$

It is convenient to define an "equivalent temperature difference for latent heat transfer", Δt_L, as that temperature difference which when multiplied by $h_C A$ will give the same heat transfer at the surface as the actual latent heat transfer. Thus:

$$\Delta t_L = 17(\phi e_{db} - e_s) \qquad \ldots 14$$

and

$$q_L = h_C A \Delta t_L \left(\frac{\lambda}{2\,430}\right)\left(\frac{100}{P}\right) \qquad \ldots 15$$

The two terms in parenthesis, $\lambda/2\,430$ and $100/P$, are small corrections to be applied depending on the actual latent heat λ (kJ/kg) and the actual barometric pressure, (kPa). For many situations they can be taken as being equal to 1. The convective coefficient, h_C, is the same as was determined earlier. Numerical values of Δt_L can be calculated from equation 14, or can be read directly from Figure 8:12, which has been prepared so as to facilitate calculation.

In using Figure 8:12, the condition of the air is located on the psychrometric chart on the right-hand side, which is valid for all barometric pressures. A horizontal line is then drawn across towards the left until it intersects the sloping straight line corresponding to the temperature of the surface, and the value of Δt_L is then read off the top scale.

On the psychrometric chart, Figure 8:12, the slopes of lines of constant wet-bulb temperature, at different barometric pressures are indicated. These lines have been drawn so as to pass through the bottom right-hand corner of the graph, and enable the chart to be used when the wet- and dry-bulb temperatures, and barometric pressure are known.

It should be noted that ϕe_{db}, being equal to the vapour pressure in the air, e, can be calculated from the wet- and dry-bulb temperatures using the well-known psychrometric equation:

$$\phi e_{db} = e = e_{wb} - B\,P(t_{db} - t_{wb}) \qquad \ldots 16$$

where B, the psychrometric constant, is given in the table below. For most purposes the psychrometric constant B can be assumed to have a fixed value of 0,000 644 per °C.

TABLE 1

PSYCHROMETRIC CONSTANT, $B(°C^{-1})$
(exact for near-saturated air)

Pressure, kPa	70	90	110	130
Wet bulb °C				
0	0,000 641 2	0,000 642 3	0,000 643 0	0,000 643
10	0,000 642 5	0,000 644 7	0,000 646 0	0,000 647
20	0,000 639 8	0,000 644 0	0,000 646 4	0,000 648
30	0,000 630 4	0,000 638 2	0,000 643 1	0,000 646
40	0,000 610 3	0,000 624 1	0,000 623 9	0,000 638

6.3 Evaporation

In the event of evaporation taking place rather than condensation, the same equations are used except that the vapour pressure difference term is reversed.

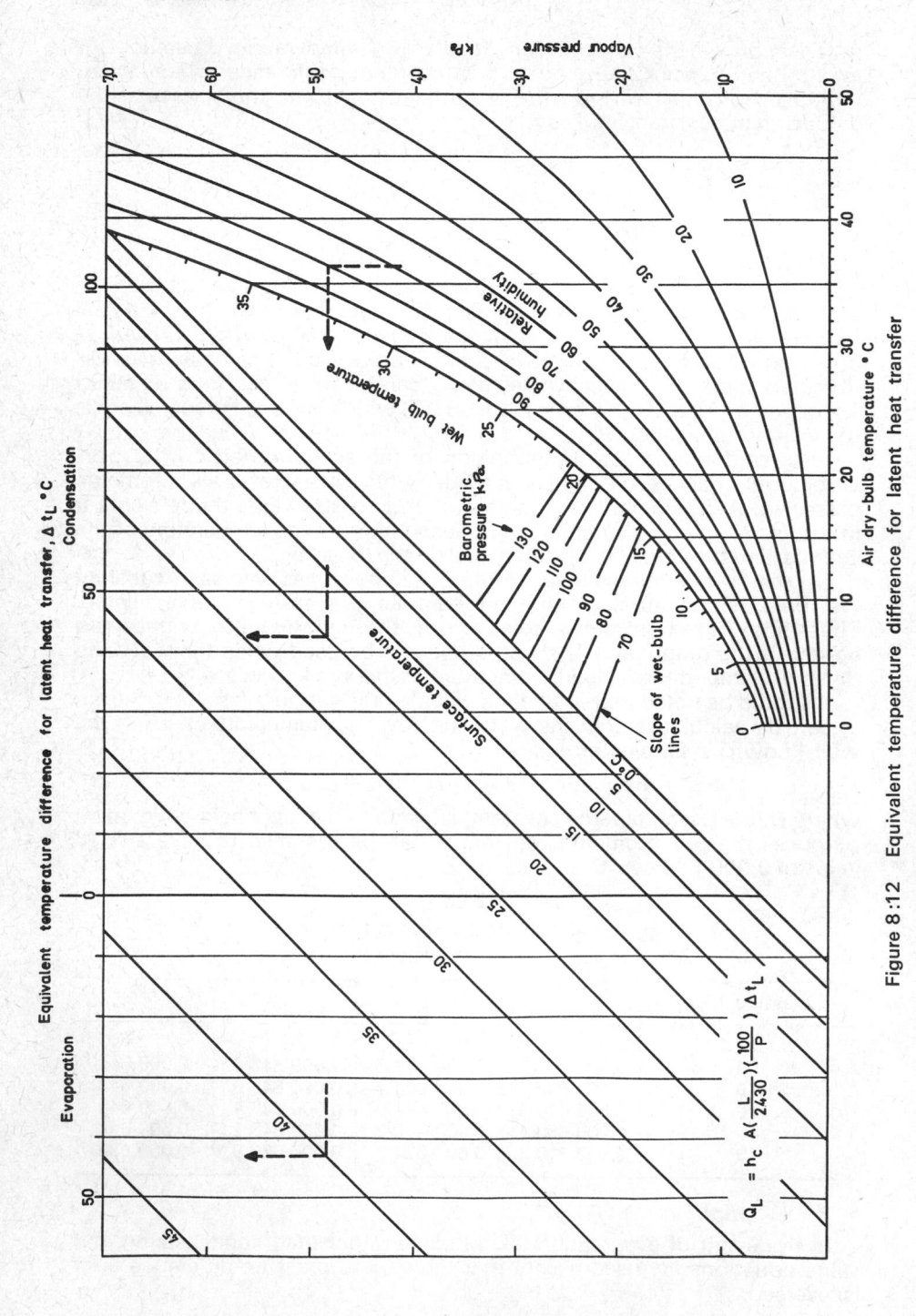

Figure 8:12   Equivalent temperature difference for latent heat transfer

EXAMPLE 10

Assume that the pipe in example 7 is not insulated, and determine the rate of heat pick-up by the water. Assume that the outer surface of the pipe is at a temperature of 11°C when the temperature of the water inside the pipe is 10°C.

ANSWER

The heat pick-up by the water will be due to the combined effects of convection, radiation and condensation, as follows:

$$q = q_C + q_R + q_L$$
$$= h_C A(t_{db} - t_s) + 0{,}95 h_R A(t_{db} - t_s) + h_C A[0{,}7\lambda(e - e_s)/P]$$

The individual terms must each be evaluated, in a manner similar to that of example 7.

$A = 0{,}503$ m^2
$h_C = 20{,}5$ W/m^2 °C (from Figure 8 :8, with $d = 160$ mm)
$h_R = 5{,}6$ W/m^2 °C (from page 146 at $(27 + 11)/2 = 19°C$)
$\lambda = 2\,501 - 2{,}378 \times 11 = 2\,475$ kJ/kg
$e_s = 1{,}312$ kPa (at 11°C)
$e = 2{,}79$ kPa (from equation 16, or charts)
$q_C = 20{,}5 \times 0{,}503 \times (27 - 11) = 164{,}9$ W
$q_R = 0{,}95 \times 5{,}6 \times 0{,}503 \times (27 - 11) = 42{,}8$ W
$q_L = 20{,}5 \times 0{,}503 \times 0{,}7 \times 2\,475(2{,}79 - 1{,}32)/100$
$\qquad\qquad\qquad\qquad = 264{,}1$ W
Total heat pick-up $= 471{,}8$ W (per m length)

It should be noted that in this example the heat transfer due to condensation accounts for more than half of the total.

The heat pick-up from the same pipe when insulated (Example 7) was only 11,35 W per m length. This shows the tremendous reduction in heat flow due to the application of insulation to the pipe.

As an exercise the reader should evaluate the *latent* heat transfer using Figure 8 :12.

7   REFERENCES

1   Whillier, A. Psychrometric charts for all barometric pressures (SI units). *J. Mine Vent. Soc. S. Afr;* Vol. 24, 1971. p. 138–43.
2   Barenbrug, A. W. T. *Psychrometry and psychrometric charts.* Chamber of Mines of South Africa. Third edition, 1974.
3   ASHRAE *Handbook of Fundamentals,* Second edition 1972.
4   McAdams, W. H. *Heat Transmission.* McGraw-Hill. Third edition 1954.

9 Elementary Thermodynamics

A. WHILLIER

Assistant Director, Mining Research,
Chamber of Mines Research Organization

Symbols

A = cross-sectional area, m²
C_p = thermal capacity, J/kg K
F = energy loss due to friction, J/kg. See equation 10.
H = enthalpy of fluid, J/kg (Once called "total heat" or "total energy")
M = mass flow rate of fluid, kg/s
r = moisture content, kg/kg of dry air
P = absolute pressure of fluid, N/m², Pa
R = gas constant, J/kg K
s = entropy of fluid, J/kg K
S = sigma energy content of air, J/kg
$\quad S = H_a - 4\,180\,r\,t_{wb}$
t = temperature, °C
T = absolute temperature, $K(T = 273{,}15 + t)$
q = rate at which heat enters the control envelope, W
W = rate at which work enters the control envelope, W
v = specific volume of fluid, m³/kg
V = velocity of fluid, m/s
w = density of fluid, kg/m³

1 INTRODUCTION

Thermodynamics is the science that is concerned particularly with the effect of heat and work on the properties of substances. The substances may be solid, liquid or gaseous. In mine ventilation the substances that are most commonly involved are air, water and refrigerants, with the latter two existing in either liquid or gaseous forms.

The purpose of this chapter is to present the fundamental laws of thermodynamics and to illustrate their application to situations which arise in mine ventilation. Readers are referred to text books for a more rigorous treatment of the laws of thermodynamics and for the derivation of the various relations that arise from these laws.

Occasionally situations arise where conditions change significantly with time. These will be ignored in this chapter and only steady-state situations will be considered.

2   PROPERTIES OF SUBSTANCES

The three most important properties of substances in relation to thermodynamics are pressure, temperature and specific volume. (Specific volume is the inverse of density.)

When the specific volume and the pressure *or* temperature of a fluid are specified, all other properties of the fluid are fixed. Other properties include thermal capacity (specific heat), latent heat, enthalpy, entropy, viscosity, thermal conductivity, etc.

Entropy is a particularly important property of substances even though in most engineering work its numerical value never has to be calculated. Its significance will become apparent later.

3   HEAT AND WORK

Heat and work are the two fundamental forms in which energy can be added to, or removed from, any substance.

Heat is the flow of energy that takes place as a result of a difference in temperature. Heat always flows from a hotter zone to a cooler zone; it cannot, according to the Second Law of Thermodynamics, flow in the opposite direction. The flow of heat into a substance results in an increase in the energy content of that substance, this energy content being referred to as the internal energy of the substance. The change in internal energy is usually manifested as a change in temperature, an exception being when there is a change in phase such as from solid to liquid.

The expression "heats up" can be quite misleading sometimes, and it should be avoided. What is usually meant is that the temperature rises. Thus, when a surface is rubbed the friction causes the temperature to rise. One should not say that it heats up because the temperature rise was the result of mechanical work, and not the result of a flow of heat from some other hotter body.

Work is the flow of energy that takes place along the drive shaft of a fan or pump, for example. Work entering a substance also causes the internal energy of that substance to rise, but in this case the rise in internal energy is manifest primarily as a rise in pressure, in addition to a rise in temperature.

4   THE LAWS OF THERMODYNAMICS

The two fundamental laws of thermodynamics govern all engineering situations. The First Law usually takes the form of the Law of Conservation of Energy. The Second Law usually takes the form that energy that is dissipated by friction cannot be returned to its original form. In most engineering work the application of these two laws is usually a matter of commonsense, as will become clearer in due course.

5   THE STEADY-FLOW ENERGY EQUATION

The relationship which serves as the basis of calculations for practically all flow processes is known as the steady-flow energy equation, or, more simply, as the energy equation. The words "steady flow" are included to indicate that the process does not vary with time.

Consider the situation shown in Figure 9:1 where a fluid is flowing steadily in a duct from position 1 to position 2, and assume that the properties of the fluid (such as pressure, specific volume and temperature) are known at these two positions. Consider further that there is a pump or fan located between the two measuring stations, which is doing work on the fluid, and that there is also a heat exchanger through which heat is being added to the fluid.

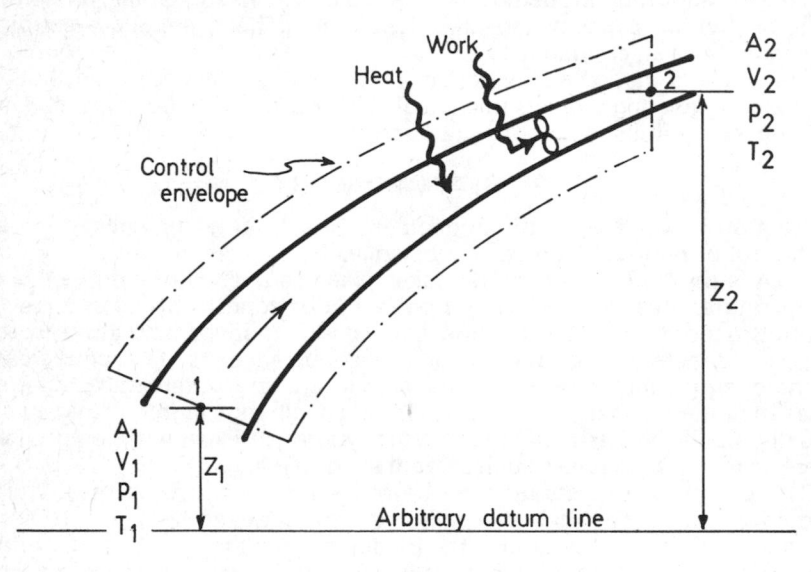

Figure 9:1

The steady-flow energy equation is derived by first drawing an imaginary "control" envelope (shown as the dashed line) around the system, and equating the sum of all in-flowing energy quantities to the sum of all out-flowing energy quantities.

Three distinct types of energy must be recognized each time an energy balance is set up for any system. These are

(a)   heat entering through heat exchangers or through the pipe walls,

(b)   work introduced through fans or pumps, and

(c)   the energy content of all fluids entering and leaving the envelope.

The energy content of any flowing liquid stream comprises three quantities namely, enthalpy, kinetic energy due to its velocity and gravitational (potential) energy due to its position in the earth's gravitational field.

The enthalpy (once known as "total heat") is the energy per unit mass of the fluid resulting from the random motion of the fluid molecules. Enthalpy includes the thermal energy stored in the fluid as "internal energy" and energy due to the pressure of the fluid. More will be said about this later.

The *kinetic energy* of a fluid flowing with average velocity V is $V^2/2$ per unit mass of fluid.

The *gravitational* or *potential* energy of a fluid is gZ per unit mass, where Z is the elevation in the gravitational field (measured from any convenient datum level) and g the local value of the gravitational acceleration. In South Africa the value of g is about 9,79 m/s^2.

According to the steady-flow energy equation for the system illustrated in Figure 9.1, the energy balance becomes:

(in-flowing energy quantities) = (out-flowing energy quantities)

$$q + W + M(H_1 + V_1^2/2 + gZ_1) = M(H_2 + V_2^2/2 + gZ_2)$$

or $q + W = M[(H_2 - H_1) + (V_2^2 - V_1^2)/2 + g(Z_2 - Z_1)]$ ...1

This is the most commonly used form of the steady-flow energy equation. It may also be written in differential form as follows:

$$dq + dW = M[dH + d(V^2/2) + gdZ]$$ ...2

Note

For those not familiar with calculus each d in equation 2 can be read as "a small addition of or small increase in". Thus dq means a small addition of heat, while $d(V^2/2)$ means a small increase in kinetic energy.

It is important to note that the symbols q, W and M refer to the flow of heat, work and mass, while the terms in the large bracket on the right-hand side represent energy *per unit mass*.

In setting up the energy balance above no reference was made to *friction* or other losses which may occur as the fluid passes from position 1 to position 2. Any such effects take place solely within the fluid, or at the pipe surface bounding the fluid. Nothing is transferred across the control envelope. Hence friction or eddy losses in no way influence the steady-flow energy equation so that the equation is *valid equally for processes with and without friction.*

Furthermore, the equation is valid for compressible and incompressible (constant density) fluids.

6   ENTHALPY

It may seem strange that the steady-flow energy equation does not contain a pressure term. It is, for example, well known that a fan doing work on an air stream will increase the pressure. The explanation for this is that the enthalpy, which is a property of the fluid, embodies all the other properties that are of importance, including pressure, specific volume, temperature and entropy. These various properties are related as follows:

$$dH = vdP + Tds$$ ...3

Thus the energy of the flowing fluid consists of a "pressure" component, vdP, and an "entropy" component, Tds.

This equation and the steady-flow energy equation are the two most important relations in thermodynamics from the point of view of everyday applications in engineering.

The term on the left of equation 3, dH, is the change in enthalpy which is another word for the change in total energy content of the fluid. Referring to the steady-flow energy equation, equation 2, and neglecting for the moment the kinetic energy and gravitational energy terms, it is seen that an addition of heat *or* work to the flowing fluid results in an increase in energy content (enthalpy) of the fluid. Thus the flow of heat or work into the flowing fluid causes the enthalpy to increase by a corresponding amount. It does not matter whether the energy flows in the form of heat or work because the change in enthalpy will be the same. However, the actual change in pressure, specific volume, temperature or entropy depend very much on whether heat or work is added.

If work only is added, *all* the energy goes towards increasing the term vdP in equation 3, and the pressure rises. The term Tds remains zero, that is, the entropy remains constant. The specific volume may or may not change; this depends mainly on whether the fluid is a gas or a liquid. Similarly, the temperature may or may not rise, again depending on the particular fluid and circumstances. (For example, if water at a temperature of 1 °C passes through a perfect pump, the temperature will *decrease* as the pressure increases. The explanation for this anomaly lies in the fact that water reaches its maximum density at about 4°C.)

If heat only is added, then *all* this heat energy goes towards increasing the term Tds in equation 3. The pressure stays constant so that the term vdP remains zero. Whether the specific volume and temperature also change depends on the particular fluid and circumstances involved. (For example, if heat is added to flowing water at 1 °C, the temperature will rise but the specific volume will decrease, because water reaches its maximum density at about 4°C. If heat is added to water at its boiling point, the temperature will remain constant, but the specific volume will increase rapidly because of the change of phase from liquid to gas.)

If a fan or pump of, say, 80 per cent efficiency is doing work on the fluid flowing through the control envelope, then 80 per cent of the fan energy goes into the term vdP and the remaining 20 per cent into the term Tds. It is this distribution of the energies which has led to the term vdP often being referred to as the "useful" energy, "useful" work, or the "useful" portion of the enthalpy.

7   THERMAL CAPACITY

The thermal capacity of a substance (solid or fluid) is defined as the increase in enthalpy per unit temperature, at constant pressure. It is often called specific heat. Thus.

$$C_p = dH/dT, \text{ at constant pressure} \qquad \qquad ...4$$

Since a large variety of engineering processes take place at almost constant pressure, equation 4 provides the basis for the simple relation that is used for calculations involving heat flow, which can be derived as follows:

From equation 2, with no work, and neglecting kinetic energy changes and changes in elevation, the steady-flow energy equation becomes:

$$dq = MdH \qquad \ldots 5$$

By using equation 4 this can be written as

$$dq = mC_p dT \qquad \ldots 6$$

It should be emphasized that equation (6) is valid only when the change in pressure is small, usually less than about 1 MPa.

8   PROPERTIES OF PARTICULAR FLUIDS AND PERFECT GASES

The fluids which are encountered in mine ventilation can be classified into two broad categories, namely, incompressible and compressible fluids.

Incompressible fluids include gases in situations where the pressure does not change by more than a few kilopascals, and liquids.

Although gases all fall into the category of compressible fluids, the change in density is negligible if the change in pressure is less than a few kilopascals. It is only with large changes in pressure or temperature that variations in density have to be taken into account.

Fortunately, all compressible fluids which are encountered in mine ventilation behave as *perfect gases* which greatly simplifies the calculations that are involved.

A *perfect gas* is defined as any gas for which the pressure, specific volume and temperature are related by the equation:

$$Pv/RT = 1 \qquad \ldots 7$$

where R, the gas constant, is given by

$$R = 8\,314/(\text{molecular mass of the gas})$$

The number 8 314 is known as the universal gas constant. Its units are J/kg K.

Values of the gas constant R and other related properties for several common fluids are given in Table 1.

TABLE 1   THERMODYNAMIC PROPERTIES OF PURE SUBSTANCES

Substance	Molecular mass	Gas constant J/kg K	Thermal capacity J/kg K	R/C_p or $(\gamma - 1)/\gamma$	Adiabatic coefficient
	m	R	C_p		γ
Water vapour	18,015	461,5	1 830	0,252	1,337
Dry air	28,97	287	1 005	0,285 6	1,400
Ambient air	28,77	289	1 014	0,285	1,398
Methane CH₄	16,042	518,2	2 300	0,225	1,290
Carbon dioxide	44,01	189	880	0,218	1,280
Carbon monoxide	28,01	296,6	1 043	0,285 6	1,400
Nitrogen	28,016	296,6	1 043	0,285 6	1,400
Oxygen	32,000	260	921	0,283	1,395

The question arises as to whether saturated water vapour can be treated as a perfect gas. To answer this question the ratio Pv/RT must be calculated from measured values of pressure, specific volume and temperature of the saturated water vapour.

Such measured values are given in tables giving properties of steam. In the table below the ratio Pv/RT is calculated for several temperatures, using $R = 461,5$ J/kg K.

Assumed temperature °C	10	50	100	200
Saturation pressure kPa	1,227	12,335	101,33	1 554,9
Specific volume m³/kg	106,4	12,05	1,673	0,127 2
Calculated Pv/RT	0,998	0,996	0,984	0.906

The table indicates that the ratio Pv/RT remains close to 1 only at low pressures, so steam can be assumed to behave as a perfect gas only at low pressures. In psychrometric work the vapour pressures are always very low, so psychrometric calculations can always be done on the basis of the perfect gas laws.

A further property of perfect gases that is particularly helpful is that the enthalpy and temperature are uniquely related, so that enthalpy is a function of temperature only and therefore independent of pressure.

Thus, for any perfect gas at any pressure,

$$dH = C_p dT \qquad \qquad \ldots 8$$

or

$$H_1 - H_2 = C_p(T_1 - T_2)$$

Because the enthalpy of a perfect gas is independent of pressure, equation 6 can always be used for calculations involving the heating of *gases*, irrespective of changes in pressure. For other substances, equation 6 should be used only where the change in pressure during the heating operation is small, say less than a megapascal.

It should be noted that equation 8 may be used for calculations involving air only if there is no change in the moisture content.

9   MIXTURES OF GASES AND VAPOURS, PSYCHROMETRY

Psychrometric calculations and psychrometric charts as used in mine ventilation work are based on two assumptions. One has already been mentioned, namely, that both the air and the water vapour can be treated as perfect gases for which $Pv/RT = 1$. The other is that the so-called Gibbs-Dalton law of partial pressures is valid, implying that each gas behaves as if the others were not present. Thus, the total pressure of a mixture of gases is the sum of the partial pressures of each component gas, calculated as if the other gases were not present.

A psychrometric chart in *SI* units that is valid for all barometric pressures is available.[1]

10   THE BERNOULLI EQUATION

The Bernoulli equation is a special form of the energy equation for the frictionless flow without heat transfer of incompressible fluids in pipes.

It may be derived from the steady-flow energy relation, equation 2, and the enthalpy relation, equation 3.

For frictionless flow without heat transfer the change in entropy will be zero and in the absence of a fan or pump the work term will also be zero.

Thus, from equation 2 with $dq = 0$ and $dW = 0$,

$$dH + d(V^2/2) + gdZ = 0$$

From equation 3 with $ds = 0$

$$dH = vdP$$

Combining these two equations, and using Δ in place of d to indicate changes in quantities

$$v\,\Delta P + \Delta(V^2/2) + g\,\Delta Z = 0$$

or

$$v(P_1 - P_2) + (V_1^2 - V_2^2)/2 + g(Z_1 - Z_2) = 0 \qquad \ldots 9$$

This is the well-known Bernoulli equation.

11   TEMPERATURE RISE DUE TO FRICTIONAL LOSSES

It is well known that when one body is rubbed against another the friction causes a rise in temperature. One might expect intuitively, therefore, that friction between air and a ventilation pipe or airway will cause a rise in temperature of the air.

Consider air flowing at constant velocity through a horizontal pipe; assume that there is no fan and no heat transfer through the wall of the pipe. All terms in the energy relation, equation 1, except the enthalpy fall away, so that

$$\Delta H = H_1 - H_2 = 0$$

or, using equation 8,

$$\Delta T = T_1 - T_2 = 0$$

Since the energy relation is valid for flow with or without friction, it follows that the temperature of the air remains constant whether there is friction or not, that is, irrespective of whether there is a pressure loss along the pipe. Thus, the intuitive expectation of a rise in temperature to accompany a drop in pressure along the pipe is incorrect.

The enthalpy relation, equation 3, shows what happens to the energy when there is friction. Since the change in enthalpy is zero, the left-hand side of this equation is zero, and any drop in the energy term vdP due to friction must be accompanied by an equal increase in the energy term Tds. Thus, friction causes a transfer of useful "pressure" energy (vdP) into unusable "entropy" energy (Tds), all at constant temperature.

In the case of pipe flow with friction the right-hand side of equation 9 will not be zero, but will equal the energy loss, F, due to the friction. Sometimes this loss is referred to as "friction work". This is an unfortunate use of the term "work" since in thermodynamics "work" is a term restricted to mechanical energy that crosses the control envelope.

The friction loss results in an increase in entropy, thus:

$$F = \int_1^2 Tds = \overline{T}(s_2 - s_1) \qquad \ldots 10$$

where $\overline{T}$ is the average temperature between measuring stations 1 and 2 (see Figure 9:1).

12   THE COOLING EFFECT OF COMPRESSED AIR

The cooling effect on the human body of compressed air leaking from a pipe in a hot area of a mine is well known. The problem is to determine the temperature of the air leaking from such a compressed air pipe.

If it is assumed that the compressed air after leaking from the pipe slows down until it has the same velocity as inside the pipe, then once again all terms in the energy equation, equation 1, except enthalpy will fall away. There is no fan or air motor involved, so there is no work done on or by the air. Hence the enthalpy of the air after leaking and slowing down is the same as the enthalpy of the compressed air within the pipe, and, therefore, (equation 8), the temperature remains unaltered. Thus, if the air inside the compressed air pipe is at 35°C, the temperature of the air after leaking will also be 35°C.

The reason why this air feels so cool in a hot area can be found in the chapter on physiology where the cooling power of ventilation air is discussed. The air in the compressed air pipe has an extremely low moisture content, so after escaping its wet-bulb temperature will be about 15°C. The cooling effect, therefore, is the combined influence of its low wet-bulb temperature and velocity.

13   AUTOCOMPRESSION

When ventilation air or compressed air flows down a mine shaft its pressure and temperature increase. When this happens in the absence of any flow of heat into the air the process is known as "autocompression". Also, the moisture content and the velocity of the air are assumed to remain constant.

The temperature change can be calculated from the energy equation with the work term zero if there is no fan in the shaft.

Thus, from equation 1:

$$H_2 - H_1 = g(Z_1 - Z_2)$$

From equation 8:

$$H_2 - H_1 = C_p(T_2 - T_1)$$

$$\therefore T_2 - T_1 = g(Z_1 - Z_2)/C_p$$

With

$$(Z_1 - Z_2) = 100 \text{ m}$$
$$g = 9,79 \text{ m/s}^2$$
$$C_p = 1\ 014 \text{ J/kg °C}$$

the temperature increase due to autocompression is

$$T_2 - T_1 = 9,79 \times 100/1\ 014$$
$$= 0,966 \text{ °C per 100 m}$$

It is important to note that this rate of temperature increase applies only for the case where there is no change in the moisture content of the air. It applies for both ventilation air and compressed air, and it is independent of whether there is any frictional pressure drop.

The rise in pressure as air passes down the shaft can be calculated from the enthalpy relation, equation 3, by assuming the flow to be frictionless. The frictional pressure loss can be subtracted to determine the actual pressure rise in a real situation.

If the flow is assumed to be frictionless, and if there is no heat transfer, the change in entropy is zero, and equations 3 and 8 give

$$dH = vd\mathrm{P}$$

and

$$dH = C_p dT$$

The specific volume, v, in the first equation can be eliminated with the aid of the perfect gas relation, equation 7, to give

$$C_p dT = vdP = (RT/P)dP$$
$$\therefore\ dT/T = (R/C_p)(dP/P)$$

Integration from station 1 to station 2 gives:

$$(T_2/T_1) = (P_2/P_1)^{R/C_p} \qquad \ldots 11$$

It is possible to write equation 11 in terms of specific volume rather than temperature by again using the perfect gas relation, equation 7. This leads to the well-known relation

$$P_1 v_1{}^\gamma = P_2 v_2{}^\gamma$$

or

$$Pv^\gamma = \text{constant} \qquad \ldots 12$$

where

or

$$\left.\begin{array}{l} \gamma = C_p/(C_p - R) \\[2mm] R/C_p = (\gamma - 1)/\gamma \end{array}\right\} \qquad \ldots 13$$

The term γ is known as the "adiabatic exponent". Numerical values of R/C_p and γ for several common gases are given in Table 1.

Equations 11 and 12 are particularly important relations between pressure, temperature and specific volume which are applicable to any perfect gas undergoing a frictionless, adiabatic process of expansion or compression without change in moisture content.

The pressure rise due to autocompression is seen to depend on both the initial temperature and initial pressure of the air. Equations 11 and 12 have been used to calculate the rates of pressure rise with depth in Table 2. The pressures shown are absolute values, not gauge pressures.

It is important to note that in deriving the pressure and temperature increases for autocompression no reference has been made to the expression "flow work". Autocompression is not the result of work being done on the air. It is solely a consequence of gravitational energy being transformed into enthalpy as a result of a change in elevation in the earth's gravitational field. Autocompression is a process in which no work is involved, so the term "flow work" should be avoided in this context.

It is quite true, of course, that if air were to flow through a frictionless, adiabatic fan or compressor where work is done on the air, the changes in pressure, temperature and specific volume would also be given by equations 11 and 12. It is this similarity which has led to the use of the expression "flow work" in the case of autocompression.

TABLE 2   AUTOCOMPRESSION OF VENTILATION AIR AND COMPRESSED AIR

		Ventilation air		Compressed air	
Initial pressure P_1 kPa		85	85	600	600
Initial temperature t_1 °C		5	25	5	25

Depth 100 m $(t_2 - t_1) = 0,966°C$

t_2	°C	5,966	25,966	5,966	25,966
P_2	kPa	86,04	85,97	607,3	606,8
$P_2 - P_1$	kPa	1,035	0,966	7,31	6,82

Depth 1 000 m $(t_2 - t_1) = 9,66°C$

t_2	°C	14,66	34,66	14,66	34,66
P_2	kPa	95,8	95,0	676,3	671,0
$P_2 - P_1$	kPa	10,81	10,05	76,3	71,0

Depth 3 000 m $(t_2 - t_1) = 29°C$

t_2	°C	34	54	34	54
P_2	kPa	120,4	117,7	849,6	830,9
$P_2 - P_1$	kPa	35,36	32,70	249,6	230,9

14   EFFICIENCY OF FANS

Assume

(a)   that air flows horizontally through a fan,

(b)   that the velocity of the air at the inlet and outlet measuring stations is the same, and

(c)   that heat transfer into the air is negligible.

The energy relation, equation 2, applied to this situation yields:

$$W = M(H_2 - H_1), \text{ or, using equation 8}$$
$$W = MC_p(t_2 - t_1)$$

In this relation W represents the rate at which work enters the fan along the drive shaft. Regardless of the efficiency of the fan, the temperature rise will be the same for a given amount of shaft work and a given air flow rate (M).

The rise in pressure across the fan, however, will depend very much on the efficiency of the fan. This can be seen from the enthalpy relation, equation 3. In the case of a fan of zero efficiency (for example, a stirrer), the rise in pressure will be zero so that $dP = 0$. In the case of a perfect fan with no losses, all of the energy goes into the term vdP since the term Tds is then zero, and equation 11 or 12 enables the pressure rise to be calculated. For such a perfect fan the increase in enthalpy of the air (using equation 3) is

$$M(H_2 - H_1) = Mv(P_2 - P_1)$$

where v is the average specific volume of the air between inlet and outlet.

The efficiency of the fan, defined as the ratio of the useful energy to the total energy input, is

$$\eta = M_a\, v_a(P_2 - P_1)/M_a C_{pa}(t_2 - t_1)$$
$$= \Delta P/w_a\, C_{pa}\Delta t$$

where w_a is the average density of the air.

This equation shows that the efficiency of a fan can be deduced from measurements of the pressure rise and temperature rise of the air, with no knowledge of the flow rate or the power input. Although this equation is valid only for perfect gases, McPherson[2] has shown that a modification to the equation enables the thermometric method of testing fans to be applied even to fans handling fogged air containing liquid water in droplet form.

15   ROCKDRILLS

Rockdrills used in mining are powered by compressed air. Consider the system illustrated in Figure 9:2, showing a rockdrill with the water supply (essential for the suppression of dust, removal of chips and cooling the cutting edge of the steel) temporarily shut off. Work passes out of the imaginary envelope along the drill rod, but heat transfer with the surroundings is negligible. During a short interval of time (a few seconds) the work done by the thrusting device in advancing the drill into the rock is negligible. It is assumed that the exhaust air is slowed down until its

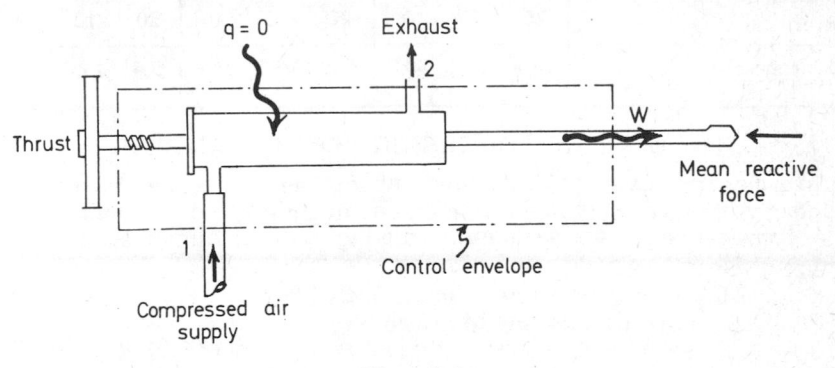

Figure 9:2

velocity is the same as that of the compressed air entering through the hose pipe.

Applying the energy relation to this system gives an expression for the rate at which work is done by the rockdrill.

$$W = M(H_1 - H_2) = MC_p\,(t_1 - t_2)$$

The maximum possible rate at which work could be done (in a perfect system) can be determined from equations 2 and 3, since the change in entropy, ds, will be zero as follows:

$$W_{max} = M\int_1^2 v\,dP$$

This equation can be integrated with the aid of equation 12 to give

$$W_{max} = MC_p T_1[1 - (P_2/P_1)^{R/C_p}]$$

In mines the temperature of the compressed air, T_1, is typically about 30°C or 303 K.

The efficiency of a rockdrill may be defined as

$$\eta = W/W_{max}$$

These equations have been used to prepare Table 4, showing how the exhaust temperature will vary with efficiency at different compressed air pressures. It is impractical to operate rockdrills with exhaust temperatures below 0°C because the exhaust ports would rapidly become choked with ice. This explains why the efficiency of utilization of compressed air in rockdrills can never be very high. It should be noted that the temperature of the exhaust gases gets lower as the efficiency of the rockdrill increases.

This illustrates the well-known fact that compressed air must be made to do work if its temperature is to be reduced; merely letting it leak through a nozzle does not reduce its temperature.

TABLE 4   EFFICIENCY OF ROCKDRILLS
($t_1 = 30$°C, $P_2 = 100$ kPa)

Assumed absolute air pressure P_1, kPa	400			600			800		
Assumed exhaust temperature t_2, °C	20	10	0	20	10	0	20	10	0
Efficiency, %	10,1	20,2	30,3	8,26	16,5	24,8	7,4	14,8	22,2

16   COOLING TOWERS OR SPRAY CHAMBERS

In a cooling tower the two fluid streams, air and water, make direct contact with each other in a chamber. The quantity of liquid water leaving the chamber is less than the quantity entering by the amount of evaporation.

Let

M_w = mass flow rate of liquid water, kg/s
M_a = mass flow rate of dry air, kg/s
C_{pw} = thermal capacity of liquid water = 4 187 J/kg K
r = moisture content of air, kg vapour/kg dry air

t_{wb} = wet-bulb temperature, °C
H_a = enthalpy of dry air, J/kg of dry air
H_v = enthalpy of vapour, J/kg of vapour
H = enthalpy of humid air, J/kg of dry air
= $H_a + r H_v$

Subscripts $_i$, $_o$ refer to inlet and outlet conditions, respectively.
The law of conservation of mass applied to water, gives

$$M_{wi} = M_{wo} + M_a(r_o - r_i)$$

The law of conservation of energy, applied to the control envelope shown in Figure 9.3 requires that the sum of the enthalpies of all entering fluid streams must equal the sum of the enthalpies of all leaving fluid streams because there is no heat or work entering the envelope. (Changes in velocity and elevation can always be neglected in heat exchanger calculations.)

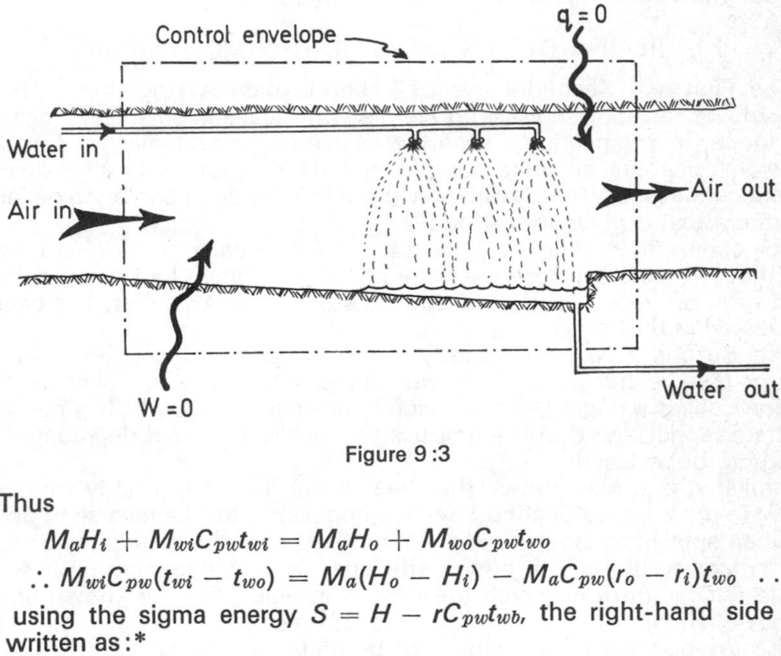

Figure 9:3

Thus

$$M_a H_i + M_{wi} C_{pw} t_{wi} = M_a H_o + M_{wo} C_{pw} t_{wo}$$

$$\therefore M_{wi} C_{pw}(t_{wi} - t_{wo}) = M_a(H_o - H_i) - M_a C_{pw}(r_o - r_i) t_{wo} \quad \ldots 14$$

or, using the sigma energy $S = H - r C_{pw} t_{wb}$, the right-hand side can be written as:*

$$M_a(S_o - S_i) + M_a C_{pw}[(r_o t_{wbo} - r_i t_{wbi}) - (r_o - r_i) t_{wo}] \quad \ldots 15$$

$$= M_a(S_o - S_i) + M_a C_{pw}[r_o(t_{wbo} - t_{wo}) + r_i(t_{wo} - t_{wbi})] \quad \ldots 16$$

---

*Sigma energy differs only slightly in numerical value from enthalpy, and is an important property of air when changes occur in moisture content. Sigma energy is a unique function of wet-bulb temperature (at a given barometric pressure). During an adiabatic process of humidification of air (adiabatic saturation process) the enthalpy of the air does not remain exactly constant, but only approximately constant. The sigma energy of the air, however, remains exactly constant during such a process. It is because of this latter fact that it is preferable to use sigma energy rather than enthalpy in calculations where the moisture content of the air changes.

On the right-hand side the second terms are small relative to the first terms, and hence are normally omitted. In equation 14, the second term on the right-hand side is usually 7 to 8 per cent, while the second term on the right-hand side in equations 15 or 16 is usually 3 to 4 per cent of the term on the left-hand side of the equation. Hence, if the second terms on the right-hand side are to be neglected it is more accurate to use the sigma energy rather than the enthalpy whenever there is a change in moisture content of the air, such as in this example.

The restrictions imposed by the Second Law in the case of a cooling tower are:

(a)   the wet-bulb temperature of the air leaving the chamber cannot be higher than the temperature of the water entering the chamber, and

(b)   the water cannot leave the chamber at a temperature lower than the wet-bulb temperature of the air entering the chamber.

It is these limitations which serve as the basis for defining the efficiency of cooling towers. This is dealt with in Chapter 10.

17   REVIEW OF THE LAWS OF THERMODYNAMICS

The First and Second Laws of Thermodynamics (together with the Law of Conservation of Mass) govern all physical and chemical processes that occur in engineering. These laws have many subtleties, and in their general forms can be quite complicated. This chapter has attempted to introduce the reader to these laws without the thorough and often pedantic treatment that is given in text books.

The steady-flow energy equation is a consequence of the First Law of Thermodynamics, and expresses the fact that energy can be transformed from one form to another, and can be stored in substances, but cannot be created or destroyed.

The Second Law of Thermodynamics limits the directions in which energy can be transformed or transferred. Thus it is well known that friction causes a degradation of useful "pressure" energy. It is a corollary of the Second Law that it is impossible for the frictional degradation of energy to be reversed.

Similarly, it is well known that heat flows from a hot body to a cold body; in terms of the Second Law it is impossible for the reverse to occur.

When applied to the generation of motive power from heat, the Second Law places an upper limit on the efficiency of such a conversion in terms of the temperatures at which the heat is available. This is known as the Carnot efficiency. The Carnot Cycle is referred to in Chapter 10.

Entropy appears as an important property of substances, but is one that is seldom involved in everyday calculations. Entropy is to heat as pressure is to work (see equation 8). Energy in the form of vdP can be transformed by dissipation into energy in the form of Tds, but the reverse cannot happen (Second Law).

The term *heat* as used in this chapter is restricted to the energy which flows as a direct consequence of a difference in temperature. The loss of energy that results from friction is a conversion of vdP energy into Tds energy, and *not* into heat. Unfortunately, no adequate concise term has ever been applied to Tds energy, with the result that this dissipation of vdP energy is referred to frequently as "friction work". The use of the word "work" in this context is at variance with the definition of "work" that has been adopted in this chapter, namely, a flow of mechanical energy across a control envelope.

The term *work* refers to a flow of mechanical energy such as would be transmitted through a shaft to a fan or pump. It could include electric power transmitted along wires into an electric motor.

Work is the highest level of energy, in that it can be converted into all other forms of energy such as electrical energy, heat, thermal energy (*Tds* energy), kinetic energy ($V^2/2$), potential energy due to pressure (*vdP* energy), potential energy (gZ) due to position in the earth's gravitational field.

18   REFERENCES

1   Whillier, A. Psychrometric charts for all barometric pressures. *J. Mine Vent. Soc. S. Afr.;* Vol. 24, 1971, p. 138–143.
2   McPherson, M. J. The isentropic compression of moist air in fans. *J. Mine Vent. Soc. S. Afr.;* Vol. 24, 1971, p. 74–89
   (See also Discussion, Vol. 25, 1972, p. 30–54.)

10   Refrigeration

J. BURROWS

Ventilation Training Officer, Chamber of Mines of South Africa

Symbols

A = area (m²)
B = constant
C_c = cooling coil capacity rate for water (kW/°C)
C_h = cooling coil capacity rate for air (kW/°C)
C_{pw} = thermal capacity of water (kJ/kg °C)
d_i = inside tube diameter (mm)
G = mass flow rate of air, per unit area, dry basis (kg/m² s)
g = gravitational acceleration (m/s²)
H = enthalpy (kJ/kg)
h_i = inside heat transfer coefficient (W/m² °C)
h_o = outside heat transfer coefficient (W/m² °C)
h_f = fouling heat transfer coefficient (W/m² °C)
k = conductivity (W/m °C)
L = mass flow rate of water entering the tower, per unit area (kg/m² s)
$LMTD$ = log mean temperature difference (°C)

M = mass flow rate (kg/s)
N = number of screens
N = effectiveness of cooling coil
P = absolute pressure (kPa)
p = pressure loss (kPa)
Q = volume flow rate (m³/s)
q = heat transfer rate (kJ/s or kW)
R = capacity factor
S = sigma heat (kJ/kg)
T = absolute temperature (K)
t = temperature (°C)
U = overall heat transfer coefficient (W/m² °C)
V = velocity (m/s)
V_T = terminal velocity (m/s)
v = specific volume (m³/kg)
w_a = air density (kg/m³)
WAR_o = reference water-air ratio
x_t = thickness of tube wall
Z = height of spray filled portion of tower (m)
Z = capacity rate ratio
η = efficiency

Subscripts

a = air,	w = water,	r = refrigerant,	i = in or inside,	o = out or outside,
t = tube,	m = mean,	ev = evaporator,	wb = wet bulb,	e = effective.

1   INTRODUCTION

Refrigeration is a process of cooling. The function of any refrigerating system is to remove heat from a substance at one temperature level and to discharge it at a higher temperature level. The removal of heat from a body produces a condition called "cold" which is, in fact, an absence or relative absence of heat. The terms "hot" and "cold" are relative and have no reference to the absolute amount of heat in a substance.

A refrigeration machine uses mechanical work to absorb heat at one temperature and to reject heat to a sink at a higher temperature. Work is therefore expended in a refrigeration machine in order to produce coolth. This is in accord with the laws of thermodynamics which state that work and heat are mutually convertible, and that heat cannot be transferred from a source at a lower temperature to one at a higher temperature without the expenditure of external energy.

Large cooling plants are used to cool water underground. This water is then used either to bulk cool downcast air, usually in direct spray chambers, or is circulated through sections of a mine and used to cool the air in water-to-air heat exchangers or cooling coils at the working places. The heat rejected by the cooling plant is transferred to water and then to the upcast air, generally in vertical, counterflow, spray-filled cooling towers, although in some cases the hot water is pumped direct to surface.

This chapter is concerned mainly with the refrigeration processes at the main plant, at the cooling coils and the method used to reject heat at the cooling tower. The siting of cooling plants and cooling coils is discussed in Chapter 18.

2   REFRIGERATION SYSTEMS

Several different refrigeration systems are used commercially, but only one of these, the vapour compression system, is suitable for both surface and underground mining operations, and this is the only system described in this chapter.

A suitable substance, known as the refrigerant, circulates continuously through vapour compression machines. It enters the evaporator as a liquid and is evaporated, the heat required for this being obtained from the substance being cooled. The resultant vapour then enters the compressor, where it is compressed to a higher pressure and then discharged into the condenser. In the condenser the refrigerant vapour is cooled and then condensed to a liquid, the latent heat released being transferred to the circulating condenser water. The liquid refrigerant leaves the condenser and passes through an expansion valve before once again entering the evaporator.

This system is shown in Fig. 10:1.

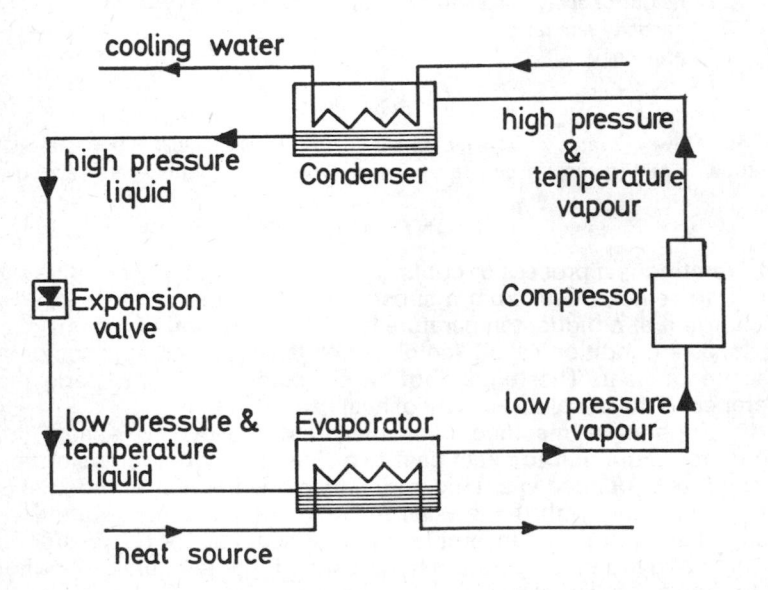

Fig. 10:1   The basic vapour compression refrigeration system

3   THE PRESSURE-ENTHALPY DIAGRAM

The pressure-enthalpy diagram is a useful means for examining and analysing the operation of a vapour compression system, and is a diagram showing the various properties of the refrigerant. The absolute pressure and enthalpy are used as the main ordinates in this diagram.

The following skeleton diagram shows the main features of a pressure-enthalpy diagram (Fig. 10:2).

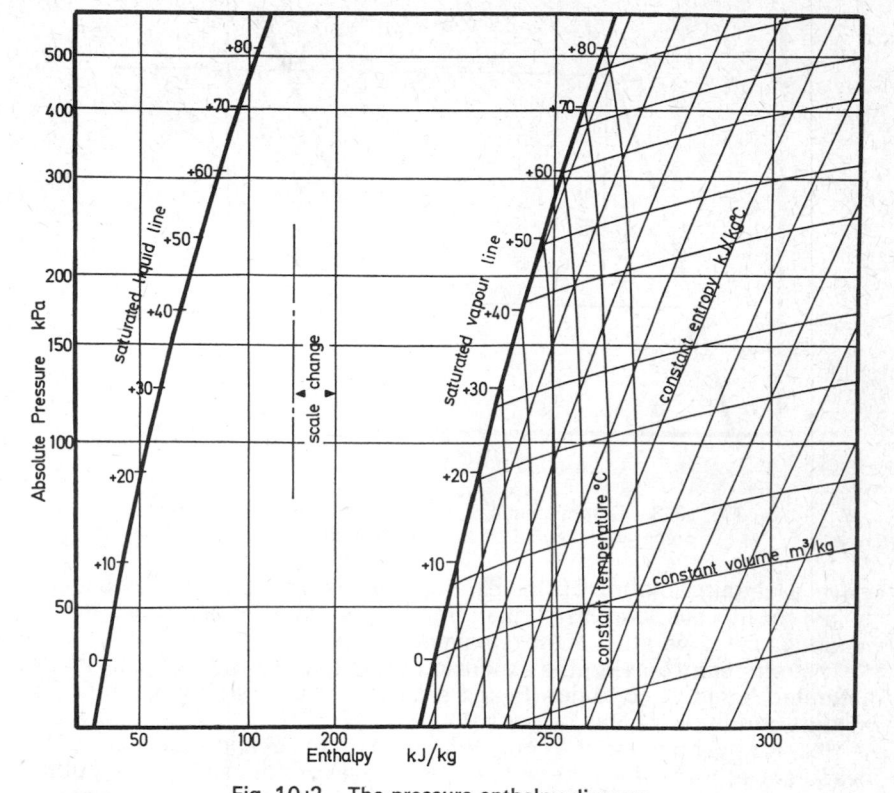

Fig. 10:2   The pressure enthalpy diagram

The area to the left of the saturated liquid line is called the sub-cooled or liquid region. Lines of constant temperature in this region will be vertical lines extending upwards from the saturated liquid line.

The area between the saturated liquid and saturated vapour lines is called the wet region and represents the condition of the refrigerant while undergoing a change of phase from liquid to vapour during the addition of latent heat at any given pressure. When a liquid changes into a vapour or *vice versa* at constant pressure, the temperature remains constant while latent heat is added or removed. Temperature lines in this region are therefore horizontal. The area to the right of the saturated vapour line is called the superheated region.

Fig. 10:3 shows a pressure-enthalpy diagram on which has been superimposed the sequence of operations of a basic single-stage vapour compression cycle.

The state of the refrigerant on leaving the condenser is shown as point A on the saturated liquid line. The liquid passes through the expansion valve where the pressure is reduced from the condenser pressure to the evaporator pressure. During this process, A to B in the diagram, no work is done by the refrigerant and a negligible amount of heat is transferred, and the process thus takes place at constant enthalpy. In passing through the expansion

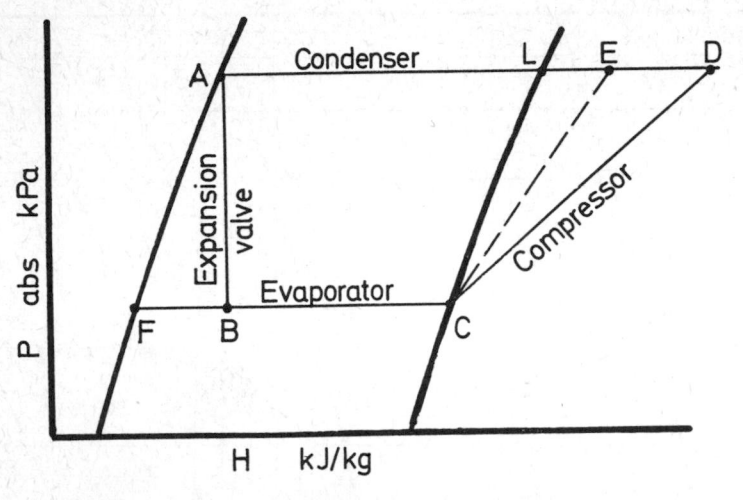

Fig. 10:3   Diagrammatic representation of the basic vapour
compression cycle on a pressure-enthalpy diagram

valve a certain amount of liquid refrigerant is evaporated. The heat required for this evaporation is taken from the liquid itself and thus causes a
reduction in temperature of the remaining liquid.

The refrigerant leaving the expansion valve thus consists of a mixture of
saturated liquid at condition F, and saturated vapour at condition C. The
mixture condition is given by point B.

Heat is now added to the liquid refrigerant in the evaporator causing it to
evaporate so that the refrigerant leaves the evaporator as a vapour, point C
on the saturated vapour line. An ideal compression process is represented
by the line CE, which is a line of constant entropy, until the gas is discharged at a higher pressure into the condenser, point E. In actual practice
inefficiencies in the compressor cause further heat to be added to the
gas during compression and the compression follows a path CD. The
gas then enters the condenser.

Point D represents the condition of the hot gas as it enters the condenser
from the compressor. In order to condense the gas, cooling must first be
provided to reduce its temperature to the saturation temperature at L.
Further cooling causes the gas to condense. The final liquid state is shown
as point A on the saturated liquid line.

The following two examples illustrate the use of the pressure-enthalpy
diagram.

EXAMPLE 1

The following measurements were obtained from a plant with a
single-stage compressor. The refrigerant used is Refrigerant 11.

Plant room barometric pressure = 100 kPa
Evaporating pressure = 54 kPa vacuum = 46 kPa (abs)
Condensing pressure = 126 kPa gauge = 226 kPa (abs)
Compressor inlet temperature = 3,4°C
Compressor outlet temperature = 70°C

The evaporator duty is calculated from measurements made in the chilled water circuit and is 1 600 kW.

Plotting the cycle on the P/H diagram

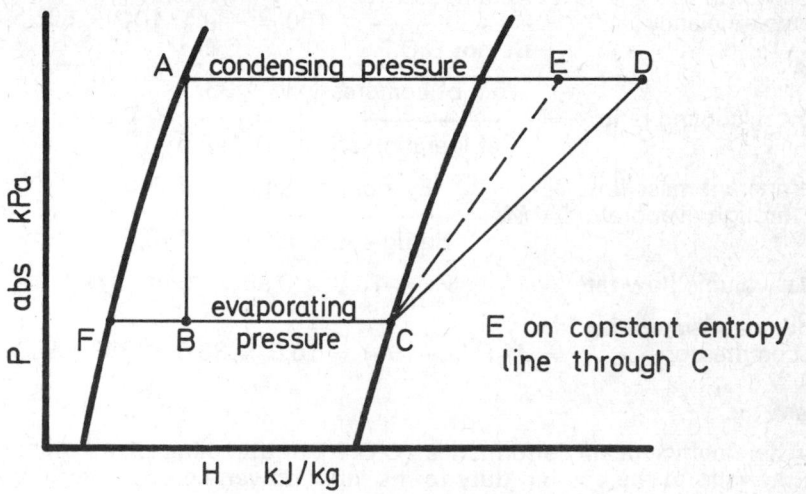

Fig. 10:4   Single-stage compressor

The horizontal lines A E D and F B C correspond to the absolute condensing and evaporating pressures, respectively.

Points D and C are plotted at the compressor outlet and inlet temperatures, respectively.

Point B lies vertically beneath point A, because no work is done and no heat transfer takes place in the expansion valve.

Calculation of performance and duty

All enthalpy, temperature and specific volume values can be read directly from the chart.

Refrigeration effect $= H_C - H_B = 224,5 - 76 = 148,5$ kJ/kg

Heat exchange at the
condenser $= H_D - H_A = 260,5 - 76 = 184,5$ kJ/kg

Work of compression $= H_D - H_C = 260,5 - 224,5 = 36,0$ kJ/kg

Ideal work of
compression $= H_E - H_C = 253,0 - 224,5 = 28,5$ kJ/kg

Compressor efficiency $= \dfrac{H_E - H_C}{H_D - H_C} \times 100 = \dfrac{28,5}{36,0} \times 100 = 79,3\%$

Percentage flash gas $= \dfrac{H_B - H_F}{H_C - H_F} \times 100 = \dfrac{39}{187,5} \times 100 = 21\%$

Carnot C.O.P. $= \dfrac{T_1}{T_2 - T_1} = \dfrac{273,15 + 3,20}{48,0 - 3,20} = \dfrac{276,35}{44,8} = 6,2$

Actual C.O.P. $= \dfrac{\text{Refrigeration effect}}{\text{Work of compression}} = \dfrac{148,5}{36,0} = 4,1$

Cycle efficiency $= \dfrac{\text{Actual C.O.P.}}{\text{Carnot C.O.P.}} \times 100 = \dfrac{4,1}{6,2} \times 100 = 66\%$

Power/cooling ratio $= \dfrac{\text{Work of compression}}{\text{Refrigeration effect}} = \dfrac{36,0}{148,5} = 0,24$

Refrigerant mass flow through evaporator $= M_r = \dfrac{\text{Evaporator duty}}{\text{Refrigeration effect}} = \dfrac{1\ 600}{148,5} = 10,8$ kg/s

Inlet volume flow rate $= M_r \times v_C = 10,8 \times 0,36 = 3,89$ m^3/s

Power consumed by compressor $= M_r(H_D - H_C) = 10,8 \times 36,0 = 389$ kW

Note

The Coefficient of Performance (C.O.P.) of a cooling plant is defined as the ratio of the cooling duty to the input power, i.e. the ratio of what is got out to what is put in. In the above example the C.O.P. obviously cannot include power required by pumps and fans and only the compressor power is taken into account. The Carnot cycle is one in which heat is absorbed and rejected at constant temperature, and where both compression and expansion processes occur adiabatically. Thermodynamic reasoning shows that the Carnot cycle is the most efficient possible, and hence the maximum possible C.O.P. is the Carnot C.O.P.

Actual refrigeration cycles are always less efficient than the Carnot cycle, and the "cycle efficiency" expresses the extent to which the actual cycle falls short of the ideal. The cycle efficiency is always less than the compressor efficiency, because the inefficiency of the compressor is only one of the factors causing an actual cycle to depart from the ideal. Other factors are that

(a)   the condensation process does not take place at a constant temperature, and

(b)   the refrigerant does no work during the expansion process. In the Carnot cycle this work provides some of the work necessary to compress the refrigerant.

EXAMPLE 2

The following measurements were obtained at a plant with a two-stage compressor. Refrigerant 11 is used.

Evaporator

Water flow rate	$= 26,5$ ℓ/s
Water temperature in	$= 23,9°C$
Water temperature out	$= 7,8°C$
Evaporating pressure	$= 50$ kPa (abs)

Condenser

Water flow rate	= 113,6 ℓ/s
Water temperature in	= 41,1°C
Water temperature out	= 45,9°C
Condensing pressure	= 238 kPa (abs)
Temperature of liquid leaving the condenser	= 50,5°C

Compressor

Interstage pressure	= 114 kPa (abs)
Temperature of gas entering compressor	= 5,3°C
Temperature of gas leaving 1st compressor stage	= 43,1°C
Temperature of gas leaving compressor	= 78,1°C

Plotting the cycle on the P/H diagram

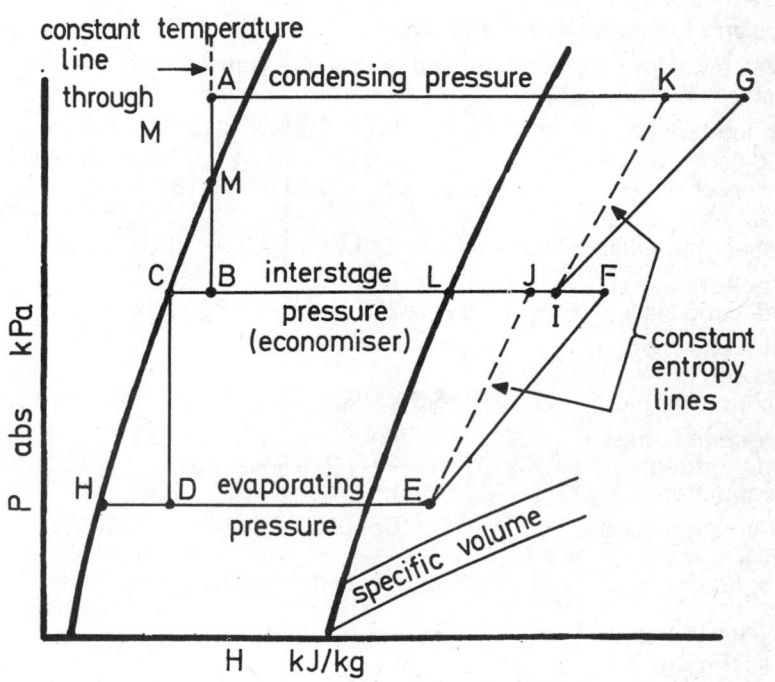

Fig. 10:5   Two-stage compressor

The three horizontal lines correspond to the absolute condenser, interstage and evaporator pressures.

G   is the measured outlet temperature of the second stage of the compressor.

M   lies on the saturated liquid line at the measured condenser outlet temperature.

A   lies on the constant temperature line passing vertically upwards through point M.

C, H   lie on the saturated liquid line.

B, D   lie vertically beneath M (or A) and C, respectively.

E   is the measured inlet temperature of the 1st stage of the compressor.

F   is the measured outlet temperature of the 1st stage of the compressor.

J   lies on a constant entropy line through E.

L   lies on the saturated vapour line at the temperature of the gas in the economiser. (This is the flash gas after the first expansion valve.)

I   is the calculated inlet condition to the 2nd stage of the compressor

K   lies on a constant entropy line through I.

Calculation of performance and duty

(All enthalpy, temperature and specific volume values can be read directly from the chart.)

Evaporator duty $= q = M_w C_{pw} \Delta t_w = 26{,}5 \times 4{,}187 \times 16{,}1 = 1\ 785$ kJ/s (kW)

Condenser duty $= q = M_w C_{pw} \Delta t_w = 113{,}6 \times 4{,}187 \times 4{,}8 = 2\ 280$ kJ/s (kW)

Refrigeration effect $= H_E - H_D = 225{,}5 - 57{,}5 = 168{,}0$ kJ/kg

Heat exchange at the condenser $= H_G - H_A = 266 - 78 = 188$ kJ/kg

Heat content of gas leaving economiser $= H_L = 236{,}5$ kJ/kg

Refrigeration mass flow through evaporator $= M_{r1} = \dfrac{\text{Evaporator duty}}{\text{Refrigeration effect}} = \dfrac{1\ 785}{168} = 10{,}6$ kg/s

Refrigeration mass flow through condenser $= M_{r2} = \dfrac{\text{Condenser duty}}{\text{Condenser heat exchange}} = \dfrac{2\ 280}{188} = 12{,}1$ kg/s

Mass flow of flash gas through economiser $= M_{r3} = M_{r2} - M_{r1} = 12{,}1 - 10{,}6 = 1{,}5$ kg/s

Note

The refrigerant mass flows as determined above are only as accurate as the condenser and evaporator duties.

Calculation of state of gas entering the second stage of the compressor (I)

$$H_I = \frac{(M_{r3} \times H_L) + (M_{r1} \times H_F)}{M_{r2}} = \frac{(1{,}5 \times 236{,}5) + (10{,}6 \times 246{,}3)}{12{,}1}$$

$$H_I = \frac{355 + 2\,610}{12,1} = \frac{2\,965}{12,1} = 245 \text{ kJ/kg}$$

Point I is plotted on the interstage pressure line at this calculated enthalpy.

Actual work of compression per unit mass

1st Stage
of compressor $= H_F - H_E = 246,3 - 225,5 = 20,8$ kJ/kg
2nd Stage
of compressor $= H_G - H_I = 266 - 245 = 21$ kJ/kg

Power consumed by compressor

1st Stage $= M_{r1}(H_F - H_E) = 10,6 \times 20,8 = 220,5$ kJ/s (kW)
2nd Stage $= M_{r2}(H_G - H_I) = 12,1 \times 21 = 254,0$ kJ/s (kW)
Total input power to compressor $= 220,5 + 254,0 = 474,5$ kJ/s (kW)

Heat balance

If the above measurements were correct, then
Condenser duty $=$ evaporator duty $+$ total input power to compressor
but $2\,280 \neq 1\,785 + 474,5$
Experience has shown, however, that it the above values are within 5 per cent of each other they are acceptable.

Ideal work of compression per unit mass

1st stage
of compressor $= H_J - H_E = 241 - 225,5 = 15,5$ kJ/kg
2nd stage
of compressor $= H_K - H_I = 259 - 245 = 14$ kJ/kg

Compressor efficiency

1st stage
of compressor $= \dfrac{H_J - H_E}{H_F - H_E} \times 100 = \dfrac{15,5}{20,8} \times 100 = 75\%$

2nd stage
of compressor $= \dfrac{H_K - H_I}{H_G - H_I} \times 100 = \dfrac{14}{21} \times 100 = 67\%$

Percentage flash gas after first expansion valve

% of mass
flow through $= \dfrac{M_{r3}}{M_{r2}} \times 100 = \dfrac{1,5}{12,1} \times 100 = 12,4\%$
condenser

or

$$= \frac{H_B - H_C}{H_L - H_C} \times 100 = \frac{78,0 - 57,6}{236,5 - 57,6} = \frac{20,4}{178,9} = 11,4\%$$

% of mass flow through evaporator $= \dfrac{M_{r3}}{M_{r1}} \times 100 = \dfrac{1,5}{10,6} \times 100 = 14,2\%$

or

$$= \frac{H_B - H_C}{H_L - H_B} \times 100 = \frac{78,0 - 57,6}{236,5 - 78,0} = \frac{20,4}{158,5} = 12,9\%$$

Note

The two methods used above differ because, as stated previously, the mass flow rates of the refrigerant are only as accurate as the condenser and evaporator duties.

Carnot C.O.P. $= \dfrac{T_1}{T_2 - T_1} = \dfrac{273,15 + 5,3}{50,8 - 5,3} = \dfrac{278,45}{45,5} = 6,1$

Actual C.O.P. $= \dfrac{\text{Evaporator duty}}{\text{Power input to compressor}} = \dfrac{1\ 785}{474,5} = 3,8$

Cycle efficiency $= \dfrac{\text{Actual C.O.P.}}{\text{Carnot C.O.P.}} \times 100 = \dfrac{3,8}{6,1} \times 100 = 62,5\%$

Power/cooling ratio $= \dfrac{\text{Power input to compressor}}{\text{Evaporator duty}} = \dfrac{474,5}{1\ 785} = 0,26$

Compressor inlet gas volume flow rate

1st stage of compressor $= M_{r1}v_E = 10,6 \times 0,34 = 3,61 \text{ m}^3/\text{s}$
2nd stage of compressor $= M_{r2}v_I = 12,1 \times 0,17 = 2,06 \text{ m}^3/\text{s}$

Note

When the interstage pressure or the temperature of the flash gas in the economiser is not measured, the interstage pressure can be estimated from the formula

Interstage pressure (absolute) $= \sqrt{\text{Evaporator pressure (absolute)} \times \text{Condenser pressure (absolute)}}$

When the temperature at the outlet of the 1st stage of the compressor is not measured, then
Total power input to compressor (kW) $= M_{r1}(H_G - H_E) + M_{r3}(H_G - H_L)$

4   PROPERTIES OF REFRIGERANTS

A large number of factors have to be taken into account in the selection of a refrigerant. The following are some of these.

Each refrigerant has a characteristic boiling point-pressure relationship. The actual temperatures in the plant will have a bearing on the most suitable refrigerant to be used so that pressures will be kept within acceptable limits. Hence the pressure-temperature relationship of a refrigerant must be such as to avoid excessively low pressures in the evaporator or very high pressures in the condenser. High pressures require costly construction of the condensers, while very low evaporator pressures mean that the compressor must handle large volume flow rates, and if the pressures are below atmospheric pressure, there is the danger of ingress of air and moisture to the machine.

Refrigerants must be cheap and should not affect the lubricant used in the compressor. They should also be non-corrosive, non-toxic, non-inflammable, non-explosive and must also be easily detectable so that leakages from the refrigerating machine can be located.

A refrigerant must have a high latent heat of evaporation so that flow rates can be kept as low as possible.

Only certain refrigerants will be suitable for any desired cooling range, as the following table will indicate.

TABLE 1

Refrigerant	Boiling point Atmos. press. (101,3 kPa)	Critical temperature (°C)
Trichlorotrifluoroethane (Refrigerant 113)	47,6	214,1
Trichloromonofluoromethane (Refrigerant 11)	23,7	197,8
Methyl chloride	13,1	182,8
Dichlorotetrafluoroethane (Refrigerant 114)	3,6	145,7
Sulphur dioxide	—10,0	157,2
Dichlorodifluoromethane (Refrigerant 12)	—29,8	112,2
Carrene 500	—33,3	105,1
Ammonia	—33,3	133,0
Monochlorodifluoromethane (Refrigerant 22)	—40,8	96,1
Carbon dioxide	—78,0	31,3

The *critical temperature* is that temperature above which the gas cannot be made to liquefy no matter how great the pressure. The critical temperature forms a limit to the usefulness in mines of such refrigerants as carbon dioxide.

It will be seen, therefore, that for a particular application, the suitability of a refrigerant is dependent on a number of factors and no particular refrigerant is universally applicable or preferable.

Table 1 gives the chemical name of the refrigerant together with its refrigerant number. The fluorinated hydrocarbon refrigerants are known almost exclusively by number, generally associated with trade names. Thus refrigerant 12, dichlorodifluoromethane, is known as Freon 12, Genetron 12, Arcton 12, etc.

Methyl chloride, sulphur dioxide and carbon dioxide are seldom used in modern industrial or commercial plants as they have been replaced by the fluorinated hydrocarbon refrigerants such as Nos. 11, 12, 22, 113, 114, etc.

Ammonia is one of the best refrigerants, but its pungent smell and toxic effects preclude its use underground.

Water is unsuitable for use as a refrigerant in the cooling plants used on mines, but can be used in absorption and steam refrigeration systems.

Tables giving the properties of refrigerants are obtainable from the various manufacturers.

Refrigerants 11 and 12 are commonly used underground in mines. Some of their properties for the range of temperatures normally encountered in mining are given in Tables 2 and 3 at the end of this chapter.[1]

5   SYSTEM COMPONENTS

5.1   *Compressors*

Reciprocating and centrifugal compressors are used with vapour-compression refrigerating machines. Reciprocating compressors are usually of the single-acting multi-cylinder type and may be driven by internal combustion engines, steam engines or electric motors. Electric motors are used exclusively underground. Since high compression ratios lead to a reduced volumetric efficiency, tandem or multi-stage compressors are used when there is a large temperature difference, and, therefore, pressure difference, between the evaporator and the condenser. Ammonia, Refrigerant 12 and Refrigerant 22, having low specific volumes, are widely used with reciprocating compressors, and compressor efficiencies vary between 70 and 80 per cent, reducing progressively as the compression ratio increases. Reciprocating compressors are limited in size to approximately 3 500 kW of refrigeration. On mines they are used in large surface plants or in small spot coolers underground. In plants of greater capacity, one or more compressors operate in parallel.

Centrifugal compressors are capable of handling large volumes of gas and are used for cooling duties from 350 kW to 10 000 kW or more per unit. In plants requiring very large cooling duties, use is made of one or more of these units operating in parallel, with each compressor on its own refrigerant circuit. Being high-speed machines they are driven by geared electric motors and internal combustion engines or by direct-coupled high-speed steam turbines. Electric motors are invariably used for mining applications. These compressors have efficiencies of between 70 and 80 per cent, depending on the pressures and operating conditions concerned. Centrifugal compressors are used in large underground cooling plants.

Reciprocating and centrifugal compressors are of either the open or closed type. The closed type is an hermetic machine in that the compressor and driving motor are contained in the same sealed enclosure. In the open type the driving motor is external to the compressor, the two components being separated by a shaft seal. Hermetic types are consequently always driven electrically whereas the open types may be driven by either electric motors, turbines or internal combustion engines. An advantage of open machines is that the driving motor can be replaced readily without any interference with the refrigerant circuit.

Centrifugal compressor performance is generally specified by means of a compressor curve, which is a plot of the adiabatic head developed by the compressor against the volume flow rate at the compressor inlet. Adiabatic head is most easily obtained from the pressure-enthalpy diagram (ideal

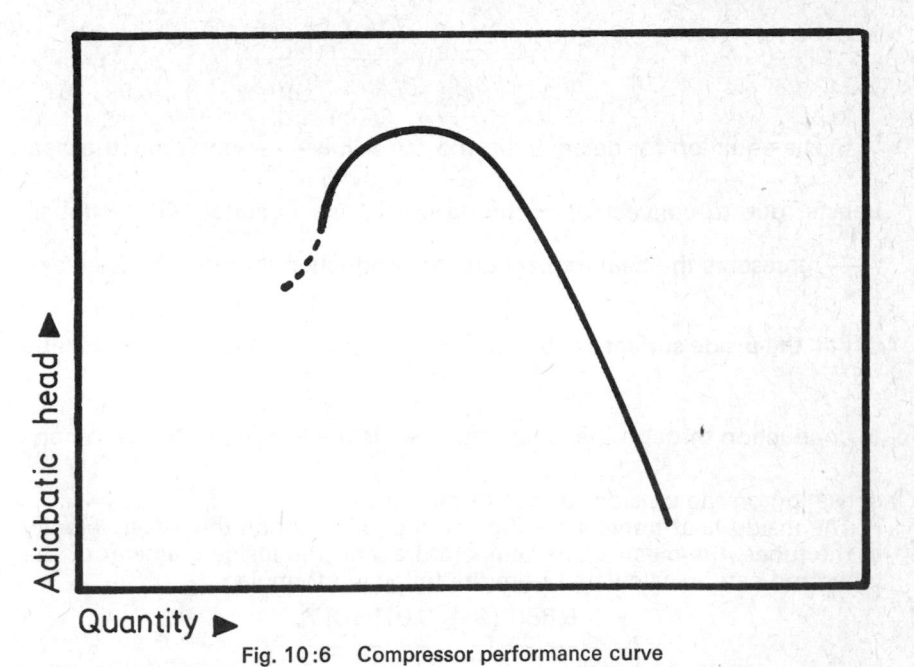

Adiabatic head ▲

Quantity ▶

Fig. 10:6   Compressor performance curve

work of compression). Fig. 10:6 shows the shape of such a compressor curve.

It should be noted that in many cases a centrifugal compressor operates over a fairly small range in inlet volume flow rate. A later section shows how this can be used to predict easily, at least in general terms, the effect of changes in conditions upon the operation of the cooling plant.

5.2   Condensers

The function of the condenser is to remove from the refrigerant gas the heat of compression and the heat extracted by the refrigerant in the evaporator. The refrigerant gas is condensed back into a liquid in the condenser.

Condensers may be air- or water-cooled, the type most commonly used in mining applications being horizontal, water-cooled, shell-and-tube condensers. In this type of condenser the cooling water passes through the tubes and the hot refrigerant gas flows over the outside of the tubes, onto which it condenses.

The heat transfer rate in the condenser can be calculated from the formulae $q = M_w C_{pw} \Delta t$, or $q = UA \times LMTD$, where

$$LMTD = \frac{\Delta t_1 - \Delta t_2}{2{,}3 \log_{10} \dfrac{\Delta t_1}{\Delta t_2}}$$

and where Δt_1 and Δt_2 are the differences in temperature between the water and the refrigerant at the inlet and outlet of the condenser.

$$\frac{1}{UA} = \frac{1}{h_iA_i} + \frac{1}{h_fA_i} + \frac{x_t}{k_tA_m} + \frac{1}{h_oA_o}$$

In the equation for determining the UA value $\dfrac{1}{h_iA_i}$ represents the heat transfer due to convection occurring on the inside surface of the tubes, $\dfrac{1}{h_fA_i}$ represents the heat transfer due to conduction through the scale and dirt on the inside surface of the tubes, $\dfrac{x_t}{k_tA_m}$ represents the heat transfer due to conduction through the tubes, and $\dfrac{1}{h_oA_o}$ is the heat transfer due to condensation on the outside surface of the tubes.

The inside heat transfer coefficient h_i depends upon the water velocity in the tubes, the mean water temperature, and the inside diameter of the tubes and can be calculated from the following formula:

$$h_i = \frac{5\,680\,(1 + 0,015\,t_m)V_w{}^{0,8}}{d_t{}^{0,2}}$$

The outside heat transfer coefficient h_o depends on both the refrigerant and the design of the condenser and can be calculated from careful plant tests if a fouling factor value can be assumed.

Typical conductivity values for copper, cupronickel (90/10) and cupronickel (70/30) are 380, 44 and 30 (W/m°C), respectively.

The term $\dfrac{1}{h_fA_i}$ makes an allowance for the build-up of scale and dirt which may occur on the inside surfaces of the condenser tubes. $\dfrac{1}{h_f}$ is known as the fouling factor and a high fouling factor can affect the performance of the plant. Condenser tubes should be cleaned regularly to remove scale and dirt. Typical figures for the fouling of condenser tubes are:

Clean tubes	0,000 1 m² °C/W
Dirty tubes	0,000 2 m² °C/W
Very dirty tubes	0,000 5 m² °C/W

5.3 Expansion valves

The expansion valve is the controlling device for the evaporator and many different types are employed for different evaporators, but in each case the action on the refrigerant is the same. When the warm liquid passes through the valve the pressure of the liquid is reduced from the condensing to the evaporating pressure, and the process is, for all practical purposes, adiabatic. A drop in pressure results in a drop in the temperature of the liquid, accompanied by boiling or evaporation. The heat required for evaporation is taken from the liquid itself during the expansion process. Thus, after passing through the valve some of the refrigerant exists as vapour and the remainder as liquid, both now at a lower temperature corresponding to the prevailing pressure conditions in the evaporator. Obviously only that part of the refrigerant that remains as a liquid is now available for heat removal by evaporation in the evaporator.

5.4   Evaporators

The evaporator removes heat from the substance being cooled and in so doing causes the refrigerant to vaporize.

Shell-and-tube evaporators, similar in construction to shell-and-tube condensers, are normally used in mine refrigeration plants.

Superheating may be obtained in the evaporator if further heat is added to the vapour by the substance being cooled. Superheating ensures that no droplets remain in the refrigerant when it enters the compressor. The presence of such droplets could result in damage to the compressor, and eliminators are fitted to prevent liquid refrigerant entering the compressor.

The method of calculation of the heat transfer rate in evaporators is similar to that used for condensers. Fouling in evaporators is generally much less than in condensers because of the closed water system.

5.5   Additional equipment

Numerous other items of equipment are included in the refrigerant circuit, but do not affect the basic cycle and sequence of operations. This additional equipment includes such items as strainers, controls, oil traps, liquid receivers, purging and charging apparatus, thermometers and pressure gauges.

6   CYCLE VARIATIONS

In order to improve efficiencies and performance, several modifications to the vapour compression cycle can be made without changing the basic principles of the cycle. These include using economizers with multi-stage compressors and subcooling the liquid refrigerant when it leaves the condenser.

6.1   Subcooling

Subcooling of the liquid refrigerant from the condenser may be obtained from an external cooling medium such as air, water or some other fluid at a temperature below that of the liquid refrigerant.

When subcooling occurs the amount of flash gas produced after the expansion valve is reduced, and for a fixed cooling duty, this means that less refrigerant has to be circulated.

The net benefit of subcooling is to increase the refrigeration effect without affecting the work of compression. This is shown in Fig. 10:7. However, as can be seen from the pressure-enthalpy diagram, the benefits are usually small.

6.2   Economizers

The properties of some refrigerants are such that in large cooling plants several stages of compression are generally necessary to achieve the

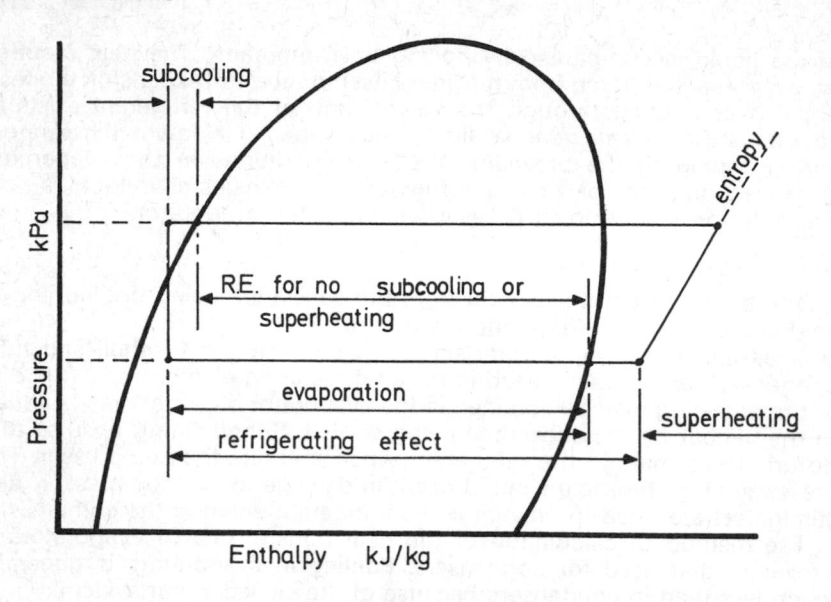

Fig. 10:7   The effects of subcooling

required duty. When two or more stages of compression are used the gas can be cooled after each stage by the addition of flash gas from the corresponding expansion valve. Therefore, the same number of expansion valves and stages of compression are required. The refrigeration cycle is similar to the basic compression cycle and is shown in Fig. 10:8.

Flash gas from the first expansion valve after the condenser is separated from the remaining liquid refrigerant in the economizer and is piped back to enter the compressor between the first and second stages. This arrangement enables the hot gas from the first stage of compression to be cooled by the flash gas.

The liquid refrigerant in the economizer is circulated to the evaporator in the usual manner.

The effects of these modifications are illustrated in Fig. 10:9 which has the same annotations as Fig. 10:8.

Flash gas inter-cooling results in an increased refrigerating effect. The flash gas from the first expansion valve, which does not contribute to the heat transfer in the evaporator is compressed only from the inter-stage pressure instead of from the evaporator pressure to the final condenser pressure. In the basic cycle the liquid refrigerant from the condenser is reduced to the evaporator pressure and consequently all the flash gas has to be compressed from the evaporator pressure to the condenser pressure.

It will be evident from Figure 10:9 that for 1 kg/s of refrigerant flowing from the condenser, x kg/s of flash gas is formed after the first expansion valve, so that only $(1 - x)$ kg/s flows to the second expansion valve. The amount of flash gas after each expansion process can be determined as explained earlier for any particular conditions of temperature and pressure.

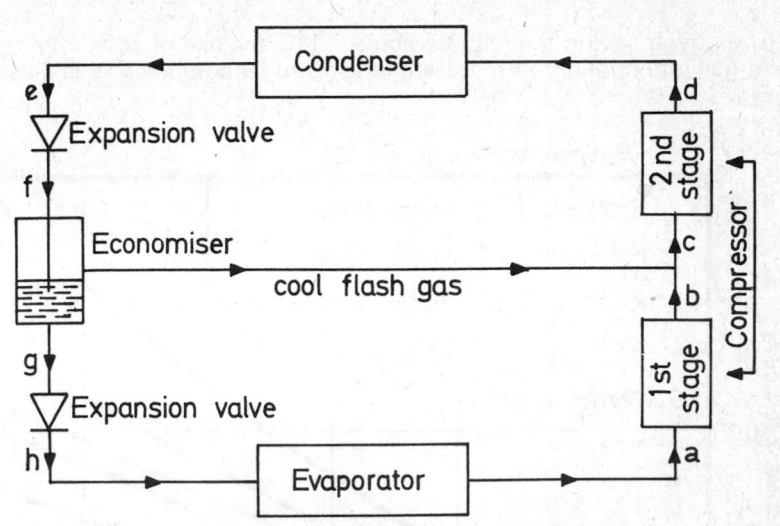

Fig. 10 :8   The vapour compression system with flash gas
intercooling and two stages of compression

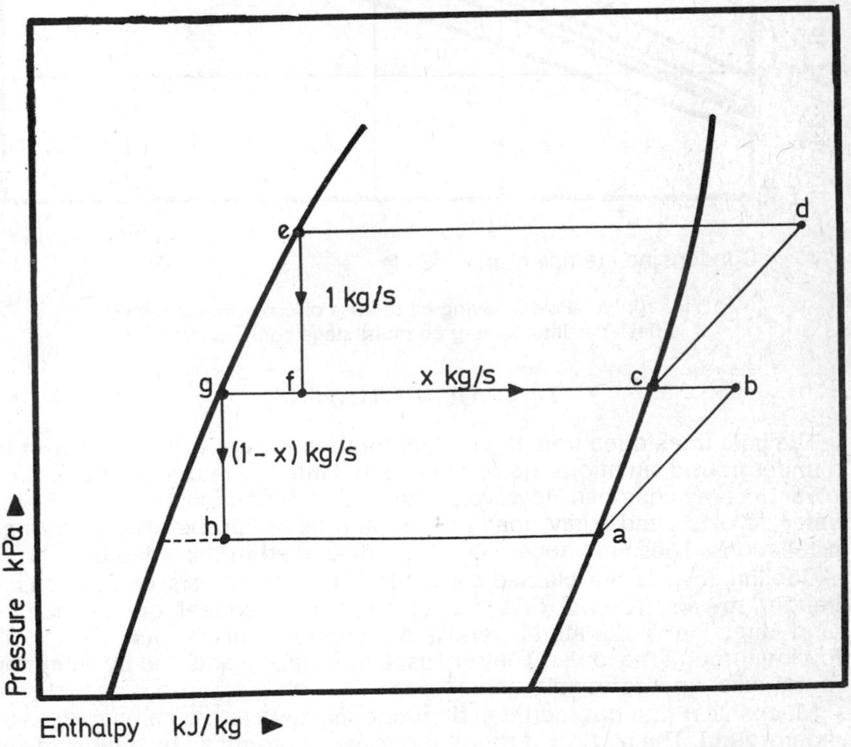

Fig. 10 :9   The vapour compression cycle on the pressure-enthalpy
diagram for two-stage compression with flash gas intercooling

The power saving that can be achieved by the use of economizers with flash gas intercooling on multi-stage centrifugal compressors is illustrated in Fig. 10:10.

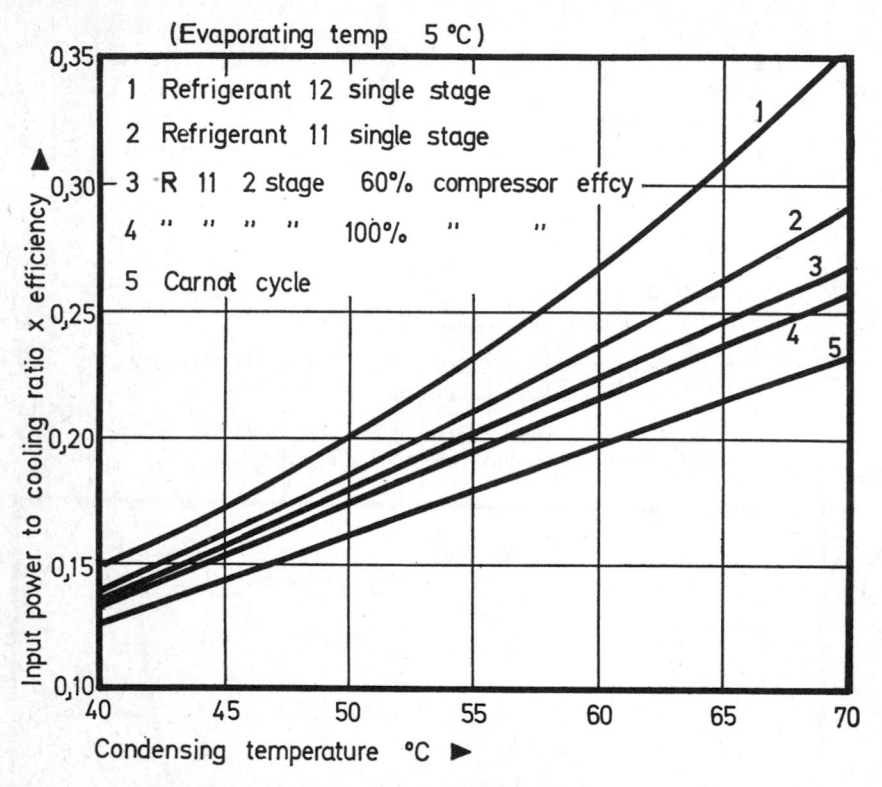

Fig. 10:10   Power saving by the use of economizers with flash gas intercooling on multi-stage compressors

7   COOLING TOWERS

The heat transferred from the refrigerant to the water in the condenser is, in underground situations, generally rejected into the return air at a cooling tower or spray chamber. However, other methods of cooling the condenser water do exist, and spray ponds, rivers and lakes can be used in surface installations. These methods will not be discussed in this chapter.

Cooling towers are classed as natural draught towers or mechanical draught towers. Natural draught towers are dependent on the natural wind direction and natural ventilation pressure for the amount of air flowing through the tower. They are used at surface plants and by definition do not exist underground.

Mechanical draught, counter-flow cooling towers are commonly used underground. The air flow through the tower is produced by a fan and the condenser water is sprayed into the air stream. The layouts of typical underground towers are shown in Fig. 10:11 (a), (b) and (c).

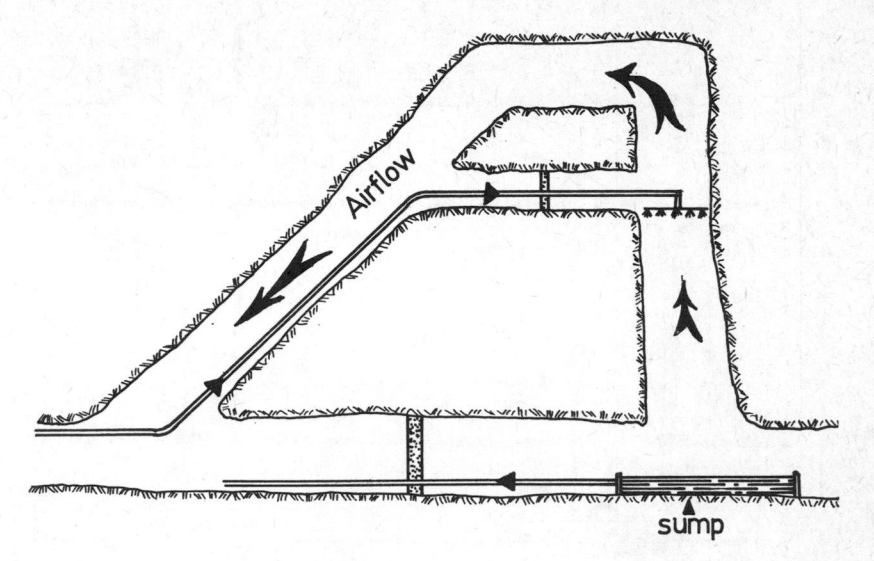

Fig. 10:11(a)

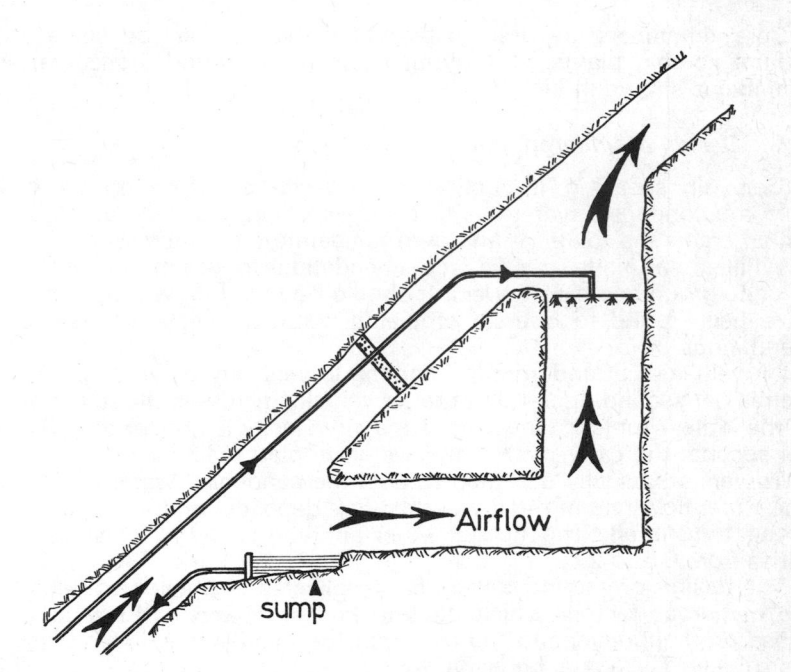

Fig. 10:11(b)

Typical underground cooling tower layouts

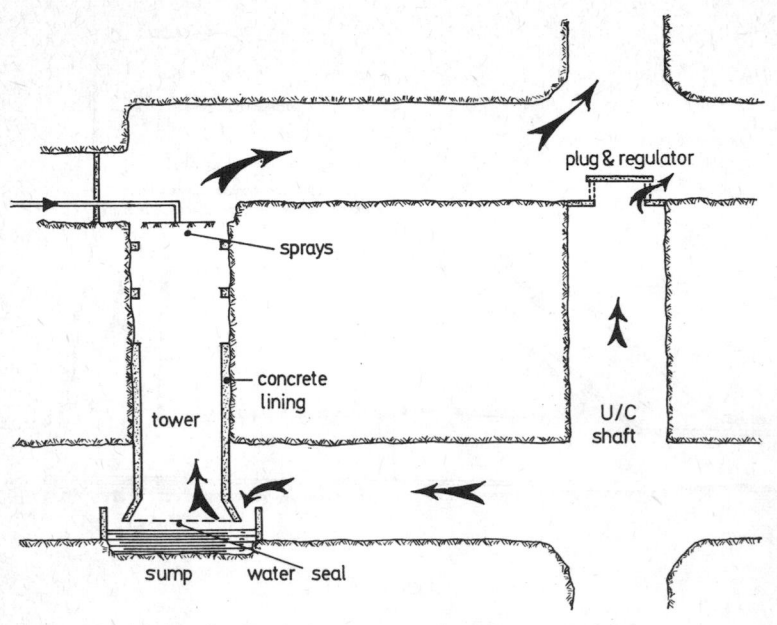

Fig. 10:11(c)   Typical underground cooling tower layouts

Spray chambers are used instead of cooling towers on some underground cooling plants. The layout of an underground, horizontal spray chamber is shown in Fig. 10:12.

7.1   Design of underground cooling towers

Generally speaking, in cooling tower design a known amount of heat from the condenser water has to be rejected into a known amount of air which enters the tower at a known temperature and humidity.

Whillier[2] has made specific recommendations for use in the construction of underground cooling towers. It should be noted, however, that towers have been found to operate efficiently without meeting these recommendations.

Air velocities in underground cooling towers vary between 2,5 and 7,5 metres per second. Increasing the air velocity increases the retention time of the water droplets. However, if the air velocity is greater than 9 metres per second, the carry-over of the water droplets is large.

Towers are usually designed to cool the condenser water by 7 to 9°C. The water flow rate in the tower therefore depends on the amount of heat to be transferred. The actual water-air ratio, L/G, in existing towers varies from 0,5 to 2,5.

The design of cooling towers is complicated and involved because of the numerous factors which have to be considered and several papers based on thermodynamic and heat transfer theories have been written on the subject. The actual behaviour or characteristics of a tower can be fully determined only by an actual test. Because no prediction method is known to be reliable it is the general practice to follow up tower design by actual

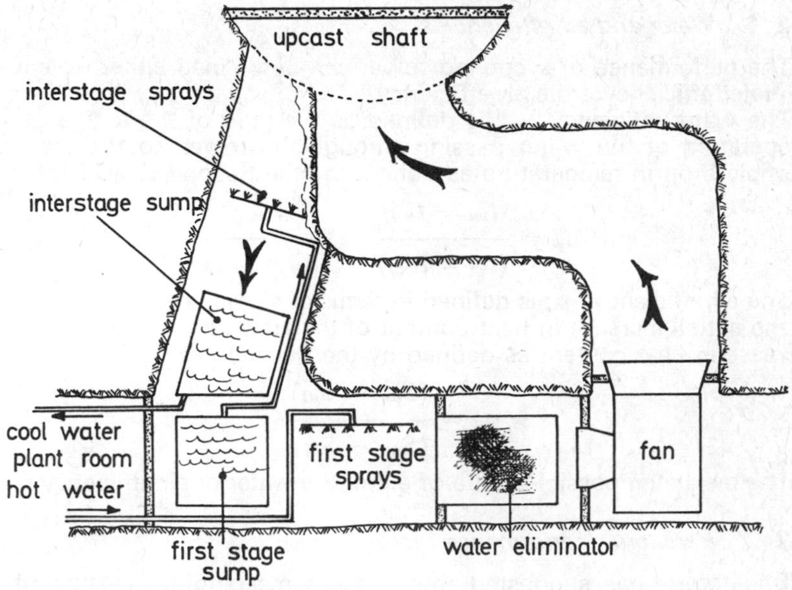

Fig. 10:12   Diagram of a horizontal spray chamber

tests before finally establishing the performance figures of any particular size and type of tower.

7.2   Cooling tower performance

The cooling processes in a tower or a spray chamber are limited by the First and Second Laws of Thermodynamics.

The limitations of the First Law of Thermodynamics are that the energy lost by the water must equal the energy gained by the air, due allowance being made for the evaporation which takes place.

This statement can be expressed approximately by the equation

$$q = LAC_{pw}\Delta t_w = GA\Delta S_a$$

In this equation only partial allowance is made for evaporation and a small additive term is omitted from the right-hand side. The magnitude of this correction is 3 to 4 per cent and its omission is generally justified.

Rearrangement of the above equation gives the following expression for the water-air ratio:

$$L/G = \frac{\Delta S_a}{C_{pw}\Delta t_w}$$

The limitations of the Second Law of Thermodynamics are that the water cannot leave the tower at a temperature lower than the wet-bulb temperature of the entering air, and the wet-bulb temperature of the air leaving the tower cannot exceed the temperature at which the water enters the tower.

7.2.1   *Water and air efficiencies*

The performance of a cooling tower can be defined either in terms of its water efficiency or its air efficiency.

The water efficiency, η_w, is defined as the ratio of the actual drop in temperature of the water passing through the tower, to the maximum possible drop in temperature as defined by the Second Law. Thus:

$$\eta_w = \frac{(t_{wi} - t_{wo})}{(t_{wi} - t_{wbi})} = \frac{\Delta t_w}{(t_{wi} - t_{wbi})}$$

The air efficiency, η_a, is defined in terms of sigma heats and is the ratio of the actual increase in heat content of the air to the maximum possible increase in heat content as defined by the Second Law. Thus:

$$\eta_a = \frac{(S_{ao} - S_{ai})}{(S_{wi} - S_{ai})}$$

The maximum possible value of either the water or air efficiency is 1,0.

7.2.2   *Barenbrug performance factor*

Barenbrug[3] has suggested that a more meaningful measure of the performance of a cooling tower is the sum of the air and water efficiencies, giving a performance factor (*BPF*). Thus:

$$BPF = \eta_a + \eta_w$$

The maximum possible value of the Barenbrug performance factor is obviously 2.

7.2.3   *Griesel factor*

Griesel[4] has proposed another performance factor which is defined either as the ratio of the actual change in water temperature to the change in temperature if water and air had left the tower at the same temperature, or as the ratio of the actual change in enthalpy of the air to the change in enthalpy which would have occurred had the air and water left the tower at the same temperature. The determination of this performance factor is most easily visualized by plotting first of all a graph of the enthalpy of saturated air against the temperature for the existing barometric pressure (Fig. 10:13 opposite).

Point A corresponds to the temperature of the entering water and the enthalpy of the entering air, and a line AB with slope $-\dfrac{LC_{pw}}{G}$ drawn. If the actual leaving water temperature and leaving air enthalpy are given by point D, the Griesel factor is given by

$$\text{Griesel factor} = \frac{t_a - t_d}{t_a - t_c} = \frac{H_d - H_a}{H_c - H_a}$$

Griesel has shown that for a particular tower the performance factor depends on the water-air ratio L/G and the air velocity in the tower.

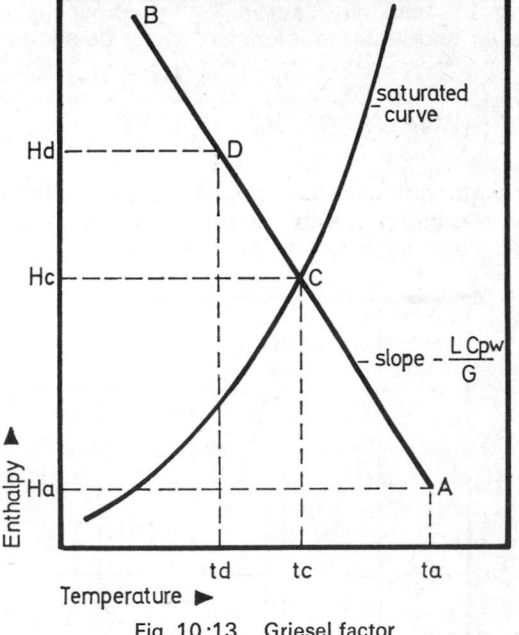

Fig. 10:13   Griesel factor

7.2.4   *Reference water-air ratios*

Because of the limitations imposed by the First and Second Laws of thermodynamics, Whillier[2] has suggested that a reference water-air ratio $(WAR)_o$ be used in determining the performance of cooling towers. This is defined as that water-air ratio at which, heat and mass transfer permitting, the water would be cooled to the wet-bulb temperature of the entering air, while the air would be heated to a wet-bulb temperature equal to the temperature of the entering water.

Expressed algebraically,

$$(WAR)_o = \frac{(S_{wi} - S_{ai})}{C_{pw}(t_{wi} - t_{wbi})}$$

The reference water-air ratio depends only on the temperatures of the air and water entering the tower, t_{wbi} and t_{wi}, and on the barometric pressure. It is independent of the type of tower, the efficiency of the tower, and of the actual water and air flow rates.

Most mine cooling towers operate at temperatures such that the reference water-air ratio $(WAR)_o$ is between 1,45 and 1,65.

Whillier has given curves showing how the reference water-air ratio varies with the barometric pressure, inlet wet-bulb temperature and the difference between inlet water temperature and the inlet wet-bulb temperature.

Having described the reference water-air ratio Whillier suggests that the water efficiency of the tower is then a function of the capacity factor (R), which is defined as the ratio of the actual water-air ratio to the reference water-air ratio, the air velocity in the tower, the inlet air wet-bulb temperature and the tower construction.

By expressing the capacity factor (R) algebraically and using the relationships for air and water efficiencies, it can be shown that:

$$R = \frac{L/G}{(WAR)_o} = \frac{\Delta S_a}{C_{pw}\Delta t_w} \frac{C_{pw}(t_{wi} - t_{wbi})}{S_{wi} - S_{ai}} = \frac{\eta_a}{\eta_w}$$

$$\eta_a = R\eta_w$$

Since neither water nor air efficiencies can exceed 1, the above relationship enables the maximum possible water efficiency to be determined as a function of the capacity factor (Figure 10:14).

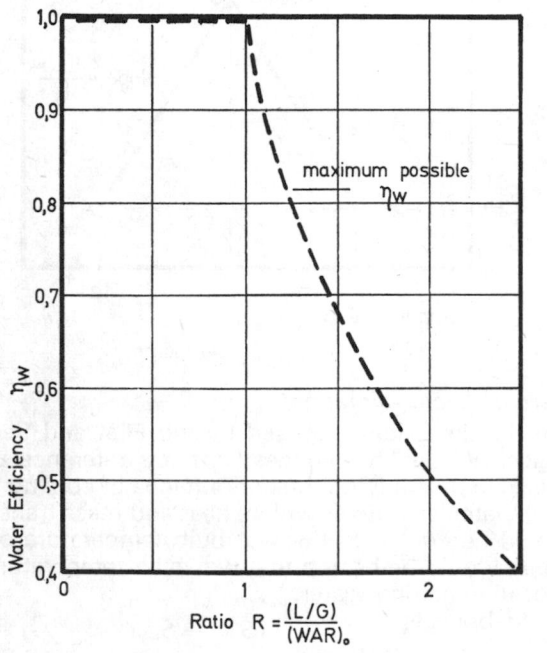

Figure 10:14   Maximum possible water efficiency in a vertical cooling tower

7.2.5   *Air pressure losses across cooling towers*

The air pressure losses which occur in a cooling tower are caused by friction, changes in air direction and velocity and the effect of falling water droplets. The power required to overcome these losses must be considered when towers are designed. Whillier[2] and Hemp[5] have published formulae to determine the value of the pressure loss. It is assumed in these equations that the actual pressure loss in a cooling tower is the sum of the pressure loss which occurs in the dry tower and the pressure loss caused by the effects of water in the tower.

The pressure loss in the dry tower depends on tower layout and the number of screens. Whillier suggests that this pressure can be calculated by means of the formula

$$p(\text{dry}) = [B + (2 \times N)]\frac{V^2 w_a}{2}$$

The pressure loss caused by the water is given by the formula

$$p(\text{wet}) = \left(\frac{LZg}{V_T - V} \right)$$

8   COOLING COILS

Cooling coils are used to transfer heat from air to the chilled water, and their performance can be analyzed in a way similar to that in which the performance of evaporators and condensers is analyzed.

Thus
$$q = M_w C_{pw} \Delta t_w = M_a \Delta S_a$$

which again does not allow fully for the condensation of water.

Heat transfer at cooling coils is more involved because the heat is transferred by both convection and condensation. A satisfactory approximation for mining purposes, where even the intake air to the coil is close to saturation and does not usually cover a wide range in temperature, is to consider the difference between the wet-bulb temperature of the air and the water temperature as the driving force for heat transfer. Thus

$$q = UA \ LMTD$$

where

$$LMTD = \frac{\Delta t_1 - \Delta t_2}{2,3 \log_{10} \dfrac{\Delta t_1}{\Delta t_2}}$$

Δt_1 and Δt_2 are the differences between the wet-bulb temperatures and the water temperature at each end of the coil.

$$\frac{1}{UA} = \frac{1}{h_i A_i} + \frac{1}{h_{fi} A_i} + \frac{x_t}{k_t A_m} + \frac{1}{h_{fo} A_o} + \frac{1}{h_o A_o}$$

This equation really serves to define h_o in terms of the approximation mentioned above.

Cooling coil performance underground can be assessed using the above relationship, the steps in the process usually being as follows:

(*a*)   The duty of the coil is calculated from the water and air observations by using the formulae

$$q = M_w C_{wp} \Delta t_w \quad \text{and} \quad q = M_a \Delta S_a$$

This serves to check the data for errors, as the two calculated values of the duty should be in reasonable agreement.

(*b*)   The logarithmic mean temperature difference between the air and water is calculated and used together with the coil duty to determine the "Actual *UA*" value since $UA = \dfrac{q}{LMTD}$

(c)   The UA value for the observed air and water flow rates is calculated on the assumption that both the inside and outside fouling factors $\dfrac{1}{h_{fi}}$ and $\dfrac{1}{h_{fo}}$ are zero, i.e., the coil is clean.

$$\frac{1}{UA} = \frac{1}{h_iA_i} + \frac{1}{h_oA_{oe}}$$

where A_{oe} is the effective outside area and the conduction term, $\dfrac{x_t}{k_tA_m}$, is ignored because it is very small compared with the other terms.

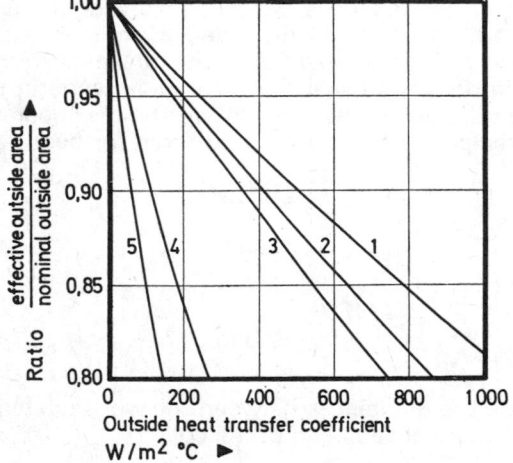

Fig. 10 :15   Effective and nominal areas of cooling coils

Fig. 10 :15 shows how the ratio of effective outside area to nominal outside area varies with h_o for different types of coils. This approach obviously requires information on h_i and h_o which can really be obtained only by carrying out a series of performance tests on a clean coil. One series of tests indicated that the formulae below can be used to calculate values for these coefficients.

$$h_i = \frac{1,4 \times 5\,680 \times (1 + 0,015t_m)V_w{}^{0,8}}{d_t{}^{0,2}}$$

$$h_o = 195 \times G^{0,549}$$

where

   V_w = water velocity, m/s
   d_t = internal tube diameter, mm
   t_m = mean water temperature, °C
   G = mass flow rate of air, per unit area, kg/m² s.

This step permits a comparison to be made between the "Actual UA value" and the "Clean UA value". The two calculated values will agree closely if the coil is clean and differ considerably if the coil is dirty. In the latter case the calculations explained in step (*d*) should be undertaken to determine the benefits to be gained by cleaning the coil.

(*d*) The duty of a clean coil supplied with the same air and water is calculated from

  (i) the "capacity rates" i.e., the heat transfer rate for a unit change in temperature for air and water (C_h and C_c) where

$$C_h = M_a \times \frac{\Delta S_a}{\Delta t_{wb}} \text{ (kW/°C)}$$

$$C_c = M_w \times C_{pw} \text{ (kW/°C)}$$

The smaller of these two capacity rates is then called C_{min} and the larger C_{max}.

  (ii) the capacity rate ratio, Z is calculated thus:

$$Z = \frac{C_{min}}{C_{max}}$$

  (iii) the "number of transfer units (*NTU*)" is calculated

$$NTU = \frac{UA \text{ of clean coil (kW/°C)}}{C_{min} \text{ (kW/°C)}}$$

  (iv) the effectiveness of the coil (*N*) is determined from the capacity rate ratio (*Z*), the number of heat transfer units (*NTU*) and the type of flow (Fig. 10:16)

  (v) the duty of the clean coil for the same operating conditions is calculated from the formula

$$q = N \times C_{min} \times (t_{wbi} - t_{wi})$$

A comparison between the duties as calculated in steps (*a*) and (*d*) will show the increase in duty which can be achieved by cleaning the coil.

It is possible to use the equations given above to derive curves which enable the *UA* value for a clean coil, for varying air and water flow rates and mean water temperatures, to be obtained rapidly. Each type of coil will obviously have its own set of curves. An example of these curves for one type of coil is given in Fig. 10:17.

It should be noted that the effect of changes in mean water temperature is not very significant.

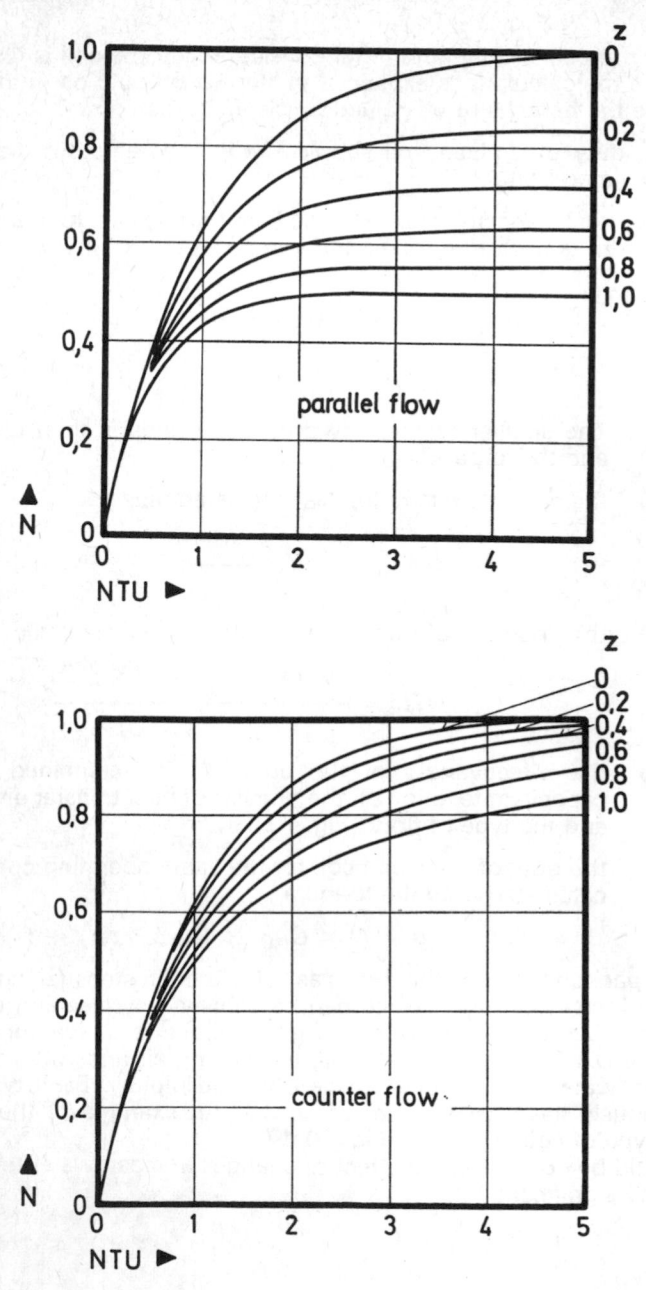

Fig. 10:16   Cooling coil effectiveness

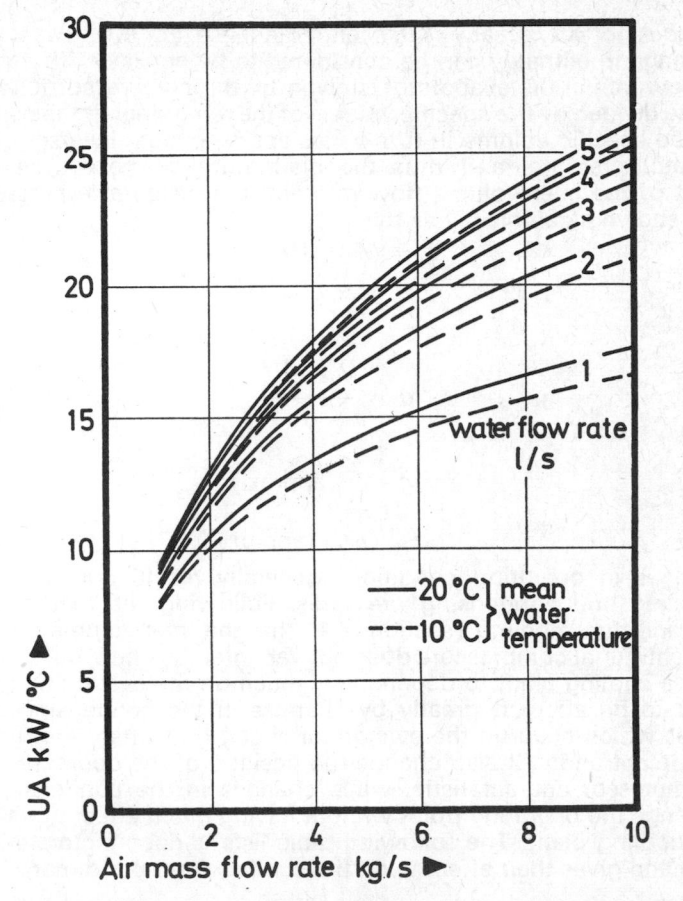

Fig. 10:17   Curves showing the determination of the overall heat
transfer coefficient for a cooling coil

9   ANALYSIS OF PLANT PERFORMANCE

The measurements made at a cooling plant are used to calculate its performance and duty. In many instances the plant performance is found to differ from its rated performance and the ventilation officer or maintenance engineer should be able to determine the reason or reasons for this difference.

This analysis can be tackled in two stages. The first stage will show how it is possible to obtain an approximate idea of the effects of changes in the operating conditions upon the cooling plant performance, while the second stage will show how it is possible to determine the plant performance more accurately.

The duty of a cooling plant is given by the product of the refrigerant mass flow rate in the evaporator and the change in the enthalpy of the refrigerant in the evaporator. Reference to section 3 shows that this change in enthalpy depends on both the condenser and evaporator pressures, but that it does not vary greatly with changes in these. For the present purpose, this change in enthalpy can be considered to be constant. The refrigerant mass flow rate in the evaporator is given by the compressor inlet volume flow rate divided by the specific volume of the refrigerant at the compressor inlet. The specific volume in turn varies approximately inversely with the evaporator pressure, and thus the plant duty is proportional to the product of the inlet volume flow rate and the evaporator pressure. This can be shown algebraically as follows:

$$q = M \times \Delta H$$

$$M = \frac{Q}{v}$$

$$q = \frac{Q \times \Delta H}{v}$$

$$v \propto \frac{1}{P_{ev}} \quad \text{(approx.)}$$

$$\therefore \ q \propto QP_{ev} \text{ (approx).}$$

Changes in operating conditions generally result in changes in the evaporating and condensing pressures. Following the reasoning given above, and remembering (section 5.1) that the inlet volume flow rate of some centrifugal compressors does not vary greatly, one would expect the duty of a cooling plant to depend very much on the evaporating pressure but not to be affected greatly by changes in the condensing pressure. Changes which occur in the evaporator circuit thus affect the duty of the cooling plant and will also change the position of the operating point on the compressor characteristic, while changes in the condensing circuit will change the operating point without having much effect upon the duty of the cooling plant. The following table lists various factors which can change and gives their effect upon the cooling plant performance.

Factor	Evaporator	Condenser
(i) Low water flow rate	Reduction in heat transfer Reduction in evaporating pressure Reduction in output	Reduction in heat transfer Increase in condensing pressure Compressor may stall Slight decrease in duty
(ii) Inlet water temperature Low	Reduction in evaporating pressure Reduction in output	Slight increase in output Reduction in power requirements
High	Compressor motor may overload	Increase in condensing pressure Increase in power requirements Compressor may stall Slight reduction in output

Factor	Evaporator	Condenser
(iii) Increased fouling factor	Reduction in heat transfer Reduction in evaporating pressure Reduction in output	Reduction in heat transfer Increase in condensing pressure Compressor may stall Slight decrease in duty
(iv) Low refrigerant level	Reduction in heat transfer Reduction in evaporating pressure Reduction in output	No affect
(v) Non-condensables in the refrigerant	No affect	Increase in condensing pressure Increase in power requirements Slight decrease in duty Compressor may stall
(vi) Leaking water box baffles	Reduction in heat transfer Reduction in evaporating pressure Reduction in output	Reduction in heat transfer Increase in condensing pressure Compressor may stall Slight decrease in duty

Other faults which can occur at a plant include incorrect capacity control at the compressor, faulty expansion valves and defective pumps, strainers and purge units.

A more accurate determination of cooling plant performance is done by determining the actual operating point of the compressor on its characteristic curve. As with a fan, this is achieved by finding the intersection of the system curve and the compressor curve. The method requires a knowledge of the overall heat transfer coefficients for both evaporator and condenser, and involves assuming a value for the duty of the cooling plant. Both evaporating and condensing temperatures and pressures are then calculated. Once these are known the adiabatic head and the inlet volume flow rate for the compressor can be calculated and used to plot one point on the system curve.

This process is continued until sufficient points on the system curve have been obtained and it is possible to determine the point of intersection of this curve with the compressor curve.

10   REFERENCES

1   Greeff, P. W. Refrigerant pressure enthalpy diagrams in S I units. *J. Mine Vent. Soc. S. Afr.,* Vol. 24, No. 12, p. 191-6.

2   Whillier, A. The design of underground cooling towers. *J. Mine Vent. Soc. S. Afr.,* Vol. 25, No. 5, p. 70-81.

3   Barenbrug, A. W. T. Contribution to discussion of reference 4. *J. Mine Vent. Soc. S. Afr.,* Vol. 22, No. 7, p. 133.

4   Griesel, G. D. Cooling tower geometry. *J. Mine Vent. Soc. S. Afr.*, Vol. 22, No. 6, p. 113-26.
5   Hemp, R. Some aspects of the design of cooling plant installations. *J. Mine Vent. Soc. S. Afr.*, Vol. 25, No. 9, p. 159-73.

BIBLIOGRAPHY

ASHRAE, *Guide and Data Book. Fundamentals and Equipment for* 1965 *and* 1966.
Stoecker, W. F. *Refrigeration and Air Conditioning*, McGraw-Hill Book Company, Inc.

TABLE 2   THERMODYNAMIC PROPERTIES OF REFRIGERANT 11

Temp. °C	Absolute Pressure kPa	Specific Volume m³/kg		Enthalpy kJ/kg			Entropy kJ/kgK
		Liquid × 0,001	Vapour	Liquid	Latent	Vapour	Vapour
−5	32,29	0,6470	0,49387	29,733	190,641	220,374	0,82967
−4	33,76	0,6480	0,47390	30,588	190,291	220,879	0,82891
−3	35,28	0,6489	0,45488	31,444	189,940	221,384	0,82816
−2	36,86	0,6499	0,43678	32.300	189,589	221,889	0,82743
−1	38,49	0,6508	0,41956	33,157	189,237	222,395	0,82672
0	40,18	0,6518	0,40314	34,015	188,885	222,900	0,82603
1	41,93	0,6528	0,38751	34,872	188,533	223,405	0,82535
2	43.73	0,6537	0,37261	35,730	188,179	223,910	0,82469
3	45,60	0,6547	0,35838	36,589	187,825	224,414	0,82404
4	47,54	0,6557	0,34480	37,448	187,471	224,919	0,82340
5	49,54	0,6567	0,33187	38,307	187,116	225,423	0,82279
6	51,60	0,6577	0,31951	39,167	186,760	225,927	0,82219
7	53,73	0,6587	0,30771	40,028	186,404	226,431	0,82160
8	55,93	0,6597	0,29644	40,889	186,047	226,935	0,82102
9	58,21	0,6607	0,28566	41,750	185,689	227,439	0,82046
10	60,55	0,6617	0,27536	42,612	185,331	227,942	0,81992
11	62,98	0,6627	0,26549	43,474	184,971	228,445	0,81938
12	65,47	0.6637	0 25607	44,337	184,611	228,948	0,81886
13	68,05	0,6648	0,24704	45,200	184,250	229,451	0,81835
14	70,70	0,6658	0,23840	46,064	183,889	229,953	0,81786
15	73,43	0,6668	0,23014	46,928	183,526	230,455	0,81738
16	76,25	0,6679	0,22221	47,793	183,163	230,956	0,81691
17	79,15	0,6689	0,21462	48,658	182,799	231,458	0,81645
18	82,14	0,6700	0,20734	49,524	182,434	231,958	0,81600
19	85,22	0,6710	0,20037	50,391	182,068	232,459	0,81557
20	88,38	0,6721	0,19367	51,257	181,701	232,959	0,81515
21	91,64	0,6732	0,18725	52,125	181,334	233,458	0,81474
22	94,99	0,6743	0,18109	52,992	180,966	233,958	0,81434
23	98,44	0,6753	0,17517	53,861	180,596	234,456	0,81395
24	101,98	0,6764	0,16949	54,730	180,225	234,955	0,81357
25	105,62	0,6775	0.16404	55 599	179,854	235,452	0,81320
26	109,37	0,6786	0,15879	56,469	179,481	235,950	0,81284
27	113,21	0,6797	0,15376	57,339	179,107	236,446	0.81250
28	117,17	0,6808	0,14891	58,211	178,732	236,943	0,81216
29	121,23	0,6820	0,14424	59,082	178,356	237,438	0,81183
30	125,39	0,6831	0,13977	59,954	177,980	237,933	0,81151
31	129,67	0,6842	0,13546	60,827	177,601	238,428	0,81120

Temp. °C	Absolute Pressure kPa	Specific Volume m³/kg		Enthalpy kJ/kg			Entropy kJ/kgK
		Liquid × 0,001	Vapour	Liquid	Latent	Vapour	Vapour
32	134,06	0,6854	0,13131	61,700	177,222	238,922	0,81090
33	138,56	0,6865	0,12731	62,574	176,841	239,415	0,81061
34	143,18	0,6877	0,12346	63,448	176,460	239,908	0,81033
35	147,92	0,6888	0,11976	64,323	176,077	240,400	0,81006
36	152,78	0,6900	0,11619	65,199	175,693	240,891	0,80979
37	157,77	0,6911	0,11275	66,075	175,308	241,382	0,80953
38	162,87	0,6923	0,10943	66,951	174,921	241,872	0,80929
39	168,10	0,6935	0,10624	67,828	174,533	242,362	0,80905
40	173,47	0,6947	0,10315	68,706	174,144	242,850	0,80881
41	178,96	0,6959	0,10018	69,585	173,753	243,339	0,80859
42	184,59	0,6971	0,09731	70,464	173,362	243,826	0,80837
43	190,35	0,6983	0,09454	71,344	172,968	244,312	0,80816
44	196,25	0,6995	0,09187	72,225	172,573	244,798	0,80796
45	202,29	0,7008	0,08929	73,105	172,178	245,283	0,80777
46	208,46	0,7020	0,08680	73,987	171,780	245,767	0,80758
47	214,79	0,7032	0,08439	74,869	171,382	246,251	0,80740
48	221,26	0,7045	0,08206	75,752	170,981	246,733	0,80722
49	227,88	0,7058	0,07982	76,636	170,579	247,215	0,80705
50	234,65	0,7070	0,07765	77,520	170,176	247,695	0,80690
51	241,58	0,7083	0,07554	78,406	169,770	248,175	0,80674
52	248,65	0,7096	0,07351	79,291	169,363	248,654	0,80659
53	255,87	0,7109	0,07155	80,177	168,955	249,133	0,80645
54	263,28	0,7122	0,06965	81,065	168,545	249,610	0,80631
55	270,84	0,7135	0,06781	81,953	168,133	250,086	0,80618
56	278,55	0,7148	0,06603	82,841	167,720	250,561	0,80606
57	286,43	0,7161	0,06431	83,731	167,305	251,036	0,80594
58	294,49	0,7175	0,06263	84,622	166,887	251,509	0,80582
59	302,72	0,7188	0,06102	85,513	166,468	251,981	0,80571
60	311,11	0,7202	0,05946	86,404	166,049	252,453	0,80561
61	319,69	0,7215	0,05794	87,297	165,626	252,923	0,80551
62	328,44	0,7229	0,05647	88,191	165,202	253,392	0,80542
63	337,37	0,7243	0,05504	89,085	164,775	253,861	0,80533
64	346,49	0,7257	0,05366	89,981	164,347	254,328	0,80524
65	355,79	0,7271	0,05233	90,877	163,917	254,794	0,80517
66	365,28	0,7285	0,05103	91,774	163,484	255,258	0,80509
67	374,97	0,7299	0,04977	92,672	163,050	255,722	0,80502
68	384,84	0,7313	0,04855	93,571	162,613	256,185	0,80495
69	394,90	0,7328	0,04736	94,471	162,176	256,646	0,80489
70	405,16	0,7342	0,04621	95,371	161,735	257,106	0,80483
71	415,63	0,7357	0,04510	96,274	161,291	257,565	0,80478
72	426,30	0,7372	0,04401	97,177	160,846	258,023	0,80472
73	437,17	0,7387	0,04296	98,081	160,399	258,479	0,80469
74	448,26	0,7402	0,04194	98,986	159,949	258,934	0,80463
75	459,55	0,7417	0,04094	99,892	159,496	259,388	0,80459
76	471,03	0,7432	0,03998	100,799	159,043	259,841	0,80456
77	482,76	0,7447	0,03904	101,707	158,585	260,292	0 80453
78	494,68	0,7463	0,03813	102,616	158,126	260,743	0,80450
79	506,83	0,7478	0,03725	103,527	157,665	261,191	0,80447
80	519,23	0,7494	0,03639	104,439	157,199	261,638	0,80444
81	531,83	0,7510	0,03555	105,352	156,731	262,084	0,80442

TABLE 3 THERMODYNAMIC PROPERTIES OF REFRIGERANT 12

Temp. °C	Absolute Pressure kPa, sub-script	Specific Volume m³/kg		Enthalpy kJ/kg			Entropy kJ/kgK
		Liquid × 0,001	Vapour	Liquid	Latent	Vapour	Vapour
−5	260,81	0,7078	0,06500	31,432	153,935	185,367	0,69907
−4	269,86	0,7094	0,06293	32,350	153,451	185,801	0,69853
−3	279,14	0,7110	0,06094	33,270	152,964	186,234	0,69800
−2	288,67	0,7126	0,05903	34,191	152,474	186,665	0,69748
−1	298,42	0,7142	0,05719	35,113	151,982	187,095	0,69698
0	308,45	0,7159	0,05542	36,038	151,486	187,524	0,69648
1	318,70	0,7176	0,05372	36,963	150,989	187,951	0,69600
2	329,23	0,7192	0,05208	37,890	150,488	188,377	0,69552
3	340 01	0,7209	0,05050	38,818	149,984	188,802	0,69506
4	351,06	0,7226	0,04898	39,748	149,477	189,225	0,69460
5	362,37	0.7244	0,04751	40,679	148,967	189,647	0,69415
6	373,95	0,7261	0,04610	41,612	148,455	190,067	0,69372
7	385,81	0,7279	0,04474	42,547	147,939	190,486	0,69329
8	397,96	0,7297	0,04342	43,483	147,419	190,903	0,69287
9	410,37	0,7315	0,04216	44,421	146,898	191,319	0,69246
10	423,08	0,7333	0,04094	45,360	146,372	191,733	0,69206
11	436,10	0,7351	0,03976	46,302	145,842	192,145	0,69166
12	449,40	0,7369	0,03862	47,245	145,310	192,555	0,69127
13	462,99	0,7388	0,03752	48,190	144,774	192,964	0,69089
14	476,91	0,7407	0,03646	49,137	144,234	193,371	0,69051
15	491,13	0,7426	0,03543	50,086	143,691	193,777	0,69015
16	505,66	0,7445	0,03444	51,037	143,144	194,180	0,68979
17	520,53	0,7465	0,03348	51,990	142,591	194,582	0,68943
18	535,69	0,7485	0,03256	52,945	142,037	194 982	0,68908
19	551,22	0,7504	0,03166	53,902	141,477	195,379	0,68874
20	567,05	0,7525	0,03079	54,861	140,914	195,775	0,68840
21	583,21	0,7545	0,02996	55,822	140,346	196,169	0,68807
22	599,71	0,7565	0,02915	56,785	139,775	196,560	0.68775
23	616,55	0,7586	0,02836	57,751	139,200	196,950	0,68743
24	633,77	0,7607	0,02760	58,719	138,618	197,337	0,68711
25	651,33	0,7628	0,02687	59,690	138,032	197,722	0,68679
26	669,24	0,7650	0,02615	60,663	137,443	198,105	0,68649
27	687,52	0,7672	0,02546	61,638	136,847	198,486	0,68618
28	706,18	0,7694	0,02479	62,617	136,247	198,864	0,68588
29	725,19	0,7716	0,02415	63,597	135,642	199,239	0,68558
30	744,58	0,7739	0,02352	64,580	135,032	199,613	0,68529
31	764,32	0,7761	0,02291	65,566	134,418	199,984	0,68500
32	784,54	0,7784	0,02232	66,556	133,794	200,350	0,68471
33	805,09	0,7808	0,02174	67,548	133,167	200,716	0,68442
34	826,04	0,7831	0,02119	68,543	132,535	201,078	0,68414
35	847,35	0,7855	0,02065	69,540	131,898	201,439	0,68386
36	869,12	0,7880	0,02013	70,542	131,253	201,795	0,68358
37	891,26	0,7904	0,01962	71,545	130,604	202,149	0,68330
38	913,88	0,7929	0,01912	72,554	129,945	202,499	0,68302
39	936,86	0,7954	0,01864	73,565	129,282	202,847	0,68274
40	960,29	0,7980	0,01818	74,579	128,612	203,191	0,68246
41	984,13	0,8006	0,01772	75,597	127,935	203,532	0,68218
42	1 008,42	0,8032	0,01728	76,619	127,251	203,870	0,68191

Temp. °C	Absolute Pressure kPa	Specific Volume m³/kg		Enthalpy kJ/kg			Entropy kJ/kgK
		Liquid × 0,001	Vapour	Liquid	Latent	Vapour	Vapour
43	1 033,10	0,8059	0,01686	77,643	126,562	204,205	0,68163
44	1 058,30	0,8086	0,01644	78,673	125,862	204,535	0 68135
45	1 083,89	0,8114	0,01604	79,705	125,157	204,863	0,68107
46	1 109,98	0,8141	0,01564	80,743	124,443	205,185	0,68079
47	1 136,46	0,8170	0,01526	81,783	123,723	205,506	0,68051
48	1 163,45	0,8198	0,01489	82,828	122.993	205,821	0,68023
49	1 190,96	0,8227	0,01453	83,879	122,252	206,132	0,67994
50	1 218,85	0,8257	0,01417	84,932	121,507	206,439	0,67965
51	1 247,28	0,8287	0,01383	85,992	120,751	206,742	0,67935
52	1 276,13	0,8318	0,01350	87,054	119,987	207,041	0,67906
53	1 305,52	0,8349	0,01317	88,122	119,212	207,335	0,67876
54	1 335,40	0,8380	0,01285	89,196	118,428	207,624	0,67845
55	1 365,82	0,8412	0,01255	90,275	117,632	207,907	0,67814
56	1 396,68	0,8445	0,01224	91,358	116,828	208,187	0,67783
57	1 428,04	0,8478	0,01195	92,447	116,015	208,461	0,67751
58	1 460,01	0,8512	0,01166	93,542	115,186	208,729	0,67718
59	1 492,43	0,8546	0,01139	94,642	114,350	208,992	0,67684
60	1 525,40	0,8581	0,01111	95,749	113.500	209,249	0,67650
61	1 558,89	0,8617	0,01085	96,861	112,639	209,500	0,67615
62	1 592,88	0,8653	0,01059	97,979	111 767	209,746	0,67580
63	1 627,50	0,8690	0,01034	99,105	110,879	209,984	0,67543
64	1 662,59	0,8728	0,01009	100,236	109,981	210,217	0,67506
65	1 698,25	0,8766	0,00985	101,374	109,069	210,442	0,67467
66	1 734,49	0,8806	0,00961	102,520	108,141	210,660	0,67427
67	1 771,32	0,8846	0,00938	103,673	107,197	210,871	0,67386
68	1 808,68	0,8887	0,00916	104,833	106,241	211,074	0,67344
69	1 846,62	0,8928	0,00894	106,001	105,268	211,270	0,67301
70	1 885,17	0,8971	0,00872	107,178	104,279	211,456	0,67256
71	1 924,33	0,9015	0,00851	108,363	103,271	211,634	0,67210
72	1 964,01	0,9060	0,00831	109,555	102,249	211,804	0,67162
73	2 004,31	0,9105	0,00811	110,757	101,208	211,965	0,67113
74	2 045,21	0,9152	0,00791	111,967	100,149	212,116	0,67062
75	2 086,80	0,9200	0,00772	113,190	99,065	212,255	0,67009
76	2 128,87	0,9250	0,00753	114,418	97,968	212,386	0,66954
77	2 171,78	0,9300	0,00735	115,663	96,839	212,502	0,66896
78	2 215,10	0,9352	0,00717	116 912	95,699	212,610	0,66837
79	2 259,19	0,9406	0,00699	118,176	94,528	212,704	0,66775
80	2 303,84	0,9461	0,00682	119,450	93,336	212,786	0,66711
81	2 349,21	0,9517	0,00665	120,737	92,116	212,853	0,66644

11   Fundamentals of Airflow

V. A. L. CHASTEAU

*Senior Lecturer, Department of Mechanical Engineering,
University of Pretoria. Formerly Senior Research Officer,
Aerodynamics Research Department of the CSIR's National
Mechanical Engineering Research Institute.*

1   INTRODUCTION

This chapter deals primarily with some of the basic principles involved in
the flow of fluids as they might be encountered in many mining applications.
It concerns mainly the flow of air but the principles are valid for any fluid.

2   DEFINITION OF A FLUID

A fluid may be defined broadly as a substance which *deforms continuously when subjected to shear stress.* To make this definition clearer,
assume the fluid to consist of layers parallel to each other and let a force
act upon one of the layers in a direction parallel to its plane. This force
divided by the area of the layer is called shear stress. As long as this shear
stress is applied the layer will continue to move relative to its neighbouring layers.

If the neighbouring layers offer no resistance to the movement, the
fluid is called *frictionless* or *ideal.* If the shear movement is resisted, the
fluid is called *real.* Strictly speaking, ideal fluids do not exist in nature, but
in many practical problems the resistance is either small or is not important.
The advantage of the concept of an ideal fluid lies in the simplicity of the
equations which describe its behaviour.

A fluid is always a continuous medium, that is, there cannot be voids in it. The properties of a fluid, such as the density, may, however, vary from place to place in the fluid.

Apart from shear forces a fluid may also be subjected to *compressive forces.* These compressive forces tend to change the volume of the fluid and in turn its density. If the fluid yields to the effect of the compressive forces and changes its volume, it is *compressible,* otherwise it is *incompressible.* The matter of compressibility will be dealt with later.

3   THE STATIONARY FLUID

Before dealing with the flow or motion of fluids, a basic equation may be noted concerning stationary fluids, that is, fluids not subjected to shear forces. This states that the pressure P exerted by a column of height H of incompressible fluid of density w is:

$$P = gwH \qquad \qquad \dots 1$$

This principle is applied to the measurement of pressure differences by means of manometers.

4   FLUID FLOW: STREAMLINES

In a flowing fluid, each particle changes its position with a certain velocity. The magnitudes and directions of the velocities of all particles may vary with position as well as with time. A very useful means of illustrating the variation of the velocity of flow with position is to consider *streamlines.*

A streamline is an imaginary line in a fluid, the tangent to which gives the direction of the flow velocity at that position, as shown in Fig. 11 :1.

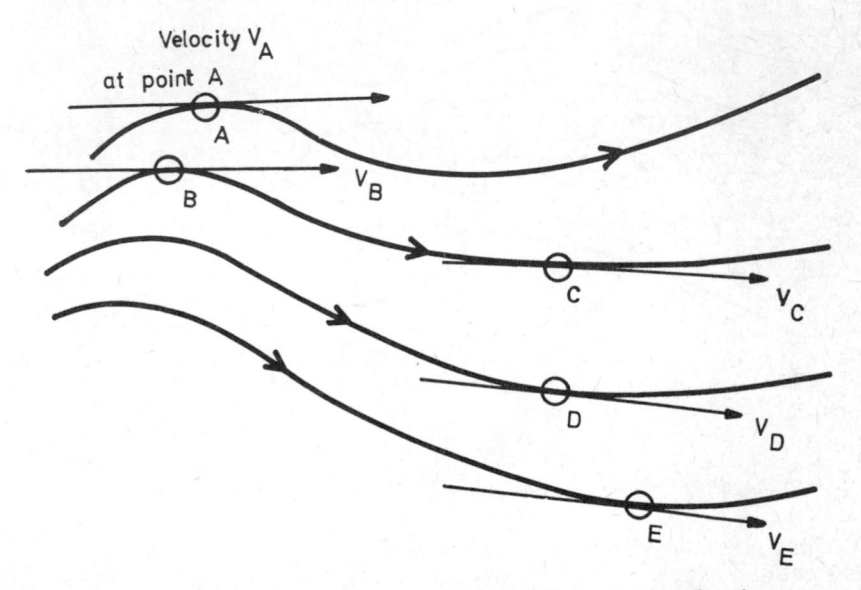

Fig. 11 :1   Streamlines showing velocity of flow at several points

The distance between two streamlines is an inverse measure of the magnitude of the velocity.

If the streamlines are smoothly curved and almost parallel to each other, as illustrated in Fig. 11 :2, the flow is known as *streamlined flow* or *laminar flow*. If the streamlines are arranged haphazardly as illustrated in Fig. 11 :3, the flow is known as *turbulent flow.*

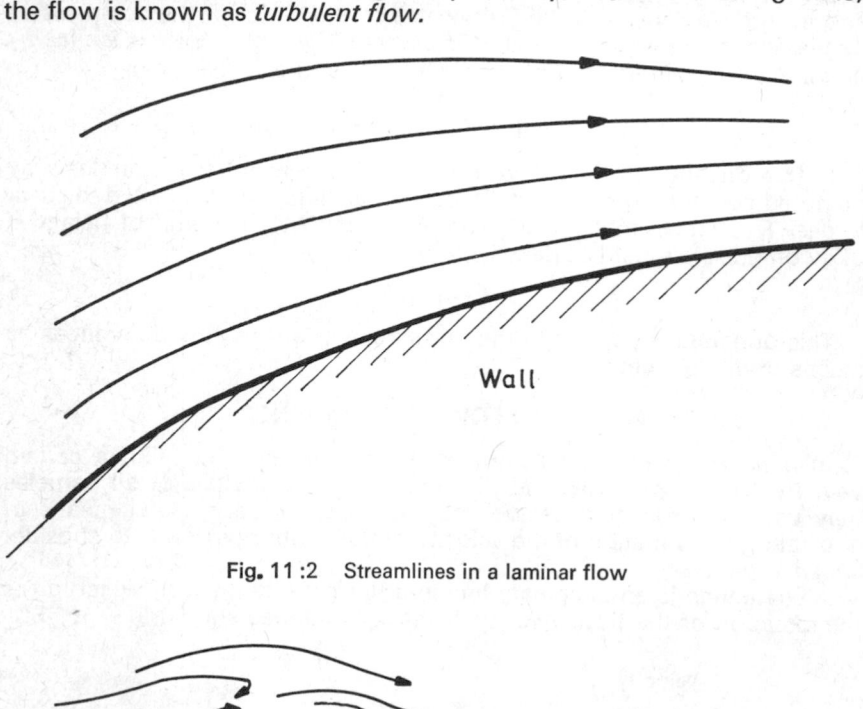

Fig. 11 :2   Streamlines in a laminar flow

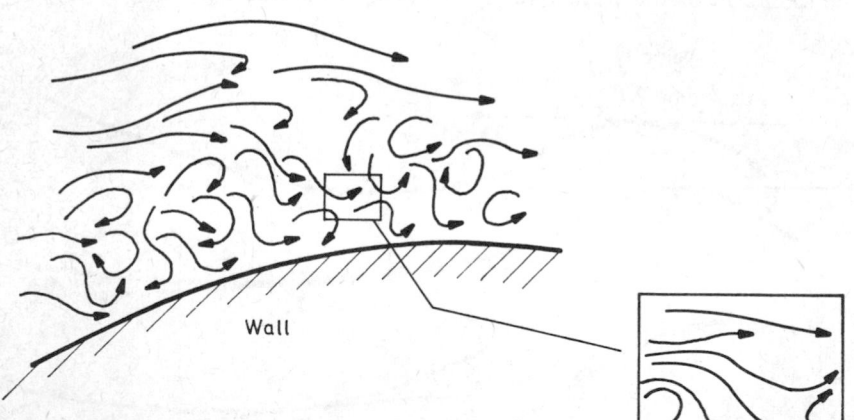

Fig. 11 :3   Instantaneous picture of streamlines in turbulent flow

If the streamline pattern of a flow remains constant with time, the flow is *steady*. If it does not, the flow is *unsteady* and in this case a streamline picture is an instantaneous one, valid only for a particular instant of time.

A greatly enlarged view of any small region of a turbulent flow shows that the flow is a randomly unsteady laminar flow (Fig. 11:3 is therefore an instantaneous picture). If the mean flow values, however, are unchanged over a period of time, it is referred to as *steady turbulent flow.*

5   THE LAW OF CONTINUITY OR CONSERVATION OF MASS

In its simplest form, for steady flow in a duct, this law takes the form
mass flow station 1 = mass flow station 2 = constant

i.e.,

$$w_1 A_1 V_1 = w_2 A_2 V_2 = w_i A_i V_i = \text{constant} \qquad \ldots 2$$

where, at points $i = 1,2 \ldots$ along the duct, w is the density and V the velocity of the fluid and A the cross-sectional area of the duct.

6   THE IDEAL INCOMPRESSIBLE FLUID: LAW OF CONSERVATION OF MOMENTUM: BERNOULLI'S EQUATION

Newton's Second Law states that the force F to accelerate a body must be equal to the product of the mass m of the body and its acceleration a. If this law is applied to an ideal (frictionless), incompressible (constant-density) fluid, *Euler's Law* of conservation of momentum is obtained.

Let such a fluid be moving steadily through an imaginary fixed volume element xyz as illustrated in Fig. 11:4(a). Consider the flow in the x-direction, that is, across plane yz.

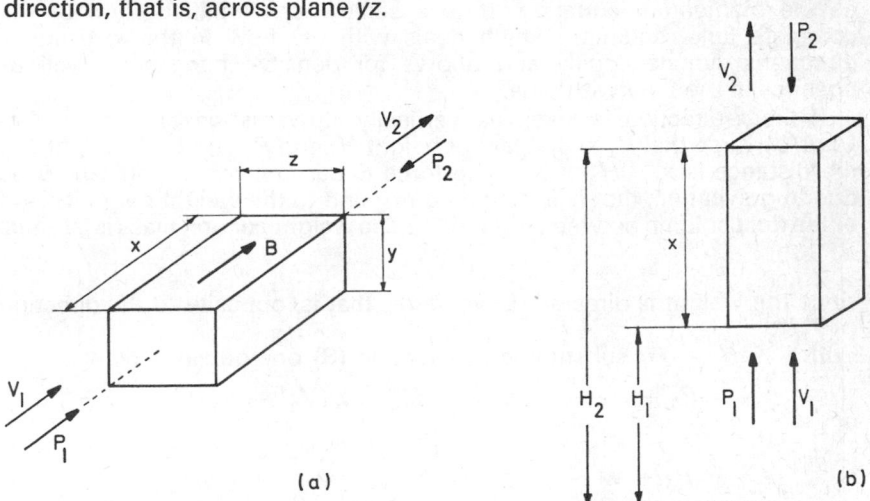

Fig. 11:4   Illustration of Euler's Law

If pressures P_1 and P_2 act upon the two opposite faces as illustrated in Fig. 11:4(a), the corresponding forces are $P_1 yz$ and $P_2 yz$. In addition to these "surface" forces, the fluid element may also be subjected to "body" or "mass" forces. If B denotes such a force per unit mass in the direction x, and w is the (constant) density of the fluid, the corresponding force is $Bwxyz$. The resultant force on the fluid in the volume element considered is then

$$F = P_1 yz - P_2 yz + Bwxyz$$

The fluid is flowing into the one end surface with velocity component normal to the surface V_1 and out of the other with velocity V_2 as shown in Fig. 11 :4(a). (In general, there will also be flows in the y- and z-directions across the planes zx and xy, but these flows do not affect the present analysis.) If x is a very small distance, the acceleration along it is constant and

$$a = (V_2 - V_1)/t$$

where t is the time for the fluid to flow through distance x.

Since the mass of the fluid element is $m = wxyz$, Newton's Law $F = ma$ for this case reads

$$P_1yz - P_2yz + Bwxyz = wxyz(V_2 - V_1)/t$$

or, after dividing by yz

$$P_1 - P_2 + Bwx = wx(V_2 - V_1)/t$$

The mean velocity over the distance x is

$$(V_1 + V_2)/2 = x/t$$

Substituting this in the previous equation yields:

$$P_1 - P_2 + Bwx = w(V_2{}^2 - V_1{}^2)/2 \qquad \dots 3$$

This is *Euler's Equation for the x-direction.* This equation is also known as the momentum equation. It is a somewhat simplified form of the complete Euler equation which deals with the flow in the x, y and z directions simultaneously and allows for density changes as well as changes in the flow with time.

If the x-direction is taken as vertically upwards as shown in Fig. 11 :4(b), such that P_1 and V_1 are at height H_1 and P_2 and V_2 at height H_2, the distance is $x = H_2 - H_1$. The force B per unit mass would now be due to gravitation, that is it would correspond to the weight per unit mass of the fluid column between H_2 and H_1. The weight per unit mass is g. Thus,

$$B = -g$$

since the weight is directed downwards, that is, opposite to the direction of P_1.

With $x = H_2 - H_1$ substituted in equation (3) one obtains

$$P_1 - P_2 - gw(H_2 - H_1) = w(V_2{}^2 - V_1{}^2)/2$$

or

$$P_1 + w\frac{V_1{}^2}{2} + gwH_1 = P_2 + w\frac{V_2{}^2}{2} + gwH_2 \qquad \dots 4$$

This is *Bernoulli's equation for the ideal incompressible fluid in terms of pressure.* The same result would have been obtained if the x-direction had been taken at any arbitrary angle. The vertically upwards direction was taken to simplify the analysis.

At this stage the units in which the physical quantities dealt with so far are measured should be noted.

In the *SI*, length is measured in *metres* (m), time in *seconds* (s) and force in *newtons* (N). Mass is measured in *kilograms* (kg). The relationship between mass and force is given by Newton's Second Law, so that a force of one newton would accelerate a mass of one kilogram one metre per second per second.

By dividing equation (4) by wg it may also be written

$$\frac{P_1}{wg} + \frac{V_1^2}{2g} + H_1 = \frac{P_2}{gw} + \frac{V_2^2}{2g} + H_2 \qquad \text{...5}$$

This is *Bernoulli's equation for the ideal incompressible fluid in terms of head.* Local variations of g on Earth are small, and in normal practice it is sufficient to use the typical value of 9,8 m s^{-2}.

The units to be used in the foregoing equations are then as follows:

Name	Symbol	Unit
Pressure	P	Nm^{-2} (Pa)
Velocity	V	m s^{-1}
Head, Height	H	m
Density	w	kg m^{-3}

7   STATIC, DYNAMIC AND TOTAL PRESSURES

The pressures P_1 and P_2 in equations 3, 4 and 5 are referred to as *static pressures;* they act in all directions regardless of the direction of the flow. The static pressure can therefore, in principle, be measured at right angles to the flow velocity, e.g., at a small hole in a surface along a streamline as illustrated in Fig. 11 :5. For this reason the static pressure is also referred to as the side-tube pressure.

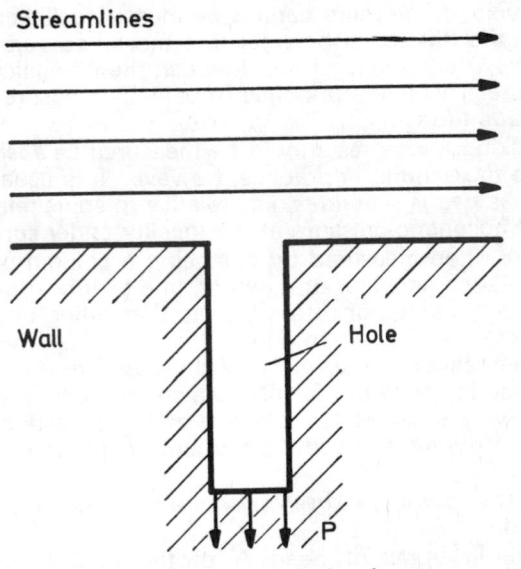

Fig. 11 :5   Measurement of static pressure

The terms $wV_1^2/2$ and $wV_2^2/2$ in equation 4 also have the dimension of a pressure and are referred to as *velocity or dynamic pressures.*

The terms $(P_1 + wV_1^2/2)$ and $(P_2 + wV_2^2/2)$ are referred to as *total pressures*, being the sum of static and velocity pressures. This is the customary definition in aerodynamics, although in some texts the total pressure is taken as $(P + \dfrac{wV^2}{2} + gwH)$, i.e., the sum of all three terms in Bernoulli's equation.

Referring to Fig. 11 :6, if a flow with static pressure P_1 and velocity V_1 is brought to rest at a point x, then according to Bernoulli's equation

$$P_1 + w\frac{V_1{}^2}{2} = P_x + w\frac{V_x{}^2}{2}$$ but $V_x = 0$, therefore the pressure at x is the

total pressure of the oncoming fluid stream. This pressure is also referred to as the *facing pressure.*

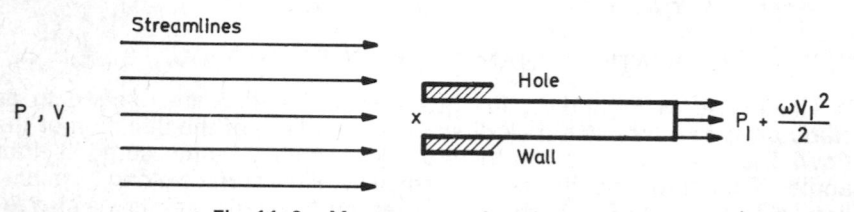

Fig. 11 :6   Measurement of total pressure

Obviously, velocity pressure cannot be measured directly but must be determined as the difference between the measured values of total and static pressures. The velocity of the flow can then be calculated from the velocity pressure. This is the principle of velocity measurement by means of the *Pitot-static* tube.

Strictly speaking, pressures should be measured as *absolute pressures,* that is, relative to vacuum. In practice, however, it is usually sufficient to measure them as *gauge pressures,* i.e., relative to some reference pressure P_0, e.g., the atmospheric pressure at the locality under consideration.

Pressures are often measured by balancing a column of another fluid, usually a liquid such as water or mercury, in a U-tube. The pressure P to be measured (either static or total pressure depending upon whether the tube is connected as shown in Fig. 11 :5 or 11 :6) then differs from the outside (reference) pressure P_0 by the pressure due to the column H_m of the measuring fluid in the tube which, according to equation 1 is $P_m = gw_mH_m$, where w_m is the density of the measuring fluid. P_m is, however, partly counterbalanced by a column H_m long of the fluid being measured.

Thus, $P - P_0 = gw_mH_m - gwH_m$, where w is the density of the fluid being measured.

The pressure in terms of head H of the fluid being measured is

$$Hgw = P - P_0 = gH_m(w_m - w).$$

Therefore $H = \dfrac{(w_m - w)}{w}H_m = \left\{\dfrac{w_m}{w} - 1\right\}H_m.$

Where the ratio of the densities is very much greater than 1, for instance for air at normal pressure and water, the equation can be simplified to

$$H = \frac{w_m}{w} \times H_m.$$

8   SOME SIMPLE APPLICATIONS OF BERNOULLI'S EQUATION

The conditions of equilibrium, that is, Bernoulli's equation (equation 4) together with the condition of continuity (equation 2), the latter simplified to $A_1V_1 = A_2V_2$ because in an incompressible fluid $w_1 = w_2 = w$, form the basis for relating pressure changes to velocity, area and height changes in ducts.

A horizontal converging duct is depicted in Fig. 11 :7. Since its axis is horizontal, $H_1 = H_2$. Thus, with reference to the cross-sections "1" and "2", equation 4 reads

$$P_1 + wV_1{}^2/2 = P_2 + wV_2{}^2/2$$

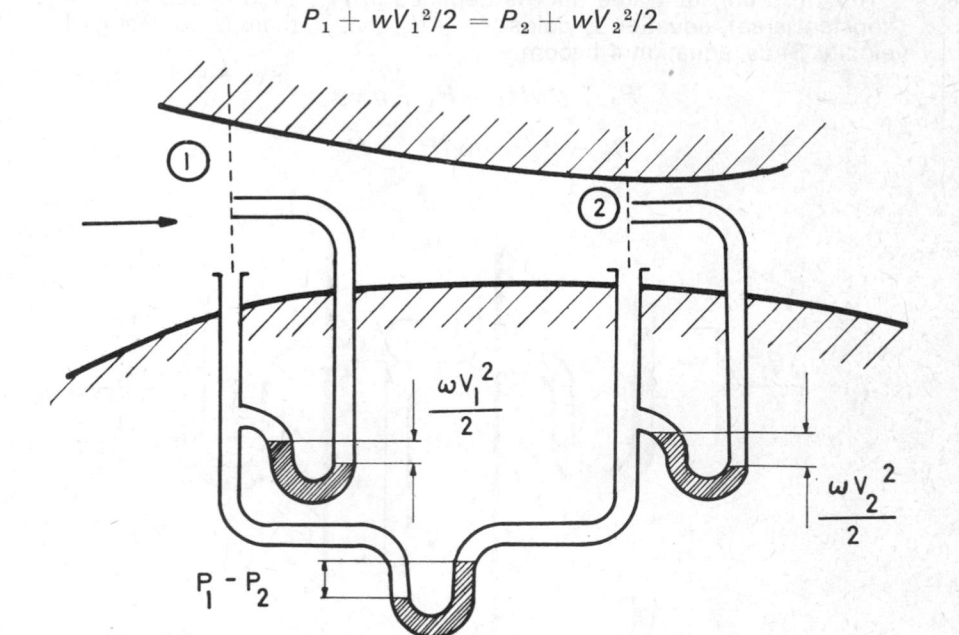

Fig. 11 :7   Horizontal converging duct pressure measurement

The total pressure at both points is therefore the same. It also follows from this equation that

$$P_1 - P_2 = \frac{w}{2}(V_2{}^2 - V_1{}^2)$$

Thus there is a static pressure drop as the velocity increases.
Further, according to equation 2

$$A_1V_1 = A_2V_2 = Q$$

where Q is the volume flow rate. Substituting from this for V_1 and V_2 in the previous equation yields

$$P_1 - P_2 = \frac{w}{2}Q^2(1/A_2^2 - 1/A_1^2) = \frac{w}{2}Q^2\frac{A_1^2 - A_2^2}{A_1^2 A_2^2}$$

or

$$Q = A_1 A_2 \sqrt{\frac{2(P_1 - P_2)}{(A_1^2 - A_2^2)w}} = A_2 \sqrt{\frac{2(P_1 - P_2)}{w[1 - (A_2/A_1)^2]}} \quad \ldots 6$$

Thus the volumetric flow rate through a horizontal converging duct can be determined conveniently by measuring the static pressure drop $P_1 - P_2$, provided the cross-sectional areas A_1 and A_2 and the density of the fluid are known. This is the basic principle underlying numerous flow measuring devices such as venturis and orifice plates. (Refer to Chapter 13.)

A vertical constant-area duct is depicted in Fig. 11:8. Since $A_1 = A_2$ (constant area), equation 2 yields $V_1 = V_2$, that is, there is no change in velocity. Thus, equation 4 becomes

$$P_1 + gwH_1 = P_2 + gwH_2$$

or

$$P_2 - P_1 = gw(H_1 - H_2)$$

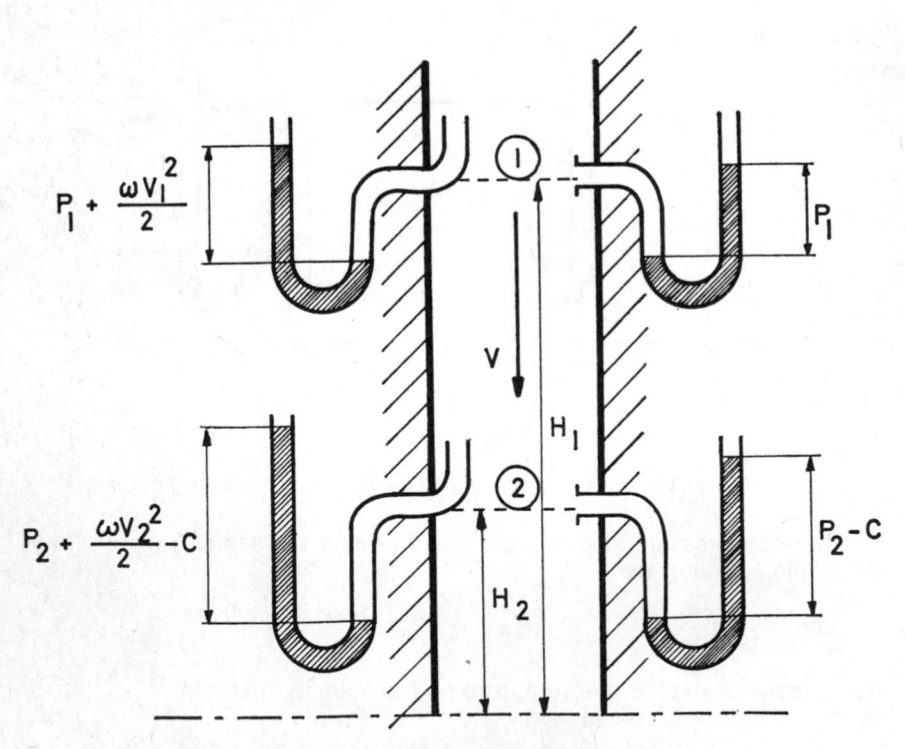

Fig. 11:8   Vertical constant-area duct: pressure measurement

The pressure P_2 is therefore greater than P_1 by the pressure due to gravity $gw(H_1 - H_2)$ between the two points '1' and '2'; gravitation thus increases the total pressure for downward flow and decreases it for upward flow. If, however, the alternative definition of total pressure mentioned previously, viz., $P + w\dfrac{V^2}{2} + gwH$ is used, there is obviously no change for upward or downward flow. If U-tubes are used to measure the pressures as illustrated in Fig. 11 :8, account must be taken of the fact that the measured pressures P_1 and P_2 are relative to the pressure of the environmental fluid (atmosphere) which will also increase from point 1 to point 2 because of its own gravity head. The lower U-tube reading should therefore be corrected relative to the reading of the upper U-tube by adding $C = gw_o(H_1 - H_2)$ where w_o is the density of the environmental fluid. If the instruments measure absolute pressure, this correction is of course not necessary.

If the environmental fluid has the same density as that of the fluid in the duct then, when measured as gauge pressures, $P_2 = P_1$.

A vertical converging duct is depicted in Fig. 11 :9. It follows from equation 2 that $V_2 = V_1(A_1/A_2)$. Thus, V_2 must be greater than V_1, since A_2 is smaller than A_1. From equation 4

$$P_1 - P_2 = \frac{w}{2}(V_2^2 - V_1^2) + gw(H_2 - H_1)$$

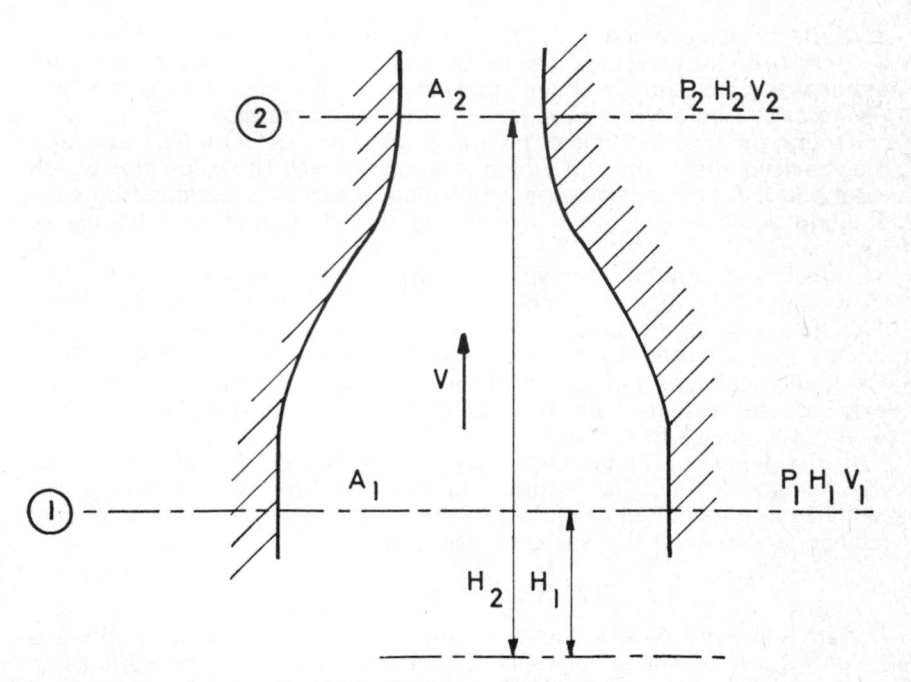

Fig. 11 :9   Vertical converging duct

The static pressure P_2 is lower than P_1 because of both the increase in velocity and the increase in height. In this connection it should be noted that heights are always measured upwards from some lower datum level, irrespective of the direction of the flow. If U-tubes are used to measure the pressures P_1 and P_2, the correction C should be made as shown in Fig. 11 :8.

9   THE LIMITS FOR INCOMPRESSIBLE FLOW

Air is a compressible fluid so that pressure changes are accompanied by volume changes, that is, density changes. Bernoulli's equation as given previously is, however, valid only for incompressible flow and the question therefore arises as to the extent to which it can be applied to compressible fluids.

Let it be assumed that a fluid may be considered as incompressible if its density does not change by more than 5 per cent. If it is assumed further that the relationship between (absolute) static pressure and density is linear, the acceptable change in static pressure would also be 5 per cent.

To find the limit in terms of air velocity, that part of Bernoulli's equation stating $P = w\dfrac{V^2}{2}$ may be used. The absolute pressure of atmospheric air is about 10^5 Nm^{-2}, 5 per cent of which is 5×10^3 Nm^{-2}. With $w = 1$ kg m^{-3} for air, the dynamic pressure $w\dfrac{V^2}{2}$ equals 5 per cent of the absolute pressure when $V^2 = 5 \times 10^3 \times 2$, or $V = 100$ ms^{-1}.

Thus, only for velocities greater than about 100 ms^{-1} for air at about atmospheric pressure, will the application of Bernoulli's equation give rise to appreciable errors because air is not incompressible.

To find the limit in terms of height, another part of Bernoulli's equation may be used, that is the part which states $P = gwH$. The value of H which results in a 5 per cent change in absolute pressure is obtained by substituting again $P = 5 \times 10^3$ Nm^{-2} and $w = 1$ kg m^{-3}, $g = 9{,}8$ ms^{-2}. This gives $H = 5 \times 10^3/9{,}81 = 510$ m.

Thus for air at about atmospheric pressure with height changes of less than about 500 m and velocity changes which do not exceed about 100 m/s, the application of Bernoulli's equation should not produce unduly great errors. In the majority of mine ventilation applications Bernoulli's equation can be used with little error being introduced. For extended surveys of shafts the higher limit will be exceeded and other methods will have to be used.

If the limits of incompressibility are exceeded, the application of thermodynamic laws is required to describe flow phenomena, since changes in the internal or molecular energy of the fluid and external heat exchange also enter the energy balance equation.

10   THE REAL FLUID : VISCOSITY

Bernoulli's and Euler's equations are valid only for ideal or frictionless fluids. As pointed out earlier, real fluids are not frictionless but are subjected to shear resistance against relative motions of their layers.

To account for shear resistance, Newton introduced a fairly simple concept stating that the *shear stress should be proportional to the rate of shear strain.*

Consider a fluid volume *xyz* subjected to shear force *S* acting upon the two opposite faces a distance *y* apart as illustrated in Fig. 11:10. The quotient of the force *S* and the area of the plane parallel to which it is acting, that is, area *xz*, is the shear stress $\tau = S/xz$. Shear stresses give rise to a continuous movement of the one face relative to the other one as also shown in Fig. 11:10. If the velocity of the one layer relative to the other is ΔV, the rate of shear strain is $\Delta V/y$. Newton postulated that

$$\tau = \mu \frac{\Delta V}{y} \qquad \ldots 7$$

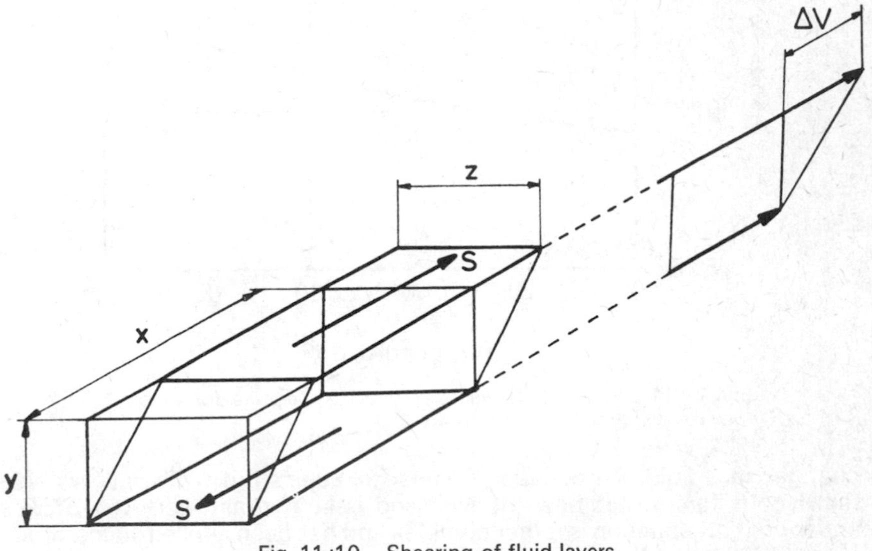

Fig. 11:10   Shearing of fluid layers

The factor of proportionality μ is called the *coefficient of dynamic viscosity* and is expressed in Nsm^{-2} or $kg\ m^{-1}\ s^{-1}$. These dimensions, Nsm^{-2} and $kg\ m^{-1}\ s^{-1}$ are identical according to the definition of the newton.

It has been found that the viscosity depends upon the temperature. This is to be expected since the shear resistance for which the viscosity is a measure, results from molecular motion within the fluid, and temperature is a measure of the degree of molecular motion. The variation of viscosity with temperature for different gases is shown graphically in Fig. 11:11.

A fluid for which μ is independent of $\Delta V/y$ is called a *Newtonian fluid* and constitutes only one, fairly simple, example of a real fluid. Fluids for which μ depends on $\Delta V/y$ are referred to as *non-Newtonian fluids* and their mathematical treatment is rather complex.

Fortunately, in many real fluids the effects of shear resistance are small and Bernoulli's concept of the ideal fluid is reasonably accurate for most practical cases concerning the relationship between pressure and velocity

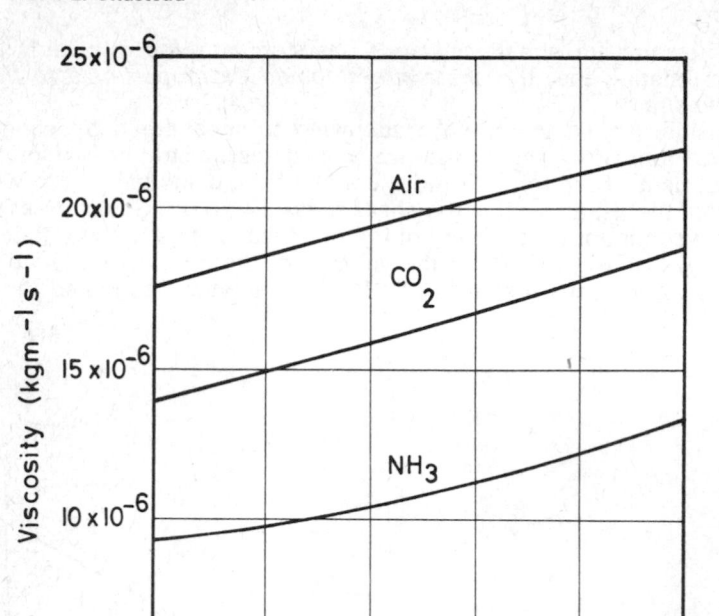

Fig. 11 :11   Variation of viscosity with temperature for various gases

changes in a fluid. An equation, similar to Euler's but which allows also for viscous forces, has been derived and is known as the *Navier-Stokes equation.* This equation is rather complex and has been applied successfully to real fluid flow in only a few simple cases.

In a general way, Bernoulli's equation may be modified to account for losses due to internal friction by adding the total pressure losses to the downstream side of the equation as follows:

$$P_1 + \frac{w_1 V_1{}^2}{2} + g w_1 H_1 = P_2 + \frac{w_2 V_2{}^2}{2} + g w_2 H_2 + p_L \qquad ...8$$

where p_L is the loss in total pressure between points 1 and 2.

If a device such as a fan which increases the total pressure is incorporated between points 1 and 2, Bernoulli's equation can be modified further by adding the total pressure rise to the pressure on the upstream side of the equation to give

$$P_1 + \frac{w_1 V_1{}^2}{2} + g w_1 H_1 + p_F = P_2 + \frac{w_2 V_2{}^2}{2} + g w_2 H_2 + p_L \qquad ...9$$

where p_F is the total pressure rise through the device.

Equations 8 and 9 are valid only if the flow is incompressible; where acceptable limits are exceeded for the change in static pressure, thermo-dynamic principles have to be used.

11 DIMENSIONAL ANALYSIS

It will be gathered from the foregoing analysis that the mathematical treatment of flow problems becomes increasingly difficult, if not impossible, if the behaviour of the fluid is more complex than that of an ideal flow. In such case resort must be made to *empirical methods* for solving flow problems.

In the empirical study of fluid flow, a technique known as *dimensional analysis* is relied upon to a large extent. This section deals briefly with the main aspects of dimensional analysis.

The measurement of every physical quantity, such as pressure, velocity, distance, etc., is performed in terms of some reference unit, or derived reference. Such references are, for instance, metres, newtons, grams, kilometres per hour, metres per second, newtons per square metre and numerous others which have become traditionally accepted and defined. Each such physical quantity consists of two components, namely, a *number* and a *unit*. If the velocity, for instance, is said to be 200 ms $^{-1}$, the number is 200 and the unit is ms $^{-1}$. This means that the quantity is 200 times greater than a reference quantity which has been chosen as 1 ms $^{-1}$. If some other reference quantity (unit) is chosen, e.g., 1 km per hour, the number of the same quantity would be different from 200. Whatever unit is chosen, it will always be a unit of length (cm, m, km) divided by a time unit (second, minute, hour). This reveals an aspect of the physical quantity which is termed its *dimension*. For instance, velocity has the dimension of length divided by time. It can be shown that the dimensions of all physical quantities can be derived from a number of *fundamental dimensions*, the choice of which is arbitrary.

In the study of aerodynamics it is customary to choose the dimensions of mass, length and time, denoted by $[M]$, $[L]$ and $[T]$, respectively, as three fundamental dimensions.

The relationship between mass and force has been discussed above and it becomes clear therefore that the dimension of force is $[F] = [M][L][T]^{-2}$.

Table 1 shows the dimensions as well as the commonly used units of the physical quantities used in this chapter. The fact that the dimension of any physical quantity can be derived from the dimensions of three fundamental quantities is now used in dimensional analysis to find relationships between the physical quantities involved in any physical process (e.g., flow of a fluid).

The method is best explained by an example:

Consider the resistance force R of a body in a fluid stream; this is the physical process. Let it be assumed (from experience or by in-tuition) that the force R depends upon the flow velocity V, the fluid density w and some convenient area A of the body. The still unknown relationship between these four physical quantities involved in the process may be written in the form:

$$R \propto w^a A^b V^c \text{ or } R = C_1 w^a A^b V^c$$

where C_1 is a non-dimensional proportionality factor and the exponents

TABLE 1   DIMENSIONS AND UNITS OF THE MORE
IMPORTANT PHYSICAL QUANTITIES

Physical quantity	Dimension $M - L - T$ System	Units S.I.
Length, height, head, distance, diameter	$[L]$	metre (m)
Time	$[T]$	second (s)
Force, weight	$[M][L][T]^{-2}$	kg m s^{-2}
Mass	$[M]$	kilogram (kg)
Pressure, stress	$[M][L]^{-1}[T]^{-2}$	kg m^{-1} s^{-2}
Velocity	$[L][T]^{-1}$	s^{-1}
Acceleration	$[L][T]^{-2}$	m s^{-2}
Volume flow rate	$[L]^{3}[T]^{-1}$	m^{3} s^{-1}
Density	$[M][L]^{-3}$	kg m^{-3}
Viscosity	$[M][L][T]^{-1}$	kg m^{-1} s^{-1}
Kinematic viscosity	$[L]^{2}[T]^{-1}$	m^{2} s^{-1}

a, b and c are unknown. Writing this relationship in terms of dimensions yields (see Table 1) :

$$([M][L][T]^{-2}) = ([M][L]^{-3})^{a}([L]^{2})^{b}([L][T]^{-1})^{c}$$

that is

$$[M]^{+1}[L]^{+1}[T]^{-2} = [M]^{+a}[L]^{-3a\,+\,2b\,+\,c}[T]^{-c}$$

Equating the exponents for the three fundamental dimensions on either side yields

$$\text{for } [M] \ldots +1 = +a$$
$$\text{,,} \quad [L] \ldots +1 = -3a + 2b + c$$
$$\text{,,} \quad [T] \ldots -2 = -c$$

Solving this set of three equations for three unknowns yields

$$a = 1, \quad b = 1, \quad c = 2.$$

Substituting this in the original relationship yields:

$$R = C_{1}wAV^{2} \text{ or } \frac{R}{wAV^{2}} = C_{1}$$

If measurements on bodies with different areas A but otherwise of the same geometrical shape, in fluid streams having different velocities V and densities w show that the factor C_{1} is not a constant, then it must be concluded from this that additional physical quantities are involved in the process. Let it be expected that the viscosity μ of the fluid is such an additional parameter. The expression for the resistance force may then tentatively be written

$$R = C_{2}w^{a}A^{b}V^{c}\mu^{d}$$

where C_{2} is some other dimensionless proportionality factor, and

$$([M][L][T]^{-2}) = ([M][L]^{-3})^{a}([L]^{2})^{b}([L][T]^{-1})^{c}([M][L]^{-1}[T]^{-1})^{d}$$

which yields

$$1 = a + d$$
$$1 = -3a + 2b + c - d$$
$$-2 = -c - d$$

There are three equations for four unknowns so that a unique solution is not possible. It is, however, possible to solve for any three of the variables in terms of the fourth. Such a solution is

$$a = 1 - d$$

$$b = 1 - \frac{d}{2}$$

$$c = 2 - d$$

Substituting in the original relationship yields

$$R = C_2 w^{1-d} A^{1-d/2} V^{2-d} \mu^d$$

$$= C_2(wAV^2) \left(\frac{\mu}{wA^{\frac{1}{2}}V}\right)^d \qquad \ldots 10$$

The value of d is unknown and dimensional analysis can yield no further information on it. The equation is therefore re-written as

$$\frac{R}{wAV^2} = f\left(\frac{\mu}{wA^{\frac{1}{2}}V}\right), \text{ or since } \frac{R}{wAV^2} = C_1 \qquad \ldots 11$$

$$C_1 = f\left(\frac{\mu}{wA^{\frac{1}{2}}V}\right)$$

where f denotes some unknown function of $\left(\dfrac{\mu}{wA^{\frac{1}{2}}V}\right)$

The value of C_2 is included in the function f.
The nature of this function is generally determined experimentally.

Each of the terms $\left(\dfrac{R}{wAV^2}\right)$ and $\left(\dfrac{\mu}{wA^{\frac{1}{2}}V}\right)$ is termed a *non-dimensional group*. For a body with a given geometrical shape, the area A can be replaced by the product of a constant factor and any convenient dimension squared, say D^2. The functional relationship between the above non-dimensional groups can then be written as

$$\left(\frac{R}{wD^2V^2}\right) = f_1\left(\frac{\mu}{wDV}\right) \text{ or } \left(\frac{R}{wD^2V^2}\right) = f_2\left(\frac{wDV}{\mu}\right) \qquad \ldots 12$$

where f_1, f_2 are once again unknown functions.
It is found in practice that certain non-dimensional groups occur frequently in the dimensional analysis of problems, and these groups have been given definite names. For instance, the group

$$\left(\frac{R}{wD^2V^2}\right)$$

is referred to as a *force or Euler coefficient,* denoted by C_f. The group

$$\left(\frac{wDV}{\mu}\right)$$

is referred to as the *Reynolds number,* denoted by R_e. The above equation can therefore be re-written as

$$C_f = f_2(R_e) \qquad \qquad ...13$$

The quotient (μ/w) is referred to as the kinematic viscosity ν. The Reynolds number may therefore also be expressed as

$$R_e = \left(\frac{DV}{\nu}\right) = \left(\frac{wDV}{\mu}\right) \qquad \qquad ...14$$

Experience leads to the expectation that in addition to Reynolds number R_e, the surface roughness of the body in the fluid stream influences the resistance force R. Surface roughness may be defined as the average height e of irregularities in the surface of the body. Again it can be investigated by dimensional analysis how R depends upon e and w, μ, D and V. The relationship may be written as

$$R = Cw^aD^bV^c\mu^de^k$$

Solving, as for the previous case, reveals that

$$\frac{R}{wD^2V^2} = f_3\left[\left(\frac{wDV}{\mu}\right), \left(\frac{e}{D}\right)\right] \qquad \qquad ...15$$

The non-dimensional group $\dfrac{e}{D}$ is referred to as the *relative roughness* and is given the symbol ϵ. The above equation can therefore be rewritten as

$$C_f = f_3(R_e, \epsilon) \qquad \qquad ...16$$

It is seen that force coefficient C_f is now a function of both Reynolds number R_e and relative roughness ϵ.

In common practice the force coefficient is often defined as

$$C_f = \frac{R/A}{\frac{1}{2}wV^2} \qquad \qquad ...17$$

The factor "$\frac{1}{2}$" has been introduced since, according to Bernoulli's equation, $\dfrac{wV^2}{2}$ is the velocity pressure of the flow. In fact then, C_f becomes the "resistance pressure" R/A per unit velocity pressure on a body in a fluid stream.

The dimensionless equation 16 still does not yield a means for calculating R since the nature of the function f_3 is still unknown. It renders available however, a basis for planning experiments, particularly model studies. In addition, dimensionless equations have the advantage that they are independent of the system of the units in which the physical quantities are measured and therefore make comparison of experimental or theoretical results from different countries or in different branches of science easy. A few more examples of non-dimensional equations are given below.

Returning to Bernoulli's equation modified for losses as given in equation (9) it will be remembered that all total pressure losses in a duct were accounted for by the pressure loss p_L included in the downstream term. This pressure loss can be made non-dimensional by dividing by the dynamic pressure $\dfrac{wV^2}{2}$. The pressure loss in non-dimensional form is then

$$K = \frac{p_L}{\frac{1}{2}wV^2} \qquad \qquad \ldots 18$$

where K is a *general pressure loss coefficient*. A component of K is the *pipe friction coefficient* defined by

$$\lambda = \frac{\Delta p}{\frac{1}{2}wV^2 L/D} \qquad \qquad \ldots 19$$

where Δp is the loss in static pressure due to wall friction in a parallel duct of diameter D and Length L.

Equation (6) may also be expressed in non-dimensional form, accounting for losses and other deviations not accounted for in Bernoulli's equation on which it is based. It then reads

$$C_d = \frac{Q/A_2}{\sqrt{2(P_1 - P_2)/w\,[1 - (A_2/A_1)^2]}} \qquad \qquad \ldots 20$$

where C_d is referred to as the *coefficient of discharge*.

12   MODEL LAWS

Based upon the principle of dimensional analysis, the very powerful technique of model studies has been developed to find relationships between physical quantities involved in a physical process. To achieve this, any model must obey the *law of similitude* which, stated in its most simple form, requires that the non-dimensional parameters involved in the process must be the same for model and prototype. This is best explained by the example already dealt with in the previous section, where equation 13 contains the non-dimensional parameters C_f and R_e.

If, for instance, it is required to find the aerodynamic resistance R_p of a body having the typical linear dimension D_p in a fluid with a density w_p and viscosity μ_p, flowing with velocity V_p, a model may be made and tested as illustrated in Fig. 11 :12. The model body must have the same geometrical shape as the prototype, but its linear dimension may be $D_m = m_1 D_p$, where m_1 is the length scale. To comply with the laws of similitude, the scales $m_2 = w_m/w_p$, $m_3 = \mu_m/\mu_p$ and $m_4 = V_m/V_p$ for density w_m, viscosity μ_m and velocity V_m in the model set-up must be made such that the Reynolds number is the same for model and prototype, that is,

$$\frac{w_m D_m V_m}{\mu_m} = R_e = \frac{w_p D_p V_p}{\mu_p}$$

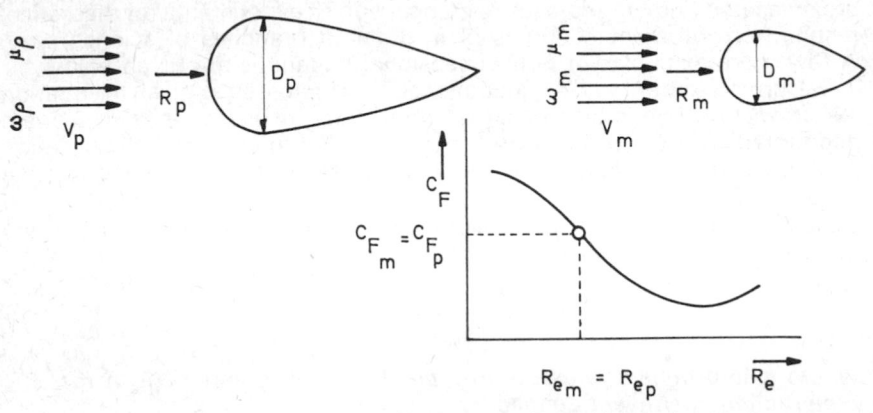

Force coefficient versus Reynolds number

Fig. 11:12 Model and prototype: aerodynamic force on body in fluid stream

The force coefficient C_f will then also be the same for model and prototype, that is,

$$\frac{R_m}{w_m V_m{}^2 D_m{}^2} = C_f = \frac{R_p}{w_p V_p{}^2 D_p{}^2}$$

From C_f the required force R_p can be calculated from given values of prototype variables.

A curve showing the relationship for the case just considered could be as given in Fig. 11:12. This curve is valid for geometrically similar set-ups of any size; as long as the value of R_e is the same in both cases they also have the same C_f.

Check measurements on models of different size may show that the curve of C_f versus R_e is not always strictly reproducible. What is referred to as a "scale" effect is then present. The occurrence of scale effects is an indication that some parameter involved in the process has not been taken into account.

Let it be assumed for the example considered that the surface roughness of the body is the missing parameter. The influence can be studied on models of different sizes for which not only the Reynolds number R_e but also the relative roughness $\epsilon = e/D$ as a non-dimensional parameter can be varied. The results are shown in Fig. 11:13 which, in fact is an extension of Fig. 11:12, just as equation 16 is an extension of equation 13. The graph can be extended further to allow for the influence of other parameters, if they are significant. The extent to which the knowledge of the parameters of influence on C_f is defined is a matter of practical necessity; if the influence of a certain parameter is negligible for practical purposes, it may of course be ignored in model studies. In studies of the flow around sharp-edged objects, for instance, unstreamlined shaft buntons, the Reynolds number is found to have a very limited influence over a wide range of test conditions. The resistance coefficients are then dependent mainly on geometrical similarity between models.

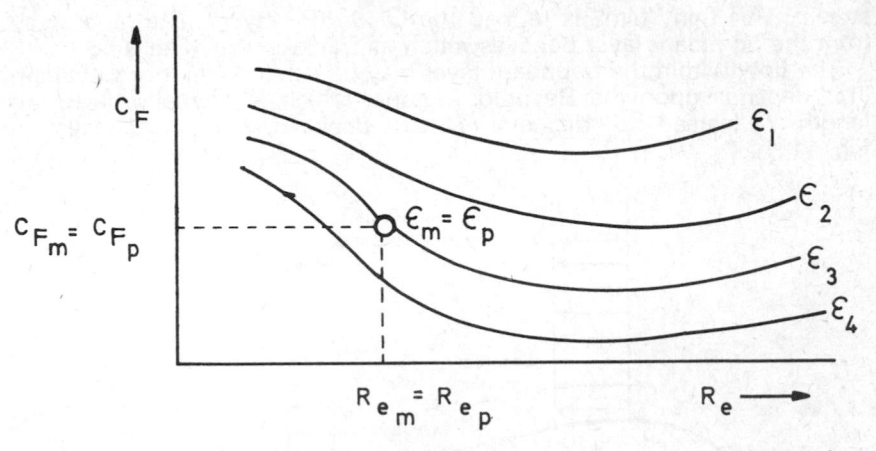

Fig. 11 :13   Force co-efficient versus Reynolds number with relative surface roughness as additional parameter

13   LAMINAR AND TURBULENT FLOW

It was stated in Section 4 that flow may be either laminar or turbulent. Reynolds, in about 1890, found that flow in pipes is laminar provided the parameter $R_e = wDV/\mu$ (the Reynolds number) does not exceed a value of approximately 2 500 (D is the pipe diameter and V the mean flow speed). For higher Reynolds numbers the flow would be turbulent.

In laminar flow the shear resistance is caused by viscous friction between layers moving at different velocities. In turbulent flow, additional shear resistance arises from turbulent mixing as a result of *eddy currents*. Consequently, shear resistance in turbulent flow is considerably higher than in laminar flow.

Laminar flow will hardly ever exist in mine airways since for a 3 m diameter airway the velocity of the air will have to be less than about 0,013 ms^{-1} or 0,8 m per minute for the Reynolds number not to exceed 2 500.

In a similar way, as for flow in pipes, the flow around bodies in fluid streams may also be either laminar or turbulent, depending upon the value of the Reynolds number.

14   TOTAL HEAD LOSSES: BOUNDARY LAYER: FLOW SEPARATION

In equation 9 energy losses were accounted for in a general way by adding p_L to the downstream side of Bernoulli's equation. Two sources of loss in energy may be mentioned briefly here.

When a real fluid flows along some wall surface, the flow of the fluid particles touching the wall is resisted by molecular adhesive forces while particles further away from the wall slip over the stationary particles. Viscous effects then lead to a shear stress on the surface and an equal and opposite drag on the fluid. The shear resistance offered by the wall causes total pressure losses p_{LB}. Prandtl made an extensive study of the behaviour of such flows and found that in practice viscous effects are confined to a relatively thin "film" near the wall or a body in the fluid stream. This thin "film" is termed the *"boundary layer"*. The fluid away from the boundary layer behaves much as if it were an ideal fluid.

The flow within the boundary layer may be either laminar or turbulent. This depends upon the Reynolds number which is normally based on length L instead of diameter D, as depicted diagrammatically in Fig. 11 :14.

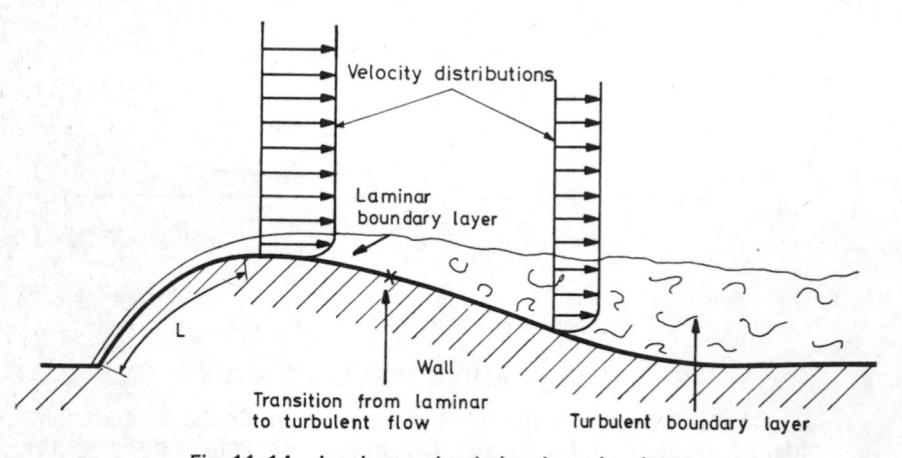

Fig. 11 :14   Laminar and turbulent boundary layers

According to Bernoulli's equation, a decrease in velocity corresponds to an increase in pressure. Whenever a flowing fluid is subjected to increasing pressure it is said to be flowing against an *adverse pressure gradient*. Both laminar and turbulent boundary layers can flow against such gradients for a limited distance only, after which the flow detaches itself from the wall or body surface leaving a *"dead fluid"* region, as illustrated in Fig. 11 :15. The flow is then said to be *"separated"*.

Consider the flow conditions at cross-sections A_1, A_2 and $A_3 = A_1$ in the duct depicted in Fig 11 :15. Since A_2 is smaller than A_1, the pressure decreases from P_1 to P_2 (negative pressure gradient over distance between A_1 and A_2). Since $A_3 = A_1$, the pressure should increase again from P_2 to $P_3 = P_1$ if the fluid behaves as an ideal fluid. Because of the adverse pressure gradient and separation over the length A_2 to A_3, the static pressure remains low, only attaining the value $P_3 = P_1 - p_{LS}$ where p_{LS} is the pressure loss due to separation.

The low pressure caused by separation may be regained to some extent if a parallel section of the airway follows the separation.

Flow separations constitute one of the major causes of pressure losses. Sharp projections such as I-beam flanges or 90° corners in ducts give rise to flow separations as illustrated in Fig. 11 :16.

Objects are said to be streamlined when they are designed so as to prevent separation as far as possible. This involves, for instance, limiting the maximum angles in diverging passages, such as fan evasees to about 7° included angle and rounding-off sharp corners, as illustrated in Fig. 11 :17.

Scale model studies are used extensively to discover design rules for optimum streamlined shapes.

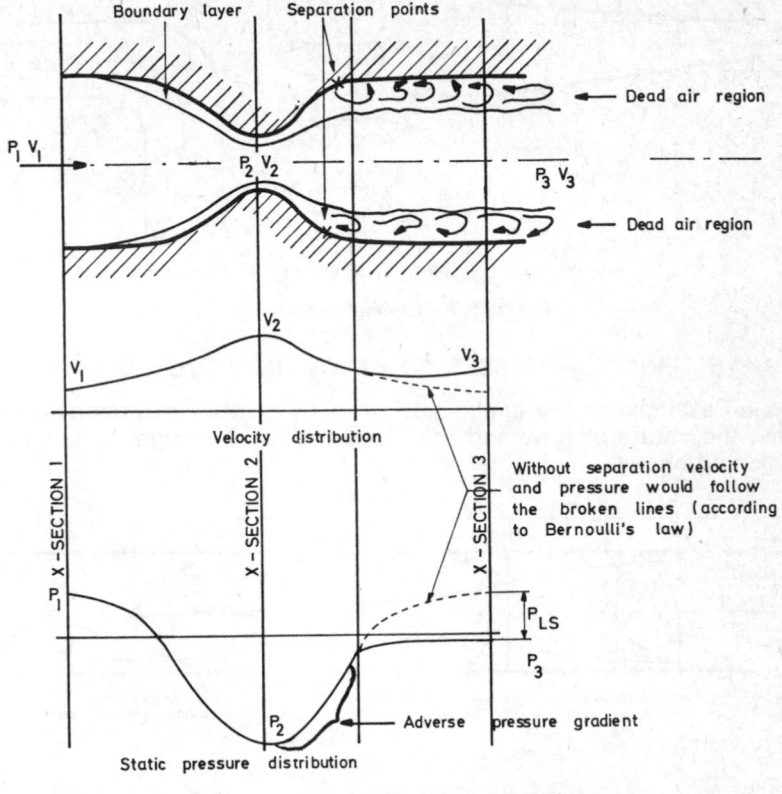

Fig. 11 :15   Flow separation

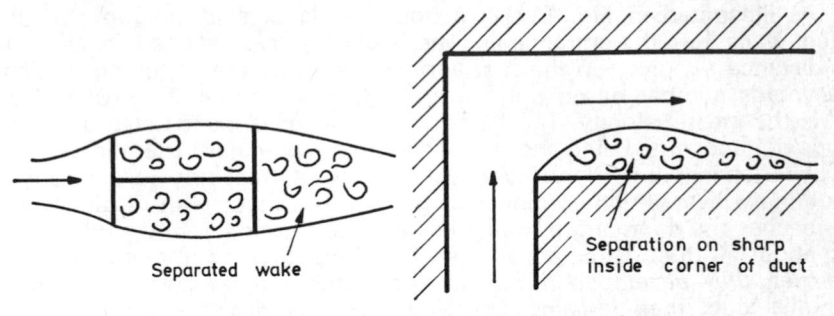

Fig. 11 :16   Practical cases of flow separation

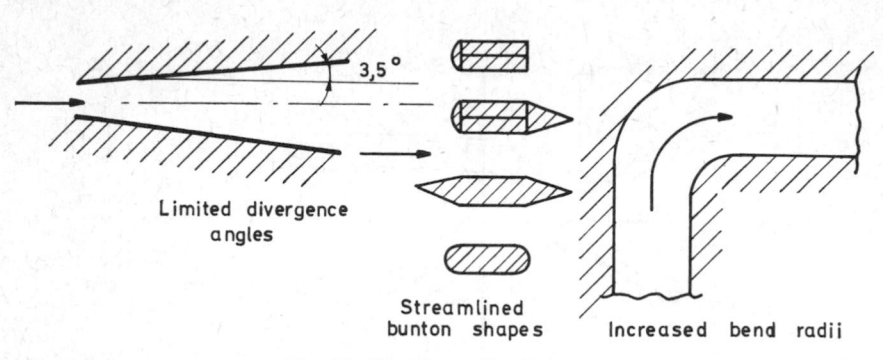

Fig. 11 :17   Streamlined shapes

15   FRICTION LOSSES FOR FLOW IN ROUGH DUCTS

As an example of the application of many of the concepts dealt with so far, the nature of flow and the friction losses in rough ducts may be considered briefly.

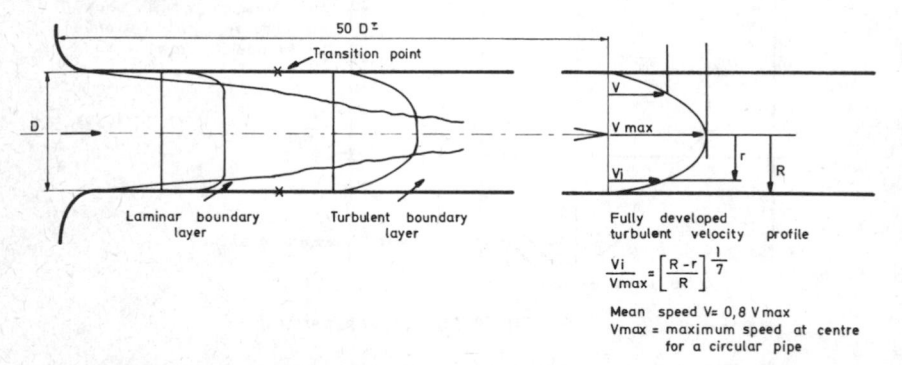

Fig. 11 :18   Stages of development of fully developed turbulent flow

As illustrated in Fig. 11 :18, a boundary layer starts to grow on the duct walls from the entrance lip. The boundary layer will be laminar up to a distance L_b, given in the first approximation by the condition that the Reynolds number based upon length, $R_e = wL_bV/\mu < 3 \times 10^5$, where V is the mean velocity. The length L_b, however, depends also upon the type of duct entry, being shorter for sharp-edged entries. After the distance L_b the laminar boundary layer will undergo a transition to a turbulent boundary layer which continues to grow in thickness with distance until it reaches the duct centre from all sides at a distance from the inlet equal to about 50 duct diameters so that the whole flow is turbulent. The flow is then *fully-developed turbulent*. The distribution of velocity across a parallel duct then remains unaltered. Any changes in duct shape and size, such as contractions, diffusers and bends will, however, alter the profile downstream again and some further distance measured from this disturbance will be required for re-establishing fully-developed turbulent flow.

It should be noted, however, that turbulent flow will never develop, that is, the flow in the duct will be laminar throughout, if the Reynolds number based on diameter, $R_e = wDV/\mu$, is less than about 2 500.

The loss of total pressure due to the wall friction in fully-developed turbulent flow can be measured by the static pressure drop Δp along the length of the duct. In general, however, if the flow is not fully developed the difference ΔP_t between the mean total pressures must be considered. $\Delta P_t = P_t,\text{mean},1 - P_t,\text{mean},2$ is the difference between the mean total pressures, determined for two measuring points "1" and "2" for which the velocity profiles differ. The mean total pressure P_t, mean at a measuring point is defined as follows:

Divide the cross-sectional area A into n area elements a_i and measure the total pressure P_{ti} and the velocity V_i for each element. Then,

$$P_t,\text{mean}, = \frac{\sum_{i=1}^{i=n} P_{ti} V_i a_i}{\sum_{i=1}^{i=n} V_i a_i} \qquad \ldots 21$$

This is not an arithmetic mean but a "weighted" mean. The mean velocity in a duct at the cross-sectional area A is given by

$$V = \frac{\sum_{i=1}^{i=n} V_i a_i}{A} \qquad \ldots 22$$

The factors upon which the pressure drop Δp in fully developed turbulent flow depends, will now be dealt with.

Many early experimenters derived formulae for calculating the pressure drop ΔP on the assumption that this value would be proportional to the square of the velocity. One of these, the Darcy-Weisbach formula, which is commonly used, states that the head loss in a circular pipe is

$$\Delta H = \frac{\lambda L V^2}{2gD} \qquad \ldots 23$$

where L is the pipe length, D its diameter, V the mean velocity and λ a non-dimensional *pipe friction coefficient.*

For non-circular ducts the equation can also be used if the diameter D is replaced by the *equivalent hydraulic* diameter D_h, defined as

$$D_h = 4 A/C \qquad \ldots 24$$

where A is the cross-sectional area and C the perimeter in contact with the fluid flowing.

The head loss ΔH in equation (23) converted to pressure drop gives

$$\Delta p = \tfrac{1}{2} w V^2 \lambda L/D_h \qquad \ldots 25$$

The above results can also be obtained by dimensional analysis (see equation 19). A more complete analysis would show further that the pipe friction coefficient is a function of Reynolds number, relative roughness and duct shape, thus

$$\lambda = f(R_e, \ \epsilon, \ s) \qquad \qquad \dots 26$$

where

$$\lambda = \frac{\Delta p}{\left(\dfrac{wV^2}{2} \ (L/D_h) \right)}$$

is the pipe friction coefficient or factor,

$R_e = wD_hV/\mu$, the Reynolds number,
$\epsilon = e/D_h$, the relative wall roughness, and
$s =$ the shape factor of the duct cross-section.

While it has been found experimentally that s has only a small influence upon λ, the influence of the other two non-dimensional parameters, R_e and ϵ, is of major importance.

The relationship between λ, R_e, and ϵ was first studied extensively by Nikuradse, while Stanton had previously studied the relationship between λ and R_e in smooth pipes so that the influence of ϵ could be neglected. The results are given in graphical form in Fig. 11 :19.

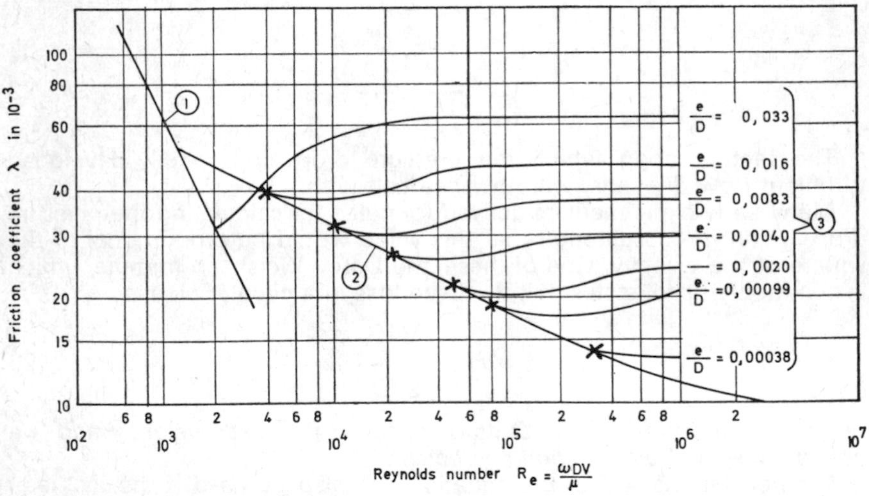

Fig. 11 :19   The Stanton and Nikuradse diagrams (after Schlichting)

Curve 1 is valid for wholly laminar flow, that is, for the case where the Reynolds number does not exceed the value $R_e = 2\,500$. The analytical equation corresponding to this curve is $\lambda = 64/R_e$. Curve 2 is valid for fully-developed turbulent flow in a smooth duct and is given by the empirical formula due to Blasius as

$$\lambda = \frac{0,316}{R_e^{\,0,25}}$$

which is valid for R_e up to 100 000. Curves 1 and 2 together form the so-called Stanton diagram.

The family of curves 3 in Fig. 11:19 is valid for rough ducts and was obtained by Nikuradse. To determine the relationships experimentally Nikuradse used sand of uniform grain size e to vary the roughness $\epsilon = e/D$ of the walls. It will be noted that for any given constant ϵ, the curves in the λ-R_e diagram follow that for smooth pipes up to certain points, marked X in the Figure. They then diverge and eventually become almost parallel to the R_e-axis, that is, λ then depends only upon ϵ and not on R_e. The explanation of this behaviour is that up to point X the roughness elements are small enough to have laminar flow over their surfaces, but beyond X they project into the turbulent flow and cause greater resistance. It is only in these regions beyond point X that pressure loss is proportional to the square of the velocity.

The Nikuradse diagram (curve 3 in Fig. 11:19) is based on experiments with rough surfaces composed of sand of uniform grain size. In practice, however, the roughness is not uniform and the value of e varies from point to point. Then , clearly defined points X as in Fig. 11:19 do not exist and the curves look more as depicted in Fig. 11:20. In this figure K_s

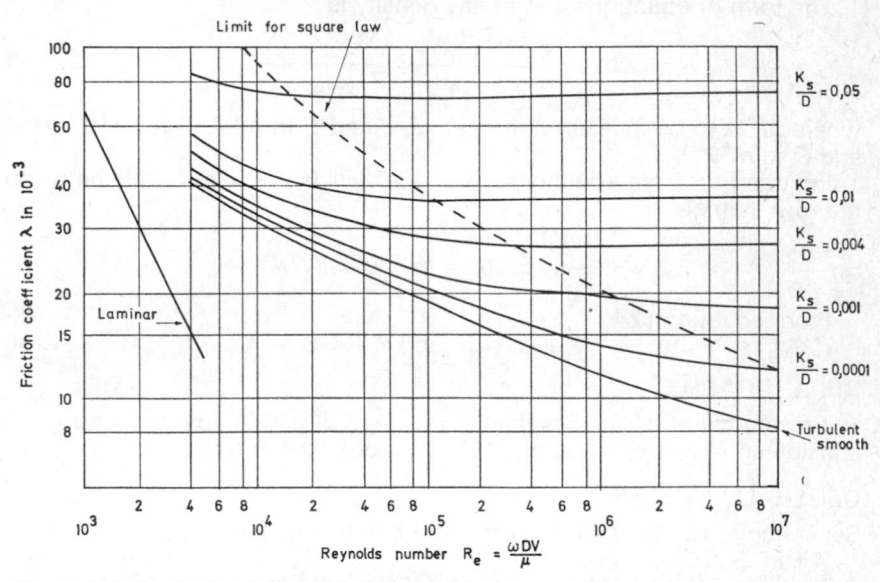

Fig. 11:20   Friction co-efficient versus Reynolds number (after Schlichting) with wall roughness as additional parameter

contained in $\epsilon = K_s/D$, is the *equivalent sand roughness* that yields the same λ as the uniform ϵ in the region where λ is independent of the Reynolds number. An empirical equation which applies to both the rough and smooth turbulent regions, due to Colebrooke and White is

$$\frac{1}{\sqrt{\lambda}} = 1{,}74 - 2\log_{10}\left(2\epsilon + \frac{18{,}7}{R_e\sqrt{\lambda}}\right) \qquad \ldots 27$$

Both rough- and smooth-walled airways in mines give results for λ versus R_e that fit on the curves of the diagram depicted in Figure 11.20. Equipped shafts, however, constitute a special case of "rough ducts", where it appears that, instead of K_s/D, the non-dimensional parameter A_b/A can be used with greater advantage, where A_b is the bunton projected cross-sectional area and A the cross-sectional area of the shaft.

In mine ventilation in South Africa, an alternative friction factor, referred to as Atkinson's friction factor K is used instead of λ. Atkinson arrived at this factor by assuming the pressure loss Δp to be proportional to the duct length L, the perimeter C, the square of the velocity V and inversely proportional to the cross-sectional area A. Thus,

$$\Delta p = K \frac{LCV^2}{A} \qquad \ldots 28$$

This equation is similar to the Darcy-Weisbach formula (equation 25) but K is not, as λ is, a non-dimensional factor since it has the dimensions $[M][L]^{-3}$. Atkinson ignored density effects in deriving equation 29 and it is therefore valid only for a standard density of 1,2 kg/m³.

The form of equation used at any density is

$$\Delta p = K \frac{LCV^2}{A} \frac{w}{1,2} = \frac{KLCQ^2}{A^3} \frac{w}{1,2} \qquad \ldots 29$$

where ΔP is to be measured in pascals, L and C in m, A in m², V in ms⁻¹ and Q in m³s⁻¹.

Equating ΔP from equations 25 and 29 yields the relationship between K and λ, namely,

$$\frac{\lambda w V^2}{2} L/D_h = KLCV^2w/1,2A$$

From equation (24)

$$D_h = 4A/C \quad \text{and} \quad \lambda = 6,67 K \qquad \ldots 30$$

BIBLIOGRAPHY

The following references deal in more detail with many of the subjects considered in this chapter, and list numerous further references.

GENERAL ASPECTS

Schlichting, H. *Boundary layer theory*. 6th ed., New York, McGraw-Hill, 1968.
Roberts, A. *Mine ventilation*. London, Cleaver-Hume Press, 1960.
Streeter, V. *Fluid mechanics*. 5th ed., New York, McGraw-Hill, 1971.
Eck, B. *Technische Stromungslehre*. 4th ed., Berlin, Springer-Verlag, 1954.
Massey, B. S. *Mechanics of fluids*. New York, Van Nostrand, 1968.

FLOW IN BENDS, DIFFUSERS, ETC.

Pankhurst, R. and Holder, D. *Wind Tunnel technique*. London, Pitman, 1952.
Ward-Smith, A. J. The flow and pressure losses in smooth pipe bends of constant cross-section. *J. R. Aeronaut. Soc.*, V. 67, No. 631 (1963) p. 437–447.

Ward-Smith, A. J. *Pressure losses in ducted flows*. London, Butterworth, 1971.

Patterson, N. Modern diffuser design. *Aircr. Engr.,* Sep. 1938, p. 267–73.

Miller, D. S. *Internal flow: a guide to losses in pipes and duct systems*. Cranfield, BHRA, 1971.

DIMENSIONAL ANALYSIS AND EXPERIMENTAL TECHNIQUE

Pankhurst, R. C. *Dimensional analysis and scale factors*. The Institute of Physics and the Physical Society, Monographs for Students, London, Chapman and Hall, 1964.

Bradshaw, P. *Experimental fluid mechanics*. London, Pergamon Press, 1964.

Ower, E. and Pankhurst, R. C. *The measurement of airflow*. 4th ed., Oxford, Pergamon Press, 1966.

Bryer, D. W. and Pankhurst, R. C. *Pressure-probe methods for determining wind speed and flow direction*. London, HMSO, 1971.

STUDIES OF THE STREAMLINING OF MINE SHAFT EQUIPMENT, AND THE PREDICTION OF MINE SHAFT RESISTANCE

Greuer, R. E. A. The determination of mine shaft resistance to airflow by the Mine Ventilation Research at Essen. *J. Mine Vent. Soc. S. Afr.,* Vol. 18 (1965), p. 45-56, 61–9.

Greuer, R. E. A. Der Wetterwiderstand von Schächten. *Bergb. Arch.,* Vol. 21, No. 1 (1960), p. 1–26.

Chasteau, V. A. L. and Gillard, D. The prediction of the resistance to airflow of mine shafts equipped with internal structures. *J. Mine Vent. Soc. S. Afr.,* Vol. 18, Nos. 10, 11 (1965), p. 133–46, 149–58.

Chasteau, V. A. L. Equipment and technique used for scale model investigations of mine shaft resistance to airflow in the CSIR Laboratories. *J. Mine Vent. Soc. S. Afr.,* Vol. 15, (1962), p. 99–106.

Chasteau, V. A. L. and Kemp, J. F. Further results of scale model measurements of mine shaft resistance to airflow by the CSIR. *J. Mine Vent. Soc. S. Afr.,* Vol. 15 (1962), p. 109–28.

Kemp, J. F. Analysis of the airflow in downcast shafts with reference to the trailing hose method of resistance measurement. *J. Mine Vent. Soc. S. Afr.,* Vol. 15 (1962), p. 1–14.

Kemp, J. F. Scale model testing in aerodynamics with special reference to the study of mine shaft resistance. *J. Mine Vent. Soc. S. Afr.,* Vol. 11 (1958), p. 251–58.

12 The Thermodynamic Approach to Mine Ventilation

A. W. T. BARENBRUG

Private Consultant. Formerly Group Ventilation Engineer, Anglo-Transvaal Consolidated Investment Company, Limited

1 INTRODUCTION

In the early days, in calculations of airflow in mines the air was regarded as being incompressible. Little error was introduced, however, because of the shallowness of the mines. However, as mining depths increased, the error introduced by assuming the air to be incompressible became progressively larger. For deep mines, the older method can, therefore, introduce errors which make the assumption of the incompressibility of air unacceptable.

Air is a compressible fluid which changes in volume continuously as it passes through a mine. Its volume can, as a result of compression in a deep downcast shaft, be reduced by as much as 20 to 30 per cent so that the compressibility of air cannot be ignored.

The flow of air through a mine, its being heated by being compressed, and by heat from rock, men and machinery, can be compared to the flow of gases in a heat engine. It is compressed in the downcast, heated in the workings and expands in the upcast.

Just as the behaviour of air in a heat engine can be examined by means of a thermodynamic analysis, so also can the airflow in mines be treated according to thermodynamic principles.

The thermodynamic flow equations are expressed in terms of energy per unit mass of air and as the mass flow is assumed to remain constant the variation in volume is incorporated automatically.

In some thermodynamic texts the work done *on* the air (compression) is negative while the work done *by* the air (expansion) is positive. However, many writers prefer the opposite practice and regard the work done *on* the air (as by a fan) and the increase in availability to do work (as through natural ventilation energy) as a positive source of energy, while the work required to lift water vapour and the loss of availability to do work (as through friction) as a negative source of energy.

As the latter method is less likely to create confusion it is the method followed in this chapter.

Bearing in mind that friction and lifting of water are always negative, and that fanpower and natural ventilation are always positive, the fundamental energy balance equation is

$$\text{Friction} + \text{lifting water} + \text{fan energy} + \text{NVE} = 0$$

In the following notes detailed information is given showing how each individual item can be determined from a mine ventilation survey.

2 BASIC THERMODYNAMIC EQUATIONS FOR AIR

The work done *by* 1 kg of air entering a circuit is given by

$$W = -P_1 v_1 \text{ Nm/kg}$$

The work done *by* 1 kg of air as the result of change in level and in kinetic energy, and in overcoming friction, causes an expansion of the air. This can be expressed by

$$W = -\int_{v_1}^{v_2} P dv \text{ Nm/kg}$$

The work done *on* the air when it is forced out of the circuit against a pressure P_2 is

$$W = P_2 v_2 \text{ Nm/kg}$$

The total work done *on* the air is thus

$$W_t = -P_1 v_1 - \int_{v_1}^{v_2} P dv + P_2 v_2 \text{ Nm/kg}$$

$$\text{or } W_t = \int_{P_1}^{P_2} v dP \text{ Nm/kg}$$

For a mine consisting of a downcast shaft, horizontal workings and an upcast shaft (Fig. 12:1), the work done *on* and *by* the air is given by the following expressions:

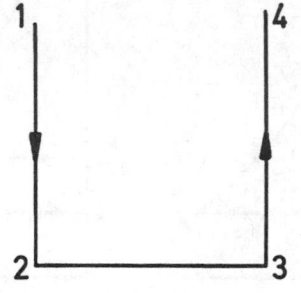

Figure 12:1

(*a*) downcast shaft: $W = \int_{P_1}^{P_2} v dP \text{ Nm/kg}$

(*b*) workings: $W = -\int_{P_3}^{P_2} v dP \text{ Nm/kg}$

(*c*) upcast shaft: $W = -\int_{P_4}^{P_3} v dP \text{ Nm/kg}$

It should be noted that when work is done *on* the air such as when air is compressed, as in a downcast shaft, the work done is positive. When the work is done *by* the air in horizontal workings and upcast shafts, the work done is negative. The total work done by the air in a mine ventilation system is then:

$$W_t = \int_{P_1}^{P_2}vdP - \int_{P_3}^{P_2}vdP - \int_{P_4}^{P_3}vdP \quad \text{Nm/kg}$$

The integrals $\int_{P_1}^{P_2}vdP$, $\int_{P_3}^{P_2}vdP$, $\int_{P_4}^{P_3}vdP$ can all be represented graphically on so-called pressure-volume, or Pv, diagrams (Fig. 12:2).

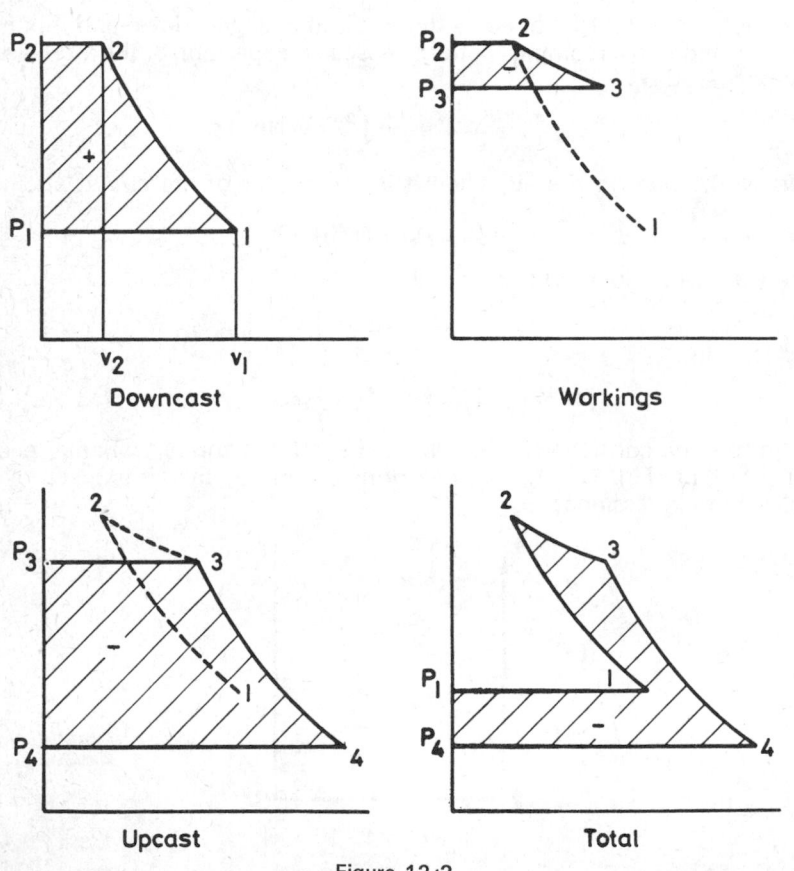

Figure 12:2

If the specific volume is plotted on the horizontal axis so that one division equals 0,005 m³/kg and the pressure (N/m²) is plotted on the vertical axis so that one division equals 500 N/m², then the area of one square will be equivalent to 0,005 × 500 or 2,5 Nm/kg.

Although the curves 1–2, 2–3 and 3–4, can sometimes be regular in shape or even sometimes almost a straight line, this is seldom so in practice, and in order to obtain the correct configuration of these lines it is necessary to make numerous observations of temperatures and pressures at regular intervals of, say, 100 metres.

The work done *on* 1 kg of air in a downcast shaft as a result of the change in elevation due to gravity, the change in kinetic energy and in work done to overcome friction (*F*), is positive, and can also be expressed by the equation

$$W_{dc} = \int_{P_1}^{P_2} v\,dP = g(Z_2 - Z_1) - \tfrac{1}{2}(u_2^2 - u_1^2) + F_{1-2} \text{ Nm/kg}$$

If the small change in kinetic energy is neglected, this expression becomes

$$W_{dc} = \int_{P_1}^{P_2} v\,dP = g(Z_2 - Z_1) + F_{1-2} \text{ Nm/kg}$$

The work done *by* 1 kg of air in horizontal workings and the upcast shaft is given in the following expressions if the small change in kinetic energy is neglected.

For the workings in which there is no change in elevation,

$$W_w = -\int_{P_3}^{P_2} v\,dP = F_{2-3} \text{ Nm/kg}$$

and fo an upcast shaft

$$W_{uc} = -\int_{P_4}^{P_3} v\,dP = -g(Z_3 - Z_4) + F_{3-4} \text{ Nm/kg}$$

so that for a mine as a whole

$$F_{1-4} = -g(Z_2 - Z_1) + \left(\int_{P_1}^{P_2} v\,dP - \int_{P_3}^{P_2} v\,dP - \int_{P_4}^{P_3} v\,dP\right) + g(Z_3 - Z_4)$$

It should be noted that *F* is always negative.

The expressions derived above permit the determination of the loss of frictional energy in any section of the mine or in the mine as a whole. The expressions apply strictly speaking only to the situation in which there is no change in mass flow (that is, no evaporation of moisture) and ignore the effects of changes in kinetic energy which are usually negligible.

The information required to calculate frictional energy losses is, therefore, as follows:

(i)   the depths below datum of the two ends of the airway of shaft, together with the value of the gravitational acceleration *g* (for most practical purposes *g* can be taken as 9,79 m/s²) and

(ii) sufficient values of true specific volume (*v*) and absolute pressure (*P*) to enable the integral term to be calculated.

Obtaining the information required under (i) usually presents no difficulty but various methods exist for calculating the integral term and these are described below.

To a very large extent the method used depends upon the degree of accuracy required and upon the purpose of the measurements. If the measurements are made to determine the energy losses in a shaft, in which the loss of frictional energy seldom exceeds 10 per cent of the value of the integral term, it is obvious that considerable care must be taken in evaluating this term. On the other hand, if the measurements extend over the whole mine and only the total frictional energy loss is required, it is not as important to achieve high accuracy in evaluating the integrals as errors in the downcast are likely to be offset by similar errors in the upcast.

The simplest method for evaluating the integral $\int vdP$ is the one already described, that is, the graphical method. Here the absolute pressure is plotted against the specific volume and the area between the curve and the vertical pressure axis is measured, either by counting squares or by using a planimeter. If several observations have been made within the airway there should be no problem in drawing a curve between the two end points. On the other hand, it often happens that only the two end-point conditions are known so that drawing the curve presents some problems. The easiest solution is to draw a straight line but this is seldom satisfactory, particularly when there is a considerable difference in elevation. It is better to assume that a polytropic process occurs between the two end points, that is, that $Pv^k = $ constant.

This equation, together with the end-point conditions, can be used to plot the curve. However, it is rarely worth plotting the curve and measuring the area when it is assumed that flow is polytropic, as the area can easily be calculated.

The second method for evaluating $\int vdP$ is to calculate the area directly. When conditions are such that the assumption of a linear relationship between absolute pressure and specific volume is justified, for example, when the difference in elevation is small, say, a few hundred metres, the area is obtained from the equation

$$\int_{P_1}^{P_2} vdP = (P_2 - P_1)\frac{v_1 + v_2}{2}$$

When several sets of observations have been made in a shaft, this equation can obviously be used to calculate the area involved for each successive pair of observations.

When only two sets of observations are made, one at each end of the airway, and it is assumed that flow is polytropic, the area is given by

$$\int_{P_1}^{P_2} vdP = \frac{k}{k-1}(P_2 v_2 - P_1 v_1), \text{ where } k = \frac{\log \dfrac{P_2}{P_1}}{\log \dfrac{v_1}{v_2}} = \frac{\log \dfrac{P_1}{P_2}}{\log \dfrac{v_2}{v_1}}$$

The use of these various methods will be illustrated later by means of numerical examples.

The determination of the correct sign for the measured or calculated area sometimes presents difficulties. The equations given above, if applied correctly, automatically yield the correct sign, but if the graphical approach is used it is only necessary to remember that

$$\int_{P_1}^{P_2} vdP \text{ is positive if } P_2 \text{ is larger than } P_1.$$

3   CORRECTIONS REQUIRED WHEN DEALING WITH A VAPOUR MIXTURE

It seldom occurs in practice that the air contains no moisture and that no moisture is evaporated in the downcast and workings, or condensed in the upcast. Although the error introduced by neglecting the gravity work due to the variation in moisture content is usually small (about 2 to 3 per cent), theoretically an allowance must be made for this variation, and as the increase or decrease in the moisture content can be very irregular it is necessary to consider these factors over small sections of the circuit.

Whereas the fundamental formula for the total work remains as before, that is,

$$W_t = \int_{P_1}^{P_2} v dP - \int_{P_3}^{P_2} v dP - \int_{P_4}^{P_3} v dP,$$

the equations for the frictional energy losses in the downcast shaft, workings and upcast shaft are, respectively,

downcast shaft: $F_{1-2} = -g(Z_2 - Z_1) - g\int_{Z_1}^{Z_2} r dZ + \int_{P_1}^{P_2} v dP;$

level workings: $F_{2-3} = -\int_{P_3}^{P_2} v dP;$

upcast shaft: $F_{3-4} = g(Z_3 - Z_4) + g\int_{Z_4}^{Z_3} r dZ - \int_{P_4}^{P_3} v dP$

(r is the moisture content, kg/kg of dry air).

Once again kinetic energy terms are ignored, and v is now the apparent specific volume of the air-vapour mixture, that is, it is the volume of the mixture per unit mass of dry air.

It is important to realize that whereas the Pv diagram indicates the total work done, the Pv area is not equal to the total friction work, but differs by the amount of work required to lift the added moisture out of the mine.

For the mine as a whole

$$F_{1-4} = -g(Z_2 - Z_1) - g(\int_{Z_1}^{Z_2} r dZ - \int_{Z_4}^{Z_3} r dZ) + (\int_{P_1}^{P_2} v dP - \int_{P_3}^{P_2} v dP - \int_{P_4}^{P_3} v dP) +$$
$$g(Z_3 - Z_4).$$

If the tops of the upcast and downcast shafts are at the same elevation

$$F_{1-4} = -g(\int_{Z_1}^{Z_2} r dZ - \int_{Z_4}^{Z_3} r dZ) + W_t.$$

The work required to lift the excess moisture out of the shaft can be obtained from the depth-moisture graph and this enables one to evaluate the integral $\int r dZ$.

The moisture content r is plotted against the depth Z so that on the depth axis, one division equals 50 m and on the vertical moisture content

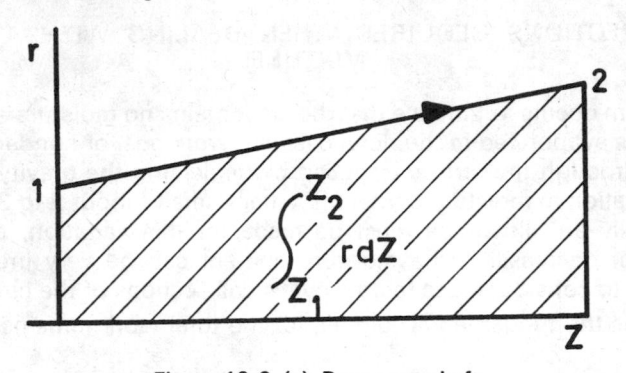

Figure 12:3 (a) Downcast shaft

axis one division equals 0,001 kg/kg. The area of one square is then $50 \times 0,001 \times 9,79 = 0,489\ 5\ \text{Nm/kg}$. Other scales can, of course, be used if necessary (Fig. 12:3 (a) and Fig. 12:3 (b)).

The variation of the moisture content of the air as the air flows up an upcast shaft requires some explanation. If air velocities are very low most of the condensed moisture will be precipitated from the airstream and the moisture content of the air will then be equal to the apparent specific humidity of the air. High air velocities, on the other hand, will cause all of the condensed moisture to be carried along with the airstream and the moisture content of the air will then be equal to the apparent specific humidity of the air entering the upcast shaft.

The value of the integral term $\int r dZ$ is determined either by a graphical method or by calculation.

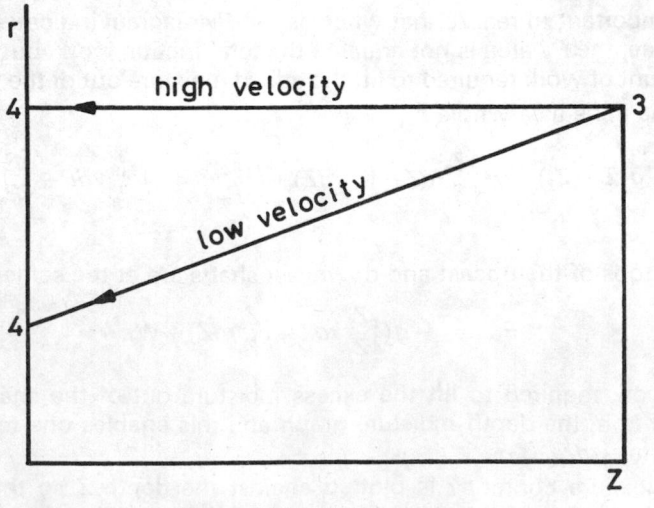

Figure 12:3 (b) Upcast shaft

The total fan energy W_f is given by the expression

$$W_f = -F_{1-4} - g\oint rdZ - (-\oint vdP) = -W_t - (-\oint vdP)$$

Total fan energy $=$ $-$friction work$-$moisture lift work$-$natural ventilation energy.

It must be remembered that both friction work and moisture lift work are negative.

The integrals $\oint rdZ$ and $\oint vdP$ are now evaluated around the entire mine circuit, that is, from the top of the downcast through the mine and back to the top of the downcast. Positive values for the integrals are obtained when the diagram is traversed in a clockwise direction for $\oint rdZ$ and an anti-clockwise direction for $\oint vdP$. This applies when the horizontal or x axes used are depth Z and specific volume v. This appears to be an anomalous situation, but if the diagrams are drawn with the variable in respect of which the integration is being carried out plotted on the horizontal or x axis, positive areas occur when each diagram is traversed in a clockwise direction. This would mean plotting depth and absolute pressure on the horizontal axis.

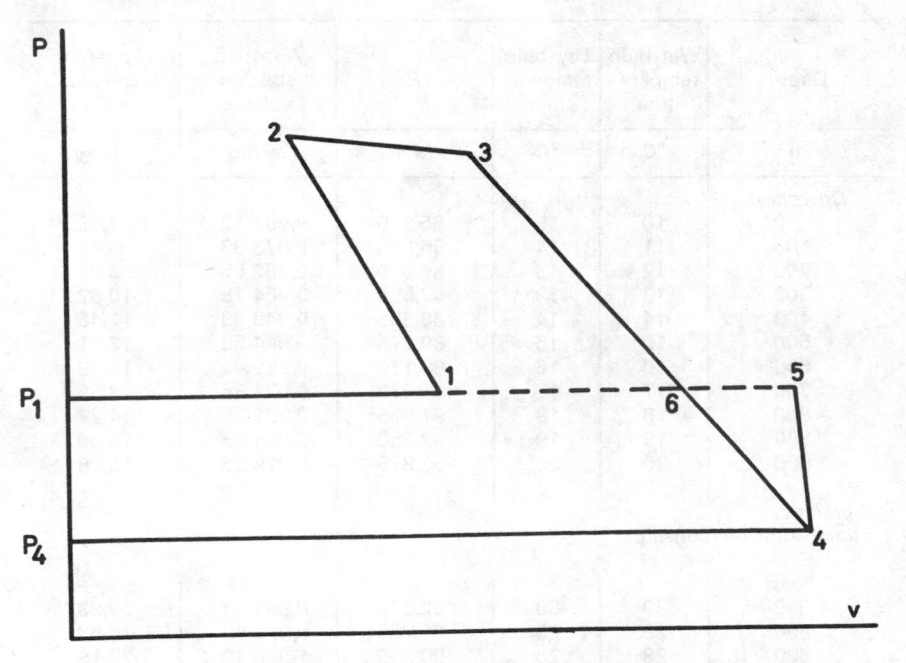

Figure 12:4

In most instances in a mine, both $\oint rdZ$ and $\oint vdP$ will be negative and the fan energy required plus the total friction losses plus the energy required to lift water out of the mine ($g\oint rdZ$) and plus the natural ventilation energy ($-\oint vdP$) is equal to zero. The relationship between the total fan energy and the total work is best illustrated on the pressure-specific volume diagram (Fig. 12:4).

Point 5 is now the condition at fan discharge, while Point 6 is the point on the upcast curve 3–4 at which the pressure equals the surface barometric pressure P_1.

$$W_t = -\text{area } (P_1-1-2-3-4-P_4)$$
$$W_f = \text{area } (P_1-5-4-P_4)$$
$$\oint vdP = -\text{area } (1-2-3-4-5-6)$$
$$= -(\text{area } (1-2-3-6) - \text{area } (4-5-6)).$$

Area (4–5–6) is in practice so small that it can be ignored.

From the above equations, $W_f = -W_t-(-\oint vdP)$

Example 1

The above discussion can be summarized by the following worked example. The following data were obtained from a pressure survey of a mine 1 000 m deep, consisting of a downcast shaft, workings and upcast shaft. (It is assumed that all the condensed water in the upcast shaft falls to the bottom of the shaft.) Readings were taken at 100 m intervals.

Depth	Wet-bulb temperature	Dry-bulb temperature	P	Apparent specific volume	Apparent specific humidity
m	°C	°C	kPa	m³/kg	g/kg
Downcast					
0	10	15	85,000	0,984 12	7,06
100	11	14	85,830	0,973 33	8,42
200	12	13	86,670	0,962 66	9,81
300	13	13	87,525	0,954 78	10,82
400	14	14	88,395	0,949 63	11,45
500	15	15	89,275	0,944 52	12,11
600	16	16	90,170	0,939 41	12,79
700	17	17	91,075	0,934 35	13,52
800	18	18	91,995	0 929 29	14,27
900	19	19	92,930	0,924 25	15,06
1 000	20	20	93,875	0,919 26	15,88
Workings					
Straight-line relationship					
Upcast					
1 000	30	30	92,375	0,987 33	29,93
900	29	29	91,285	0,993 69	28,53
800	28	28	90,205	1,000 19	27,19
700	27	27	89,135	1,006 84	25,90
600	26	26	88,075	1,013 62	24,67
500	25	25	87,025	1,020 55	23,49
400	24	24	85,985	1,027 62	22,35
300	23	23	84,955	1,034 83	21,26
200	22	22	83,935	1,042 18	20,22
100	21	21	82,925	1,049 66	19,22
0	20	20	81,925	1,057 29	18,27

The first step is to determine the frictional energy losses. Integral terms are evaluated by calculating the areas. Details are not given of all the calculations, but the method used will be illustrated by calculating $\int_{P_4}^{P_3} v dP$ for the upcast shaft, all the calculations being summarized in the table below:

n	$P_n(Pa)$	$v_n(m^3/kg)$	$P_n-P_{n+1}(Pa)$	$\dfrac{v_n+v_{n+1}}{2}(m^3/kg)$	$(P_n-P_{n+1})\dfrac{v_n+v_{n+1}}{2}(Nm/kg)$
1	92 375	0,987 33	1 090	0,990 51	1 079,66
2	91 285	0,993 69	1 080	0,996 94	1 076,70
3	90 205	1,000 19	1 070	1,003 52	1 073,77
4	89 135	1,006 84	1 060	1,010 23	1 070,84
5	88 075	1,013 62	1 050	1,017 09	1 067,94
6	87 025	1,020 55	1 040	1,024 09	1 065,05
7	85 985	1,027 62	1 030	1,031 23	1 062,17
8	84 955	1,034 83	1 020	1,038 51	1 059,28
9	83 935	1,042 18	1 010	1,045 92	1 056,38
10	82 925	1,049 66	1 000	1,053 48	1 053,48
11	81 925	1,057 29			
				Total area	10 665,27

Frictional energy losses are then calculated.

(i) *Downcast*

$$F_{1-2} = -g(Z_2-Z_1)-g\int_{Z_1}^{Z_2} r dZ + \int_{P_1}^{P_2} v dP$$

$Z_2 = 1\ 000$ m

$Z_1 = 0$ m

$\therefore g(Z_2-Z_1) = 9,79 \times 1\ 000 = 9\ 790$ Nm/kg

$g\int_{Z_1}^{Z_2} r dZ = 117$ Nm/kg

$\int_{P_1}^{P_2} v dP = 8\ 393$ Nm/kg

$\therefore F_{1-2} = -9\ 790 - 117 + 8\ 393 = -1\ 514$ Nm/kg.

(ii) *Workings*

$$F_{2-3} = -\int_{P_3}^{P_2} v dP$$

$\int_{P_3}^{P_2} v dP = 1\ 430$ Nm/kg.

$\therefore F_{2-3} = -1\ 430$ Nm/kg.

(iii) *Upcast*

$$F_{3-4} = g(Z_3 - Z_4) + g\int_{Z_4}^{Z_3} r\,dZ - \int_{P_4}^{P_3} v\,dP$$

$Z_3 = 1\ 000$ m

$Z_4 = 0$ m

$g(Z_3 - Z_4) = 9{,}79 \times 1\ 000 = 9\ 790$ Nm/kg

$g\int_{Z_4}^{Z_3} r\,dZ = 232$ Nm/kg

$\int_{P_4}^{P_3} v\,dP = 10\ 665$ Nm/kg

$\therefore F_{3-4} = 9\ 790 + 232 - 10\ 665 = -643$ Nm/kg.

The total mine frictional energy losses are thus:

$$F_{1-4} = -1\ 514 - 1\ 430 - 643 = -3\ 587 \text{ Nm/kg.}$$

The total mine losses, that is, the frictional energy losses plus the work required to lift water out of the mine, are:

$$-1\ 514 - 1\ 430 - 643 - (232 - 117) = -3\ 702 \text{ Nm/kg}$$

The same result can be obtained from the Pv diagram and the depth-moisture diagram without the need to make the long calculations (Fig. 12:5 (*a*) and Fig. 12:5 (*b*)).

Friction = total work—water lifting work = $-3\ 702 - (-115)$
$$= -3\ 587 \text{ Nm/kg.}$$

4   FAN REQUIREMENTS

If air is to continue to flow through the circuit, energy must be supplied to the air in an amount equal to the total work required. In the example, this is equal to 3 702 Nm/kg

This energy is usually supplied in two forms:

(*a*) in the form of heat, moisture increase, etc., and

(*b*) from a fan;

or, expressed in better terms:

(*a*) energy produced by the expansion of the air, and

(*b*) energy produced by a fan.

The amount of energy produced by the expansion of the air is difficult to calculate as heating, cooling, evaporation, condensation, compression and expansion can take place randomly. It can, however, be determined easily from the Pv diagram.

The total fan energy required is obtained as follows:

$$W_f = -F_{1-4} - g\oint r\,dZ - (-\oint v\,dP)$$

$$F_{1-4} = -3\ 587 \text{ Nm/kg.}$$

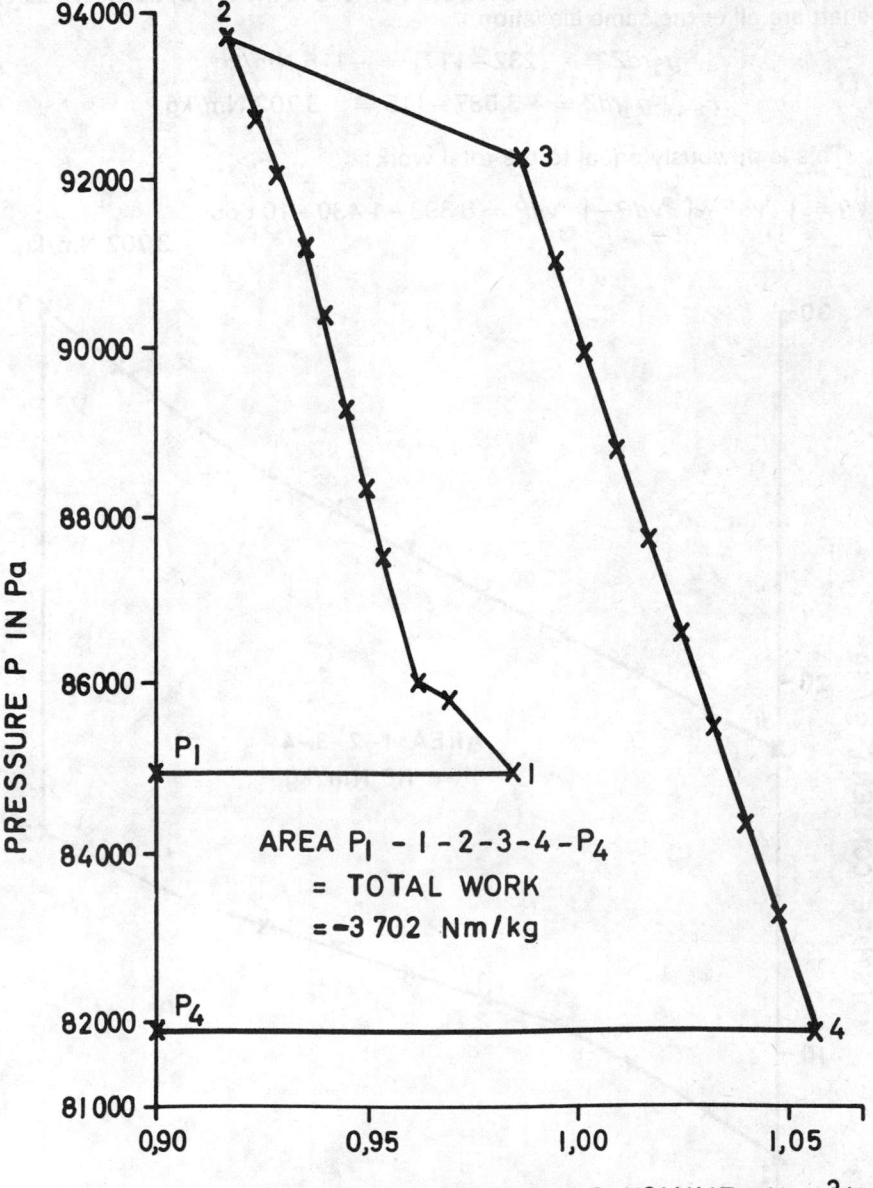

AREA P_1 - 1 - 2 - 3 - 4 - P_4
= TOTAL WORK
= -3 702 Nm/kg

APPARENT SPECIFIC VOLUME IN m³/kg
Pv DIAGRAM.

Figure 12:5 (a)

The moisture content-depth diagram is traversed in an anti-clockwise direction and since the fan inlet, fan discharge, and the top of the downcast shaft are all at the same elevation,

$$g \oint r dZ = -(232-117) = -115 \text{ Nm/kg}$$

$$F_{1-4} + g \oint r dZ = -3\,587 - 115 = -3\,702 \text{ Nm/kg}.$$

This is obviously equal to the total work:

$$W_t = \int_{P_1}^{P_2} v dP - \int_{P_3}^{P_2} v dP - \int_{P_4}^{P_3} v dP = 8\,393 - 1\,430 - 10\,665$$

$$= -3\,702 \text{ Nm/kg}.$$

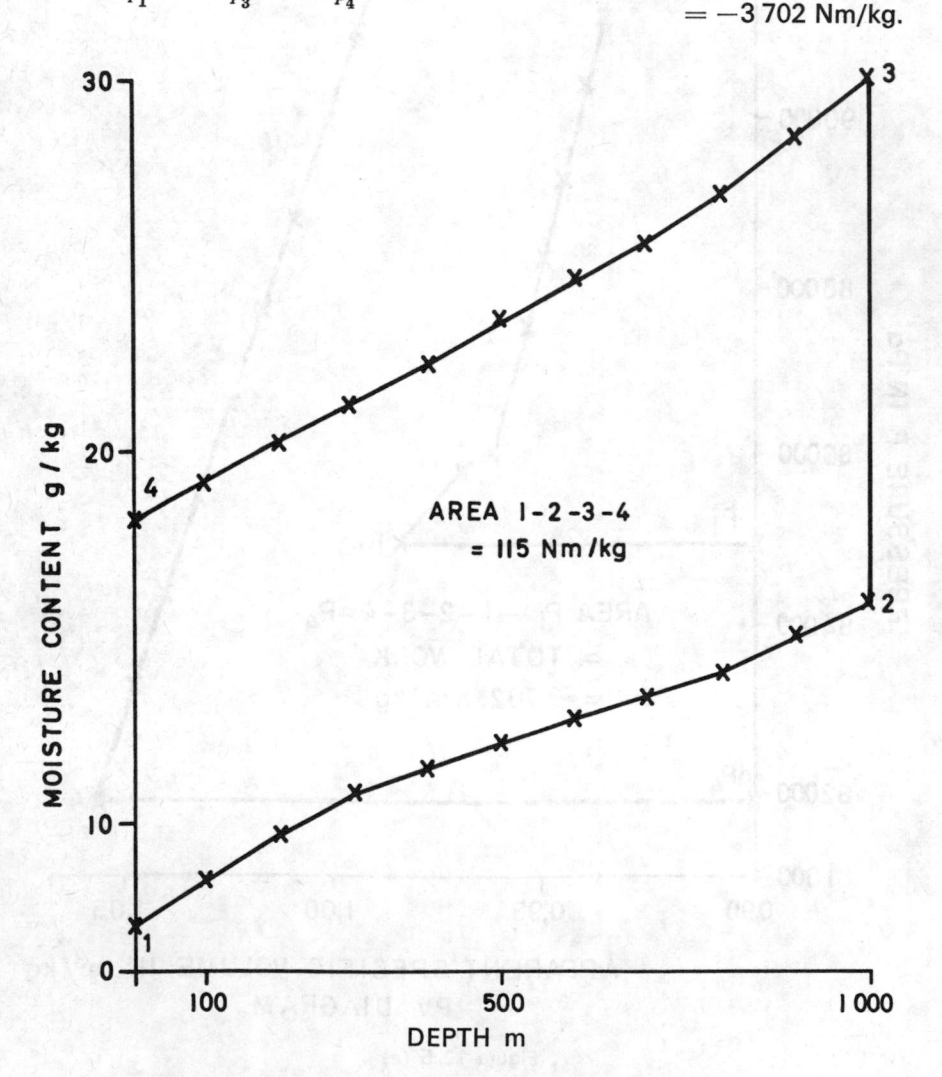

Figure 12:5 (*b*) Depth—Moisture diagram

If the change in specific volume as air passes through the fan is ignored,

$$W_f = (P_1 - P_4)v_4 = (85\,000 - 81\,925) \times 1{,}057\,29$$

$$= 3\,075 \times 1{,}057\,29 = 3\,251\ \text{Nm/kg}$$

$$-\oint v dP = -W_t - W_f = 3\,702 - 3\,251 = 451\ \text{Nm/kg}.$$

The natural ventilation energy is thus 451 Nm/kg.

If allowance is made for the change in specific volume of the air on passing through the fan, the natural ventilation energy will be slightly larger than the approximate figure calculated above.

Example 2

Chapter 15 gives details of a pressure survey carried out in a downcast shaft.

The following observations were obtained:

Depth (m)	Corrected mean barometric pressure (kPa)	Air temperatures	
		Wet-bulb (°C)	Dry-bulb (°C)
0	87,20	17,7	23,0
125,3	88,34	17,9	23,2
299,0	89,97	18,7	23,1
596,2	92,85	20,1	24,5
894,9	95,87	21,2	27,1

The frictional energy loss is calculated as follows:

(a) $\int_{P_1}^{P_2} vdP$

n	P_n (Pa)	v_n (m³/kg)	$P_{n+1} - P_n$ (Pa)	$\dfrac{v_n + v_{n+1}}{2}$ (m³/kg)	$(P_{n+1} - P_n)\dfrac{v_n + v_{n+1}}{2}$ (Nm/kg)
1	87 200	0,994 56	1 140	0,988 47	1 126,86
2	88 340	0,982 38	1 630	0,973 98	1 587,59
3	89 970	0,965 57	2 880	0,953 46	2 745,96
4	92 850	0,941 36	3 020	0,930 49	2 810,08
5	95 870	0,919 62			
				Total area	8 270,49

(b) $\int_{Z_1}^{Z_2} r\,dZ$

n	Z_n	r_n	$Z_{n+1}-Z_n$	$\dfrac{r_n+r_{n+1}}{2}$	$(Z_{n+1}-Z_n)\dfrac{r_n+r_{n+1}}{2}$
	(m)	(kg/kg)	(m)	(kg/kg)	(kg.m/kg)
1	0	0,012 57	125,3	0,012 57	1,575
2	125,3	0,012 56	173,7	0,012 99	2,256
3	299,0	0,013 42	297,2	0,013 87	4,122
4	596,2	0,014 31	298,7	0,014 29	4,268
5	894,9	0,014 28			

Total area 12,221

$$F_{1-2} = -g(Z_2-Z_1)-g\int_{Z_1}^{Z_2} r\,dZ+\int_{P_1}^{P_2} v\,dP$$

$$= -9,79\times894,9-9,79\times12,221+8\,270,5$$

$$= -8\,761,1-119,6+8\,270,5 = -610,2 \text{ Nm/kg.}$$

It is interesting to compare this value with the values that would have been obtained if only the two end observations had been used to determine

$\int_{P_1}^{P_2} v\,dP$ and $\int_{Z_1}^{Z_2} r\,dZ$.

(i) Linear variation of P with v and r with Z:

$$\int_{P_1}^{P_2} v\,dP = (P_2-P_1)\frac{v_1+v_2}{2}$$

$$= (95\,870-87\,200)\frac{0,994\,56+0,919\,62}{2}$$

$$= 8\,670\times0,957\,09=8\,298,0 \text{ Nm/kg.}$$

$$g\int_{Z_1}^{Z_2} r\,dZ = g(Z_2-Z_1)\frac{r_1+r_2}{2}$$

$$= 9,79\,(894,9-0)\frac{0,012\,57+0,014\,28}{2}$$

$$= 9,79\times894,9\times0,013\,43 = 117,7 \text{ Nm/kg.}$$

$$F_{1-2} = -8\,761,1-117,7+8\,298,0$$

$$= -580,8 \text{ Nm/kg (4,8 per cent lower than the initial result).}$$

(ii) Polytropic flow:

$$k = \frac{\log \dfrac{P_1}{P_2}}{\log \dfrac{v_2}{v_1}} = \frac{\log \dfrac{P_2}{P_1}}{\log \dfrac{v_1}{v_2}}$$

$$= \frac{\log(\dfrac{95\,870}{87\,200})}{\log (\dfrac{0,994\,56}{0,919\,62})}$$

$$= \frac{\log 1,099\,43}{\log 1,081\,49} = \frac{0,041\,168}{0,034\,022} = 1,210\,04$$

$$\int_{P_1}^{P_2} v\,dP = \frac{k}{k-1}(P_2 v_2 - P_1 v_1)$$

$$= \frac{1,210\,04}{1,210\,04-1}(95\,870 \times 0,919\,62 - 87\,200 \times 0,994\,56)$$

$$= 5,761 \times 1\,438,34 = 8\,286,3 \text{ Nm/kg}.$$

$$F_{1-2} = -8\,761,1 - 117,1 + 8\,286,3$$

$$= -592,5 \text{ Nm/kg (2,9 per cent lower than the initial result)}.$$

The previous examples have been concerned with comparatively simple situations and the following example is given to show how the method can be used to analyse more realistic and hence also more complex situations.

Example 3

The following line diagram represents a mine consisting of two downcast shafts and one upcast shaft with the main fan situated at the top of the upcast shaft (Fig. 12:6). A survey of the mine yielded the figures given in the table which follows.

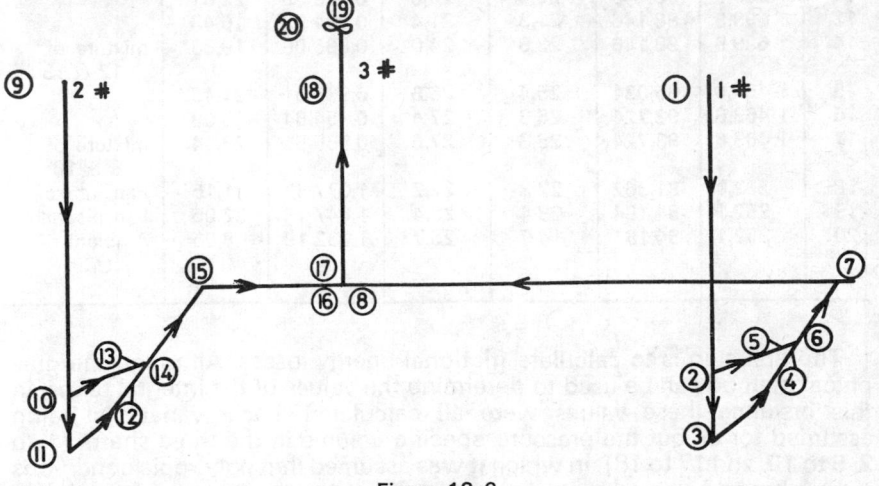

Figure 12:6

The following volume flow rates were measured:

Point	m³/s
2	106,0
3	104,0
10	88,5
11	81,5

All of the water condensed in the upcast shaft is carried out of the shaft by the airstream.

Point	Depth below datum	Baro-metric pressure	Temperatures		Apparent specific volume	Apparent specific humidity	Remarks
			Wet-bulb	Dry-bulb			
	(m)	(kPa)	(°C)	(°C)	(m³/kg)	(g/kg)	
1	253,0	84,193	14,7	25,8	1,032 36	8,01	
2	1 716,0	99,254	21,0	22,6	0,876 36	15,30	
3	1 819,2	100,426	21,5	22,5	0,866 61	15,87	
4	1 712,5	98,831	25,5	25,9	0,897 97	21,06	
5	1 712,5	98,831	21,8	22,6	0,881 81	16,54	
6	1 712,5	98,831	23,7	24,2	0,889 71	18,79	mixture of 4 & 5
7	1 468,8	95,519	26,0	26,7	0,933 50	22,38	
8	1 463,6	93,724	27,2	27,8	0,958 20	24,63	
9	232,9	84,000	14,7	25,6	1,034 22	8,12	
10	1 702,6	98,763	20,8	21,0	0,876 60	15,77	
11	1 806,8	99,941	21,3	21,5	0,868 16	16,08	
12	1 699,9	98,146	26,4	26,6	0,908 39	22,51	
13	1 699,9	98,146	21,3	21,4	0,884 22	16,43	
14	1 699,9	98,146	23,9	24,0	0,896 08	19,33	mixture of 12 & 13
15	1 467,6	95,034	25,4	26,6	0,936 61	21,46	
16	1 463,6	93,724	26,3	27,4	0,954 64	23,08	
17	1 463,6	93,724	26,8	27,6	0,956 55	23,94	mixture of 8 & 16
18	252,1	81,362	22,2	22,2	1,077 42	21,15	Fan intake
19	252,1	84,184	23,4	23,4	1,047 13	22,05	Fan discharge
20	252,1	84,184	14,7	25,7	1,032 19	8,05	Ambient at fan

The first step is to calculate frictional energy losses. Although the graphical method can be used to determine the values of the integral terms, in this instance these values were all calculated, linear variations being assumed for all but the pressure-specific volume in the three shafts (1 to 2, 9 to 10, and 17 to 18), in which it was assumed that polytropic conditions were obtained.

Details of most of the calculations will not be given, but the calculation of $\int_{P_1}^{P_2} v\,dP$ for No. 1 shaft will be given in detail.

$$P_1 = 84\ 193\ Pa \qquad v_1 = 1{,}032\ 36\ m^3/kg$$
$$P_2 = 99\ 254\ Pa \qquad v_2 = 0{,}876\ 36\ m^3/kg$$

$$k = \frac{\log \dfrac{P_1}{P_2}}{\log \dfrac{v_2}{v_1}} = \frac{\log \dfrac{P_2}{P_1}}{\log \dfrac{v_1}{v_2}}$$

$$\frac{P_2}{P_1} = 1{,}178\ 89 \qquad\qquad \log \frac{P_2}{P_1} = 0{,}071\ 473$$

$$\frac{v_1}{v_2} = 1{,}178\ 01 \qquad\qquad \log \frac{v_1}{v_2} = 0{,}071\ 149$$

$$k \qquad = 1{,}004\ 55$$
$$P_1 v_1 \quad = 86\ 917{,}5\ Nm/kg$$
$$P_2 v_2 \quad = 86\ 982{,}2\ Nm/kg$$

$$\int_{P_1}^{P_2} v\,dP = \frac{k}{k-1}(P_2 v_2 - P_1 v_1)$$

$$= \frac{1{,}004\ 55}{1{,}004\ 55 - 1}(86\ 982{,}2 - 86\ 917{,}5)$$

$$= \frac{1{,}004\ 55}{0{,}004\ 55} \times 64{,}7 = 14\ 284{,}5\ Nm/kg$$

The accuracy of this result must obviously be suspect, depending as the value does on small differences between large numbers. This is because in this instance the observed pressure-specific volume values fall very nearly on an "isothermal" curve passing through the two end points ($k = 1$, or $Pv = $ constant).

For an isothermal curve the integral is given by

$$\int_{P_1}^{P_2} v\,dP = P_1 v_1 \log_e \frac{P_2}{P_1} = P_2 v_2 \log_e \frac{P_2}{P_1}$$

A better value for $\int_{P_1}^{P_2} v\,dP$ will be obtained in this instance by calculating two values from the above and taking the average.

Thus $\int_{P_1}^{P_2} v\,dP = P_1 v_1 \log_e \dfrac{P_2}{P_1}$

$$= 86\ 917{,}5 \times 2{,}302\ 59 \times 0{,}071\ 473$$
$$= 14\ 304{,}3\ Nm/kg$$

and $\quad \int_{P_1}^{P_2} v\,dP = P_2 v_2 \log_e \dfrac{P_2}{P_1}$

$$= 86\ 982{,}2 \times 2{,}302\ 59 \times 0{,}071\ 473$$
$$= 14\ 314{,}9\ Nm/kg$$

The mean value is 14 309,6 Nm/kg.

In the following tables are presented values used in determining the frictional energy losses.

1 Shaft to 3 Shaft circuit

		1	2	3	4	5	6	7
					$3-1-2$		$\dfrac{4\times5}{1\,000}$	$\dfrac{2\times5}{1\,000}$
	Airway	$g(Z_2-Z_1)$	$g\displaystyle\int_{Z_1}^{Z_2}rdZ$	$\displaystyle\int_{P_1}^{P_2}vdP$	F_{1-2}	Mass flow rate (M)	$M\times F_{1-2}$	$gM\displaystyle\int_{Z}^{Z_2}rdZ$
		Nm/kg	Nm/kg	Nm/kg	Nm/kg	kg air/s	kW	kW
Downcast {	1— 2	14 323	167	14 310	−180	241	−43,4	40,2
	2— 3	1 010	16	1 021	−5	120	−0,6	1,9
	2— 5	−34	−1	−372	−337	121	−40,8	−0,1
Workings {	3— 4	−1 045	−19	−1 407	−343	120	−41,2	−2,3
	6— 7	−2 386	−49	−3 019	−584	241	−140,7	−11,8
{	7— 8	−51	−1	−1 698	−1 646	241	−396,7	−0,2
Upcast	17—18	−11 861	−284	−12 539	−394	241*	−95,0	−68,4
Surface	20— 1	9	0	9	0	241	0	0
Totals							−758,4	−40,7
Fan	18—19	0	0	2 998	2 998	241*	722,5	0

* The mass flow rate in these sections is that applicable to the particular circuit considered.

$$\text{Friction} + \text{moisture lift work} + \text{fan} + \text{NVE} = 0$$
$$-\ 758,4 - 40,7 + 722,5 + \text{NVE} = 0$$
$$\text{NVE} = 76,6\text{kW}$$

2 Shaft to 3 Shaft circuit

		1	2	3	4	5	6	7
					$3-1-2$		$\dfrac{4\times5}{1\ 000}$	$\dfrac{2\times5}{1\ 000}$
	Airway	$g(Z_2-Z_1)$	$g\int_{Z_1}^{Z_2} rdZ$	$\int_{P_1}^{P_2} vdP$	F_{1-2}	Mass flow rate (M)	$M\times F_{1-2}$	$gM\int_{Z_1}^{Z_2} rdZ$
		Nm/kg	Nm/kg	Nm/kg	Nm/kg	kg air/s	kW	kW
Downcast $\big\{$	9—10	14 388	172	14 041	−519	195	−101,2	33,5
	10—11	1 020	16	1 028	−8	94	−0,8	1,5
Workings $\big\{$	10—13	−26	−0	−543	−517	101	−52,2	−0,0
	11—12	−1 047	−20	−1 594	−527	94	−49,5	−1,9
	14—15	−2 274	−46	−2 852	−532	195	−103,7	−9,0
	15—16	−39	−1	−1 239	−1 199	195	−233,8	−0,2
Upcast	17—18	−11 861	−284	−12 539	−394	195*	−76,8	−55,4
Surface	20— 9	−188	−2	−190	0	195	0	−0,3
Totals							−618,0	−31,8
Fan	18—19	0	0	2 998	2 998	195*	584,6	0

* The mass flow rate in these sections is that applicable to the particular circuit considered.

$$\text{Friction} + \text{moisture lift work} + \text{fan} + \text{NVE} = 0$$
$$-\ 618,0 - 31,8 \qquad\qquad +\ 584,6 + \text{NVE} = 0$$
$$\text{NVE} = 65,2 \text{ kW}$$

For the mine as a whole

	Friction	+ moisture lift work	+ fan	+ NVE	= 0
1 Shaft	− 758,4	− 40,7	+ 722,5	+ 76,6	= 0
2 Shaft	− 618,0	− 31,8	+ 584,6	+ 65,2	= 0
Mine	1 376,4	− 72,5	+ 1 307,1	+141,8	= 0

It should be noted that in evaluating $g\oint MrdZ$ it is necessary to take into account airflow from the upcast shaft to the tops of the two downcast shafts (20–1 and 20–9). In the example, these two terms are negligible, but this will not necessarily be so when there are considerable differences in elevation between the collars of the shafts.

When dealing with a comparatively complex mine circuit, such as this one, the use of the above approach together with the pressure-volume diagram is necessary to get a complete picture of the problem. The following graph (Fig. 12:7) gives the pressure-volume diagram for this example.

Thus far it has been shown how the thermodynamic method is used to determine frictional energy losses in the various airways of a mine and to

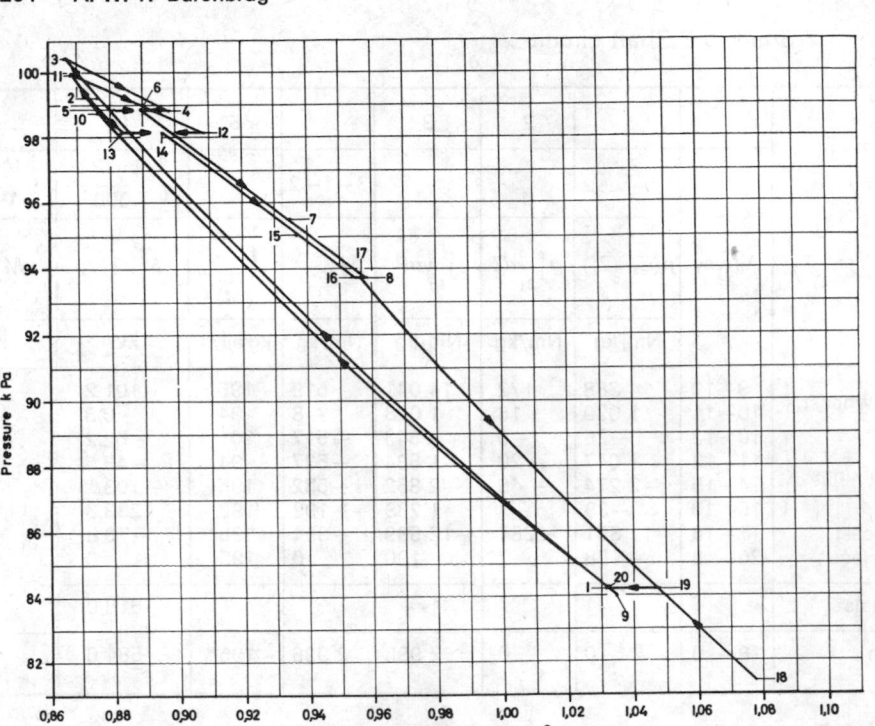

Figure 12:7

draw up an energy balance for the mine as a whole. A second problem is that of predicting fan requirements necessary to establish a given flow pattern either in an existing mine or in one in the planning stage. This is a very complex problem if it is to be tackled thoroughly, but there are several approximations which can be made to simplify the situation without affecting the accuracy of the end result significantly, bearing in mind the inevitable uncertainties associated with mining.

It can be shown that the fan energy required is given by

$$W_f = -\Sigma F - g \oint r dZ + \oint v dP$$

$$\text{or, } M_f W_f = -\Sigma MF - g \oint Mr dZ + \oint Mv dP.$$

In a given airway the frictional energy loss varies with the square of the volume flow rate and is not dependent upon air density.

The power required to lift water, both vapour and liquid, out of the mine, on the other hand, varies directly with the mass flow rate provided changes to the flow rate do not affect the variation of humidity throughout the mine and do not result in water droplets being carried by the airstream where formerly they were not, or *vice versa*.

If it is assumed that changes in the flow rate do not result in changes in the density or humidity patterns in the mine, it is a simple matter to estimate both the frictional energy requirements and the energy required to lift water vapour out of the mine. Changes which result in changes to the pattern of droplet transport are also easily dealt with.

The one remaining factor is the natural ventilation energy. This is given by the area enclosed in the pressure-volume curve and perhaps the easiest assumption to make here is that this remains constant.

Example 4

To illustrate this aspect, assume that the fan energy required is that which will cause an airflow 1,5 times greater than measured in the preceding example, that is, 654 kg/s instead of 436 kg/s.

$$\varSigma F = 1,5 \times 1,5 \times 1,5 \times (-1\,376,4) = -4\,645,4 \text{ kW}$$
$$-g \oint MrdZ = 1,5 \times 72,5 = 108,8 \text{ kW}$$
$$\oint MvdP = 141,8 \text{ kW}$$
$$\therefore M_f W_f = 4\,645,4 + 108,8 - 141,8$$
$$= 4\,612,4 \text{ kW}$$
$$W_f = \frac{4\,612,4}{1,5 \times 436} = 7\,053 \text{ Nm/kg}.$$

(This is 2,35 times teh previous figure of 2 998 Nm/kg).

It should be noted that while the frictional energy losses, expressed per unit mass of air, vary with the square of the volume flow rate, the frictional power losses vary both with the square of the volume flow rate and directly with the mass flow rate.

BIBLIOGRAPHY

Hinsley, F. B. Airflow in mines: a thermodynamic analysis. *Proc. S. Wales Inst. Engrs.* Vol. 59, 1943, p. 95–137.

Van Esbroeck, G. Thermodynamics of mine ventilation. *Colliery Eng.* Vol. 27, 1950, p. 68–72, p. 149–53, p. 366–9. Vol. 28, 1951, p. 11–14 and p. 34.

Hall, C. J. Thermodynamics of mine ventilation. *Colliery Eng.* Vol. 30, 1953, p. 66–9, p. 102–5, p. 158–62, p. 189–94, p. 246–50.

Rees, J. P. A note on the mine as a heat engine. *Bull. Mine Vent. Soc. S. Afr;* Vol. 8, 1955, p. 49–52.

Barenbrug, A. W. T. Fundamental thermodynamics applied to mine ventilation. *Bull. Mine Vent. Soc. S. Afr;* Vol. 9, p. 2–151.

McPherson, M. J. Mine ventilation thermodynamics – the entropy approach. University of Nottingham, *Mining Department Magazine.* Vol. 19, 1967, p. 47–57.

Hinsley, F. B. The assessment of energy and pressure losses due to airflow in shafts, airways and mine circuits. *J. Mine Vent. Soc. S. Afr;* Vol. 16, 1963, p. 25–44.

Barenbrug, A. W. T. Natural ventilation – a review. *J. Mine Vent. Soc. S. Afr;* Vol. 23, 1970, p. 89–100.

Hemp, R. Contribution to above paper. *J. Mine Vent. Soc. S. Afr;* Vol. 24, 1970, p. 138–47.

13 The Measurement of Airflow

J. A. DRUMMOND

Group Ventilation Engineer, Union Corporation, Limited

1   INTRODUCTION

An efficient, effective and economic ventilation system is dependent to a large extent on the accuracy and reliability of the measurement of air flow. Air velocity and volume are major factors in calculations involving power requirements, fan efficiencies, heating and cooling loads and filtration requirements. The importance and need for greater accuracy in so-called "routine measurements" is becoming more evident. Increasing statistical use is being made of the data obtained and unless these data are reasonably correct, interpretations are likely to be misleading. Incentive bonus schemes for the correct installation and use of ventilation equipment are also based on these routine measurements.

The degree of accuracy required depends on the circumstances of each individual case but in general it may be said that all measurements should be correct to at least within 5 per cent.

2   UNITS

The unit of flow most commonly used in the industry is m³/s and is the product of the average speed in m/s and the area of the duct in m² at the point of measurement. This can be represented by the expression

$$Q = VA$$

where

Q = quantity or volume in cubic metres per second
V = velocity in metres per second
A = area of the duct in metres.

It is frequently convenient to express the flow in terms of mass.

$$M = Q \times w$$

where

M = mass flow rate in kg/s
Q = quantity in m³/s
w = density in kg/m³

3   MEASUREMENT OF VELOCITY

The volume or mass of air and other gases cannot be measured easily or directly and it is necessary to measure either the physical effects caused by motion of the air or gas, or to add a tracer gas and determine the composition by chemical analysis.

The main physical effects are :

(a)   The mechanical effect on light dusts or vanes suspended in the air stream.

(b)   The pressure effect of air in motion.

(c)   The effect of velocity on the rate of cooling of a hot body.

3.1   *Mechanical effects of air in motion*

Instruments operated by the mechanical effects of air in motion include the smoke tube, rotameter, velometer and anemometer.

3.1.1   *The anemometer*

Details of the instruments and the use of the calibration chart for routine work have been dealt with in *Routine Mine Ventilation Measurements,*[1] but for more accurate and reliable results certain precautions must be taken.

In addition to calibrating the instrument the following factors must be considered:

EFFECT OF DENSITY

Most calibration tests on the Rand are conducted under surface atmospheric conditions where the air density is approximately $1,0 \text{ kg/m}^3$ while the instrument is used in underground air where the density may be 30 per cent greater than that of the air at surface.

The effect of air density on the accuracy of anemometer readings was investigated by Ower[2] whose findings were later confirmed by Swirles and Hinsley.[3] Ower recommends that when a correction factor is necessary the following procedure should be used:

(*a*)   Multiply the observed velocity by the ratio $\sqrt{\dfrac{w_1}{w_0}}$

(*b*)   Apply the correction to the velocity obtained under (*a*) from the calibration curve.

(*c*)   Multiply this corrected velocity by the ratio $\sqrt{\dfrac{w_0}{w_1}}$

where $w_1 =$ actual density and $w_0 =$ calibration density.

EFFECT OF NON-UNIFORM DISTRIBUTION

The velocity distribution across a duct is not uniform over the area of the anemometer. The difference in velocity may be appreciable especially in ducts of small cross-section. For example, a velocity of 2,5 m/s could be acting on one blade or part of a blade while at another point the force equivalent to 5 m/s could be applied and the question arises whether the anemometer in such cases will give a correct measurement of the velocity of the air passing the centre of the anemometer disc or will record some other velocity.

Ower's analysis of this problem showed that to obtain an accuracy of 1 per cent an anemometer should not be used in an airway which has a diameter less than six times that of the diameter of the instrument.

EFFECT OF THE INERTIA OF THE RECORDING MECHANISM

When the clutch of the anemometer is engaged, the gearing acts as a brake on the vanes and a certain time is required for the vanes to rotate and indicate the correct speed. The effect of this acceleration period is negligible provided the time of the test exceeds 30 seconds. For most mine work 50 seconds is recommended as the minimum period.

EFFECT OF PULSATING FLOW

Anemometers in air having a pulsating flow tend to overmeasure air speed because of the insensitivity of the instrument to a sudden decrease in velocity. The effect is unimportant, however, provided the amplitude of the pulsation does not exceed 14 per cent of the mean observed value. When the pulsation exceeds this percentage the errors rise rapidly and must be corrected according to the formula

$$E = \frac{100\lambda^2}{2}$$

where

E = percentage error.

λ = amplitude of the pulsation expressed as a fraction of the mean velocity.

This means that for a pulsation of ± 14 per cent about the observed mean value the value of E is approximately $+1$ per cent.

In practice it is usual to avoid taking measurements in places where pulsations are excessive.

EFFECT OF TRAVERSING

Movement of the instrument introduces some sources of error. These are:

(a)   The movement may cause air movement which is not part of the airstream.

(b)   The casing of the moving anemometer can alter the flow pattern.

(c)   Movement from a zone of high speed to one of low speed will give incorrect results.

Swirles and Hinsley's tests[3] under practical flow conditions showed that the combination of low air velocities and high traverse speeds would result in errors of considerable magnitude, as shown in Table 1.

TABLE I

True velocity m/s	Percentage error		
	Traverse speeds (m/s)		
	0,15	0,30	0,60
1	1,1	4,4	15,6
1,5	0,5	2,0	8,0
2	0,3	1,1	4,4
2,5	0,2	0,7	2,8
3	0,1	0,5	1,9

Correction factors could be deduced from the above table but for practical purposes it is best to standardize on, practice and perfect a particular traverse speed, say 0,2 m/s.

EFFECTS OF MISALIGNMENT

For correct operation, an anemometer should be held parallel to the airstream, but under practical underground conditions a certain yaw or misalignment is inevitable. This misalignment does not affect the accuracy of the results materially, provided the yaw does not exceed 20°.[3]

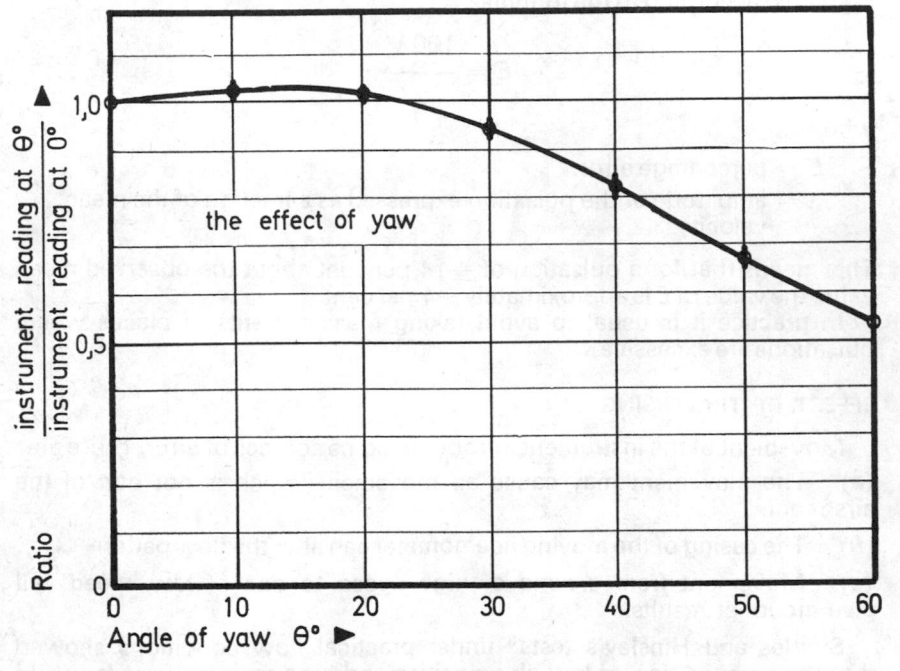

Figure 13:1

EFFECT OF INTERFERENCE BY THE OBSERVER

Interference by the body of the observer has been found to be one of the main sources of error. If the body was within 1 metre of the instrument, errors of up to 40 per cent could occur. Table 2 summarizes the effects of interference by the observers body.[3]

An obvious reaction to the results of tests showing the effects of the observer's body was the development of rods for holding the anemometer. Besides enabling the observer to keep the instrument at a reasonable distance away from his body, the traversing of large cross-sectional areas is made easier.

3.1.2   Use of the anemometer in underground airways

As explained previously, the velocity of the air may vary considerably over the cross-section of an airway or pipe, so that to obtain an accurate average it is necessary to take readings over the complete area of the airway.

For routine work the instrument is usually traversed across the airway but where a more accurate result is required, such as in fan tests, the method

TABLE 2

Proximity of the observer (m)	Error % Observer downstream			Error % Observer upstream		
	Airway areas m²					
	6,5	8,5	11	6,5	8,5	11
0,3	38	43	42	13	18	14
0,6	17	18	17	7	8	7
1,0	8	10	8	4	4	4
1,2	5	4	4	3	3	3
1,5	2	2	2	2	2	2

adopted is to divide the airway or duct into a number of geometric areas of shape similar to that of the main area and then to traverse the anemometer slowly and evenly over each of these areas. If small equal areas are used the average of the corrected velocities in each of these areas is assumed to be the average velocity of the air at the test section.

A section across a typical underground airway on which isovels have been drawn is given in Fig. 13 :2.

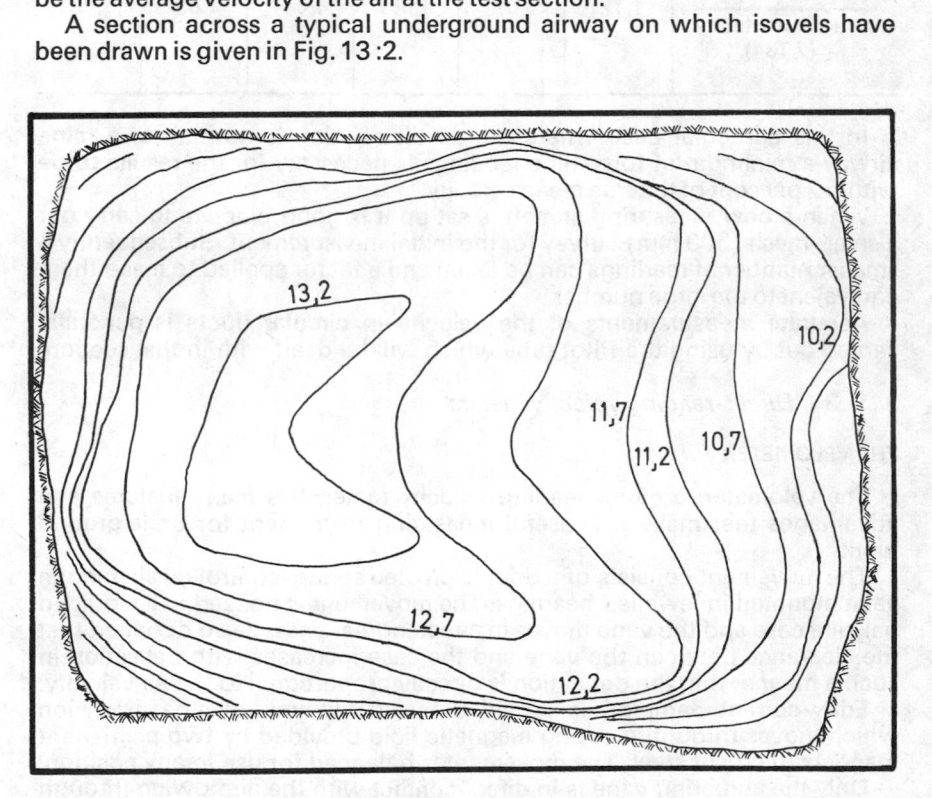

Figure 13 :2

It is always difficult to assess the number of sub-divisions necessary for accurate results, but the general tendency in practice is to make the sub-divisions too large, thus missing the rapid fall-off of velocity towards the perimeter.

If grids are placed over the isovels shown in Fig. 13:2 dividing the airway into 4, 9, 16, 25, 36 and 49 equal areas and the velocity corresponding to the centre of each rectangle is read off from the isovels, the following results are obtained:

TABLE 3

	Number of equal areas					
	4	9	16	25	36	49
Average area of each section m²	2,88	1,28	0,72	0,46	0,32	0,295
Mean corrected vel. m/s	8,66	8,28	8,13	8,05	7,98	7,88
Velocity as above / True mean velocity (7,734)	1,12	1,07	1,051	1,041	1,032	1,02

In this particular case where the air distribution is normal for a mine airway a minimum of forty-nine readings is necessary for the results to be within 2 per cent of the true mean velocity.

When a new measuring station is set up it is good practice to carry out a small-mesh (300 mm) survey for the initial measurement. Subsequently a smaller number of readings can be taken and a factor applied to make them equivalent to the large number.

Accurate measurements of the velocity in circular ducts is generally carried out by using the Pitot tube which will be dealt with in that section.

3.1.3   Direct-reading velocity meters

THE VELOMETER

The velometer, a direct-reading velocity meter, has many features and advantages that make it a useful measuring instrument for underground work.

The movement consists of a double pivoted spring-controlled aluminium vane mounted in jewelled bearings. The movement is housed in a moulded bakelite case and the vane moves in a rectangular passage so designed that the clearance between the vane and the case increases with deflection in such a manner that the deflection is directly proportional to the air velocity.

Eddy-current damping is provided by an aluminium vane extension which moves through a strong magnetic field provided by two permanent magnets of cobalt steel. The movement is balanced for use in any position.

Only the actuating vane is in direct contact with the air flowing through the meter, the spring control bearings, etc., being in a separate part of the case. Zero correction devices are fitted together with a clamp which fixes the movement during transport.

The use of delicate bearings and springs makes the velometer extremely sensitive and measurements down to 0,03 m/s are possible, though the lower limit is given as 0,15 m/s.

A series of interchangeable jets are used to extend the measuring range to 30 m/s. Pitot-type jets are available for making measurements inside pipes as well as types suitable for obtaining average velocities at grills. For each particular jet fitted there is a scale on the dial.

A typical velometer and its fittings are illustrated below.

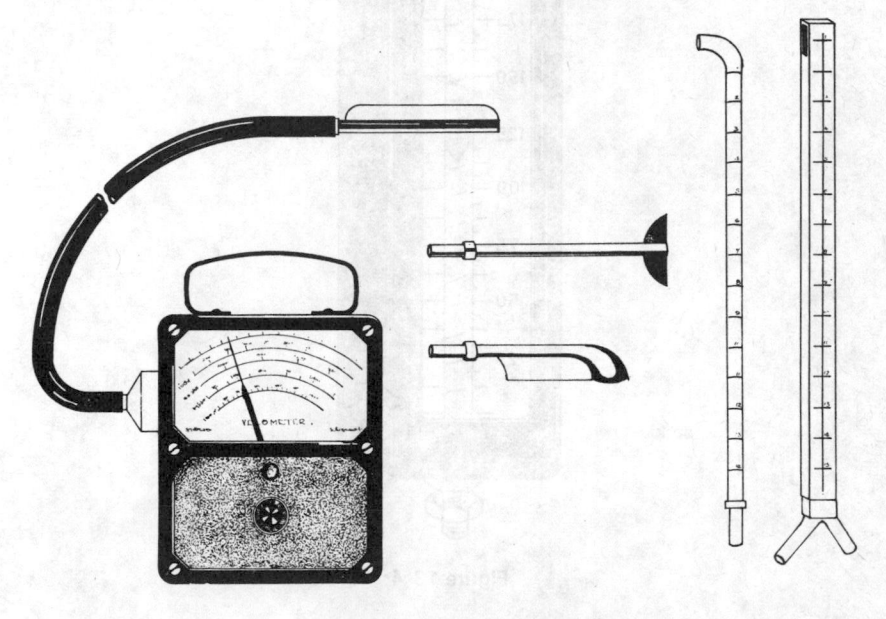

Figure 13 :3

The instrument is not affected by dust and moisture normally present in mine air but if these are present in the air in large amounts the use of special filters is recommended.

During calibration the meters are fitted with scales marked in degrees on a master jig. The blank instrument scale is then fitted into the master jig and the velocities corresponding to the measured velocities are marked in. The makers claim that the calibration remains accurate with normal usage but they recommend that it be checked every two years or more frequently if used for important work.

THE ROTAMETER

Rotameters are convenient instruments for metering the volume flow rate of air where the air is under pressure and the flow rate of the order of 0,02 to 60 ℓ/s as would be found in dust- and gas-sampling instruments.

The essential features of the meter are shown in Fig. 13 :4.

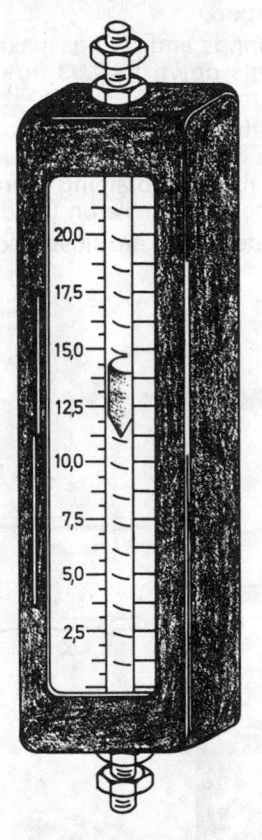

Figure 13 :4

The fluid being measured flows vertically upwards through the gauge conveying the metering float or ball until a position is reached in the tapered tubes where the weight of the float is balanced by the force of the fluid flowing past it. The height to which it is raised is a function of the flow rate.

Glass-tube rotameters are normally "tailor-made" instruments calibrated individually for a particular duty and fluid, producing an instrument of very high accuracy.

Improvements in manufacturing technique now make it possible to produce rotameters in which the essential elements, i.e. tapered metering tubes and floats, are made to accurate specifications and do not require individual calibration for normal industrial applications. This "metric series" has an additional feature in that the flow scale is not engraved on the metering tube but on a separate plate, an arrangement permitting a great deal of flexibility.

The series is based on eight standard sizes of metering tubes with standardized floats of stainless steel for liquids, light alloy for air and non-corrosive gases and a ceramic material for corrosive gases. Each metric tube has an engraved scale graduated in millimetres which is sufficient if relative volumes are required. These graduations can also be related to the absolute values through the medium of a correction chart.

For flows of 0,15 ℓ/s the metering error would not exceed 5 per cent. The error in the larger instrument handling up to 35 ℓ/s would be of the order of 2 per cent.

As the meter is installed in series with the flow, a certain loss of pressure is incurred varying from 50 Pa for the small instrument to 425 Pa for the larger ones at maximum capacity.

Meters calibrated for one density can be corrected to another by means of the formula :

$$Q_2 = Q_1 \sqrt{\frac{w_1}{w_2}}$$

where

Q_2 = corrected volume
Q_1 = indicated flow
w_1 = calibration density
w_2 = density of fluid being measured.

3.2   *The pressure effects of air in motion*

Several types of meters employing the principle of pressure changes are available. In the first group the air does not flow through the meter but registers a pressure equal to the velocity head, which can be used to calculate the velocity. The second group consists of nozzles and orifice plates through which the air passes. The reduced cross-section of the nozzle or orifice produces pressure changes which can be related to the flow.

3.2.1   *Pitot tubes*

3.2.1.1   Using the Pitot tube

Pitot tubes consist essentially of two co-axial tubes, one arranged to face directly into the air stream and so measure the total pressure while the other is open to the flow only through some small holes a short distance back from the facing tube and measuring the static pressure. The head containing the facing and static holes is carried on a stem of suitable length set at right angles to the head.

While the facing tube reflects accurately the total pressure, the static holes are subject to some interference by the facing tube and stem and have to be sized and located correctly if the true static pressure is to be obtained.

By experiment the correct proportions have been found and most Pitot tubes conform to one or other of those shown in Fig. 13 :5.

All the types of tubes sketched have right-angled heels but it is sometimes convenient to have a radius on the heel to facilitate insertion of the tube into a duct.

Tubes are usually 8 mm in diameter but there is no reason why larger or smaller tubes should not be used provided they are constructed in the proportions shown.

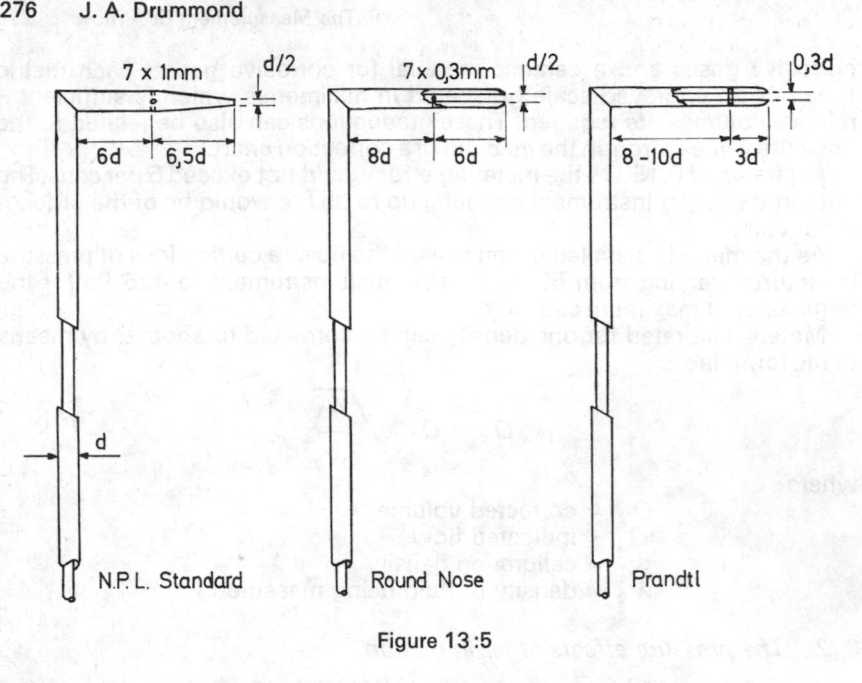

Figure 13:5

The sharp nose of the standard N.P.L. Pitot static tube is very vulnerable to damage and round-nosed instruments are generally preferred for mining and industrial use. The Prandtl tube which employs an annular slit in place of the static holes is used where dust or moisture are present, as the slit does not choke up as readily as the holes.

TEST HOLES

As far as possible the test holes in the metal pipe should be drilled to avoid leaving ragged burrs on the inside of the pipe which would upset the flow lines to some extent. It is normal to traverse two diameters at right angles to each other.

Marking-off of the test holes in horizontal piping can be simplified by use of a suitable length of thin cord, weighted at both ends and draped over the pipe, as shown in Fig. 13:6.

The points at which the cord leaves the pipe represent the ends of the horizontal diameter while the point on the circumference midway between the cords gives the position of the vertical diameter.

SUPPORT OF THE PITOT TUBE

The correct positioning of the Pitot head is most important. In Figure 13.14 it can be seen that at least four test points are situated in a region where velocity changes rapidly with position and where even the smallest error in placing the Pitot static head would make a considerable difference to the velocity obtained.

The apparatus shown in Fig. 13:7 has been found to be useful for

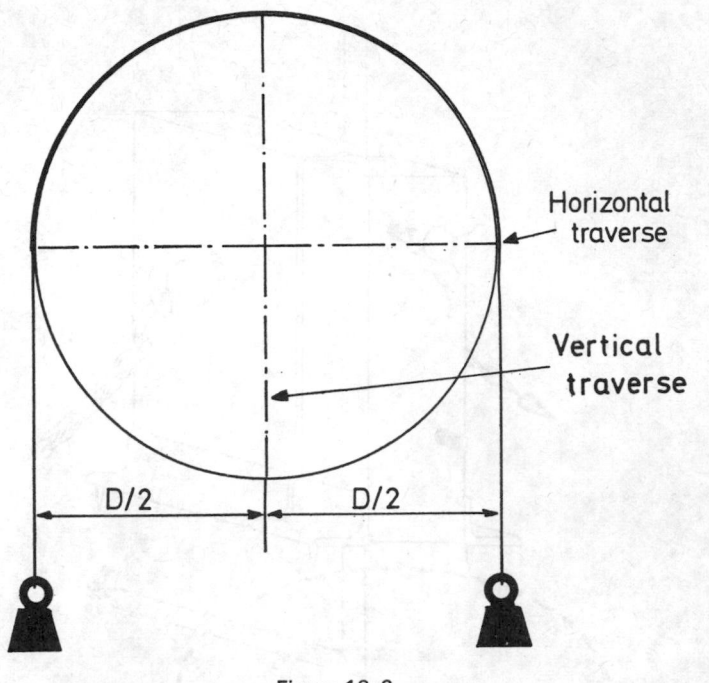

Figure 13:6

holding the Pitot tube steady in the correct position when the flow in pipes is being measured.

The Pitot tube is clamped to the device and inserted through the hole in the duct. The chain is then passed around the pipe and a suitable link is fastened to the loose turnbuckle. These buckles are then tightened and adjusted to make the Pitot tube either horizontal or vertical.

Provision is made on the device for an additional static connection for use on occasions when free moisture or dust tend to choke the rather small static holes of the standard tube. The Pitot static tube is replaced with a facing tube which is traversed across the pipe while the second clamp holds a short copper pipe firmly over a 3 mm hole drilled through the duct wall. It is assumed that the static pressure is equal at all points in the pipe; this assumption is normally true for long straight runs of piping.

TUBES

Clear plastic tubing is very suitable for Pitot tube use. This type does not kink readily and, being transparent, it is comparatively easy to check for cuts, punctures or water blockage.

The length required depends on circumstances but 6 m should be adequate for most situations. This length has the effect of damping-out fluctuations to some extent, especially if the tube used to measure the

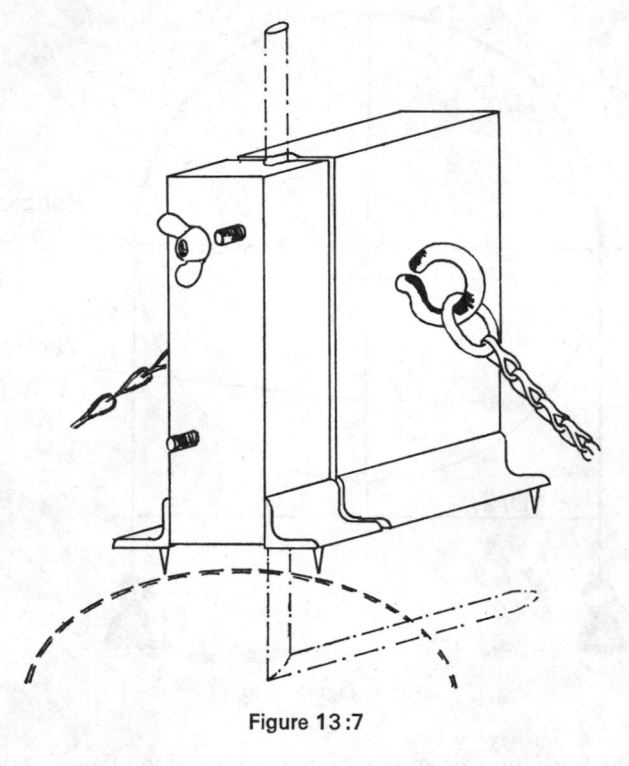

Figure 13:7

total pressure is smaller in diameter. The use of different-sized tubes also facilitates connections to the correct points on the gauge and Pitot tube.

LEAKAGE CURRENTS

To prevent high-velocity leakage currents from affecting the readings it is usual to fit a small piece of light, flexible rubber to the Pitot stem. Under suction the seal will stay against the pipe but some form of clamp is required for pressure columns.

ZERO SETTING

It is sometimes necessary to set up the gauge in strong air currents which impinge on the gauge opening making levelling and zero setting difficult operations. One simple way of eliminating this difficulty is to bridge the two connections on the gauge with a short length of rubber tubing.

PULSATIONS

Fluctuations or pulsations in the velocity head are to be expected in any flow but provided the degree of fluctuation does not exceed 25 per cent of the arithmetic mean of the maximum and minimum readings, no great error is introduced. The approximate error caused by pulsation is shown in Fig. 13:8.

Excessive pulsations can be controlled to some extent by inserting a few millimetres of capillary tubing into the total pressure connection. Under these conditions pressure response becomes somewhat sluggish and time must be allowed for the liquid to adjust itself to the changed pressures.

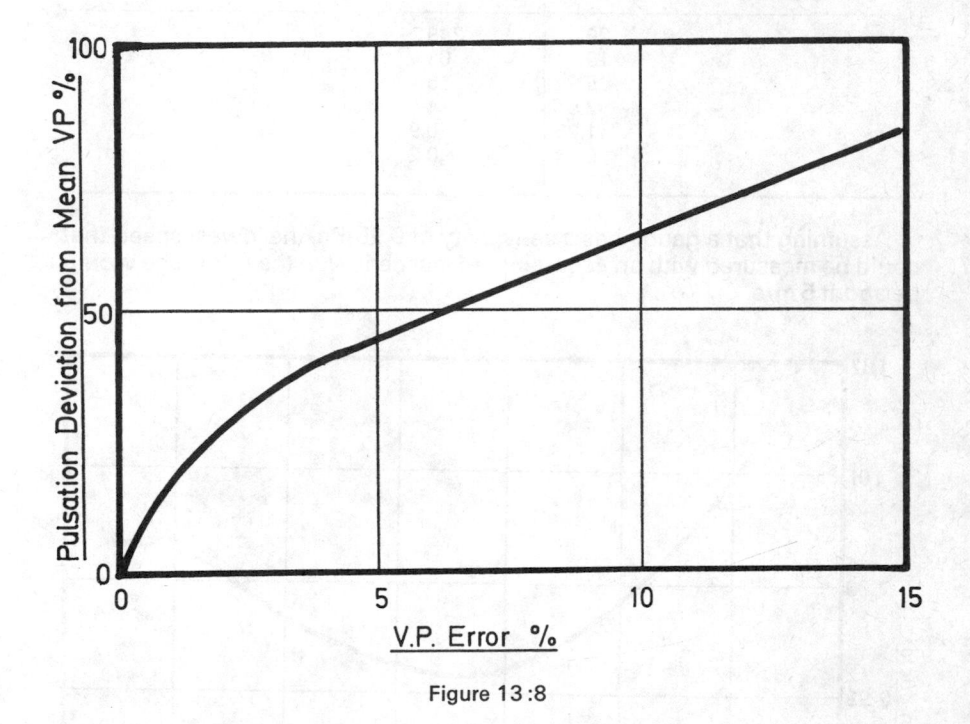

Figure 13 :8

PROTECTION AGAINST THE EFFECTS OF LARGE PRESSURE DIFFERENCES

Care must be taken to protect the fluid in the gauge against large pressure differences when inserting the Pitot head into the duct. With soft tubing this is usually accomplished by fitting a spring clip near the gauge but with the comparatively rigid plastic tubing it is necessary to insert a glass stopcock near the gauge in one or both of the tubes.

As the instrument has no moving parts it is inherently accurate and reliable, and if constructed to the specifications given, the correction factor may be assumed to be unity over the range 6 m/s to 51 m/s. However, for very accurate work in the low velocity range (see Fig. 13 :9) the Pitot tubes have to be calibrated.

A difficulty does arise when measuring low velocities, not particularly with the Pitot tube, but with the differential gauge which has to be extremely sensitive and accurate to measure the low differential heads set up by these low velocities, as can be seen from the Table 4.

TABLE 4

Velocity m/s	Velocity Pressure Pa (Density 1,2 kg/m³)
20	249
10	63
5	15
2,5	4
1,25	0,9
0,64	0,2

Assuming that a gauge has a sensitivity of 0,25 Pa, the lowest speed that could be measured with an accuracy of 1 per cent with the Pitot tube would be about 5 m/s.

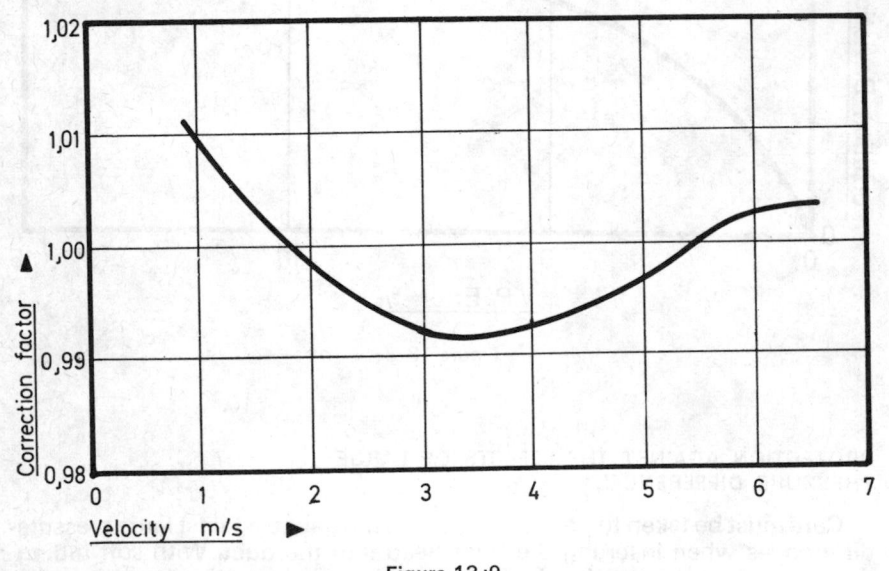

Figure 13:9

THE EFFECTS OF YAW OR MISALIGNMENT OF THE PITOT HEAD

Ower[1] states that "For accurate results the Pitot tube must have its head aligned with the direction of the air current. Appreciable errors occur if the axis of the head is inclined at more than five or six degrees to the direction of flow."

Fig. 13:10 shows the correction factor needed for various angles of yaw for the N.P.L. standard Pitot tube shown in Fig. 13:5.

The diagram shows clearly that the correct alignment of the standard tube corresponds to the maximum reading and this position can be found

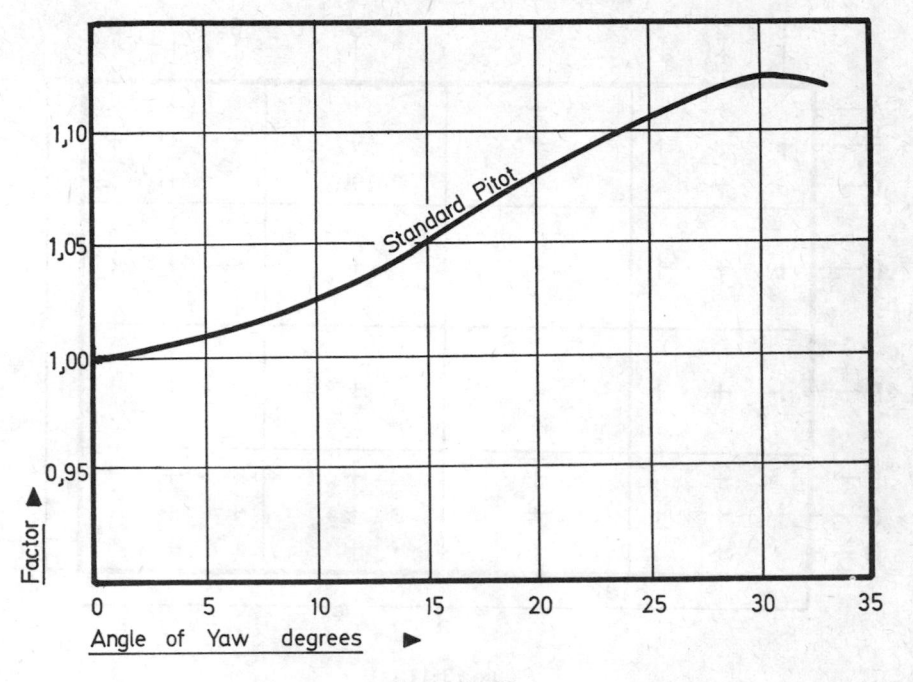

Figure 13:10

by yawing the Pitot head and noting the position at which this reading occurs.

MEASURING POINTS

(i) Rectangular ducts

For fan test measurements and others of similar importance BSS 848/63 recommends dividing the airway into sixteen areas of the same geometric shape and measuring the velocity pressure at the positions shown in Fig. 13:11 (a) and (b).

The average velocity in each sub-section is calculated and the average velocity of the airway is taken as the mean of the averages.

The precise positioning of the Pitot head is a requirement of the code and a convenient method of achieving this is to fasten small non-ferrous hooks to the hanging- and footwalls in wooden plugs or by "rock glue" at the indicated horizontal positions. Each of the eight sets of hooks is then fitted with a light chain carrying 10-mm diameter curtain rings set into the chains at the intervals required by the code. (Fig. 13:12).

(ii) Circular ducts

Circular ducts are normally divided into a number of concentric areas, generally five, and readings are taken at the centre of each area along the horizontal and vertical diameters. (Figure 13.13).

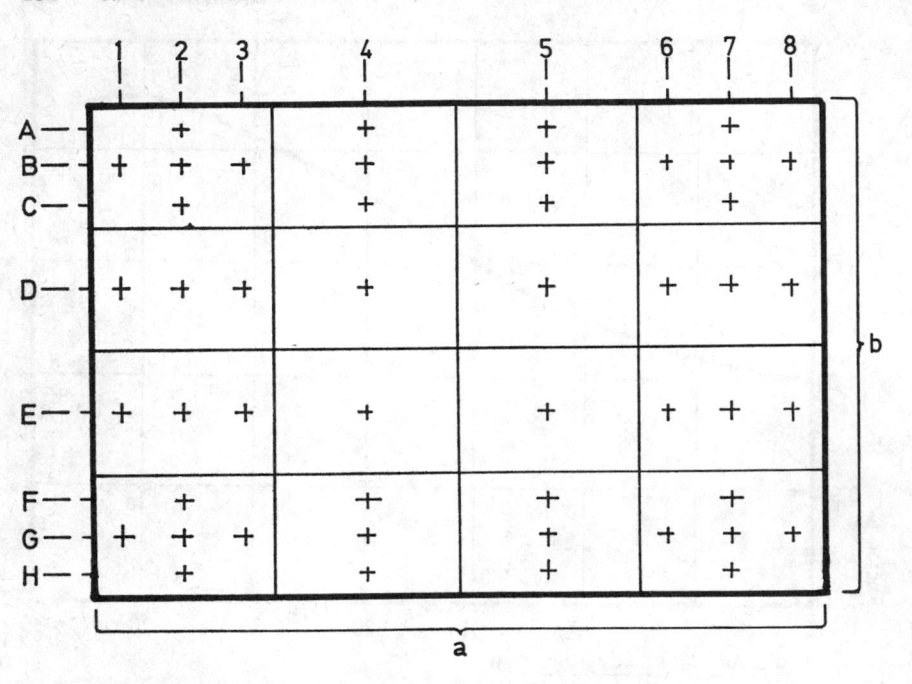

Figure 13:11 (a)

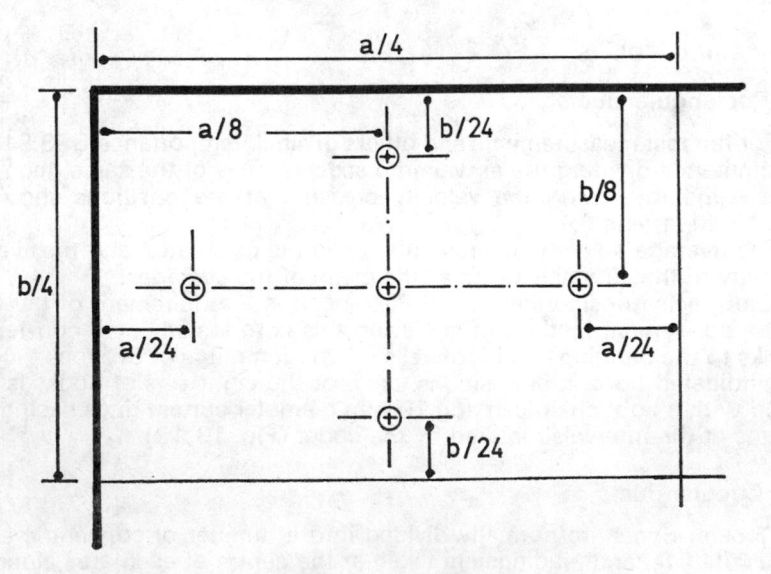

Figure 13:11 (b)

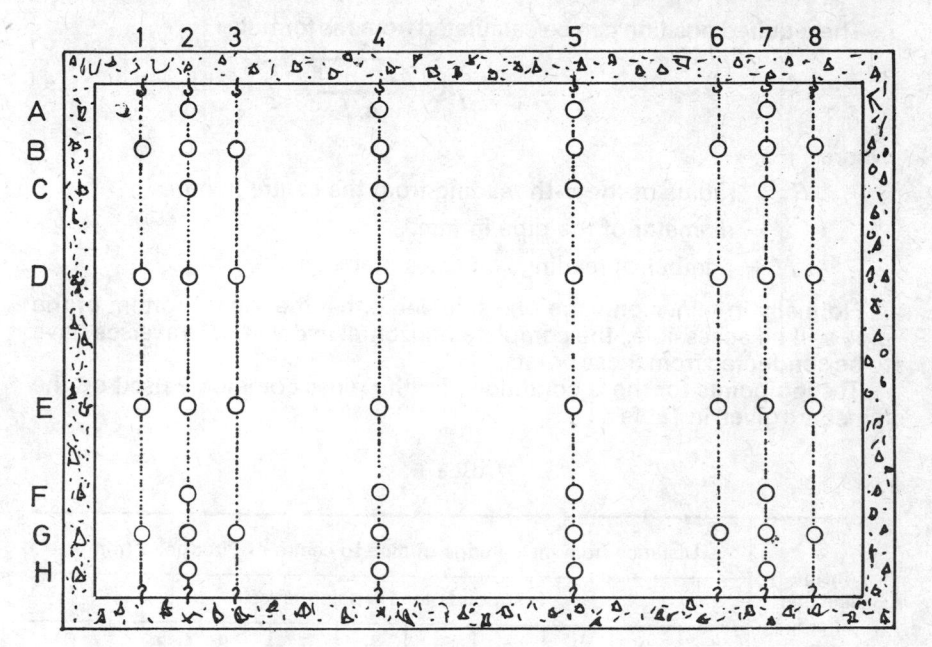

Figure 13:12

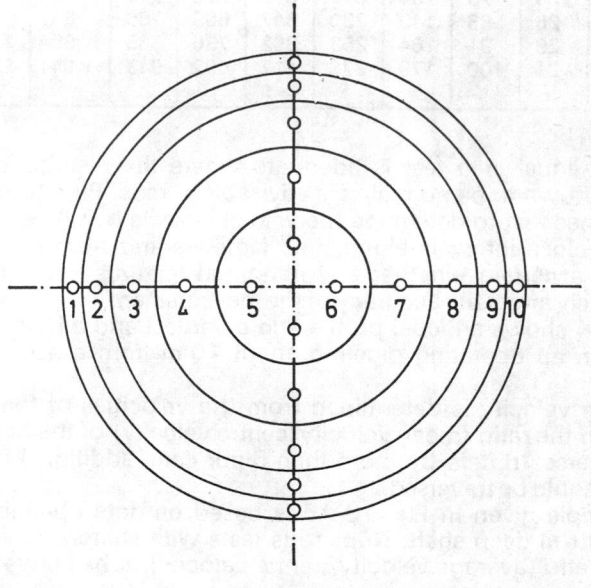

Figure 13:13

The required position can be calculated from the formula:

$$R_n = d\sqrt{\frac{2n-1}{4N}}$$

where

R_n = radius of the n-th reading from the centre in mm.

d = diameter of the pipe in mm.

N = number of readings across a diameter.

Normally in mines only the one side and either the top or bottom of the pipe will be accessible; the complete horizontal and vertical traverses have to be conducted from these points.

Testing points for these conditions for the pipes commonly used on the mines are given in Table 5:

TABLE 5

Inside diameter of pipe mm	Distance from inside edge of pipe to centre of Pitot head (mm)									
	Test points for 10-point traverse									
	1	2	3	4	5	6	7	8	9	10
305	8	25	45	69	104	201	236	260	280	297
406	10	33	60	92	139	267	315	347	373	396
572	15	47	84	129	195	376	442	488	525	557
762	20	62	112	172	261	501	590	650	699	743
914	24	75	134	207	313	602	708	780	840	891
1 016	26	83	149	230	347	669	786	867	933	990
1 118	29	91	164	253	382	736	865	954	1 026	1 089
1 219	31	100	179	276	417	802	943	1 041	1 120	1 188

While an equal-area test is adequate where the distribution of air in the duct is known to be normal, it is advisable in most Pitot tube surveys of mine pipe lines first to determine the velocity profile by taking a number of readings at close intervals along the diameters and from a plot of these readings to ascertain whether any abnormal features are present which could seriously affect the accuracy of the measurement.

Fig. 13:14 shows an ideal profile and a vertical and a horizontal profile measured on an operating pipeline about 10 m from a partially blocked intake.

The mean velocity is determined from the velocities of the equal area test points. If the ratio (mean velocity/centre velocity) of the horizontal and vertical traverses differs by more than 5 per cent, additional intermediate diameters should be traversed.

The example given in Fig. 13:15 is based on data obtained in a 3-m diameter 180-m deep shaft. Numerous tests with shafts of this type have shown the ratio (average velocity/centre velocity) to be between 0,86 and 0,88.

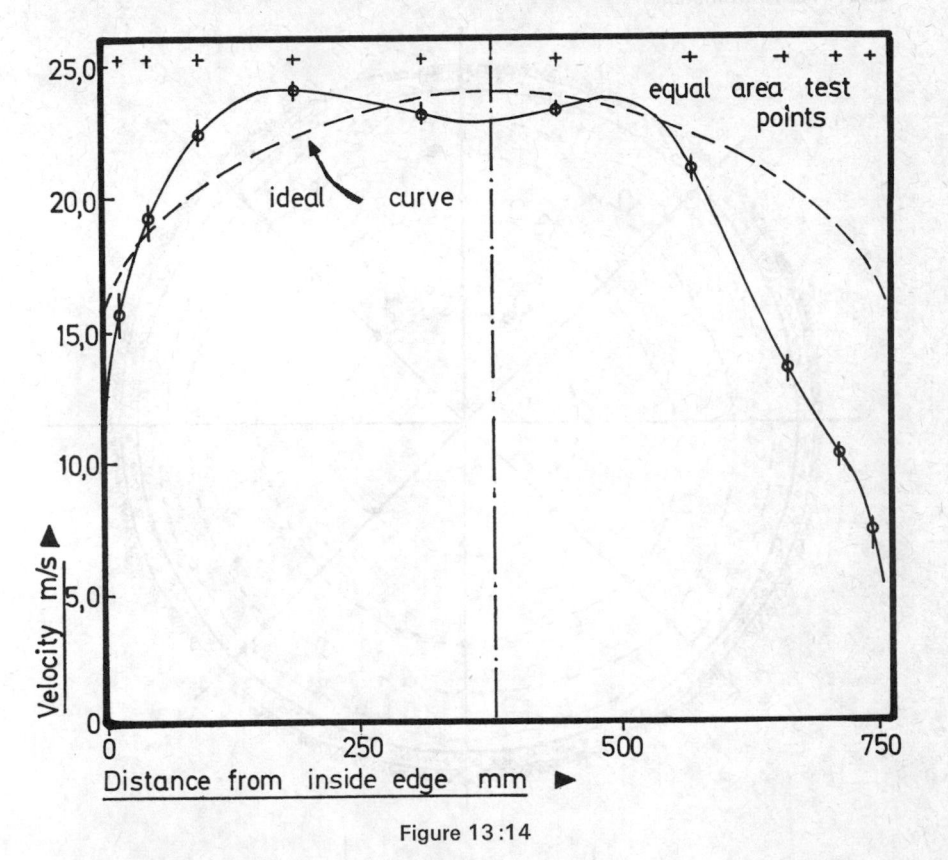

Figure 13:14

The shape of the duct affects the value of the ratio. Measurements taken in the semicircular upcast compartments shown in Fig. 13:16 gave a ratio of 0,85.

3.2.2 *Orifice plates*

Measurement of the change in pressure across an orifice is a convenient method of measuring airflow. Most of the experimental work was conducted with incompressible fluids but the formulae can be used to assess the flow of gases provided the pressure difference across the orifice is not sufficient to change the density materially (BSS 1042:1964).

Fig. 13:17 below indicates the airflow pattern in a horizontal pipe with an orifice plate between the flanges and shows the tapping points at D and $D/2$.

As the fluid approaches the orifice, the flow lines converge and continue to do so for a short distance beyond the orifice.

This minimum area which is approximately 0,67 of the orifice area is known as the "vena contracta". The flow at this point is uniform with a velocity pressure nearly equal to the static pressure in the upstream pipe if the discharge is free to atmosphere.

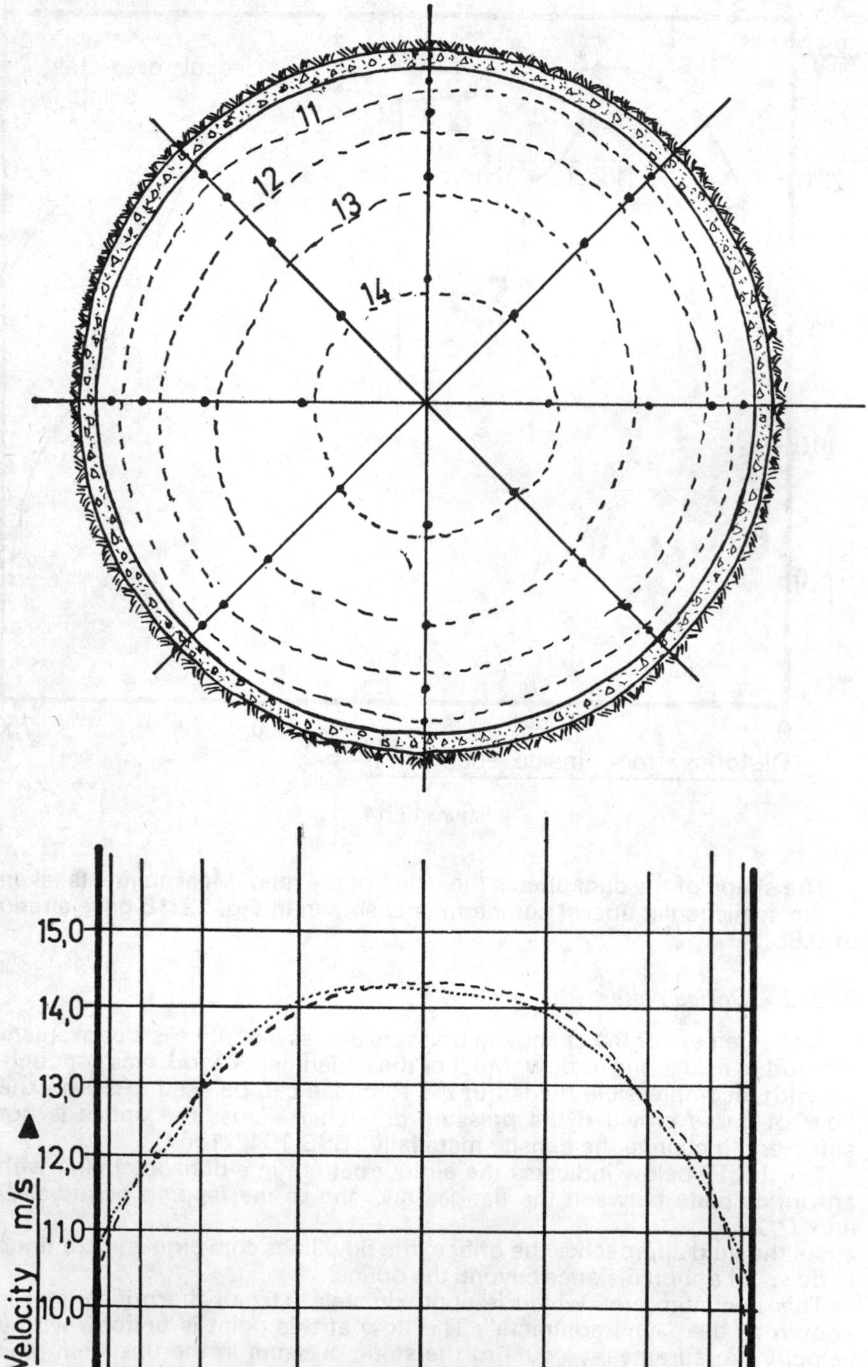

Figure 13:15

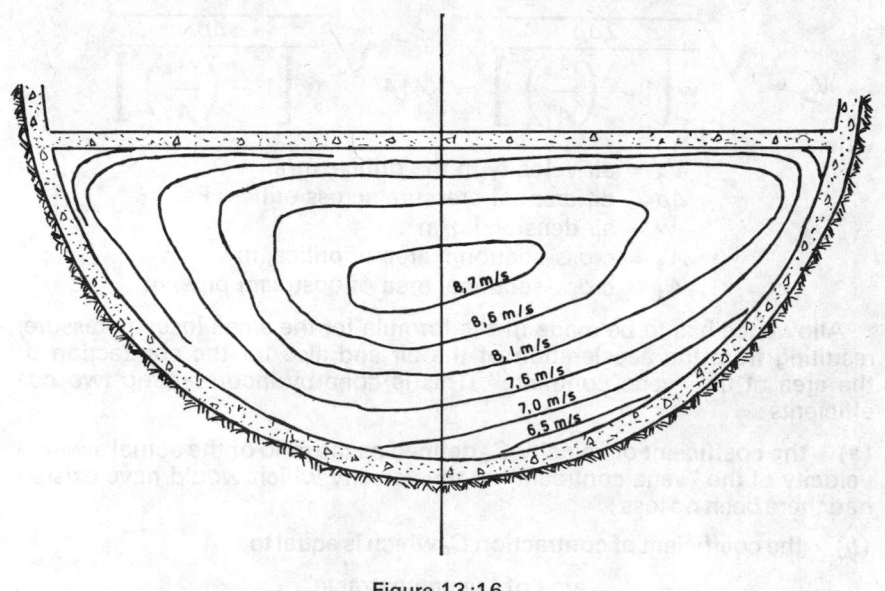

Figure 13:16

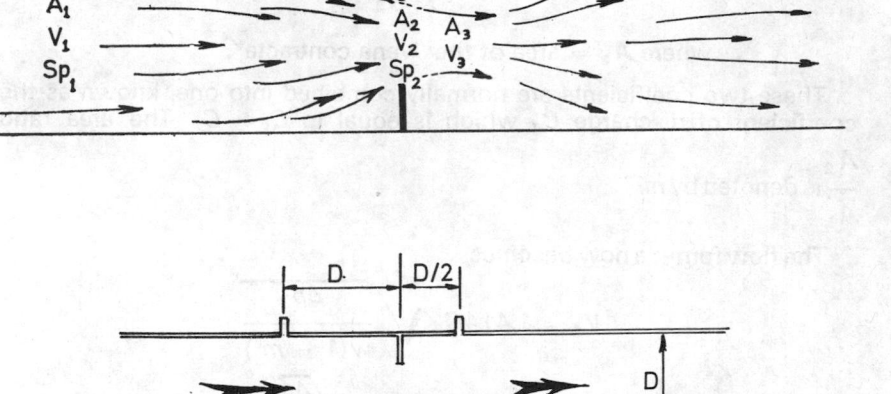

Figure 13:17

The Bernoulli equation is used as the basis for the following formula to calculate the velocity of the air and hence the airflow (assuming the pipe to be horizontal and the density remains constant) :

$$V_2 = \sqrt{\dfrac{2\Delta p}{w\left[1 - \left(\dfrac{A_2}{A_1}\right)^2\right]}} = 1{,}414\sqrt{\dfrac{\Delta p}{w\left[1 - \left(\dfrac{A_2}{A_1}\right)^2\right]}}$$

where

$V_2 =$ air velocity in the orifice, m/s.
$\Delta p =$ differential pressure across orifice, Pa.
$w =$ air density, kg/m^3.
$A_2 =$ cross-sectional area of orifice, m^2.
$A_1 =$ cross-sectional area of upstream pipe, m^2.

Allowance has to be made in the formula for the small loss in pressure, resulting from the acceleration of the air and also for the contraction of the area of the "vena contracta". This is done by incorporating two co-efficients:

(a)   the coefficient of velocity C_v defined as the ratio of the actual average velocity of the "vena contracta" to the velocity which would have existed had there been no loss;

(b)   the coefficient of contraction C_c which is equal to

$$\frac{\text{area of "vena contracta"}}{\text{area of orifice}}$$

then $C_c = \dfrac{A_3}{A_2}$

where $A_3 =$ area of the "vena contracta".

These two coefficients are normally combined into one, known as the coefficient of discharge C_d which is equal to $C_c \times C_v$. The area ratio $\dfrac{A_2}{A_1}$ is denoted by m.

The flow formula now becomes

$$V_2 = 1{,}414 C_d \sqrt{\frac{\Delta p}{w(1 - m^2)}}$$

$$\text{and } Q = 1{,}414 A_2 C_d E \sqrt{\frac{\Delta p}{w}}$$

$$= 1{,}414 \frac{\pi d^2}{4} C_d E \sqrt{\frac{\Delta p}{w}}$$

$$= 1{,}11 d^2 C_d E \sqrt{\frac{\Delta p}{w}}$$

where

$$Q = \text{air volume m}^3/\text{s.}$$
$$C_d = \text{coefficient of discharge.}$$
$$d = \text{diameter of orifice m.}$$
$$E = \frac{1}{\sqrt{1 - m^2}} = \text{velocity of approach factor.}$$

C_d is dependent on the area ratio; the Reynolds Number and type of orifice and can be obtained from tables and graphs.

The coefficient of discharge remains practically constant over a wide range of Reynolds numbers for values of m between 0,3 and 0,6. (Fig. 13:18).

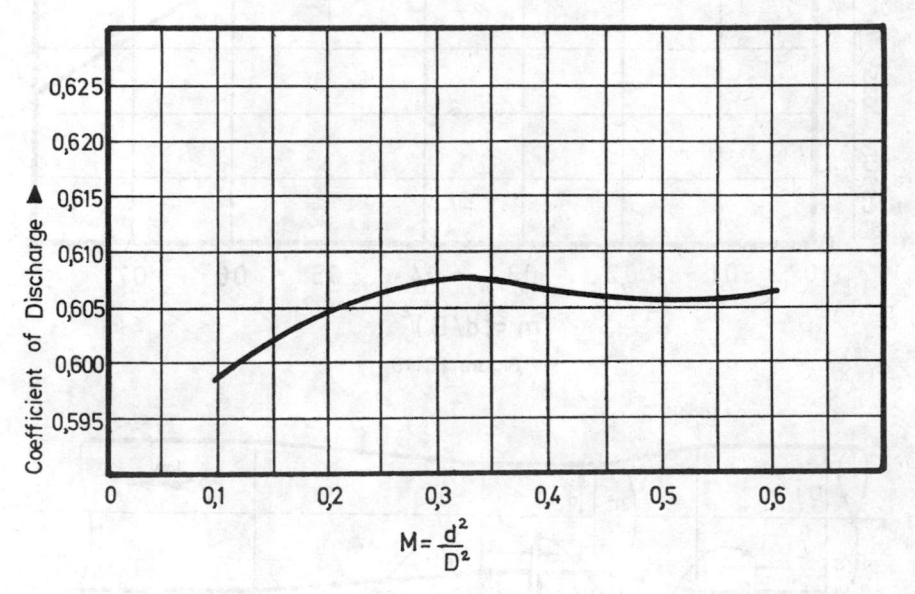

Figure 13:18

Rabson[4] contends that for mining purposes the shape of the orifice is not critical and that square and rectangular openings have substantially the same coefficient of discharge as circular ones of the same area. Also for these purposes the thick-edged openings are not materially different from the sharp-edged plates.

An orifice inserted into a circuit causes a loss of pressure depending on the differential head and the value of m as shown in Fig. 13:19.

3.2.3 Venturi meters

Another form of pressure differential device is the venturi meter. Details of a standard conical venturi meter are given in Fig. 13:20.

100
50
0
Pressure loss % of diff. pressure
0
0,1
0,2
0,3
0,4
0,5
0,6
0,7
m =(d/D)²

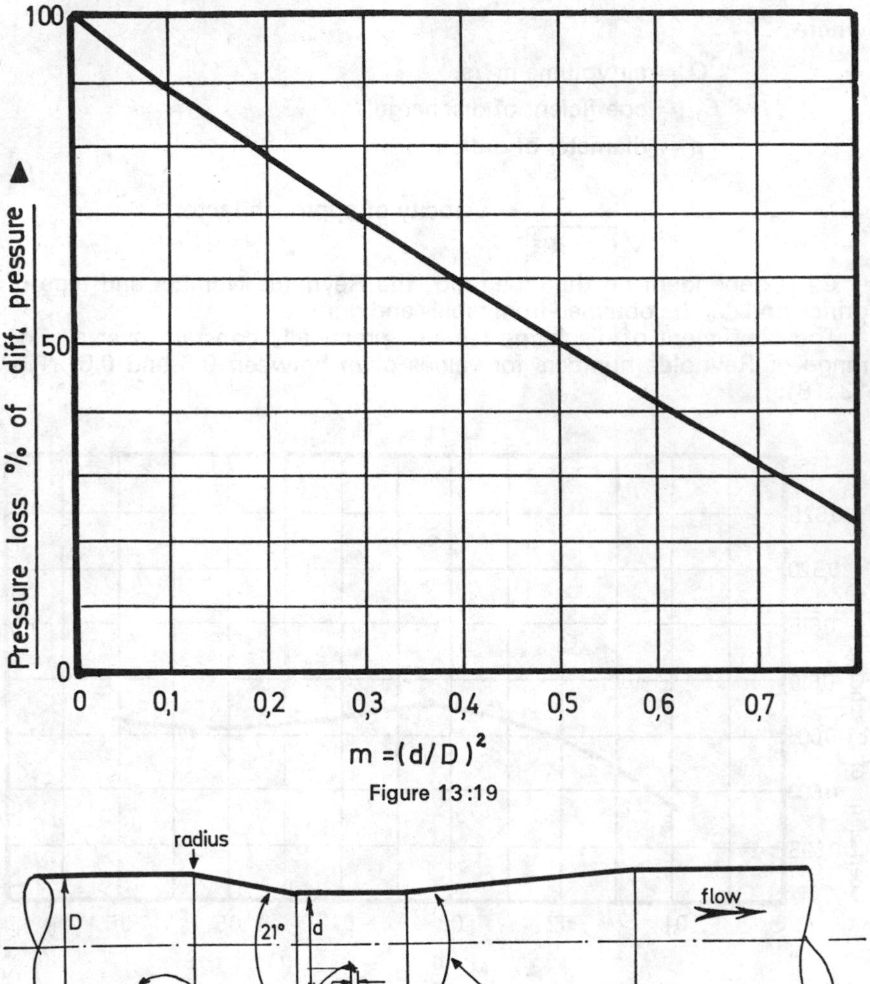

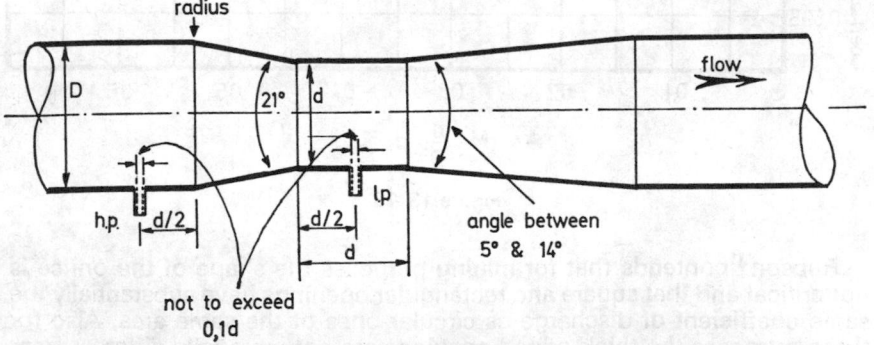

Figure 13:19

radius
flow
D
21°
d
h.p.
d/2
d/2
l.p
d
angle between
5° & 14°
not to exceed
0,1d

Figure 13:20

The flow formula is similar to that for the sharp-edged orifice i.e.

$$Q = 1{,}11 d^2 C_d E \sqrt{\frac{\Delta p}{w}}$$

A slight tendency to the formation of a "vena contracta" which results in a stable coefficient of discharge close to unity is shown in Fig. 13:21.

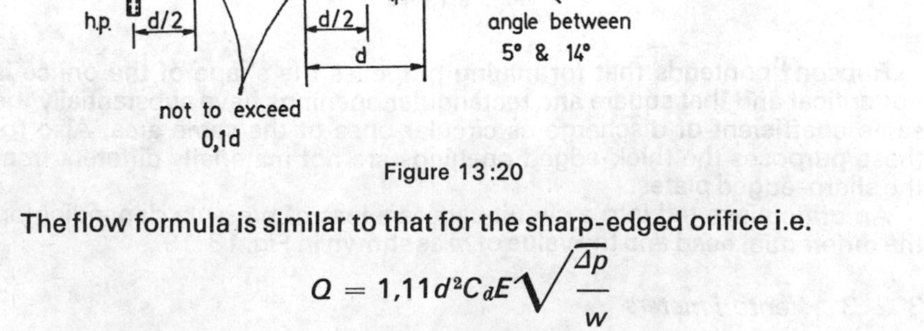

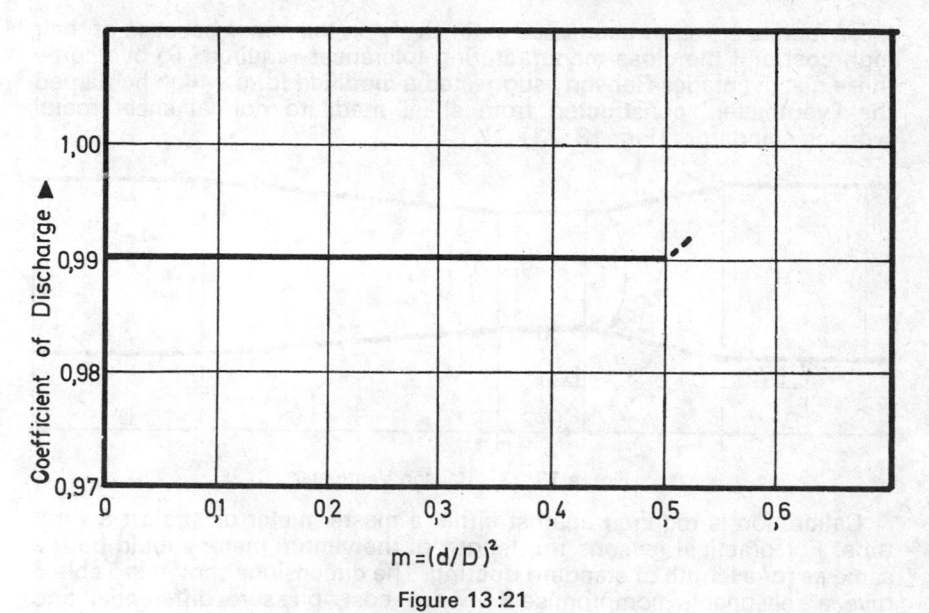

Figure 13:21

The loss in pressure caused by the venturi is shown in Fig. 13:22.

Additional accuracy is obtained by the inclusion of a factor Z covering the effects of expansion, various Reynolds numbers, duct size and roughness as outlined in BSS 1042/64

Despite the obvious advantages of venturi meters for monitoring fluids,

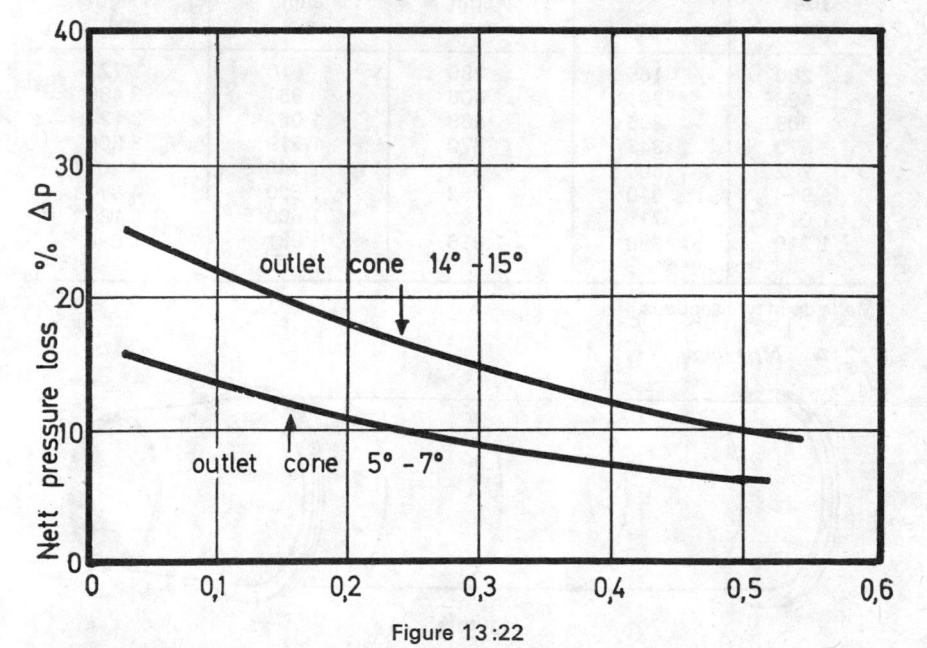

Figure 13:22

these meters have not been used extensively on the mines because of their high cost and the close manufacturing tolerances required. To overcome these disadvantages Rabson[4] suggested a modified form which he named the "ventmeter" constructed from sheet metal to normal sheet metal working standards. (Fig. 13:23)

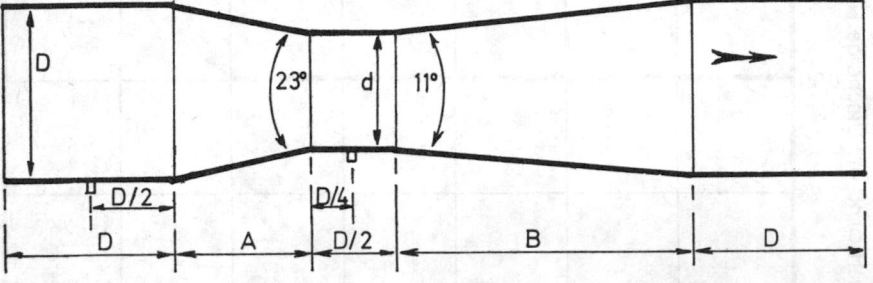

Figure 13:23   Rabson Ventmeter

Calibration is required against either a master meter or against a Pitot tube. For practical reasons the length of the venturi meter should be the same as for a length of standard ducting. The dimensions shown in Table 6 give a reasonable compromise between cost, pressure differential and pressure loss.

TABLE 6

D Duct size mm	d Throat mm	A Inlet cone length mm	B Outlet cone length mm	L Overall length mm
280	165	280	610	1 727
406	241	406	864	2 489
508	305	508	1 067	3 124
570	343	570	1 219	3 505
762	508	635	1 346	4 267*
914	610	762	1 600	4 877*
1 016	711	762	1 600	5 182*
1 219	838	1 016	1 981	6 096*

*Made up in two sections.

3.2.4 *Nozzles*

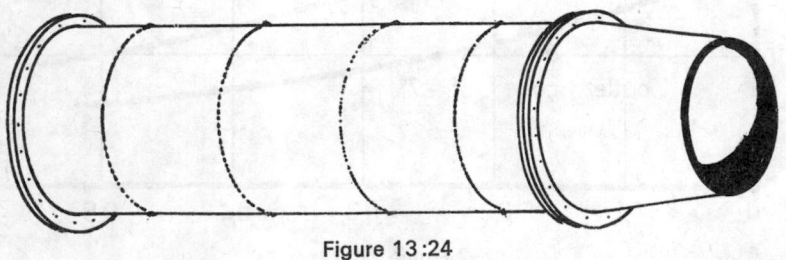

Figure 13:24

Fittings of the type shown in Fig. 13:24 are common items of mine ventilation equipment and can be adapted for metering purposes. The volume flowing through a nozzle of this type is calculated from the formula:

$$Q = 1,11d^2C_dE\sqrt{\frac{\Delta p}{w}}$$

where in this case Δp = difference in static pressure Pa.

As the nozzle is discharging to atmosphere the static pressure at the "vena contracta" is zero and the above formula simplifies to

$$Q = 1,11d^2C_dE\sqrt{\frac{SP}{w}}$$

where SP = upstream static pressure, Pa.

The coefficient of discharge C_d depends on the angle of convergence as shown in Fig. 13:25.

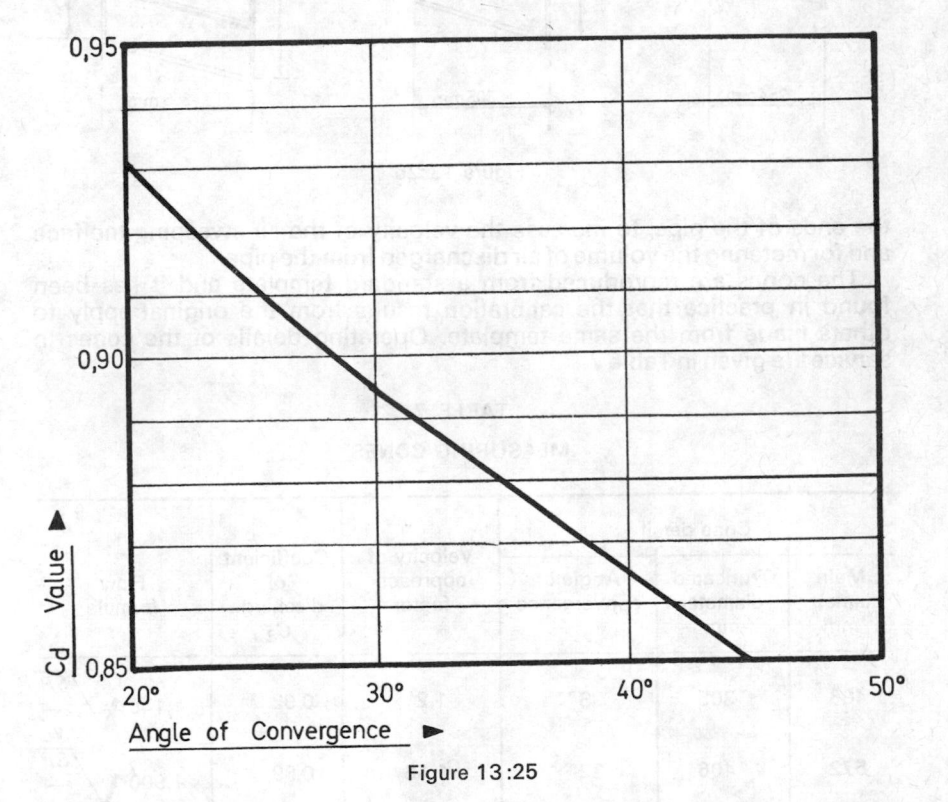

Figure 13:25

Figs. 13:26 (a), (b) and (c) give details of nozzles, used in development ends, operating on the "force only" system of ventilation, to protect

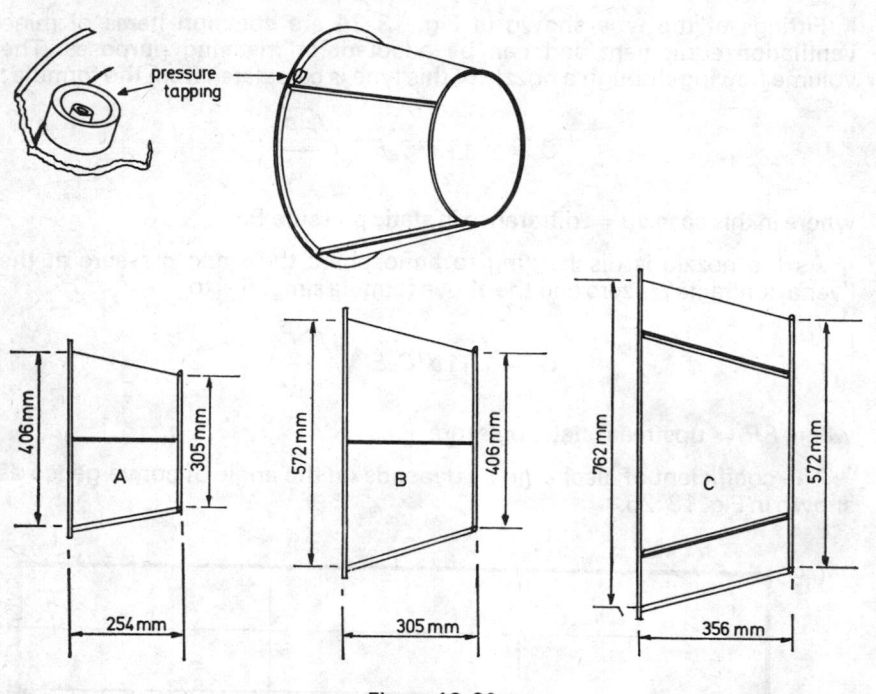

Figure 13:26

the ends of the pipe, to increase the velocity of the air sweeping the face and for metering the volume of air discharged from the pipe.

The cones are reproduced from a standard template and it has been found in practice that the calibration results from the original apply to others made from the same template. Operating details of the cones in service are given in Table 7.

TABLE 7

MEASURING CONES

Cone detail			Velocity of approach factor	Coefficient of discharge C_d	Flow formula
Main diameter mm	Truncated diameter mm	Angle of convergence			
406	305	23°	1,21	0,92	$1,145\sqrt{\dfrac{SP}{w}}$
572	406	32°	1,16	0,89	$1,900\sqrt{\dfrac{SP}{w}}$
762	572	30°	1,21	not obtained	

3.3   TRACER GAS TECHNIQUE

The tracer gas technique[5] offers important advantages in that it is the *quantity* of air flowing and *not* the *velocity* which is measured; the cross-sectional area is not needed and the method can be applied successfully to highly turbulent and pulsating flow.

For underground use the tracer gas should be inexpensive, non-toxic, not subject to absorption or change by the walls of the airway or the air into which it is injected and, lastly, must be easily measurable in low concentrations. Gases which have been considered are hydrogen, ozone, nitrous oxide and carbon dioxide, and of these gases nitrous oxide and carbon dioxide appear most suited to mining work.

Briefly, the recommended method consists of injecting a known mass of the selected gas, sufficiently far upstream of the sampling point to allow the gas and the air to be thoroughly mixed, and taking samples at frequent intervals from before the release of the tracer until the concentration of tracer gas becomes too small to measure. A concentration-time curve is then drawn and the area (A) under this curve evaluated (see Fig. 13:27).

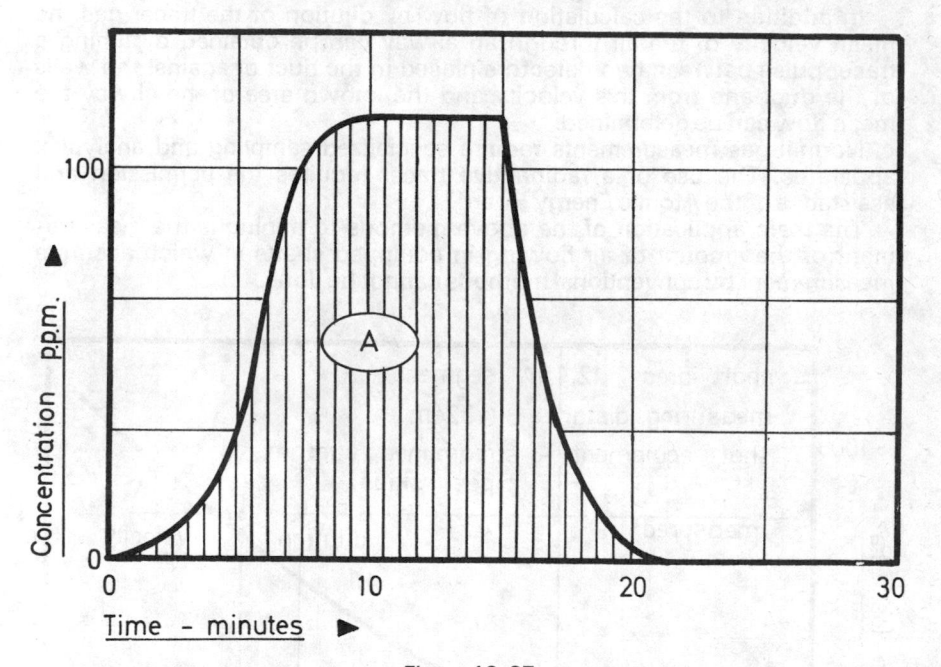

Figure 13:27

The airflow Q is determined as follows:

Let C = concentration at the sampling point at time t.
   M = mass of tracer gas kg.
   w_g = density of tracer gas kg/m^3.
   A = area under curve.

At time t, the volume rate of flow of tracer past the sampling cross-section is CQ. Hence the volume of tracer contained in the whole of the pulse passing the cross-section is

$$\int_0^\infty CQdt$$

where the time of commencement of the passage of the pulse is taken as zero. Assuming no loss of tracer between release and sampling points and an airflow which is constant, then

$$\frac{m}{w_g} = Q \int_0^\infty Cdt = QA$$

$$\therefore Q = \frac{m}{w_g A}$$

The above technique has been employed successfully using radioactive krypton 85 gas as the tracer. Radionuclides are usually easier to detect and measure than normal tracer gases.

In addition to the calculation of flow by dilution of the tracer gas the mean velocity of the air through an airway can be obtained by timing a tracer pulse between two detectors placed in the duct or against the walls of the duct and from this velocity and the known area of the airway the mean flow can be determined.

Normal gas measurements require specialized sampling and analytical apparatus. The use of a radioactive tracer requires the permission and assistance of the Atomic Energy Board.

The main application of the above methods to mining is the measurement of the amount of air flowing in equipped shafts in which accurate measurement by conventional methods cannot be done.

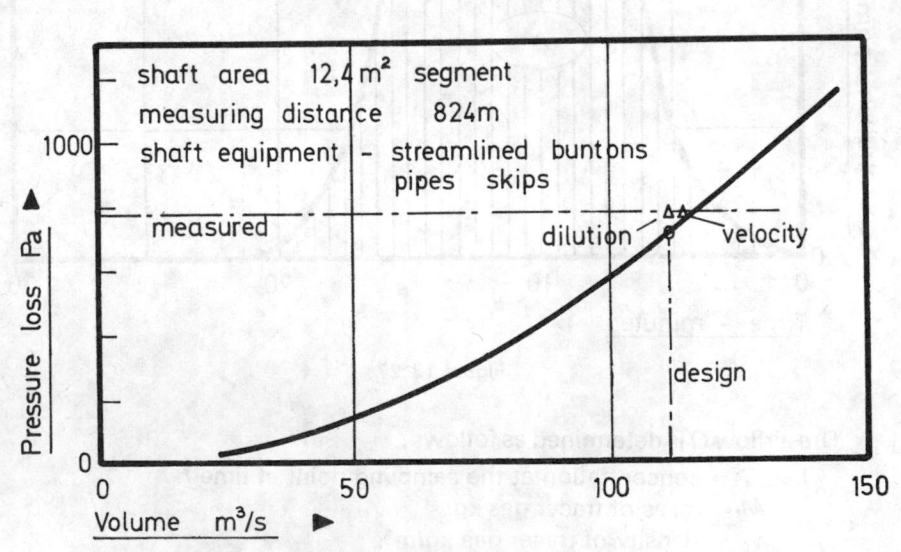

Figure 13:28

The results of measurements in operating shafts are given in Figs. 13:28 and 13:29.

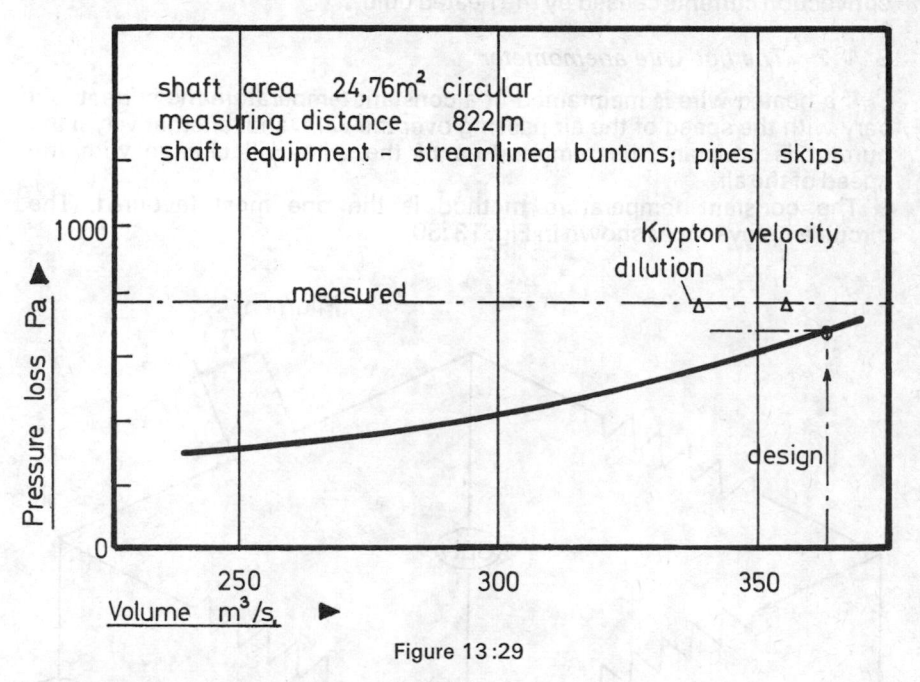

Figure 13:29

3.4   *Methods based on the rate of cooling of hot bodies*

3.4.1   *Kata thermometer*

This instrument is used to determine the cooling power of the air underground and can also be used as an anemometer to measure air velocities ranging from 0,1 m/s to, say, 1 m/s.

It was formerly recommended that when it is used for this purpose the bulb and stem should be completely dry and the bulb silvered to reduce radiant heat effects. For most underground conditions, however, the normal wet condition of the bulb and the use of the wet-bulb temperature are acceptable.

The two main factors affecting the reading, namely, wet-bulb temperature and wind velocity are related by the equation

$$K = 0,7\theta + \theta\sqrt{V}$$

where K = Kata reading
θ = 36,4°C − unventilated wet-bulb temperature °C
V = velocity m/s

thus $V = \left(\dfrac{K - 0,7\theta}{\theta}\right)^2$

The formula is approximately correct for all barometric pressures. Values of velocities below 0,1 m/s are unlikely to be reliable because of convection currents caused by the heated bulb.

3.4.2   *The hot-wire anemometer*

If a heated wire is maintained at a constant temperature the current will vary with the speed of the air passing over the wire, and, alternatively if the current is constant the temperature of the wire will change with the speed of the air.

The constant temperature method is the one most favoured. The circuit employed is as shown in Fig. 13 :30.

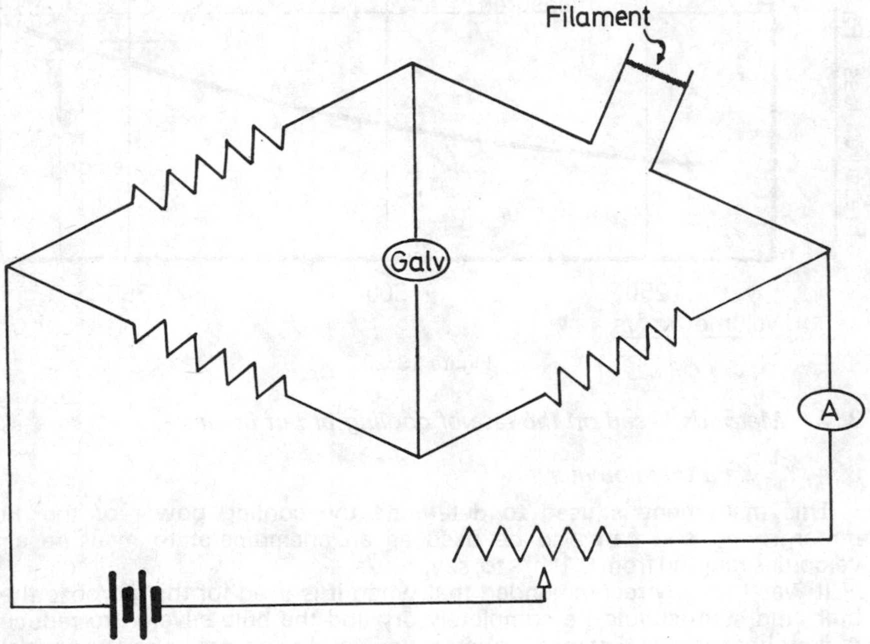

Figure 13 :30

The resistances of the three arms of the bridge are balanced at the required temperature of the filament in still air. Exposure of the wire to airflow causes the temperature of the wire and consequently its resistance to decrease, which necessitates the rebalancing of the bridge by an increase of heating current. This increase of current is related to the change of velocity.

The relationship between current and velocity for a wire maintained at a constant temperature is shown in Fig. 13 :31.

A special characteristic of this anemometer is the high degree of sensitivity for low air velocities, a feature particularly useful for the measurement of airflow in stopes.

These anemometers have not been used to any extent on gold mines as those available commercially are unsuited to underground conditions.

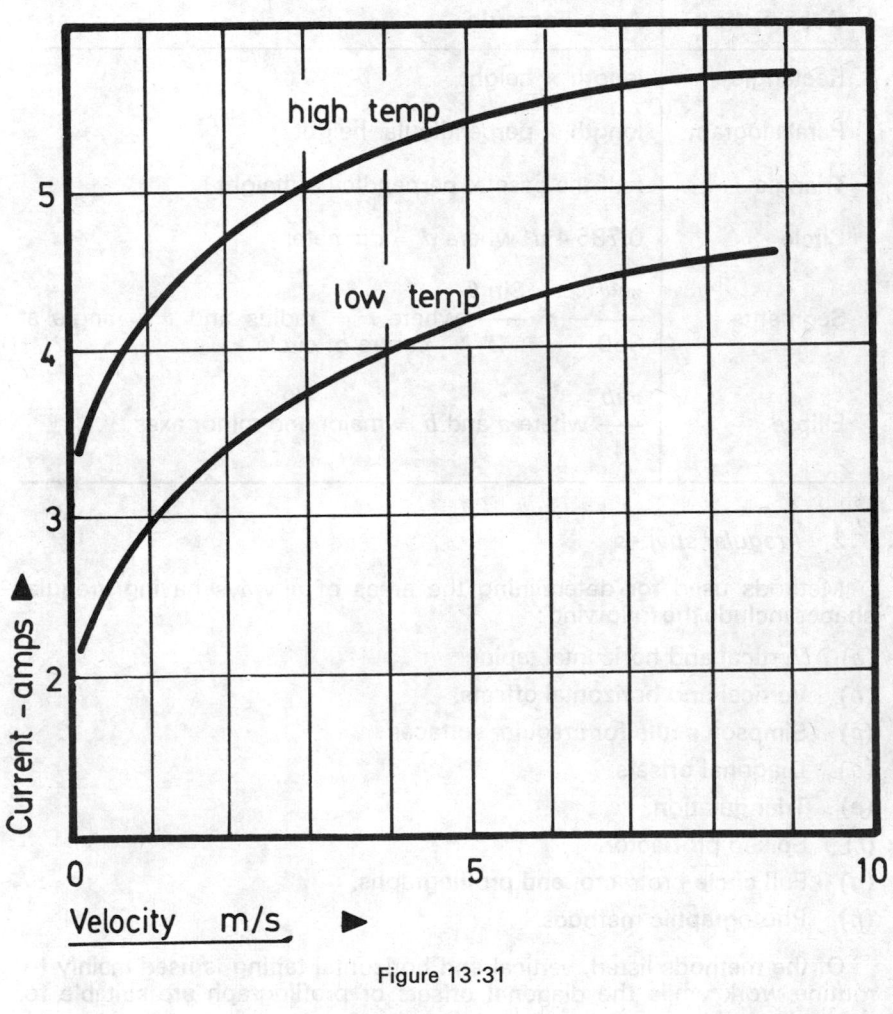

Figure 13:31

4   MEASUREMENT OF AREAS OF AIRWAYS

Area determinations are required for both regular and irregular shapes.

4.1   *Regular shapes*

Description	Area Formula
Rectangle	length $\times$ height
Parallelogram	length $\times$ perpendicular height
Triangle	half the base $\times$ perpendicular height
Circle	0,785 4 d^2 where d = diameter
Segments	$\dfrac{\pi r^2\theta}{360} - r^2\dfrac{\text{Sin }\theta}{2}$ where r = radius and θ = angle at centre of circle
Ellipse	$\dfrac{\pi ab}{4}$ where a and b = major and minor axes

4.2   *Irregular shapes*

Methods used for determining the areas of airways having irregular shapes include the following:

(*a*)   Vertical and horizontal taping.

(*b*)   Vertical and horizontal offsets.

(*c*)   Simpson's rule for irregular surfaces.

(*d*)   Diagonal offsets.

(*e*)   Triangulation.

(*f*)   Spiked protractor.

(*g*)   Full circle protractor and profilographs.

(*h*)   Photographic methods.

Of the methods listed, vertical and horizontal taping is used mainly for routine work while the diagonal offsets or profilograph are suitable for determining the areas of permanent measuring stations.[6]

5   REFERENCES

1   *Routine Mine Ventilation Measurements*. Chamber of Mines of South Africa, 1972.
2   Ower, E. *The measurement of airflow*. 3rd edition Chapman & Hall, 1949.
3   Swirles, J. and Hinsley, F. B. The use of vane anemometers in the measurement of airflow. *Trans. I.M.E.* Vol. 113, 1954, p. 895–919.
4   Rabson, S. R. The ventmeter. *J. Mine Vent. Soc. S. Afr;* Vol. 13, 1960, p. 193-200.
5   Higgins, J. and Shuttleworth, Sheila. A tracer gas technique for the measurement of airflow in headings. *Colliery. Eng.* Nov. 1958, p. 483–81.
6   Quilliam, J. H. A note on the methods of measuring cross-sectional areas in underground airways. *Bull. Min. Vent. Soc. S. Afr;* Vol. 8, 1955, p. 114–18.

14   Pressure-measuring Instruments

W. HOLDING

Group Ventilation Engineer,
Anglo Transvaal Consolidated Investment Co., Ltd.

1   INTRODUCTION

"Pressure" usually means pressure difference when related to ventilation
or reticulation systems, and the instruments by which this parameter is
measured can be grouped according to the terms in which the pressure
difference is expressed. The instruments are of two types, namely, manometers and barometers.

1.1   *Manometers*

Manometers measure directly differences between pressures at points. These readings can vary from very small to relatively large.

1.2   *Barometers*

Barometers measure the absolute pressure of the air at the site of the instruments. The pressure reading so obtained is called the barometric pressure at that particular point and its value depends on the altitude at that point, its latitude (as the gravitational acceleration varies with latitude) and the "atmospheric conditions" prevailing at the point. These atmospheric conditions are subject to natural changes (diurnal changes) which would be indicated by a barometer operating outside a controlled ventilation system. When a barometer operates in a controlled ventilation system, artificial atmospheric changes associated with changes in flow, resistance and so on, are superimposed on the natural changes.

Barometric pressure readings in mine ventilation are usually taken for one or more of the following reasons:

(*a*)   To measure variations in the natural atmospheric pressure which affect underground conditions. For example, if extensive worked-out areas or cavities contain methane or other gases (sealed off or otherwise) falling barometric pressure will result in heavy emissions of the gases.

(*b*)   To determine the barometric pressure at a point for use in conjunction with temperature readings to calculate the air density and other psychrometric conditions at that point.

(*c*)   To measure precisely the barometric pressures at a number of related points in a ventilation circuit as a means for determining indirectly the ventilation pressure difference between the points. This is possible because the readings at all the points are measured in relation to a common datum (absolute zero).

2   MANOMETERS

A manometer is an instrument in which the difference between the pressures applied to two different surfaces of a body of liquid is balanced by a displacement of the liquid. The surface to which the higher pressure is applied is depressed and the other surface is raised.

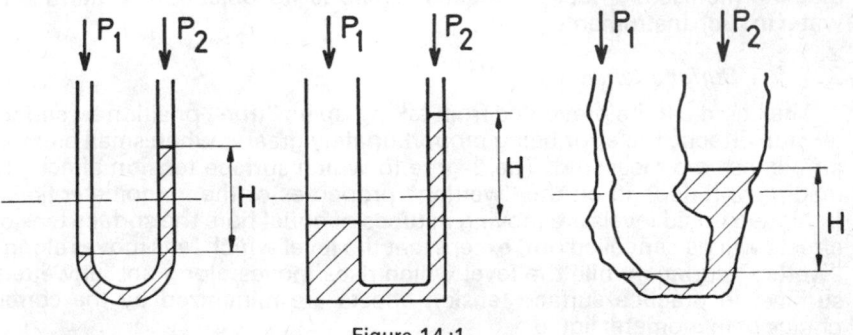

Figure 14 :1

For a given pressure difference and a given liquid the vertical difference between the levels of the surfaces is the same irrespective of the shape of the vessel containing the liquid.

In all three cases (Figure 14 :1) if H can be measured and if w the density of the liquid is known

$$P_1 - P_2 = \Delta P = w \times H \times g$$

where

ΔP = pressure difference (Pa)
w = density of the liquid (kg/m^3)
H = vertical difference in level (m)
g = gravitational acceleration (m/s^2)

In practice it is not always convenient to measure the vertical difference between the liquid levels and to multiply by w and g to calculate the pressure difference, and practical instruments are so arranged that the graduated scale incorporated gives a direct reading in Pascals.

It is useful to know, however, that *when the liquid in the manometer is water* a difference between levels of one centimetre corresponds approximately to a pressure difference of about 100 Pa or, more accurately, 1 cm corresponds to 98 Pa.

2.1 Sources of error

Sources of error in manometers are those which :

(*a*)   prevent the liquid levels from reaching their true positions relative to the pressure difference being measured or prevent the difference between the liquid levels from being measured precisely, or

(*b*)   prevent the true conversion of the "difference in level" reading to a "direct difference in pressure" reading.

2.1.1 Meniscus

The true level of a liquid is that indicated by the centre of the meniscus. If the meniscus is not well formed erroneous readings can result. For this reason water is not a good manometer liquid in small bore tubing as it does not form a good meniscus. In instruments incorporating small-bore tubing other liquids are preferred.

In certain sophisticated manometers large-diameter vessels are used so that the meniscus effect is reduced. There is no objection to the use of water in such instruments.

2.1.2 Surface tension

The liquid can be prevented from taking up its "true" position by surface tension effects, the error being proportionately greater when small pressure differences are measured. The degree to which surface tension affects the reading will depend on the "wetting" properties of the manometer liquid. If the two liquid levels are moving in tubes of equal bore the surface tension effects will be cancelled out, except that the level which falls moves along a "wetted" surface while the level which rises moves along an "unwetted" surface. In practice surface tension effects are minimized by the correct choice of manometer liquid.

2.1.3 *Visibility*

Transparent liquids are not suitable as manometer liquids as they are sometimes difficult to see, especially underground. Another "visibility" requirement is that the whole liquid should be visible so that the presence of air bubbles can be detected. Visibility can be improved by using a coloured liquid or by adding a dye to a transparent liquid, provided this does not alter the liquid's other properties such as density and viscosity.

2.1.4 *Density*

The scale graduations of a manometer are "designed around" the density of the manometer liquid. The density must be stable and accurately predictable over the range of temperatures likely to be encountered, otherwise errors will result.

2.1.5 *Scale and reading errors*

The scale graduations, as described later, depend on the dimensions of the manometer and the density of the liquid, so that the accuracy of direct pressure readings can be affected by the degree of precision of manufacture of the gauge as well as of the scale itself. Parallax errors can be significant especially when comparatively small pressure differences are involved. These errors must therefore be minimized by careful design.

A further factor which affects errors in reading is the density of the liquid. For a given pressure difference use of a low-density liquid will result in a greater, and therefore more easily measurable displacement than would be the use of a high-density liquid. However, high-density liquid, for example mercury, is sometimes used where a wide measuring range is required in an instrument of small dimensions. This naturally results in limited sensitivity.

2.2 *Types of manometer*

2.2.1 *Vertical U-tube*

This is the instrument upon which all other manometers are based. The fluid used is usually water. It is easy to use and simple to construct from materials which are readily available.

Its disadvantages stem mainly from the use of water as the gauge liquid with its inferior wetting qualities and poor meniscus. A further disadvantage is that the position of both liquid levels must be read simultaneously, which can be difficult especially when a fluctuating pressure difference is being read.

For these reasons the vertical U-tube is suitable to use where great accuracy is not important, for example, in routine measurement of fan pressures, or general pressure differences across ventilation doors where the readings are of the order of 300 Pa or over.

2.2.2 *Well- or reservoir-type vertical manometer* (Figure 14 :2)

In this instrument one limb of the U-tube is replaced by a reservoir in which the surface area of the liquid is large compared with that of the liquid in the measuring limb. When a pressure difference is measured the high-pressure tube is always connected to the reservoir. The drop in liquid level in the reservoir is very small compared with the rise in level in the

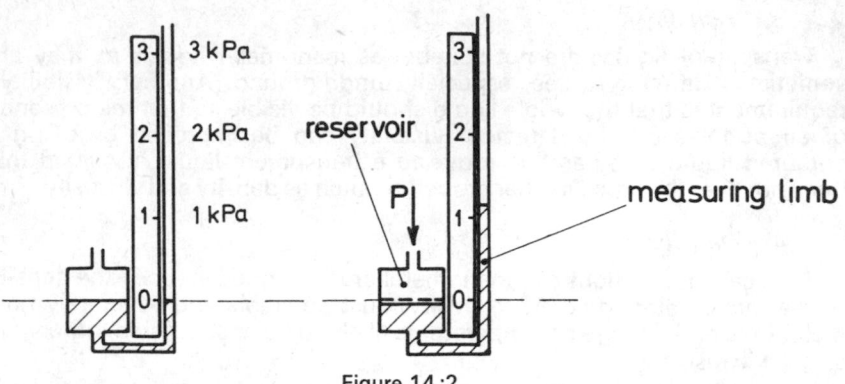

Figure 14 :2

measuring limb, and by designing the scale graduations to take into account the change in level in the reservoir, it is possible for the reading to be taken by observing the level in the narrow limb only. It is usual in manometers of this type to use a liquid other than water, paraffin or other petroleum-base oils containing a colouring agent being used quite commonly.

It follows that the size of the scale graduations must be such as to allow for the drop in level of the liquid in the reservoir, and must also take into account the density of the particular liquid being used in order to give a direct pressure reading. The well or reservoir-type vertical manometer is therefore superior to the vertical U-tube manometer for the following reasons:

(a)   The readings can be obtained by observing the level in only one limb. An advantage of this is that the scale can be situated very close to the limb, making it easy to "line-up" the liquid level with the scale graduations.

(b)   The measuring liquid reacts more easily to small changes in pressure than does water.

(c)   Since the liquids used in this type of gauge usually have a density less than that of water (e.g., $SG = 0,8$) the physical displacement of the liquid is slightly greater than that of water for the same pressure difference, which makes for increased sensitivity.

It should be noted that the reservoir-type vertical manometer is not an "absolute" instrument as is the U-tube manometer. Whereas the vertical difference between the levels in the two limbs of a U-tube manometer (within the limits of the instrument's sensitivity) will always reflect the true pressure difference whether the tube bore is uniform or not, the reading of a reservoir-type vertical manometer is correct only if the dimensions of the reservoir and measuring limb, the density of the gauge liquid, and the design of the scale graduations are as specified.

Modern manufacturing techniques, especially the use of plastics, make it possible to reproduce these parameters to very close tolerances, so it is not usually necessary to calibrate individual instruments.

Although the reservoir-type vertical manometer is superior to the U-tube, it is not a precision instrument and is best suited to the type of application described in relation to the U-tube.

2.2.3   *Well- or reservoir-type inclined manometer* (Figure 14 :3)

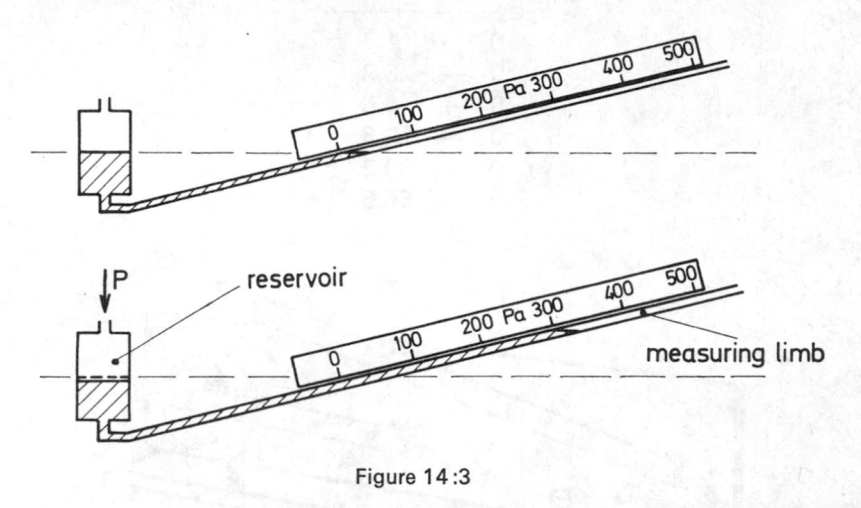

Figure 14 :3

If the measuring limb of a reservoir-type manometer is inclined instead of being vertical, a small vertical change in the level of the liquid results in a relatively large displacement of the liquid along the limb, so that the instrument is much more sensitive than a vertical manometer. The size of the scale graduations must be such that the small change in level in the reservoir caused by movement of the liquid along the inclined limb (which is based on the relative dimensions of the reservoir and measuring limb), the density of the liquid and inclination of the measuring limb are taken into account. The inclination varies between 1 in 4 and 1 in 10 and the minimum size of scale graduation usually corresponds to 2,5 Pa. Because of the inherent sensitivity of the inclined manometer, certain design features must be incorporated if correct readings are to be obtained :

(*a*)   Precise means of levelling and zero-setting must be provided.

(*b*)   The inclined tube must be straight to within close tolerances.

(*c*)   The measuring scale must actually touch the inclined tube so that the liquid level can be lined up precisely with the graduations.

(*d*)   A mirrored surface must be provided behind the inclined tube so that parallax errors can be avoided.

If an inclined manometer is used at extreme temperatures it may be necessary to take into account the change in density of the liquid and the change in the length of the scale, and to adjust the readings accordingly.

An excellent example of an inclined manometer is that illustrated in Figure 14 :4. This instrument has two inclined manometers mounted on one base. The larger gauge can be located vertically or in two alternative inclined positions while the smaller one can be located vertically or in three alternative inclined positions. The scale lengths are 320 and 643 mm and the following ranges are available :

	kPa
0 —	1,7
0 —	3,2
0 —	6,6
0 —	13,3
0 —	33,2
0 —	66,5

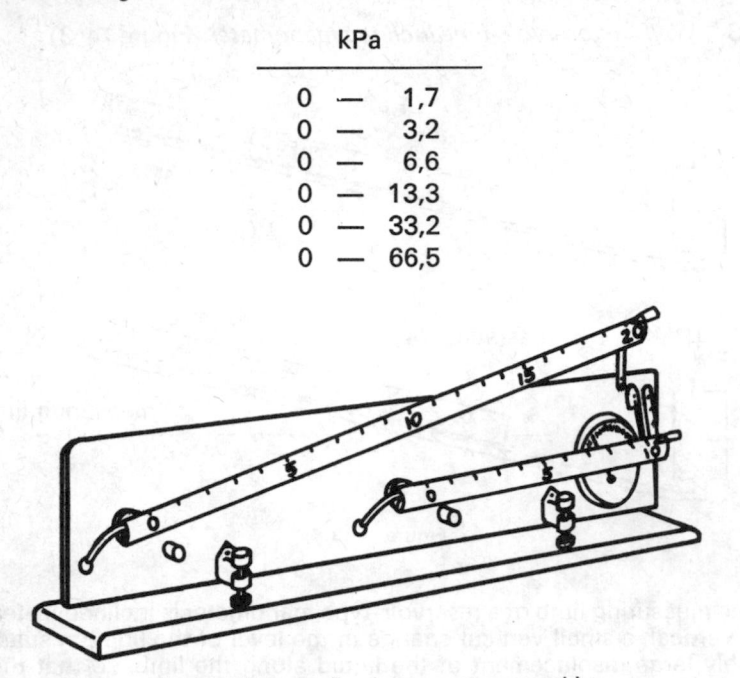

Figure 14:4   Inclined manometer assembly

The provision of two manometers mounted together is particularly useful when it is required to measure velocity pressures and static or total pressures simultaneously, as in fan testing. An alternative set of scales is provided for reading velocities directly (valid for standard air density only) and a small aneroid barometer and thermometer are included to provide data from which local air densities can be calculated.

One possible disadvantage of the instrument is that the measuring liquid is visible only in the inclined tubes and detection of the presence of air bubbles is difficult.

A reservoir-type inclined manometer is, strictly speaking, not an absolute instrument because the accuracy of the readings depends on the precision of manufacture, but again in practice modern instruments can be assumed not to need calibration for most purposes. Calibration when necessary is usually carried out against a water-filled Hook gauge or micromanometer with an accuracy of 0,25 Pa.

It is suitable for measuring pressure differences of less than 300 Pa where an accuracy of ±1,25 Pa is required, as for example in the determination of velocity pressures.

2.2.4   *Inclined/vertical manometer* (Figure 14:5)

Instruments of this type are designed to combine the sensitivity of an inclined manometer with the wider measuring range of a vertical manometer.

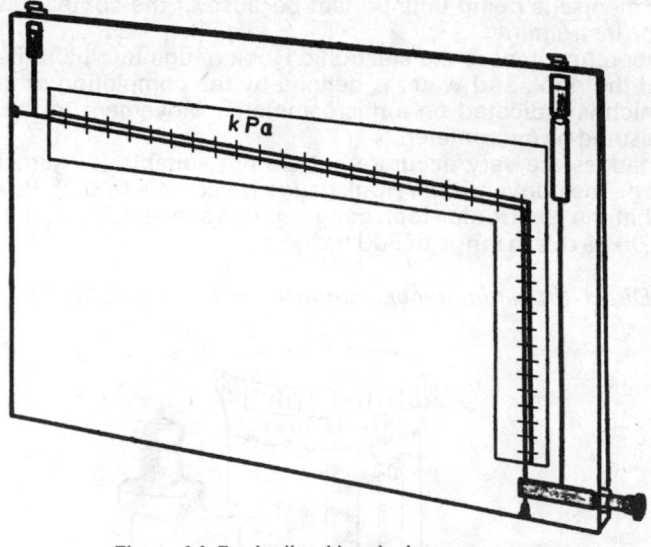

Figure 14:5   Inclined/vertical manometer

2.2.5   *Hook-type manometer* (Figure 14:6)

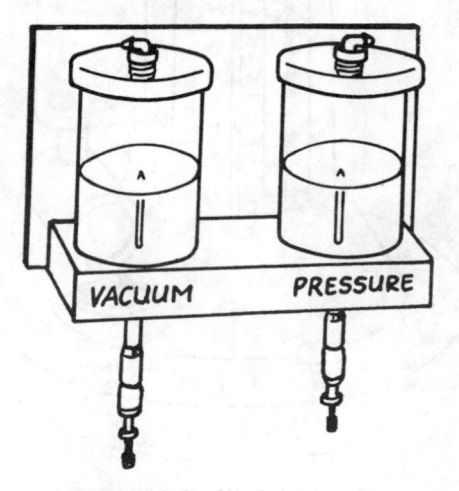

Figure 14:6   Hook manometer

In this type of instrument pointed hooks or rods are provided which can be moved vertically to follow movements of the liquid surfaces under various pressure conditions. The exact position at which the point coincides with the liquid surface can be located by the appearance of a "dimple" which forms when the point contacts the liquid. Readings are obtained by measuring precisely the movements of hooks using the micrometers provided for the purpose. Water containing fluorescein is usually used, the quality of meniscus being unimportant because of the comparatively wide limbs of the instrument.

A further refinement is the electronic Hook gauge in which the point of contact of the hook and water is defined by the completion of an electric circuit which is indicated on a microammeter. Movement of the hooks is again measured by micrometer.

Hook gauges are very accurate but are not suitable for general underground use. The conventional Hook gauge is accurate to 0,25 Pa while it is claimed that the electronic Hook gauge can give repeatable readings to the nearest 0,06 Pa over a range of 500 Pa.

2.2.6   *Direct-lift minimeter or micromanometer* (Figure 14:7)

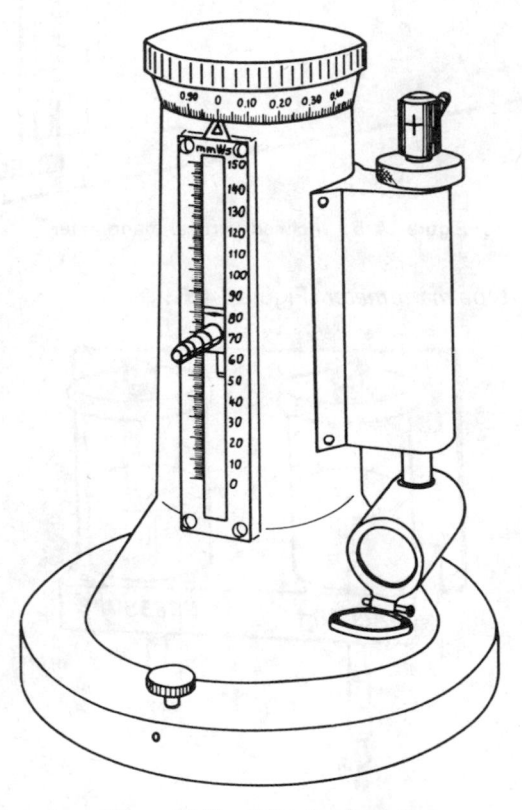

Figure 14:7   Askania minimeter

These instruments are based to some extent on the same principle as that of the Hook gauges in that the liquid level is located precisely by its being contacted with a pointer. In this case a mirror is provided through which the pointer and its image can be seen. The pointer and image appear to be apart when the pointer is below the liquid level, appear to overlap when the pointer protrudes above the liquid and appear to be just touching when the pointer is at the surface of the liquid. The instrument is set to zero before the pressure difference is applied. On application of the pressure difference the liquid is displaced in the "visible" limb. It is then restored to its original level by raising the other "movable" limb, the movement of which is measured by micrometer.

Micromanometers are usually accurate to 0,25 Pa and are very reliable but they are difficult to manipulate under conditions of fluctuating pressure.

2.2.7   *Magnehelic manometer*

This instrument is not related to any of the manometers described previously and is, strictly speaking, a form of aneroid barometer. It consists of a diaphragm across which the pressure difference is applied, causing it to move against a spring. At the end of the diaphragm is a magnet and adjacent to the magnet is a helix which is free to turn so as to maintain the minimum air gap between itself and the magnet. The rotation of the helix is therefore controlled by the movement of the diaphragm which in turn depends on the pressure difference. The position of the helix is indicated by a pointer on a dial graduated in pressure units.

This instrument is produced in a wide variety of ranges, the lowest being 0 to 100 Pa with minor divisions of 2 Pa and the highest being 0 to 130 kPa with minor divisions of 20 kPa. It can be used for pressure surveying, one advantage being that it does not need levelling at each setting.

For accurate work individual instruments must be calibrated.

2.2.8   *Differential liquid manometers* (Figure 14 :8)

Manometers of this type are not usually suitable for use as field instruments, especially in mining. They are very sensitive and are used mainly as laboratory instruments and for calibration purposes.

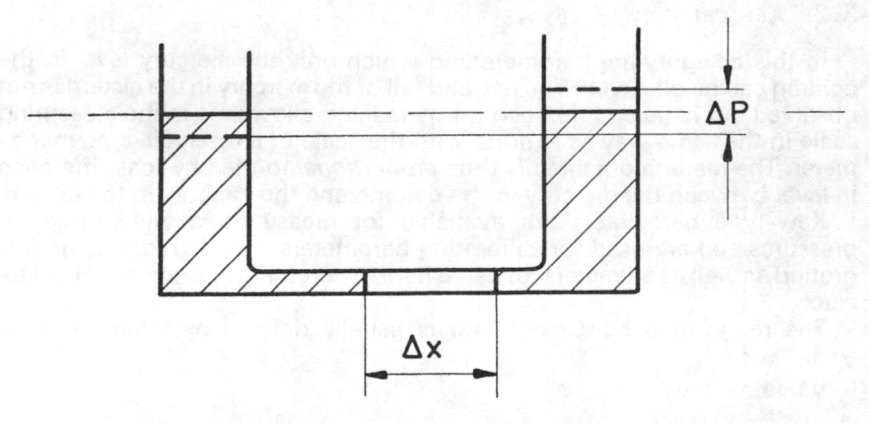

Figure 14 :8   Differential liquid manometer

If vertical limbs of large cross-section are connected by a horizonta tube of much smaller cross-section and a small pressure difference is applied, the small change in liquid level in the vertical limbs results in a very much magnified movement of liquid along the horizontal connecting tube. In order to be able to measure this movement it is necessary to provide a "marker" which is free to move with the liquid but which will not allow any liquid to "slip" past it. One way of achieving this is to use a different liquid in each limb. It is essential that the two liquids do not readily mix so that the demarcation line between them can be used as a marker. In calculating the pressure difference from the observed Δx, the respective densities of the two liquids must be taken into account, and in this respect it is an advantage if the densities of the liquids are as close as possible.

3   MERCURY BAROMETERS

All types of mercury barometers are based on the simple Torricelli barometer. Modern versions are usually divided into two categories, namely, the Fortin and Kew categories.

3.1   *Fortin category*

In this category fall all kinds of mercury barometers in which both mercury surfaces can be observed (i.e., that in the mercury cistern and that in the measuring column). The purpose of this is to enable the observer either to be able to read the exact difference in height between the mercury in the cistern and the mercury in the column or to be able to set the mercury level in the cistern to the same point before each reading. The latter provision is more common.

Fortin barometers are usually used to measure pressures over a range limited to normal atmospheric pressures on the surface and are therefore not suitable for use underground nor for the calibration of barometers intended for use underground.

3.2   *Kew category*

In this category are barometers in which only the mercury level in the column can be observed. The rise and fall of the mercury in the cistern is not observed but is taken into account by making allowance in the measuring scale in the same way as is done with the scale of a reservoir-type mano-meter. The reading obtained is thus *proportional* to the physical difference in level between the mercury in the column and the mercury in the cistern.

Kew-type barometers are available for measuring a wide range of pressures and are used for calibrating barometers intended for use under-ground as well as altimeters for use where the pressure approaches absolute zero.

The range of a Kew barometer is usually defined by referring to its $\dfrac{V}{A}$ — value, where

$$\frac{V}{A} = \frac{\text{total volume of mercury in the barometer}}{\text{effective area of horizontal cross-section of cistern}}$$

Short-range Kew barometers (Meteorological Office Specification) have a V/A value of 38 mm. Kew barometers with other V/A values are available for special uses as described and are known as "test barometers".

3.3   Barometer conventions and corrections

Mercury barometers are not "absolute" standard instruments but the readings which they provide can be used as absolute standards provided corrections are made according to internationally agreed conventions. These conventions are set out in British Standard 2520 : 1967 — *Specification for Barometer Conventions and Tables.*

The corrections to be applied are :

3.3.1   Index or calibration correction

This is the correction required to take into account slight discrepancies in manufacture and in the manufacturer's calibration. The index correction is obtained by individual calibration carried out by an authority such as the National Physical Laboratory or the C.S.I.R.

3.3.2   Temperature correction

Mercury barometers are designed by convention to give the correct pressure readings when the temperature is 0 °C so that a pressure reading in practice is meaningless unless the temperature *of the instrument* at the time of taking the reading is stated as well. Temperature corrections are based on the appropriate coefficients of expansion of mercury and brass (the material from which the scale is made) in the case of Fortin barometers with a further correction for the Kew-type based on the V/A value. For a Kew barometer of the Meteorological Office pattern the correction for a reading of 100 kPa at 20°C would be $-0,341$ kPa.

3.3.3   Gravity correction

A mercury barometer is agreed by international convention to give the correct pressure reading at a standard gravity value of 9,806 65 m/s². A correction must therefore be applied to allow for the difference between local gravity and standard gravity, the local gravity value depending mainly on latitude and altitude.

A reading of 80 kPa taken at a latitude of 30° and an altitude of 2 000 m above sea level would require two corrections, one for latitude only based on sea level conditions ($-0,109$ kPa from the table) and a further correction for altitude ($-0,05$ kPa). The net correction would therefore be $-0,159$ kPa.

3.4   Accuracy and limitations of mercury barometers

Under laboratory conditions a good quality mercury barometer is accurate to ± 7 Pa after all the conventional corrections have been applied. It is eminently suitable for measuring pressures when it is in a fixed position, but it must be used with a great deal of discretion when moved from one position to another, especially if a change in temperature is involved.

One authority[1] concludes that "if a barometer is moved from one position to another, several hours must be allowed to elapse before the barometer is read, should the temperature change be greater than 1 °C". This limitation, plus the general fragility and size of the mercury barometer, makes the instrument unsuitable for underground survey work and its use in mining is limited to monitoring the barometric pressure at fixed points and to calibrating aneroid barometers for use underground.

4   ANEROID BAROMETERS

Aneroid means "without liquid" and barometers of the aneroid-type have been in common use underground for many years as pressure survey instruments. They also find use as altimeters and as survey levelling instruments. Some authorities have cast doubts on the suitability of aneroid barometers for measuring small pressure differences, but the fact remains that the aneroid barometer method of surveying the general pressure distribution in a mine ventilation circuit is very convenient, and now that computer programs are available which eliminate the tedious calculations involved[2] the use of aneroid barometers is more likely to increase than decrease.

The fundamental mechanism of all aneroid barometers is based on the expansion and contraction of a hollow evacuated flexible metal tube (Bernoulli-type) or capsule (often in the form of a helix) which is fixed at one end. The tube or capsule contracts and expands as the pressure outside it rises and falls, the movement being restrained by a spring in some instances, while in a helical tube the motion takes the form of coiling and uncoiling.

Sensitivity is governed both by the design of the tube or capsule itself and by the linkage between the tube and the reading dials. In some instruments a mechanical linkage is employed while in others an optical or electronic linkage is employed. Generally speaking, a non-mechanical linkage would be more sensitive than a mechanical one.

4.1   *Calibration*

Aneroid barometers should be calibrated frequently (once or twice a year with additional calibration before a major survey) against a mercury barometer. This is necessary because it has been found that the characteristics of an aneroid barometer can change over a period and the previous calibration can be rendered invalid. Changes take place in the temperature compensation characteristics and there is a definite zero shift which can continue throughout the life of the instrument.

This varies from instrument to instrument as is indicated in the Table I below[3] and can be evaluated only by calibrating individual instruments.

Another phenomenon which must be taken into account when calibrating and using aneroid barometers is that in many cases the reading given by the instrument will differ depending on whether the pressure increased to or decreased to that particular value. In other words the *indicated* barometer reading, at say, the mid-point in a shaft will have one value if the barometer is brought to that point from the surface (i.e. from a lower pressure), but will have a different value if the barometer is brought to the same point from the shaft bottom (i.e. from a higher pressure).

The correction required to obtain the true pressure will therefore be different in the two cases, and is ascertained by conducting the calibration so that two curves can be drawn, one for "pressures increasing to a point" and one for "pressures decreasing to a point".

In South African practice it has been found that satisfactory results can be obtained with a good quality aneroid barometer by using the "increasing" and "decreasing" curves subject to the following provisos:

(a) When the barometer has not been subjected to a large change in pressure, as, for example, after it has been transported from a surface office to the shaft bank, the curve for pressures reducing to a point should be used to correct the observed readings.

(b) Changes from the "increasing" curve to the "reducing" curve or vice versa should not be made by virtue of a fluctuation of less than 0,65 kPa.

TABLE 1

DRIFT OF CALIBRATION OF ASKANIA MICROBAROMETERS WITH TIME

Barometer	Date of calibration	Average correction Pa	Drift Pa/month
1	June 1954	−650	
	Jan 1957	−970	−11
	Aug 1957	−730	+35
2	June 1955	−1 780	
	Feb 1957	+2 110	+16
	Aug 1957	−2 150	−7
3	Oct 1955	−13	
	July 1956	−125	−12
	Aug 1957	−284	−12
	Dec 1957	−42	+82
4	Aug 1954	−1 024	
	Oct 1955	+173	+85
	July 1956	−28	−23
	July 1957	−198	−15
	Dec 1957	−214	−4
5	Feb 1955	+102	
	May 1955	+158	+19
	June 1955	+82	−76
	Nov 1955	−160	−48
	June 1956	+58	+31
	Dec 1957	−77	−8

4.2 *Accuracy*

Probably the most sensitive of aneroid barometers in general use is the Askania microbarometer. This instrument has an optical linkage and incorporates a thermometer which registers the temperature of the core of the instrument. The accuracy of Askanias depends on the pressure differences as shown below.

Pressure difference kPa	Approx. percentage accuracy
15	0,1
0,65	2
0,13	10

Less sensitive and relatively inexpensive aneroid barometers are the Paulin and Fuess.

Between these extremes there are instruments such as the Barolux and Baromec which, while being somewhat less sophisticated than the Askania, are nevertheless high-quality instruments. The degree of accuracy of these instruments in measuring pressure differences can be obtained from the results given by Craig[3].

5   SPECIAL PRESSURE MEASURING DEVICES

The most commonly used pressure measuring instruments in mining, namely, the manometer and the aneroid barometer have been discussed but there are other devices available which, though by no means in common use, are nevertheless worthy of mention.

5.1 *The Airostat*

An Airostat is essentially a manometer, one limb of which is connected to a sealed chamber which is maintained at a constant temperature and therefore at a constant pressure. The "free" limb of the manometer is open to atmosphere and the reading represents the pressure difference between the absolute pressure of the atmosphere and the pressure in the sealed chamber. The sealed chamber is therefore a controlled datum.

A single reading at a particular site is meaningless but a series of readings at a site will indicate the variation of absolute pressure with time.

Readings taken at a series of stations in a survey will indicate the difference in absolute pressure around the circuit. The readings can be corrected in the same way as barometer survey readings for variation in surface barometric pressure, variation in elevation and density in order to calculate ventilation pressure differences.

The actual numerical value of the readings depends on the pressure in the fixed pressure chamber (the controlled datum) which can be varied for the needs of the survey. It is usual to fix this datum before taking the initial reading of a survey and it may be necessary to change the datum pressure during the course of a survey if variations in absolute pressure beyond the range of the manometer occur. In this respect the carrying out of an Airostat survey requires a judicious approach and a good knowledge of the theoretical principles involved.

The advantages of the Airostat over aneroid barometers are that no hysteresis characteristics are evident and that there are no moving parts.

The physical construction of an Airostat has been described by Finn and Quilliam[4] but improvements in design are still being made. The major changes which have been made concern the manner of insulating the "fixed pressure chamber" to ensure constant temperature and the substitution of water for ice in the constant temperature chamber.

5.2 *Differential barometer* (Fig. 14:9)

The differential barometer is a mercury barometer in which the vertical movement of the mercury is magnified in much the same way as in the differential liquid manometer.

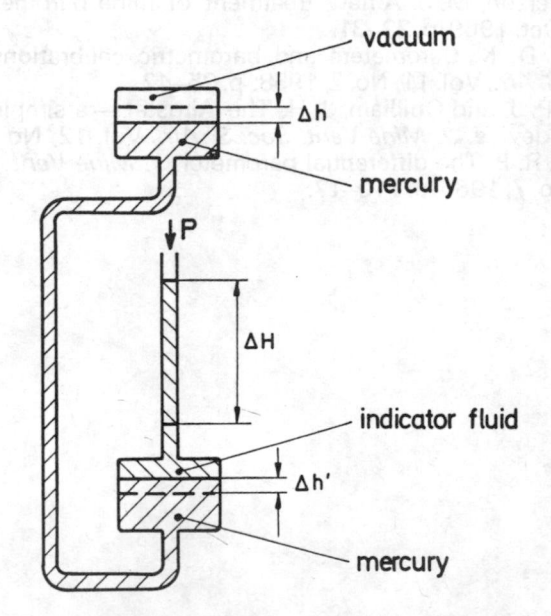

$$\Delta h + \Delta h' = \text{change in mercury column height}$$
$$\Delta H = \text{change in indicator fluid level}$$

Figure 14:9   Differential barometer

Mercury is contained in the upper and lower vessels and an indicator fluid floats on the mercury in the lower vessel, the surface of the indicator fluid being visible in a measuring limb the diameter of which is small compared with that of the mercury vessels. This measuring limb is open to atmosphere.

A small change in the level of mercury results in a large movement in the level of the indicator fluid. A "magnification" of the mercury movement of 15 to 1 is common.[5]

It is important that the density of the indicator fluid should be low compared with that of mercury so that the liquid plays a negligible part in the hydrostatic balance against the atmospheric pressure.

The differential barometer has distinct advantages over the Fortin- and Kew-type mercury barometers in that it is easier to read when small pressure differences are being measured, and over aneroid barometers by virtue of its being free from zero drift characteristics. Its main disadvantages are its bulk and the fact that it requires the corrections applicable to all types of mercury barometers, namely, index, temperature and gravity corrections.

6   REFERENCES

1   Halliday, E. C. Temperature corrections for commercial barometers. *S. Afr. J. Sci.,* Vol. 52, No. 8, 1956. p. 178–81.
2   McPherson, M. J. A new treatment of mine barometer surveys. *Min. Eng.* Oct. 1969. p. 23–31.
3   Craig, D. K. Barometers and barometric calibrations. *J. Mine Vent. Soc. S. Afr.,* Vol. 11, No. 2, 1958. p. 25–42.
4   Finn, P. J. and Quilliam, J. H. The Airostat — a simple pressure differential device. *J. Mine Vent. Soc. S. Afr.,* Vol. 12, No. 1, 1959. p. 4–8.
5   Kislig, R. E. The differential barometer, *J. Mine Vent. Soc. S. Afr.,* Vol. 19, No. 7, 1966. p. 110–17.

15 Pressure Surveys

J. H. QUILLIAM

Chief, Dust Division, Physical Sciences Laboratory, Chamber of Mines Research Organization.

1 INTRODUCTION

Mine ventilation departments are responsible for the distribution of air to the working places in a mine. This involves maintaining the desired air quantities and advising on the fans and airways necessary to ventilate new areas.

The determination of pressure losses in mine ventilation circuits is thus an important aspect of ventilation engineering. The object of pressure surveys is essentially to determine the pressure loss over a known length of airway for the flow of a known volume of air.

By conducting pressure surveys throughout a mine it is possible to determine existing conditions and to obtain information upon which to plan for the future. These surveys comprise the measurement of pressure losses, air quantities, airway dimensions and air density throughout either a whole mine or sections of a mine. The results can be used to identify airways in which the pressure drop is abnormally high and to determine resistance figures for the various airways.

319

2   OBJECTS

A carefully conducted pressure survey will enable the pressure losses to be determined; this knowledge is essential for the correct estimation of shaft and airway resistances. It is also of great importance in ventilation planning and network analysis, especially when fan duties and dimensions of shafts and airways have to be determined.

The results of pressure surveys will indicate the total power being used in different sections of any particular circuit, and, in addition, permit the natural ventilation energy of the air to be determined. This is of great value in estimating any additional fan power that may be required to increase the airflow, and to ensure that the power put into the air by the fans and natural ventilation is being utilized properly.

The extent of air leakages will be revealed, recirculation reduced, and excessive pressure losses will indicate where redistribution of the air current may be advisable.

Therefore, for the efficient distribution of the ventilating air in a mine, it is necessary to know the pressure losses along airways and districts as accurately as possible. In some instances, only pressure drops will be required, while in others, airway resistances may have to be determined, and in shaft pressure surveys the object may be to calculate the coefficient of friction (K-factor) of the shaft.

3   AIRFLOW FORMULAE

The energy of air flowing through a continuous horizontal section of a mine airway is reduced in proportion to the change in total pressure between the two extremities of the airway. For most practical purposes it can be assumed that the change in static pressure in the section will be the same as the corresponding difference in total pressure, since it is simpler to measure static pressures (or static pressure differences) with reasonable accuracy than it is to measure total pressures (or differences). Resistance surveys in mines are invariably designed to enable static pressure losses to be measured.

The basic formula for all mine airflow is the so-called "square-law" relationship, by which the pressure loss is calculated by:

$$p = RQ^2 \qquad \qquad \dots 1$$

where

p = pressure loss (Pa)
R = a resistance coefficient (Ns^2/m^8)
Q = airflow (m^3/s)

Normally the value of R is given at standard density.

In terms of the above convention, R is related to the K factor in Atkinson's formula as:

$$R = \frac{KCL}{A^3} \qquad \qquad \dots 2$$

where

K = Atkinson's friction factor (Ns^2/m^4)
C = perimeter (m)
L = length (m)
A = area (m^2)

Normally a pressure survey is conducted with the object of measuring the pressure loss in an airway in order to determine the value of R, so that equation 1 may be rewritten as:

$$R = \frac{p}{Q^2} \qquad \ldots 3$$

The total airflow in a shaft can often be determined only by measuring the individual flows in the secondary airways in the ventilation circuit, and it is therefore convenient for purposes of calculation to work on a mass flow basis throughout. To calculate R the volume flow at the point of mean density in the shaft is calculated from the total mass flow, so that equation 3 becomes:

$$R = p\frac{w_m^2}{M^2} \qquad \ldots 4$$

where

$$w_m = \text{mean density in shaft (kg/m}^3\text{)}$$
$$M = \text{mass flow (kg/s)}$$

4   INSTRUMENTS

The more important parameters which are measured in pressure surveys are:

(a)   wet- and dry-bulb temperatures of the air,

(b)   volume of air flowing,

(c)   pressure differences measured either directly by trailing hose with manometer, or indirectly by measuring differences in absolute pressure, and

(d)   absolute pressure.

4.1 Air temperatures

Whirling hygrometers are used to measure wet- and dry-bulb temperatures. These temperatures and the absolute pressure at the point of measurement are required to determine the air density.

Air temperatures in semi-dry or wet shafts are normally measured by observers situated on the top of the shaft conveyance. Under such conditions and when whirling hygrometers are used, the dry bulb may inadvertently become wet due to water falling in the shaft and consequently give an inaccurate reading. This can be prevented by using psychrometers of the aspiration type[1] in which the bulbs are protected. In these instruments the bulbs are also shielded from radiation effects, the rate of aspiration is steady, the thermometers can be read continuously while being ventilated, and final temperatures noted accurately.

4.2 Air volume

Vane anemometers are used to measure air velocity so that it is necessary that the cross-sectional area of the airway at the point of measurement should be known accurately.

It is relatively simple to measure airflow in airways; in shafts it can be determined only by measuring the individual flows in the secondary airways elsewhere in the same circuit leading from the shaft.

Pitot tubes are not considered suitable for the measurement of airflow, except in upcast shafts, but the tracer gas technique[2] (referred to in Chapter 13) appears to be promising. The complexity of modern shaft layouts adds materially to the difficulty of measuring airflow and consideration should be given to the use of tracer gas techniques.

4.3 *Pressure differences*

Various types of manometers are available for direct measurement of pressure differences. The measuring range of any manometer must, however, be able to accommodate the expected pressure difference.

A constant-volume pressure differential device known as the "Airostat"[3] is used to measure differences in absolute barometric pressure, with greater accuracy than can be obtained with certain barometers used at present.

Kislig,[4] adopting the principles of the "Airostat" designed a differential barometer, the basic component of which is a mercury column, one end of which is exposed to a vacuum, while the other end carries an indicator fluid which can be exposed either to atmospheric or other pressures. Pressure variations can be measured and magnified by the indicator fluid on a vernier scale.

4.4 *Absolute pressures*

A large number of barometers are available for measuring absolute pressures. These are of two main types, i.e., mercury and aneroid barometers, the latter employing either the flat diaphragm or the helical spring tube.

Mercury barometers are represented by two well-known types, i.e., the Fortin barometer and the Kew or "fixed-cistern" type, and give accurate readings of absolute pressures.

Because of their size, fragility and the inherent time lags that exist after sudden changes in temperature, these barometers are essentially laboratory instruments and are seldom used in underground pressure surveys or other field work.

Aneroid barometers such as the Paulin and Fuess types and the more expensive Barolux and Askania micro-barometers have been used for field investigations. When the latter micro-barometers became available it was thought that they were a considerable advance on the types used previously. Unfortunately, these instruments have not proved to be as reliable in practice as was originally expected and the accuracy with which the micro-barometer can be read tends to be misleading.

The accuracy of barometers depends on several factors listed by Craig in 1958.[5] Generally, it would seem that with most barometers maximum accuracy can be obtained when the instrument is allowed to remain stationary for some time under reasonably steady pressure and temperature conditions and then used to measure sudden and relatively small pressure differences. These conditions can usually be satisfied with the variable volume flow method of making pressure surveys.

Calibration tests have shown that there is quite often a significant difference between the corrections obtained when the instruments are subjected to either pressure increases or decreases. (See Chapter 14).

5   PRESSURE SURVEY METHODS

5.1   *Direct methods*

5.1.1   *Trailing-hose method*

In the trailing-hose method an airtight pipe or hose is laid between the two ends of the airway, and a manometer at some convenient point in the tube is used to measure directly the difference between the pressures at the two ends. This is by far the most common and usually the simplest method of measuring pressure differences in ordinary mine airways.

The basic requirements are two airtight tubes or hoses connecting the extremities of the section of airway being surveyed to the limbs of a mano-meter. When the object is to measure differences in static pressure, as is usually the case, static pressure-measuring devices should be attached to the "open" ends of the hoses; for this purpose polythene bottles with several small holes drilled through their walls can be used. If the trailing-hose method is used for long sections of a shaft, the observed pressure difference will not reflect the true pressure difference in the shaft, because the mean density of the air inside the tube may not be the same as that of the air in the shaft (because there is no flow inside the tube, and the mean density is therefore affected by the very pressure difference which is being measured).

Hinsley[6] has suggested suitable correction formulae which vary according to the position of the manometer in relation to the tubes, but normally the correction can be ignored in all cases. Reference should also be made to Kemp[7] on this aspect.

In surveys in shafts these difficulties can be reduced to a certain extent by confining the survey to a relatively short, representative section of the shaft, say, less than 300 m, so that the total resistance of the shaft can be determined by simple proportion.

The trailing hose method can be applied to horizontal airways without difficulty and no corrections are required.

Example of the trailing-hose method

Despite its basic simplicity, the trailing-hose method is not used widely in deep shafts because of the disadvantages mentioned above. The following example is taken from a paper[8] describing a trailing hose survey of a comparatively short section of a deep shaft.

The shaft was a typical "Witwatersrand" timbered rectangular shaft, of which the top 1 760 m carried the full downcast quantity of air. Two 6-mm internal diameter polythene tubes were suspended in the shaft from the surface collar, the lower end of one being connected to a static pressure measuring device attached to the shaft support at a point 12,5 m below the collar, while the lower end of the second tube was attached to a similar device located 152,4 m below the collar. Frequent measurements were made over a period of about 90 minutes of the static pressure difference between atmosphere and the respective points in the shaft, using an Askania micro-barometer set up on the bank. These observations are given in the table below.

During the same period airflow measurements to determine the total flow in the shaft were recorded at three airflow measuring stations

Time	Static pressure differences measured at collar (Pa)	
	12,5 m b.c.	152,4 m b.c.
10.08	—	78,4
10.15	28,5	—
10.20	28,5	—
10.25	—	77,3
10.32	28,3	—
10.34	—	78,4
10.42	27,6	—
10.44	—	74,0
10.52	28,2	—
10.54	—	74,0
11.03	28,2	—
11.04	—	73,5
11.14	27,8	—
11.16	—	65,7
11.24	27,5	—
11.26	—	76,0
11.33	30,3	—
11.35	—	76,0
11.40	28,3	—
11.42	—	74,2
Means	28,2	74,4

Mean pressure loss in 139,9 m
of shaft = 46,2 Pa

underground. Observers travelling down the shaft (on top of a cage) recorded wet- and dry-bulb temperatures and barometric pressures at predetermined points in the shaft to determine air density. The results of these additional observations were:

Mean total mass flow during period of test = 172,5 kg/s
Mean air density in 139,9 m section of shaft = 1,022 kg/m³
Mean density in 1 760 m of shaft = 1,126 kg/m³

From the pressure loss of 46,2 Pa in the 139,9 m section of the shaft, the pressure loss p in the 1 760 m of shaft proper was calculated as follows:

$$p = 46,2 \times \frac{1\,760}{139,9} \times \frac{1,022}{1,126} = 527,5 \text{ Pa}$$

It was estimated from the observations given in the above table that the static pressure loss at the shaft collar, i.e., the "entrance" loss, at the time of the test, was 24,9 Pa, so that the overall static pressure loss p in the shaft would have been 527,5 + 24,9 = 552 Pa.

Applying Hinsley's correction formula [6] to the observed mean pressure difference between surface atmospheric pressure and the pressure 152,4 m below the shaft collar (i.e., 74,4 Pa) gives a correction of 1,25 Pa which, strictly speaking, should be *added* to the observed value. The correction to the difference between surface atmospheric pressure and that 12,5 m below collar would have been correspondingly smaller. Over greater distances the correction would become significant.

It is assumed that exit losses would be included in the R factors for the various airways leading off the lower end of the shaft.

The trailing-hose method is simple, requiring a minimum of time, can be done during the normal shift, and provides information which can be used to perform more accurate and detailed surveys. It will not necessarily pinpoint an actual area of high pressure loss, but it will, in certain instances, provide a means for the rapid checking of the results of pressure surveys made by other methods.

Perhaps the greatest advantage of the trailing-hose method is that the pressure loss can, subject to what is said later, be read directly from the manometer. This means that an experienced observer can interpret his observations as they are made so that the reason for any anomalous readings can be sought immediately. With barometric methods, on the other hand, various calculations may be necessary to determine the significance of the recorded observations, particularly if indirect-reading barometers are used, and anomalies usually appear long after the survey has been completed.

The main disadvantages of the trailing-hose method are:

(*a*)   the difficulty of installing long lengths of airtight tubing in busy hoisting shafts and of ensuring that the tubing remains airtight throughout the test;

(*b*)   the danger of the hose being blocked by kinks or by water droplets inside the tube;

(*c*)   the tendency for the response to pressure changes to become sluggish when long lengths of tubing are used;

(*d*)   the effect of small differences between the temperatures of the air in the shaft and the hose;

(*e*)   the possible cumulative effect of any errors made during the survey.

5.1.2   The modified trailing-hose method[9]

Because of the disadvantages of the indirect and trailing-hose methods of determining pressure losses in shafts, a modified trailing hose for the direct measurement of pressure losses has been developed.

This method is reliable, easier to use than any of the conventional methods and requires only a small amount of apparatus and few personnel.

It requires the installation of a thin small-diameter plastic tube down the shaft between any two observation points between which the pressure difference is to be measured. The lower end of the tube is connected to a 20- or 30-litre aspirator bottle containing water. Water is allowed to flow from the aspirator so as to draw air down the tube. The flow rate is adjusted so that the manometer reads zero, indicating that the pressure loss of the air flowing through the tube is equal to the actual pressure drop in the shaft. The water flow rate from the bottle is determined by means of a measuring cylinder and a stop watch. The pressure loss of the air flowing through the tube and therefore of the air flowing down the shaft is then read from a calibration curve for the tube.

The effects of variations in air density and viscosity and in the tube diameter due to changes in temperature and humidity are self-cancelling. This method has the advantages of the conventional trailing-hose method and is relatively insensitive to temperature differences between the air in the tube and in the shaft. It is easy to operate and takes little time.

The main disadvantage of the method appears to be the difficulty of installing the tube in a busy hoisting shaft. The method has not yet been used extensively enough to reveal any other disadvantage which may arise under underground conditions.

Calibration of the plastic tubing

Various measured volumes of air are caused to flow through a plastic tube and the pressure losses measured. As the flow through the tubing is laminar the pressure losses are proportional to the rates of airflow.

If the pressure losses are plotted against the relevant air flows, the mean slope of the curve can be determined.

Example of the direct measurement of pressure loss in a downcast shaft

Length of test section 169 m.

The flow rates of water and, therefore, of the air obtained at the lower observation point for a static pressure difference of zero between the tube and the shaft are shown below:

Test	Time	Water and hence airflow rate (cm³/min)
1	10.29	26,4
2	10.45	27,0
3	11.02	25,8
4	11.14	26,0

For a tube of length 169 m the mean slope of the curve (tan α) is 1,48 that is,

$$\frac{\text{pressure loss}}{\text{air flow}} = \tan \alpha = \text{mean slope} = 1,48$$

∴ pressure loss = air flow rate (water flow rate) × 1,48

From this information the pressure losses are obtained as follows:

Test	Airflow rate (cm³/min)	Pressure loss (Pa)
1	26,4	26,4 + 1,48 = 39,1
2	27,0	27,0 + 1,48 = 40,0
3	25,8	25,8 + 1,48 = 38,2
4	26,0	26,0 + 1,48 = 38,5
		Mean pressure loss = 38,9

5.2   Indirect methods

The indirect methods are based on the measurement of absolute barometric pressure at the two extremities of the airway and are termed "indirect" in as much as where the two barometric stations are at different elevations a correction must be applied to take into account the "natural" difference in barometric pressure between the two stations. The four variations of the barometric method used locally are generally referred to as:

(a)   the full volume-reduced volume method (also known as the variable volume method);

(b)   the density method;

(c)   the meteorological method; and

(d)   the energy method.

5.2.1   Full volume-reduced volume method

In this method absolute pressures at an upstream station and a downstream station are measured by means of sensitive barometers with a constant volume of air flowing between the stations. The observations are then repeated with a smaller volume flow between the stations. The airflow is usually reduced by switching off a main fan. Because of the different airflow, the pressure difference between the stations will change. From these pressure changes and the respective volume flows, the pressure losses can be calculated.

Thus, if the barometric pressure is observed at the bottom of the shaft and if the reading is observed with a lower airflow, then by solving two simultaneous equations, the pressure drop in the shaft for both flows can be found from the change in barometric pressure and the ratio of the two flows (assuming that the barometric pressure on surface remains constant).

The formula used to calculate the pressure loss by the full volume-reduced volume method is:

$$p_f = \frac{\Delta P + g\Delta H(w_{mf} - w_{mr})}{1 - w_{mr}/w_{mf}[Q_r/Q_f]^2} \quad \text{for a downcast shaft}$$

and

$$p_f = \frac{\Delta P - g\Delta H(w_{mf} - w_{mr})}{1 - w_{mr}/w_{mf}[Q_r/Q_f]^2} \quad \text{for an upcast shaft}$$

where p_f = pressure loss for full volume flow (Pa)
  ΔH = difference in elevation (m)
  g = gravitational acceleration (m/s^2)
  w_{mf} = mean density at the full volume flow (kg/m^3)
  w_{mr} = mean density at the reduced volume flow (kg/m^3)
  Q_f = full volume flow (m^3/s)
  Q_r = reduced volume flow (m^3/s)
  ΔP = difference in barometric pressure with full and reduced flow (Pa)

When using this method in sub-vertical systems it is necessary to measure the changes in pressure at both the upstream and downstream observation points resulting from the use of two different air volumes.

The full volume-reduced volume method is useful for investigations in shafts in which it is easy to make appreciable changes in airflow rates. Since the main measurements are the two airflow rates and the corresponding change in barometric pressure, for investigations in a vertical shaft it is necessary to measure accurately only the pressure differences at one point, i.e., at the shaft bottom.

The *advantages* of this method are:

(a)   All measurements can be made at fixed points.

(b)   Observations can be taken over a short period of time by means of simple instruments.

The *disadvantages* of the method are:

(a)   It usually involves switching off a main fan and therefore cannot be used during the working shift.

(b)   If the difference between the rates of flow is not large any inaccuracy in the airflow measurements could seriously affect the results.

Example on the full volume-reduced volume method

The table below is an extract from the summary of the results made in a full volume-reduced volume pressure survey of a deep *upcast* ventilation shaft. Air quantities in the shaft were varied by starting or stopping one or more of the main fans situated underground.

An Askania micro-barometer was set up on surface and a similar micro-barometer and Fuess aneroid barometer were used on 6 level to measure the changes in barometric pressure when the airflow was altered.

The air volumes were measured at the main fans. The average density of the air in the shaft was calculated from the temperatures and pressures obtained on 6 level and on surface.

No.	Test condition	Surface baro-metric pressure (Pa)	6 Level baro-metric pressure (Pa)	Quantity flow (m³/s)	Calculated mean density (kg/m³)	
					w_{mf}	w_{mr}
1	All fans running	86 956	102 085	252,8	1,089 4	
2	All fans stopped	86 990	101 431	56,7		1,085 4
3	All fans running	87 051	102 220	259,2	1,089 4	

Depth of shaft 1 356,4 m (upcast)

Calculation of pressure loss

The formula to calculate the pressure loss in an *upcast* shaft is

$$p_f = \frac{\Delta P - g\Delta H(w_{mf} - w_{mr})}{1 - \dfrac{w_{mr}\,(Q_r)^2}{w_{mf}\,(Q_f)^2}}$$

Using the information provided under 1 and 2 in the above tabulation

$$\Delta P = (102\,085 - 101\,431) - (86\,956 - 86\,990) = 688 \text{ Pa}$$

$$\therefore p_f = \cfrac{688 - (9,79 \times 1\,356,4 \times 0,004\,0)}{1 - \cfrac{1,085\,4}{1,089\,4}\left(\cfrac{56,73}{252,85}\right)^2}$$

$= 668$ Pa for a volume of 252,85 m³/s

Similarly, using the information provided under 2 and 3 in the above tabulation

$$\Delta P = (102\,220 - 101\,431) - (87\,051 - 86\,990) = 728 \text{ Pa}$$

$$\therefore p_f = \cfrac{728 - (9,79 \times 1\,356,4 \times 0,004\,0)}{1 - \cfrac{1,085\,4}{1,089\,4}\left(\cfrac{56,73}{259,22}\right)^2}$$

$= 708$ Pa for a volume of 259,22 m³/s

5.2.2 The density method

The density method is based on the fact that the pressure loss between two points in an airway is equal to the difference between the observed increase in barometric pressure between the upper and lower points, and what the increase would have been had there been no pressure loss between the points. This can be expressed for flow in a downcast shaft by the equation:

$$p = M + P_1 - P_2$$

where

P_1 and P_2 = observed barometric pressures at upper and lower points, respectively (Pa)

M = estimated increase in pressure due to the intervening air column.

Provided the vertical distance ΔH between the two points is not large, M can be replaced by $\Delta H w_m g$ where w_m is the mean density of the intervening air column in kg/m³. Thus the pressure loss p in Pa is given by:

$$p = \Delta H w_m g - \Delta P \text{ (downcast airway)}$$

or

$$p = \Delta P - \Delta H w_m g \text{ (upcast airway)}$$

where

p = pressure loss (Pa)

ΔH = difference in elevation (m)

w_m = mean density (kg/m³)

g = gravitational acceleration m/s²

ΔP = actual pressure difference between the measuring stations (Pa)

In this method a barometer is set up at each end of an airway, and simultaneous readings of the barometric pressure at each point are made and an actual difference in pressure obtained. The actual difference in pressure can be compared with the theoretical difference due to elevation and density differences, and the pressure loss determined.

If only one barometer is available, corrections must be made for any possible change in the pressure at the first station, while readings are taken at the second station. This is generally done by taking two readings at the first station, one before and one after the reading at the second station. The correct pressure is obtained by linear interpolation.

Another variation of this method is to take barometer readings at regular intervals at a "control station". A second barometer is taken to the various other measuring stations and the pressure and time recorded. After making the necessary time, elevation and density corrections, the pressure loss is calculated.

In deep shafts the density pattern may be unpredictable, and when using this method observation points must be set up reasonably near to one another to ensure that the calculated mean density in each section approximates closely the true mean density. This usually necessitates travelling up and down the shaft, and the observed barometric pressures must be corrected for diurnal variations in atmospheric pressure between successive observations.

In addition, the variations in ambient air temperatures and pressures found in deep shafts, together with the unstable flow conditions almost invariably found in underground airways, make it difficult to measure the barometric pressure with the required degree of accuracy.

The density method is suitable for performing an extended survey over a mine or part of a mine because the errors are non-cumulative and because it is quicker and entails much less effort than does the trailing-hose method. The instruments used are easy to handle and read.

The principal disadvantages of this method are:

(a)   Laborious calculations are involved. This disadvantage can be overcome by using a computer to perform the calculation. This aspect is discussed in detail under Section 70.

(b)   Two large numbers (the barometric pressures at the top and bottom stations) must be subtracted from each other and subsequently a second subtraction of large numbers (the vertical distance multiplied by the mean density multiplied by the gravitational acceleration) is needed. Thus there is a very large magnification of any experimental or instrument errors. In addition it is not accurate when pressure losses over short sections have to be measured.

An advantage of this method is that where shafts are not uniformly equipped it is possible to obtain the resistance offered by certain sections, and to exclude exit and entrance losses in the measured resistance.

Example of the use of the density method

This example is based on measurements made by means of a single Askania micro-barometer in a conveyance which was moved between the bank and to each of the four points in the shaft.[10] Wet- and dry-bulb temperatures and barometric pressures were observed at all these points, and frequent observations of barometric pressure and temperatures were made on the bank throughout the test.

Barometric pressure readings in the shaft were corrected to compensate for changes in surface barometric pressures, although these were, in fact, very small.

The observations made are summarized below.

	Shaft conveyance				On surface		
Observa-tion point	Time	t_{wb}/t_{db} (°C)	Bar. pressure (Pa)		Time	t_{wb}/t_{db} (°C)	Bar. press. (Pa)
			Observed	Corrected			
Bank	9.54	17 7/23,0	87 260	87 200	9.54	18,1/22,9	87 310
Point 1	10.05	17,9/23,0	88 340	88 340	10.08	18,1/22,9	87 300
Point 2	10.10	18,7/23,1	89 980	89 970	10.10	18,1/23,3	87 290
Point 3	10.17	20,1/24,5	92 850	92 850	10.17	18,1/22,9	87 310
Point 4	10.25	21,2/27,1	95 870	95 870	10.28	18,1/23,5	87 290

Specimen calculation for determining the pressure loss between points 3 and 4 in the shaft.

At point 3

Corrected barometric pressure	92 850 Pa
Air temperature	20,1/24,5 °C
Density	1,078 kg/m^3

At point 4

Corrected barometric pressure	95 870 Pa
Air temperature	21,2/27,1 °C
Density	1,103 kg/m^3

Between points 3 *and* 4

Difference in elevation	ΔH =	298,6 m
Mean density	w_m =	1,090 5 kg/m^3
Observed increase in pressure	ΔP =	3 020 Pa
Estimated increase in pressure $\Delta H \times w_m \times 9,79$	=	3 188 Pa
∴ Pressure loss by difference (at mean density)	=	168 Pa

5.2.3 The meteorological method[11]

In a downcast shaft barometric pressures are measured at upper and lower observation points, and an estimate is then made of what the pressure at the lower point would have been in relation to the pressure at the upper point had there been no flow in the shaft. The pressure loss is then equivalent to the amount by which the estimated pressure at the lower point exceeds the observed pressure.

However, in the meteorological method, the no-flow pressure at the lower observation point is estimated by using an empirical logarithmic formula taken from the International Meteorological Tables. This formula gives the "no-flow" difference between barometric pressures at two points at different elevations as a function of the vertical difference in elevation, the mean (dry-bulb) air temperature between the two elevations, and the mean humidity between the two points, the latitude of the place and the mean elevation above sea level. The formula is given by Lambrechts[11] quoting Jones[12] as follows:

$$3,281 \, \Delta Z = PQRS \log \frac{B_2}{B_1}$$

or

$$\log (\log B_2 - \log B_1) = $$
$$(\log 3,281 + \log \Delta Z) - (\log P + \log Q + \log R + \log S)$$

where

$B_1 =$ barometric pressure at upper station (Pa)
$B_2 =$ barometric pressure at lower station (Pa)
$\Delta Z =$ difference in elevation between stations (m)
$P =$ a factor depending on the mean dry-bulb temperature ($°C$) between the stations
$Q =$ a factor depending on the numerical mean moisture content (g/kg) between the stations
$R =$ a factor depending on the latitude
$S =$ a factor depending on mean elevation above sea level
$\log R = 0,000 \, 7$ for the Witwatersrand (latitude 26 °S)
$\log R = 0,000 \, 6$ for the Orange Free State (latitude 28 °S)

The value of $\log S$ does not exceed 0,000 1 and it can be neglected for all practical purposes.

Normally, the meteorological method is based on the use of barometric pressures (and wet- and dry-bulb temperatures) measured at the top and bottom of the shaft, using either two instruments so as to obtain simultaneous readings, or using one instrument and correcting for diurnal variations in pressures between the two observations.

Lambrechts[11] suggests that, locally, this time correction can be estimated from figures for the mean daily variation, thus eliminating the need for observing barometric pressures on surface throughout the test.

The meteorological method is certainly the least time-consuming of all the methods as regards the measurements which have to be made, because it is based on the use of only two barometric pressure readings and it is not necessary to change the volume as in the full volume-reduced volume method. Obviously the accuracy of the method depends on how closely the increase predicted by the empirical formula approaches the no-flow increase in any given shaft; for fairly old, dry, downcast shafts, reasonably close agreement could be expected, but for any shaft the accuracy of the method is likely to be improved by measuring air temperatures at one or more intermediate points so as to obtain a better estimate of the mean of the temperatures between the two major observation points.

Example on the meteorological method

The observations shown below were made to determine the pressure losses in a downcast shaft by the meteorological method. The shaft was in the Orange Free State and the mean quantity downcasting was 194,9 m³/s.

Observations

Station	Time	Elevation below datum (m)	Air temp. (°C)	Barometric pressures (Pa)	
				Instrument A	Instrument B
Surface	11.30	474,9	16,7/22,2	87 376	87 399
23 Level	12.30	2 018,4	21,9/32,5	103 628	103 659

Calculations

Latitude 28 °S; log S = 0,000 1; Difference in elevation ΔZ = 1 543,5 m.

	Barometers (Pa)	
	A	B
Observed pressure on surface at 11.30	87 376	87 399
Time correction at 12.30 (from tables)	−55	−55
Corrected pressure on surface at 12.30 (B_1)	87 321	87 344
Observed pressure on 23 level at 12.30 (B_2)	103 628	103 659
Mean pressure (surface — 23 level)	95 474	95 501

∴ Mean barometric pressure   95 488 Pa
Mean temperatures   19,3/27,3 °C
Moisture content at mean barometric
pressure and temperature   11,6 g/kg

Log P = 4,822 9 (from tables)   Log ΔZ (1 543,5) = 3,188 5
Log Q = 0,003 1 (from tables)   Log   3,281   = 0,516 0
Log R = 0,000 6 (latitude 28 °S)
Log S = 0,000 1 (given)   Log   3,281 ΔZ = 3,704 5

Log $PQRS$ = 4,826 7

∴ Log 3,281 ΔZ − Log $PQRS$ = $\overline{2}$,877 8

	Barometer A	Barometer B
Antilog	0,075 48	0,075 48
Log observed B_1	4,941 11	4,941 23
Add	5,016 59	5,016 71
Calculated B_2	103 890	103 920
Observed B_2	103 628	103 659
Pressure difference (at mean density)	262 Pa	261 Pa

∴ Pressure loss in downcast shaft for a mean quantity flow of 194,9 m³/s is 262 Pa.

5.2.4 *The energy method*

This method is similar to the other barometric methods and involves measuring barometric pressures at either end of an airway and determining the energy loss from the difference between the theoretical and the actual work inputs. The advantages and disadvantages of the method are similar to those of the other barometric methods.

The formula used to calculate the frictional energy loss in a downcast airway is as follows:

$$F = g\Delta H - R\Delta P \, \frac{LMT_{1-2}}{LMP_{1-2}}$$

(For an upcast airway the right-hand side of the equation must be multiplied by -1,)

where F = frictional energy loss (J/kg)

g = gravitational acceleration (9,79 m/s²)

ΔH = difference in elevation (m)

R = gas constant (J/kg K)

ΔP = difference in pressure between the stations (Pa)

$$LMT_{1-2} = \frac{T_2 - T_1}{2{,}303 \log \dfrac{T_2}{T_1}}$$

(where T_1 is the dry-bulb temperature (K) at station (1) and T_2 is the dry-bulb temperature (K) at station (2))

$$LMP_{1-2} = \frac{P_2 - P_1}{2{,}303 \log \dfrac{P_2}{P_1}}$$

(where P_1 is the pressure (Pa) at station (1) and P_2 is the pressure (Pa) at station (2))

Example on the energy method

The Table below shows observations made during a pressure survey conducted in a main downcast shaft.

Station	Corrected barometric pressure (Pa)	Air temperature (°C)	Elevation below datum (m)	Moisture content (g/kg)	Air density (kg/m³)	*Gas constant R (J/kg K)
Bank	86 618	15,6/21,1	470,9	10,7	1,020 1	288,8
17 Level	99 040	19,5/31,0	1 691,9	9,8	1,126 4	288,8

Calculation of the gas constant (R)

The gas constant for dry air is 287,1 J/kg K

The value of the gas constant for an air-water vapour mixture varies according to the amount of water vapour present in the mixture and can be calculated by the formula:

$$R_{mixture} = \frac{R_{dry\ air}\left(1 + \dfrac{r}{0,622}\right)}{(1 + r)}$$

where

$R_{mixture}$ = gas constant for the air-water vapour mixture (J/kg K)

$R_{dry\ air}$ = gas constant for dry air = 287,1 J/kg K

r = moisture content of the mixture (g/kg)

Typical values of the gas constant for various moisture contents are given below:

Moisture content (g/kg)	Gas constant of air-water vapour mixture (J/kg K)
0	287,1
5	288,0
10	288,8
20	290,5
30	292,1
40	293,8
50	295,4

Calculation of frictional energy and pressure loss

$$F = g\Delta H - R\Delta P \frac{LMT_{1\ -\ 2}}{LMP_{1\ -\ 2}}$$

where

F = frictional energy loss (J/kg)

g = 9,79 m/s^2

ΔH = 1 691,9−470,9=1 221,0 m

R = 288,8 J/kg K from table

ΔP = 99 040−86 618=12 422 Pa

$$LMT_{1\ -\ 2} = \frac{304,15 - 294,25}{2,303 \log \dfrac{304,15}{294,25}} = 299,119$$

$$LMP_{1-2} = \frac{12\,422}{2{,}303 \log \dfrac{99\,040}{86\,618}} = 92\,674$$

$$\therefore F = (9{,}79 \times 1\,221{,}0) - \left(288{,}8 \times 12\,422 \times \frac{299{,}119}{92\,674}\right) = 360 \text{ J/kg}$$

Arithmetic mean density in shaft

$$= \frac{1{,}020\,1 + 1{,}126\,4}{2} = 1{,}073\,2 \text{ kg/m}^3$$

$$p = F \times w_m$$

where

p = pressure loss (Pa)
F = frictional energy loss (J/kg)
w_m = mean density (kg/m³)
$\therefore p = 360 \times 1{,}073\,2 = 386$ Pa

Pressure loss in the shaft = 386 Pa at the mean density

6   GENERAL COMMENTS ON THE METHODS

Each of the six methods dealt with above has its own particular advantages and disadvantages which should be borne in mind when considering the method which should be adopted in any particular set of circumstances.

The various examples given are intended merely to demonstrate the different techniques of determining pressure losses, and should not be used to judge the relative accuracies of the methods themselves.

The basic principles underlying the six methods of measuring shaft resistance outlined above are simple. Nevertheless, numerous difficulties tend to arise in practice, which may be one reason why ventilation staff are sometimes reluctant to carry out resistance surveys in shafts. Some of the more common of these difficulties are discussed below.

Changes in the pressure of the atmosphere during a barometric survey will affect the accuracy of the results unless appropriate corrections are made. To monitor such changes a control or master barometer should be sited at a fixed point and read at regular intervals during the period of the survey.

The density of the air will in general not be the same at the control and the other measuring points, so that changes in atmospheric pressure will not be followed precisely by the barometers at the other stations.

Let

P_{cb} = control barometric reading
ΔP_{cb} = a change in the control barometric reading
ΔP_n = the corresponding change in the traverse barometric reading.

Provided the flow between the two stations remains constant, and polytropic, and the temperature at the two stations remains reasonably constant, the correction applicable at any station, n, to the change ΔP_{cb} is:

$$\Delta P_n = \frac{P_n}{P_{cb}} \times \Delta P_{cb} \qquad (13)$$

Thus the simple atmospheric pressure correction should be multiplied by the ratio of the traverse to the control barometer readings in order to obtain the true effect at the traverse section.

The greatest difficulty of all is that the value to be measured, i.e., the pressure loss, invariably fluctuates continuously in sympathy with fluctuations in the airflow itself. These fluctuations can be, and usually are, due to a combination of causes, the most important of which are:

(a)   Changes in the overall system resistance, caused, for example, by the opening and/or closing of ventilation doors, the movement of conveyances in shafts and haulages, the cleaning of stope faces, the effect of falling water in upcast shafts, and variations in leakage through ore passes caused by rock being tipped or drawn.

(b)   Changes in imparted energy such as the (usually) minor fluctuations which occur even when fans are operating normally, and the fairly drastic fluctuations which may arise when fans operate in or close to the stall zone.

(c)   Changes due to "natural" causes, i.e., changes in natural ventilation pressure due to the effect of atmospheric air temperature changes on downcast air temperatures.

Some of the above sources of fluctuations can be anticipated and steps taken to ensure that interference is reduced to a minimum. Nevertheless, in a large mine it is often impossible, for example, to maintain a constant watch of every possible source of leakage while a survey is in progress, particularly if the survey takes place during an ordinary shift; generally it is more satisfactory to do surveys off-shift.

The fluctuations dealt with here would be less important if "instantaneous" measurements of airflow and pressure could be made. Existing methods of measuring pressure loss are reasonably adequate, but instantaneous measurements of airflow cannot be made easily. One reason for this is that anemometers are basically integrating instruments, and therefore incapable of giving "spot" readings. A further reason is that with many shaft layouts the total airflow in the shaft can be determined only by measuring the individual flows in several secondary airways.

One partial solution to this problem is to take all observations according to a fixed timetable; however, this is not always possible in practice, and what usually happens is that all observers are instructed to take as many observations as they conveniently can between specified times, leaving it until later to decide which observations are to be used for calculation purposes.

Before conducting a survey it is essential that all observers should be thoroughly briefed to ensure that they fully understand the tasks assigned to them.

A particular feature of most shaft resistance surveys is that observers are scattered over a considerable area of the mine so that the majority of them cannot communicate with each other. It is therefore advisable whenever possible to establish check measuring points to guard against human and/or instrumental errors. The extent to which this can be done will depend in every case on the particular circumstance of the survey, but it should be possible in every instance to establish at least certain key observations which can be checked in this way.

Barometric methods or the trailing-hose technique have their own ranges of application and a choice between the two procedures for any given exercise may be made on purely practical grounds.

7   THE USE OF COMPUTERS FOR THE ANALYSIS OF PRESSURE SURVEY RESULTS[14]

In designing the future ventilation system of an existing mine, two procedures are involved:

(a)   obtaining the physical details of the current layout by means of ventilation surveys, and

(b)   the use of these data in a feasibility study of suggested future changes, namely, ventilation network analysis (see Chapter 16).

As most air quantity surveys are made by conventional anemometer traverses and measurement of cross-sectional areas, there is no point in automating the very simple calculations involved. Air quantities should be calculated on the spot during a survey in order to check the consistency of the measurements so as to be able to eliminate gross errors.

During a full ventilation survey, air quantity measurements are normally made in conjunction with one or other of the pressure surveying techniques.

It is in the treatment of the pressure survey data that the computer is most useful. In the trailing-hose method the calculations are not complex, and consist mainly of corrections for instrument calibration and air density. In accurate surveys, corrections must be applied to allow for the position of the manometer with respect to the end stations. Due to practical limitation of the length of tubing which can be employed, a large number of observations have to be made on the more extended surveys.

A computer can be used to advantage in relieving the ventilation engineer of the tedium of the large number of repeated calculations required. In surveys where the barometer is used a formidable number of calculations are involved. Computer programs are now available which permit true thermodynamic relationships to be applied to the observed data without over-approximated corrections.[14] Manual calculations are eliminated and an accuracy which is perfectly adequate for most planning purposes can be obtained by taking reasonable care in making the observations. Thus the application of a digital computer has removed the major disadvantages of the barometric surveying method.

7.1   The pressure survey program[13,15]

The cycle of operations is such that the observations made during a ventilation survey of an existing mine are used in a pressure survey program to determine branch pressure drops, resistance, quantities and power losses. The output from this program can be used in current ventilation planning or fed into the next program, the network analysis programme. The output from the network analysis program can be used for future ventilation planning.

The advantages of using the pressure survey program are that exact thermodynamic relationships are used to calculate the pressure losses and the use of simplified formulae and manual calculations is eliminated.

Two barometers are normally used to conduct the ventilation survey, one being placed at a control station and the other traversed along the underground section. The input data which are recorded on a standard pro-forma comprise:

(a)   control barometer readings at time intervals usually not exceeding 5 minutes and extending over the period of the survey;

(b)   temperature corrections for the traverse barometer; and

(c)   a set of traverse observations at each station; the records must included the station number, time of observation, barometer reading, air temperature and velocity and the elevation of the station.

The output data from the computer are given in the three sections which are:

(i)   the station parameters, that is, relative humidity, moisture content and density of the air;

(ii)   the branch parameters, that is, the pressure drop, the resistance and the power loss in each airway; and

(iii)   the mesh parameters, that is, the standardized pressure drops around each mesh. If the meshes are closed the natural ventilation pressure is given for that mesh.

The input and output data for the pressure survey programme are shown below:

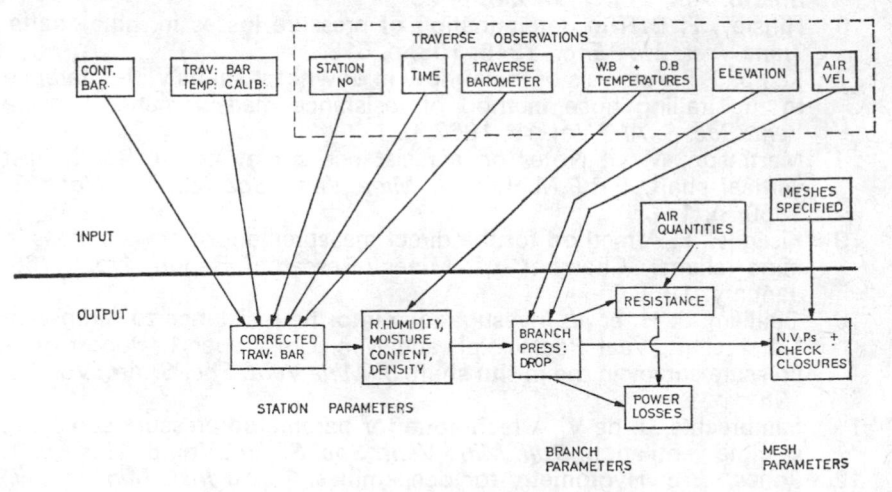

Figure 15:1

8   ACCURACY OF THE RESULTS

When the results from a pressure survey are examined the question is invariably asked, "How accurate are these figures?"

To be able to give a quantitative answer to this question involves a fairly complex statistical analysis of all the relevant test data, but it can be stated qualitatively that, all other things being equal, the overall accuracy is a function of the accuracy of all the individual instruments used in the survey.

It may be worthwhile to recall that, insofar as random errors are concerned, the precision of the mean of a series of n observations is $\sqrt{n}$ times that of a single observation, that is, the standard error of the mean is $\dfrac{1}{\sqrt{n}}$ times that of a single observation. Thus if the mean of a series of six observations is compared with the mean of a series of three observations, the mean of the six observations is 1,414 times as precise as the mean of the three observations.

9   REFERENCES

1   Quilliam, J. H. The measurement of air temperatures in semi-dry downcast shafts. *J. Mine Vent. Soc. S. Afr.;* Vol. 10, 1957, p. 286.

2   Kemp, J. F. Gas tracer method of flow measurement and its possible application to mine shafts, *Mine Vent. Soc. S. Afr.;* Vol. 14, 1961, p. 160.

3   Finn, P. J. and Quilliam, J. H. The Airostat — a simple pressure differential device. *J. Mine Vent. Soc. S. Afr.; Vol.* 12, 1957, p. 4.

4   Kislig, R. E. The differential barometer, *J. Mine Vent. Soc. S. Afr.;* Vol. 19, 1966, p. 110.

5   Craig, D. K. Barometers and barometer calibration. *J. Mine Vent. Soc. S. Afr.;* Vol. 11, 1958, p. 25.

6   Hinsley, F. B. The determination of pressure losses in mine shafts. *Trans. Inst. Min. Eng.,* 1949, 108, p. 613.

7   Kemp, J. F. Analysis of the airflow in downcast shafts with reference to the trailing hose method of resistance measurement. *J. Mine Vent. Soc. S. Afr.;* Vol. 15, 1962, p. 1.

8   Martinson, M. J. Notes on a resistance survey of the South East vertical shaft, E.R.P.M. Ltd. *J. Mine Vent. Soc. S. Afr.;* Vol. 11, 1958, p. 1.

9   Kislig, R. E. A method for the direct measurement of pressure loss in mine shafts. Chamber of Mines Research Report No. 1/68, January, 1968.

10   Quilliam, J. H. *et al.* Investigations into the resistance to airflow of No. 1 shaft, Vaal Reefs Expl. and Min. Co., Paper 1. Report on a pressure survey in the in situ shaft. *J. Mine Vent. Soc. S. Afr.;* Vol. 14, 1961, p. 1.

11   Lambrechts, J. de V. A technique for barometric pressure surveying in mine ventilation, *Bull. Mine Vent. Soc. S. Afr.;* Vol. 6, 1953, p. 1.

12   Jones, J. S. Hygrometry for deep mines, *Trans. Inst. Min. Metall.,* 1924–25, 34, p. 3.

13   McPherson, M. J. A new treatment of mine barometric surveys, *Min. Eng.* No. 109, October, 1969, p. 23–4.
14   The use of computers in mine ventilation, published in the *Min. Eng.,* Feb., 1970. Presented at a colloquium on mine ventilation held at meetings of the Federal Institutes.
15   Burrows, J. H. J. Contribution to The planning of ventilation and refrigeration requirements in deep level mines, (Grave, D. F. H. and Stroh, R. M.) *J. Mine Vent. Soc. S. Afr.;* Vol. 25, 1972, p. 113.

BIBLIOGRAPHY

Symposium. *Mine shaft design and its effect on airflow.* Johannesburg, November, 1963.
Kislig, R. E. A theoretical and critical analysis of the various methods of determining energy and pressure losses in shafts. *J. Mine Vent. Soc. S. Afr.:* Vol. 17, 1964, p. 89.

16 Ventilation Network Analysis

M. J. McPHERSON

Department of Mining, University of Nottingham, England

1 INTRODUCTION

If the geometrical layout of a mine ventilation system is known, together with the resistance values for the branches and the position and pressure-volume characteristic of each fan, how can the distribution of airflow be calculated? If, in an existing mine, it is decided to change the ventilation system, perhaps by driving new roadways, closing off old workings, changing the positions or duties of fans or merely by altering an airway resistance, how can the new pattern of airflows be forecast? It is these problems and others like them which the techniques of ventilation network analysis attempt to solve.

As underground mines become deeper and more extensive, ventilation costs rise. It becomes increasingly important that the power expended in creating air movement be utilized efficiently. Ventilation network analysis enables the engineer to plan future airflow distributions based on a firm quantitative foundation, rather than on the intuitive estimates which have necessarily been all too common in the past.

For very simple networks, straightforward analytical techniques will suffice. Unfortunately, such methods can be applied only to localized sections of mines. In general, when applied to complete mine layouts, the analytical methods result in high-order equations which are difficult to solve.

Modelling or analogue methods, so popular in the nineteen fifties and early nineteen sixties have largely been superseded by iterative methods of numerical analysis using high-speed digital computers. This chapter deals with the techniques available for the solution of mine ventilation networks and the impact of digital computers in the field of airflow planning.

2   FUNDAMENTALS OF FLUID NETWORKS

2.1   *Terminology*

Before proceeding with the techniques of ventilation network analysis a few basic terms must be defined :

(*a*)   A *ramified network* is a closed and interconnected system of branches through which the fluid may flow. In a mine ventilation network, the fluid is air and surface-connecting branches such as shafts are effectively closed through the free atmosphere.

(*b*)   A *junction* is a point at which three or more airways meet. In general, however, the ventilation engineer may define any specified point in the network as a junction. This is useful in defining the end points of planned, but as yet unconstructed, airways.

(*c*)   A *branch* is a single airway connecting two junctions. It follows that any one branch may have junctions only at its end points.

(*d*)   A *mesh* (or *loop*) is any closed path of connected branches within the network.

2.2 *Kirchhoff's Laws*

In the analysis of fluid networks, it is assumed that Kirchhoff's two Laws are applicable. Originally applied to electrical networks, these laws may be restated for fluid networks as follows :

Kirchhoff's First Law states that the algebraic sum of all mass flow rates at any junction is zero, that is,

$$\sum_{i=1}^{s} M_i = O \qquad\qquad \dots 1$$

where mass flow rate $M_i = w_i Q_i$ kg/s

w_i and Q_i are the air density and volume flow rate, respectively, in the *i*-th branch connected to the junction, there being s such branches.

Where changes in density are small or all measurements have been corrected to a standard density, equation 1 reduces to

$$\sum_{i=1}^{s} Q_i = 0 \qquad \qquad \dots 2$$

These formalized statements of Kirchhoff's First Law refer simply to the check made by a ventilation engineer during observations of airflow; that is, the sum of all air quantities flowing towards a junction must equal the sum of all air quantities flowing away from that junction.

Kirchhoff's Second Law states that the algebraic sum of all energy transforms which take place within the airflows around any closed mesh is zero.

Here again, this formal enunciation of the law can be changed into a form having more meaning to the ventilation engineer. Consider one single branch (subscript i). Then from the steady flow energy equation, the following relationship applies:

$$\Delta\left(\frac{u_i^2}{2}\right) + \Delta Z_i g + W_{fi} = \int_i VdP + F_i \text{ Nm/kg} \qquad \dots 3$$

where $\Delta\left(\dfrac{u_i^2}{2}\right)$ = *Change* in kinetic energy along the branch Nm/kg

ΔZ_i = Change in level along the branch, m

g = Gravitational acceleration, m/s^2

W_{fi} = Work input of fans in the branch, Nm/kg

$\int_i VdP$ = Flow work along the branch, Nm/kg

and

F_i = Heat generated by internal friction within the airflow (Nm/kg)

For a number, *m*, of such branches forming a closed mesh,

$$\sum_{i=1}^{m} \Delta Z_i g = 0$$

and

$$- \sum_{i=1}^{m} \int_i VdP = \text{Natural ventilating energy } (nve)_m$$

(The latter expression is given by the area enclosed by the mesh on a pressure-volume or temperature-entropy diagram and is the flow work arising from heat additions to the ventilating airstream).

Summing the terms of equation 3 around a closed mesh gives

$$\sum_{i=1}^{m}\left(F_i - W_{fi} - \Delta\left(\frac{u_i^2}{2}\right)\right) - (nve)_m = 0 \text{ Nm/kg} \qquad \dots 4$$

Now the changes in kinetic energy $\sum_{i=1}^{m} \Delta\left(\dfrac{u_i{}^2}{2}\right)$ are normally very small com-

pared with the other terms and may be neglected in the subsequent analysis. Furthermore, it is convenient in practice to express each term as a pressure differential rather than an energy transform. This is achieved by choosing a standard value of air density (normally $w_{st} = 1{,}2$ kg/m^3) and multiplying throughout.

$$\sum_{i=1}^{m} \{w_{st}F_i - w_{st}W_{fi}\} - w_{st}(nve)_m = 0 \qquad \dots 5$$

Each of the three factors in this latter equation may now be expressed in terms more familiar to the practising engineer:

$w_{st}F_i = p_i =$ frictional pressure drop, Pa
$w_{st}W_{fi} = p_{fi} =$ Difference in total pressure across the fan, Pa

and

$w_{st}(nve)_m = (nvp)_m =$ natural ventilating pressure, Pa
Kirchhoff's Second Law may therefore be written as

$$\sum_{i=1}^{m} (p_i - p_{fi}) - (nvp)_m = 0 \qquad \dots 6$$

That is, the algebraic sum of all frictional pressure drops around any closed mesh, less any fan and natural ventilating pressure, is equal to zero.
In the simplest case of a mesh containing no fan and no natural ventilating effects, Kirchhoff's Second Law reduces to

$$\sum_{i=1}^{m} p_i = 0 \qquad \dots 7$$

It should be remembered that equations 6 and 7 are strictly true only when all terms are referred to the same standard density, w_{st}. Observed pressure differentials, p_o, measured at air density w_o, may be standardized to p_{st} by the relationship

$$p_{st} = \frac{w_{st}}{w_o} p_o \ \text{Pa} \qquad \dots 8$$

2.3 The laws of airflow

In the application of Kirchhoff's Second Law (equation 6) the ventilation engineer must be able to calculate the frictional pressure drop, p_i, for any given volume flow along the branch.
From basic fluid mechanics it can be shown that provided the flow remains fully turbulent, the frictional pressure drop is proportional to the square of the volume flow, Q, and directly proportional to the fluid density, w. Removing the subscript i, gives

$$p \propto wQ^2$$

or

$$p \propto rwQ^2 \qquad \text{Pa} \qquad \dots 9$$

where the constant of proportionality, r, is dependent upon the geometry and surface lining of the branch and has units of m^{-4}. When the flow is not fully turbulent, r also varies with Reynolds' Number, Re[1]

$$Re = \frac{wud}{\mu} \quad \text{(dimensionless)}$$

where

u = fluid velocity, m/s
d = hydraulic mean diameter of branch, m

and

μ = dynamic viscosity, Ns/m²

For mine airways, the value of Reynolds' Number is given approximately by

$$Re = 261\ 000\ \frac{Q}{C}$$

where

Q = volume flow, m³/s

and

C = airway perimeter, m

If the Reynolds Number is greater than 3 000 the flow may be assumed to remain fully turbulent.

If the frictional pressure drop is referred to a standard density of 1,2 kg/m³ then equation 9 may be written simply as

$$P = RQ^2 \quad \text{Pa} \quad \quad \text{....10}$$

where

$$R = 1,2r \quad R = \text{resistance of airway, } Ns^2/m^8$$

Equation 10 is commonly referred to as the Square Law of mine ventilation and is the basis of most airflow planning exercises.

Where fully developed turbulence does not exist, the theoretical treatment is to retain the Square Law but to adjust the value of r (and hence resistance, R) according to known Reynolds Number against friction coefficient curves. However, it is often more convenient in practice to allow for such variations by restating equation 10 as

$$p = RQ^n \quad \text{Pa} \quad \quad \text{....11}$$

The results obtained by numerous investigators have shown that the index, n, lies in the range 1,8 to 2,2 for ventilated places underground. For unventilated regions such as worked-out areas, the value of n may decrease to as low as 1,0, that is, the flow is laminar. In the majority of cases, the assumption of the simple Square Law (equation 10) for all ventilated branches will give an accuracy which is adequate for routine ventilation planning.

3   TECHNIQUES FOR THE SOLUTION OF NETWORKS

Four methods may be employed for solving ventilation networks. The first of these involves the compounding of series- and parallel-connected airways into single equivalent resistances. The second method is the analytical solution of equations obtained by direct application of Kirchhoff's

Laws. The third is the use of physical models or analogues to represent the mine ventilation system and, finally, methods of successive approximation have come to the forefront with the evolution of electronic digital computers. The method chosen for a particular problem depends upon the complexity of the network to be analysed.

3.1   Equivalent resistances

This technique is useful for those networks, or parts of networks, which are made up of a number of airways connected in series and/or in parallel. Such systems may be defined as "simple" networks. Conversely, systems which cannot be resolved into a series/parallel configuration may be defined as "complex" networks. Unfortunately, very few mines can be described completely in terms of series/parallel connections. The equivalent resistance technique is, nevertheless, very useful for airflow investigations in localized parts of a mine.

3.1.1   Series circuits

When airways are connected in series, as shown in Fig. 16:1, the mass flow, wQ, is common to each branch. If all measurements are corrected to a standard density and the law of flow is the same for each branch, then

$$p_1 = R_1 Q^n$$
$$p_2 = R_2 Q^n$$
$$p_3 = R_3 Q^n$$

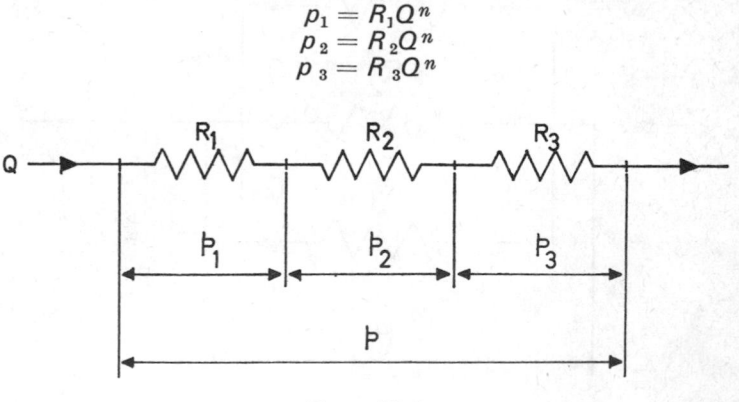

Figure 16:1

The sum of these equations is the total frictional pressure drop, p, for the system.

$$p = p_1 + p_2 + p_3 = (R_1 + R_2 + R_3)Q^n$$

If the equivalent resistance for the complete series circuit is R_s, then

$$p = R_s Q^n$$

Hence

$$R_s = R_1 + R_2 + R_3$$

In general, for b branches connected in series

$$R_s = \sum_{i=1}^{b} R_i \qquad Ns^2/m^8 \qquad \qquad ....12$$

3.1.2 *Parallel circuits*

In this case, the frictional pressure drop, p, is common to each parallel airway as shown in Fig. 16:2. Again, assuming that the same law of flow applies throughout, then

$$p = R_1 Q_1{}^n = R_2 Q_2{}^n = R_3 Q_3{}^n$$

or

$$Q_1 = \left(\frac{p}{R_1}\right)^{1/n}$$

$$Q_2 = \left(\frac{p}{R_2}\right)^{1/n}$$

and

$$Q_3 = \left(\frac{p}{R_3}\right)^{1/n}$$

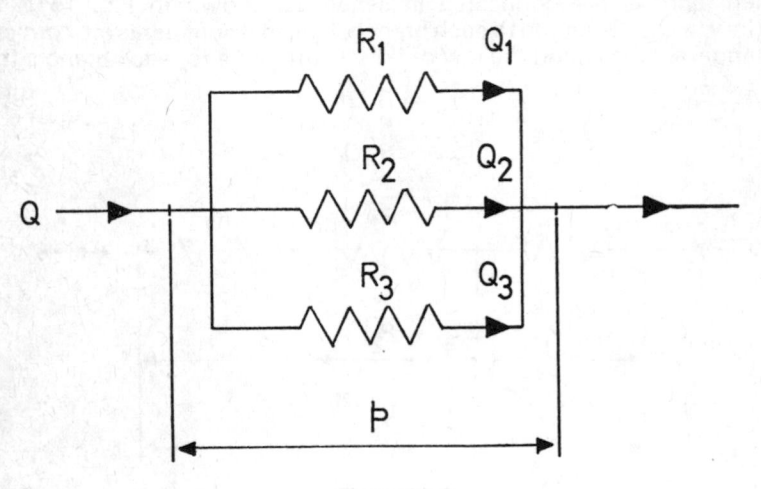

Figure 16:2

Adding these three equations gives

$$Q = Q_1 + Q_2 + Q_3 = p^{1/n} \left\{ \frac{1}{R_1{}^{1/n}} + \frac{1}{R_2{}^{1/n}} + \frac{1}{R_3{}^{1/n}} \right\}$$

Now, if the equivalent resistance for the parallel circuit is R_p, then

$$Q = \left(\frac{p}{R_p}\right)^{1/n}$$

Hence

$$\frac{1}{R_p{}^{1/n}} = \frac{1}{R_1{}^{1/n}} + \frac{1}{R_2{}^{1/n}} + \frac{1}{R_3{}^{1/n}}$$

In general, for b branches connected in parallel,

$$\frac{1}{R_r^{1/n}} = \sum_{i=1}^{b} \frac{1}{R_i^{1/n}} \qquad \dots 13$$

In the normal case of $n = 2$, equation 13 becomes

$$\frac{1}{\sqrt{R_p}} = \sum_{i=1}^{b} \frac{1}{\sqrt{R_i}} \qquad \dots 14$$

EXAMPLE

Part of a mine can be resolved into two branches connected in parallel across the bottoms of two shafts. Given the information shown in Fig. 16:3, and assuming that the Square Law holds throughout, calculate the airflow and frictional pressure drop for each airway.

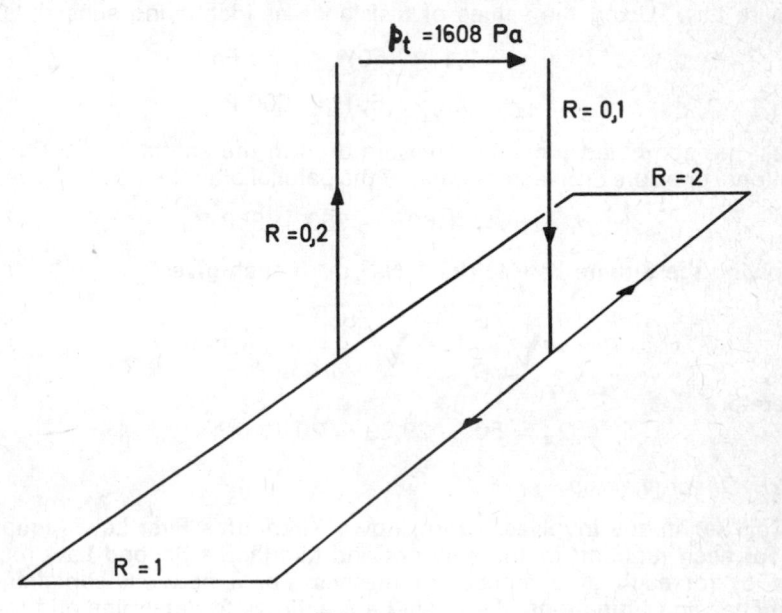

p_t =1608 Pa

R = 0,1

R = 2

R =0,2

R = 1

Figure 16:3

SOLUTION

The equivalent resistance for the two parallel branches, R_p, is given by equation 14

$$\frac{1}{\sqrt{R_p}} = \frac{1}{\sqrt{2}} + \frac{1}{\sqrt{1}} = 0{,}707\ 2 + 1$$

$$R_p = \frac{1}{(1{,}707\ 2)^2} = 0{,}343\ 1 \qquad Ns^2/m^8$$

This equivalent resistance is connected in series with the shafts. Hence, the equivalent resistance for the complete circuit, R_t, is given by equation 12.

$$R_t = 0,1 + 0,343\ 1 + 0,2 = 0,643\ 1 \qquad Ns^2/m^8$$

A great advantage of connecting airways in parallel is shown here. Even including the shafts, the total resistance is less than either of the individual parallel branches.

The total flow in the shafts, Q_t, is given by the Square Law:

$$Q_t = \sqrt{\frac{p_t}{R_t}} = \sqrt{\frac{1\ 608}{0,643\ 1}} \qquad m^3/s$$

$$= \sqrt{2\ 500} = 50\ m^3/s$$

The frictional pressure drop in each shaft is again calculated using the Square Law. Using the values of resistance as identifying subscripts,

$$p_{0,1} = 0,1 \times (50)^2 = 250\ Pa$$

$$p_{0,2} = 0,2 \times (50)^2 = 500\ Pa$$

Thus, the combined frictional pressure drop in the shafts is 750 Pa. The frictional pressure drop across each of the parallel branches is then given as

$$p_1 = p_2 = 1\ 608 - 750 = 858\ Pa$$

Applying the Square Law to the 1 Ns^2/m^8 branch gives

$$Q_1 = \sqrt{\frac{p_1}{R_1}} = \sqrt{\frac{858}{1}} = 29,29\ m^3/s$$

Therefore

$$Q_2 = 50 - 29,29 = 20,71\ m^3/s$$

3.2   Direct analysis

This technique involves writing down Kirchhoff's First Law (equation 2) for each junction in the network and Kirchhoff's Second Law (equation 6) for each of a number of meshes. For a network containing b branches and j junctions, there will be b airflows to determine and therefore b equations must be solved. Equation 2 gives j equations. However, only $j - 1$ of these are independent; the flows at the j-th junction are already defined by the flows at other junctions. There are therefore $b - (j - 1)$ remaining equations to construct. These are obtained by choosing a minimum of $b - j + 1$ meshes and writing down equation 6 for each of them. This gives

$j - 1$ junction equations from Kirchhoff's First Law

and

$b - j + 1$ mesh equations from Kirchhoff's Second Law

that is, a total of b equations to be solved for b branch airflows.

Expressions can be derived for the analytical solution of particular types of network problem. However, the mechanics of the direct analysis technique are best illustrated by a numerical example.

EXAMPLE

A two-mesh network is shown diagramatically in Fig. 16:4. A differential pressure of 2 500 Pa is applied across the circuit and a natural ventilating pressure of 500 Pa acts in the direction of airflow within mesh 1. A regulator, R_6, is constructed in the rightmost branch in order to limit the airflow in that branch to 20 m³/s. Given the resistances of all airways, find the distribution of airflow and the resistance of the regulator.

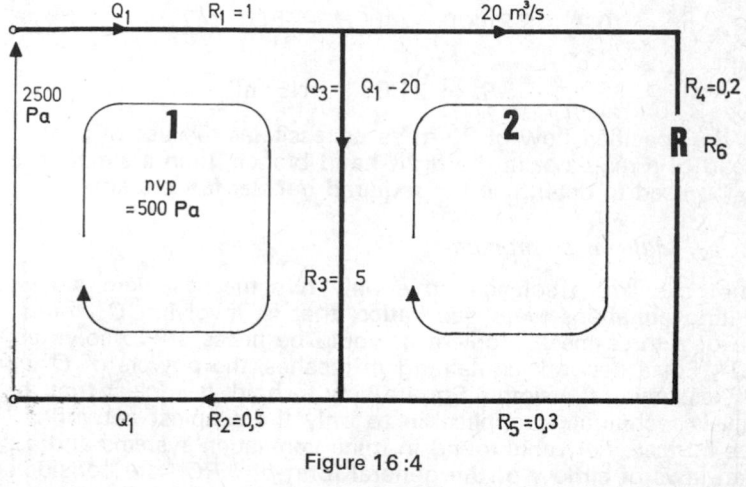

Figure 16:4

SOLUTION

If the total airflow entering the circuit is Q_1 and 20 m³/s is the flow around the regulated branch, then the flow through the centre branch is $Q_1 - 20$ m³/s. Thus Kirchhoff's First Law is satisfied by the airflows shown on Figure 16.4.

The choice of meshes is quite arbitrary provided that the minimum number $(b - j + 1)$ is satisfied and that all branches are included in the mesh pattern. A third mesh, $R_1 - R_4 - R_6 - R_5 - R_2$, may equally well have been chosen. Similarly the choice of positive direction around each mesh is arbitrary, provided that the direction chosen for each mesh is adhered to throughout the analysis. Applying Kirchhoff's Second Law (equation 6) to each of the two chosen meshes and assuming the Square Law to hold the following equations can be constructed:

Mesh 1

that is
$$R_1Q_1{}^2 + R_3(Q_1 - 20)^2 + R_2Q_1{}^2 - p_f - (nvp) = 0$$

or
$$1Q_1{}^2 + 5(Q_1 - 20)^2 + 0,5\,Q_1{}^2 - 2\,500 - 500 = 0$$

$$6,5\,Q_1{}^2 - 200\,Q_1 - 1\,000 = 0$$

This is a straightforward quadratic equation which can be solved to give

$$Q_1 = 35,147 \text{ m}^3/\text{s}$$

The flow through the R_3 branch is therefore

$$Q_3 = 15,147 \text{ m}^3/\text{s}$$

Mesh 2

$$R_4 20^2 + R_6 20^2 + R_5 20^2 - R_3(Q_1 - 20)^2 = 0$$

(Note the change of sign for the R_3 branch, due to the mesh direction being opposite to the branch flow).
that is

$$(0{,}2 + 0{,}3)400 + 400R_6 - 5(15{,}147)^2 = 0$$

giving

$$R_6 = 2{,}368 \quad \text{Ns}^2/\text{m}^8$$

If the specified flow of 20 m³/s necessitates the use of a booster fan instead of a regulator in the right-hand branch, then a similar procedure may be used to determine the required booster fan pressure.

3.2.1   Multi-mesh problems

In the example solved above only two meshes were required. The resulting equations were quadratics, that is, involving Q^2 terms. In the case of a three-mesh problem it would be necessary to solve equations in Q^4. For a network containing m meshes, the powers of Q would be 2^{m-1}, assuming the simple Square Law to hold. It is clear that the direct analysis technique is applicable to only the simplest networks. For the more intricate networks found in mine ventilation systems and especially when laws of airflow of the general form $p = RQ^n$ are considered, it is clear that other techniques of network analysis must be used. Nevertheless, like the equivalent resistance method, direct analysis has an application for localized areas within a mine.

3.3   Ventilation analogues

These are physical models which have been designed to simulate the flow of air through the branches of a ventilation network. Pneumatic and hydraulic analogues have been built using resistance elements of orifice plates and capillary tubes. Such devices suffer from scale effects in addition to very practical difficulties of dust, grease and air contamination. For these reasons, direct fluid analogues have not found general use.

The major developments in this field took place early in the nineteen fifties by the introduction of electrical analogues.[2,3,4] Kirchhoff's Laws apply to both fluid and electrical networks. Unfortunately, the basic laws governing the flow of air and the flow of electrical current differ. In the case of a ventilation network, a logarithmic law applies, $p = RQ^n$. For a straightforward electrical network, the law, that is, Ohm's Law, is linear, $E = RI$, where E is the applied voltage, I is the electrical current and R is the electrical resistance. Two methods have been used to overcome this difficulty. The first was to construct electrical analogues using non-linear resistance elements. Various analogues have been designed using tungsten lamps and, more recently, electronic circuits to simulate a logarithmic law.[5] For a ventilation analogue to remain economically viable the index n in the law $p = RQ^n$ must remain fixed for each resistance element. Many such analogues, which operate according to the Square Law, have been applied successfully in a number of countries. Similar analogues are often employed for water and gas distribution networks.

The second approach was to produce less expensive analogues in which linear resistances were retained throughout. By a method of successive adjustment of the resistances any logarithmic law of airflow could be approached. It was on this principle that the very successful National Coal Board ventilation network analyser was developed at the University of Nottingham by Scott and Hinsley in 1952.[3] In this analogue, every branch is represented by a rheostat, and a geometrical representation of the ventilation circuit is built up by making the appropriate connections on a plug board. Voltages are applied across the relevant branches to simulate fan pressures. An initial flow, Q_0, is estimated for each branch and the corresponding electrical resistance settings, S_0, are calculated as $S_0 = ARQ_0$, where R is the airway resistance and A is a constant. The flow through each resistor, Q_1, is read from an ammeter calibrated in airflow units. The rheostats are then adjusted to new values given by $S_1 = \frac{1}{2}(S_0 + ARQ_1)$. The procedure is repeated successively until the flow through each branch becomes sensibly constant. The network is then balanced and follows the Square Law. For any other law of flow, $p = RQ^n$, the values of Q in the calculation of electrical resistance must be raised to the power $(n - 1)$.

The main advantage of ventilation analogues is that they give a direct visual representation of the airflow system. Furthermore, in the case of the linear resistor type of analogue, the ventilation engineer can modify the network during the process of successive approximation if it becomes clear that an unsatisfactory solution is being approached.

The disadvantages of analogues are: (a) the time required for setting up the network on the plug board, (b) the dependence of accuracy upon the precision of manufacture, a feature common to all analogue devices and, (c), in the case of linear resistance analogues, the calculations which are necessary at each approximation. Because of these disadvantages, the use of ventilation analogues has largely been superseded by iterative techniques conducted on electronic digital computers.

3.4   Iterative techniques

These techniques of fluid network analysis involve making an initial estimate of the flow distribution, calculating an approximate correction to be applied to each branch flow and repeating the correcting procedure iteratively until an acceptable degree of accuracy has been attained.

Since the foundations of ventilation planning were laid down by John Job Atkinson in 1854[6] several iterative methods of analysing the flow through networks have been suggested. The technique which has found widest application has been that originated by Professor Hardy Cross at the University of Illinois in 1936.[7] Originally devised for water distribution systems, the method has been modified considerably in order to improve its reliability and efficiency in dealing with mine ventilation networks.[8,9]

3.4.1   *The Hardy Cross method of analysis*

Consider a volume flow of fluid, Q, passing through a duct of resistance R and obeying a law $p = RQ^n$ where p is the frictional pressure drop along the duct and n is a constant for the range of flow considered (Fig. 16:5).

In order to determine the true value of the quantity, Q, an estimated value, Q_a, is first assumed.

$$Q = Q_a + \Delta Q \qquad \qquad \ldots.15$$

where ΔQ is the error involved in the assumed quantity. Similarly, Δp is the corresponding error in the frictional pressure drop, p. The problem now becomes one of finding the correction, ΔQ, to be applied to the assumed quantity.

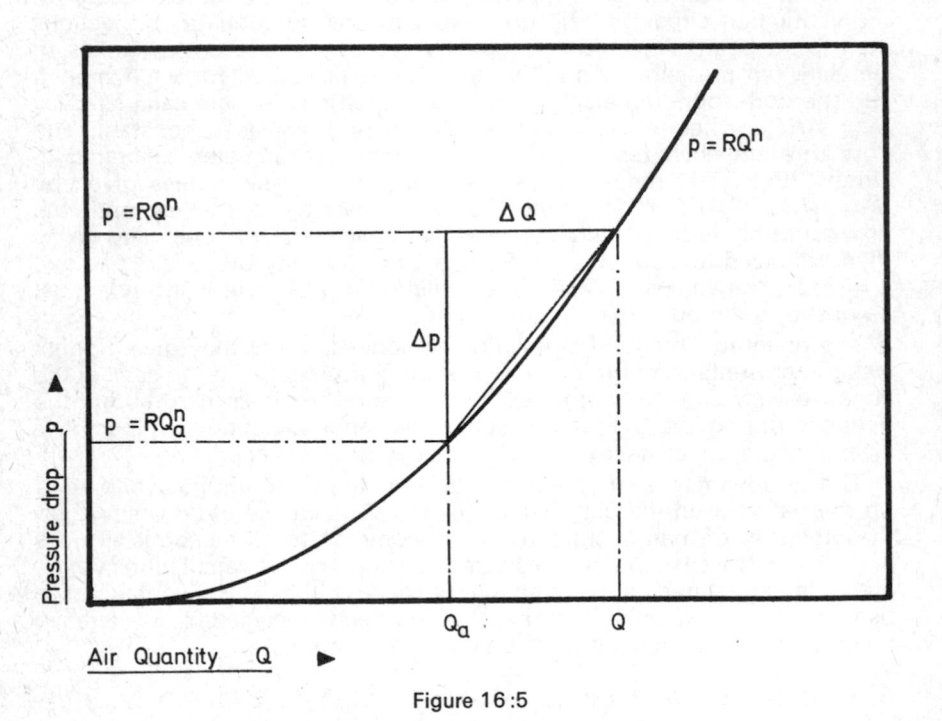

Figure 16:5

From Fig. 16:5 it will be seen that the slope of the curve in the region of Q and Q_a is given approximately by $\dfrac{\Delta p}{\Delta Q}$. In the limit this becomes $\dfrac{dp}{dQ}$.

Differentiating the law $p = RQ^n$ gives

$$\frac{dp}{dQ} = nRQ^{n-1} \quad \text{or} \quad nRQ_a^{n-1}$$

at the assumed quantity. Therefore,

$$\frac{\Delta p}{\Delta Q} = nRQ_a{}^{n-1} \quad \text{approximately,}$$

or

$$\Delta Q = \frac{\Delta p}{nRQ_a{}^{n-1}}$$

But

$$\Delta p = RQ^n - RQ_a{}^n,$$

giving

$$\Delta Q = \frac{RQ^n - RQ_a{}^n}{nRQ_a{}^{n-1}} \qquad \dots\text{.16}$$

In practical terms, the numerator of this latter equation may be called the "out-of-balance" pressure drop and the denominator is the slope of the pQ curve. So far, this analysis has been concerned with one single duct. If a series of b branches is now considered, forming a closed mesh within a network then, the mean "out-of-balance" pressure drop is given by

$$\frac{\sum\limits_{i=1}^{b} (R_i Q_i{}^{n_i} - RQ_{ia}{}^{n_i})}{b}$$

and the mean pQ slope is

$$\frac{\sum\limits_{i=1}^{b} n_i R_i Q_{ia}{}^{n_i-1}}{b}$$

Combining these two expressions in the form of equation 16 gives a composite value of flow correction, ΔQ_m, known as the mesh correction factor:

$$\Delta Q_m = \frac{\sum\limits_{i=1}^{b} (R_i Q_i{}^{n_i} - R_i Q_{ia}{}^{n_i})}{\sum\limits_{i=1}^{b} n_i R_i Q_{ia}{}^{n_i-1}} \qquad \dots\text{.17}$$

Now the frictional pressure drop along branch i is $R_i Q_i{}^{n_i}$ at the true quantity Q_i. Furthermore, Kirchhoff's Second Law states that in the absence of applied ventilating pressures the algebraic sum of frictional pressure drops around a closed mesh is zero (equation 7).

That is

$$\sum\limits_{i=1}^{b} R_i Q_i{}^{n_i} = 0$$

and equation 17 reduces to

$$\Delta Q_m = \dfrac{-\displaystyle\sum_{i=1}^{b} R_i Q_{ia}^{n_i}}{\displaystyle\sum_{i=1}^{b} n_i R_i Q_{ia}^{n_i-1}} \qquad \dots 18$$

When summing the pressure drops, $R_i Q_{ia}^{n_i}$, due account must be taken of sign, the frictional pressure drop always being positive in the direction of flow (in the absence of a fan). The slopes $n_i R_i Q_{ia}^{n_i-1}$ are always positive so that signs may be ignored in the denominator of equation 18. For each mesh a sign convention is chosen for referencing the branch flows around that mesh (as in Example 3.2.1). For manual application of the technique it is convenient to choose a clockwise traverse around each mesh as the positive direction. In actual fact, it is quite irrelevant which direction is taken as positive provided that the convention chosen for each individual mesh is maintained throughout the analysis.

Fans or natural ventilation pressures in the mesh are included by using the fuller form of Kirchhoff's Second Law (equation 6) and the slope of the fan characteristic in equation 18.

$$\Delta Q_m = \dfrac{-\left\{\displaystyle\sum_{i=1}^{b} (R_i Q_{ia}^{n_i} - p_{fi}) - (nvp)_m\right\}}{\displaystyle\sum_{i=1}^{b} (n_i R_i Q_{ia}^{n_i-1} - S_{fi})} \qquad \dots 19$$

where p_{fi} and S_{fi} are the pressure and slope of the characteristic of a fan in branch i at a volume flow of Q_{ia}. It is assumed that natural ventilating pressure, nvp, is independent of air quantity.

Because of the approximations made in the derivation of the Hardy Cross formula, the application of mesh correction factors given by equation 19 will not result immediately in a perfectly balanced flow pattern. It is therefore necessary to apply the technique repeatedly until all the mesh correction factors, ΔQ_m, approach sufficiently close to zero for the required accuracy to be met. For most practical networks, these repeated calculations make the method extremely tedious and time-consuming if computed manually.

In the majority of cases involving ventilated airways underground, the application of the Square Law of flow gives adequate accuracy. Equation 19 then becomes

$$\Delta Q_m = \dfrac{-\left\{\displaystyle\sum_{i=1}^{b} (R_i Q_{ia}|Q_{ia}| - p_{fi}) - (nvp)_m\right\}}{\displaystyle\sum_{i=1}^{b} (2R_i|Q_{ia}| - S_{fi})} \qquad \dots 20$$

where $|Q_{ia}|$ = absolute value of Q_{ia}

The choice of meshes determines the rapidity with which the flow pattern converges towards balance. Badly chosen meshes will require far more iterations than well chosen meshes. High resistance branches decelerate the convergence. In order to maintain a good computing efficiency, each high-resistance branch should appear in one mesh only.

The procedure to be followed for the manual application of the Hardy Cross method may be summarized as follows:

(a) Estimate the air quantity flowing through each branch of the network and the pressures developed by the fans. The estimated airflows should normally obey Kirchhoff's First Law at each junction. Inequalities at junctions will be maintained throughout the analysis.

(b) Examine the network and decide upon a pattern of closed meshes. The *minimum* number of meshes is given by

$$\text{No. of branches} - \text{No. of junctions} + 1$$

(Care should be taken to ensure adequate representation of all parts of the network in the mesh pattern. No mesh should contain more than one high resistance branch and such a branch should not appear in more than one mesh.)

(c) For each mesh, evaluate the mesh correction factor from equation 20 (or equation 19 if there are significant deviations from the Square Law).

(d) Correct the flow in each branch.

(e) Repeat steps (c) and (d) until all values of ΔQ_m are below a prescribed level. A satisfactory flow balance will then have been reached.

(f) Repeat steps (b) to (e) for each of a number of proposed changes to the network.

EXAMPLE

Given the ventilation circuit and resistances shown in Fig. 16:6 (a) determine the distribution of airflow. Assume that the fan pressure remains constant at 2 000 Pa and that there is no natural ventilation.

SOLUTION

The network is re-drawn in a diagrammatic manner as shown in Fig. 16:6 (b). There are six branches and four junctions giving

$$b - j + 1 = 6 - 4 + 1 = 3 \text{ meshes.}$$

The network cannot be solved easily by direct analysis, nor can it be resolved into series and parallel equivalent resistances. It will therefore be solved by the Hardy Cross method, continuing iterations until all mesh correction factors fall below 0,5 m³/s.

The three meshes are chosen such that the highest resistance, 4 Ns²/m⁸, appears in one mesh only. The estimated air quantities are given on Fig. 16:6 (b). Mesh correction factors, ΔQ_m, are calculated from equation 20 with $S_{fi} = 0$ because the fan pressure is constant. There is no natural ventilating energy, hence natural ventilation pressure equals 0.

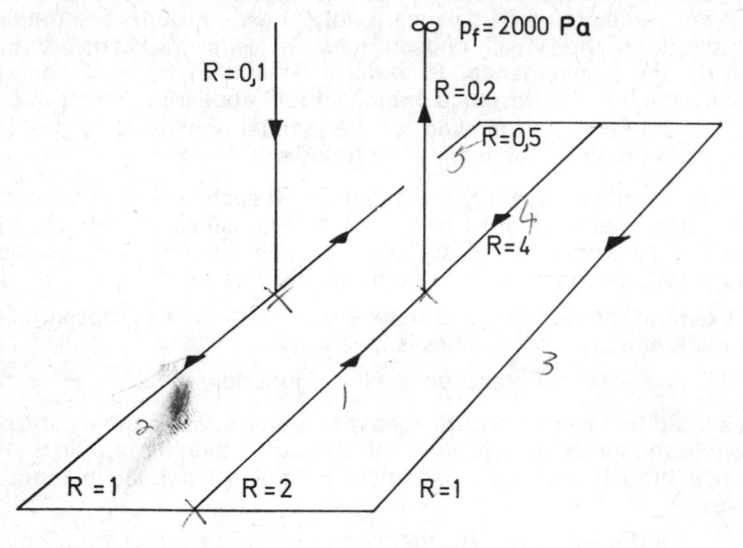

Figure 16:6 (a)

ITERATION 1

Mesh 1

$$\Delta Q_1 = \frac{-(1 \times 25^2 + 2 \times 45^2 - 4 \times 15^2)}{2(1 \times 25 + 2 \times 45 + 4 \times 15)} = -10,79 \text{ m}^3/\text{s}$$

Mesh 2

$$\Delta Q_2 = \frac{-(-0,2 \times 60^2 - 2 \times 45^2 - 1 \times 20^2 - 0,1 \times 60^2 + 2\,000)}{2(0,2 \times 60 + 2 \times 45 + 1 \times 20 + 0,1 \times 60)}$$
$$= +13,79 \text{ m}^3/\text{s}$$

Mesh 3

$$\Delta Q_3 = \frac{-(1 \times 25^2 - 1 \times 20^2 + 0,5 \times 40^2)}{2(1 \times 25 + 1 \times 20 + 0,5 \times 40)} = -7,89 \text{ m}^3/\text{s}$$

Applying these mesh correction factors to the estimated air quantities gives the flow pattern shown in Fig. 16:6 (c). The process is then repeated using the revised air quantities.

ITERATION 2

Mesh 1

$$\Delta Q_1 = \frac{-(1 \times 6,32^2 + 2 \times 20,42^2 - 4 \times 25,79^2)}{2(1 \times 6,32 + 2 \times 20,42 + 4 \times 25,79)} = +5,94 \text{ m}^3/\text{s}$$

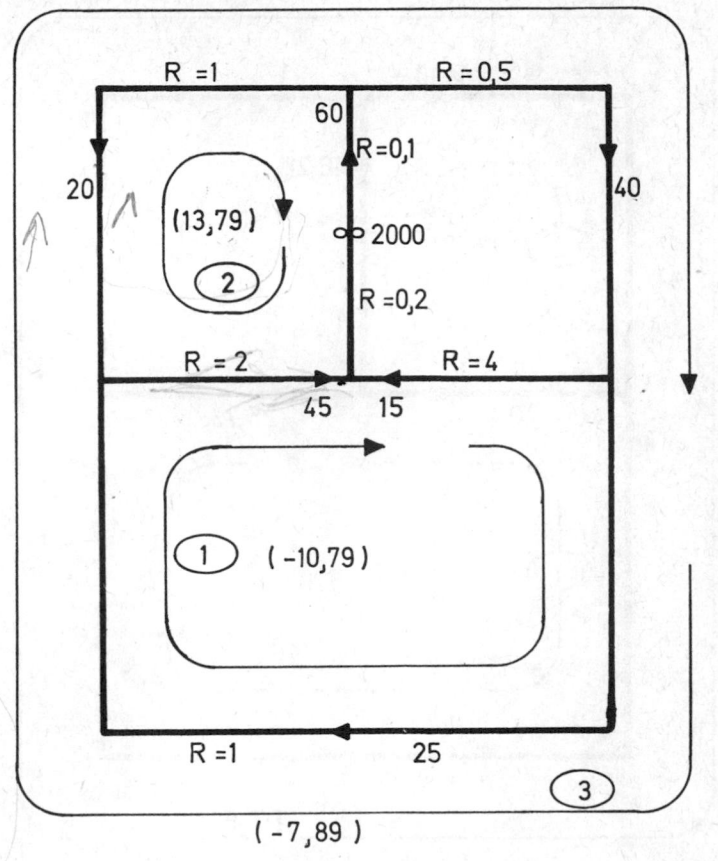

Figure 16:6 (b)

Mesh 2

$$\Delta Q_2 = \frac{-(-0,3 \times 46,21^2 - 2 \times 20,42^2 - 1 \times 14,10^2 + 2\,000)}{2(0,3 \times 46,21 + 2 \times 20,42 + 1 \times 14,10)}$$

$$= -2,37 \text{ m}^3/\text{s}$$

Mesh 3

$$\Delta Q_3 = \frac{-(1 \times 6,32^2 - 1 \times 14,10^2 + 0,5 \times 32,11^2)}{2(1 \times 6,32 + 1 \times 14,10 + 0,5 \times 32,11)} = -4,89 \text{ m}^3/\text{s}$$

The mesh correction factors are again applied to the air quantities shown in Fig. 16:6 (*c*) and a third flow pattern defined.

The complete process is repeated successively until all ΔQ values fall below the specified 0,5 m³/s. Table I shows the mesh correction factors at each iteration. In this case, eight iterations have been necessary to achieve the required accuracy. The final flow pattern then defined is shown in Fig. 16:6 (*d*).

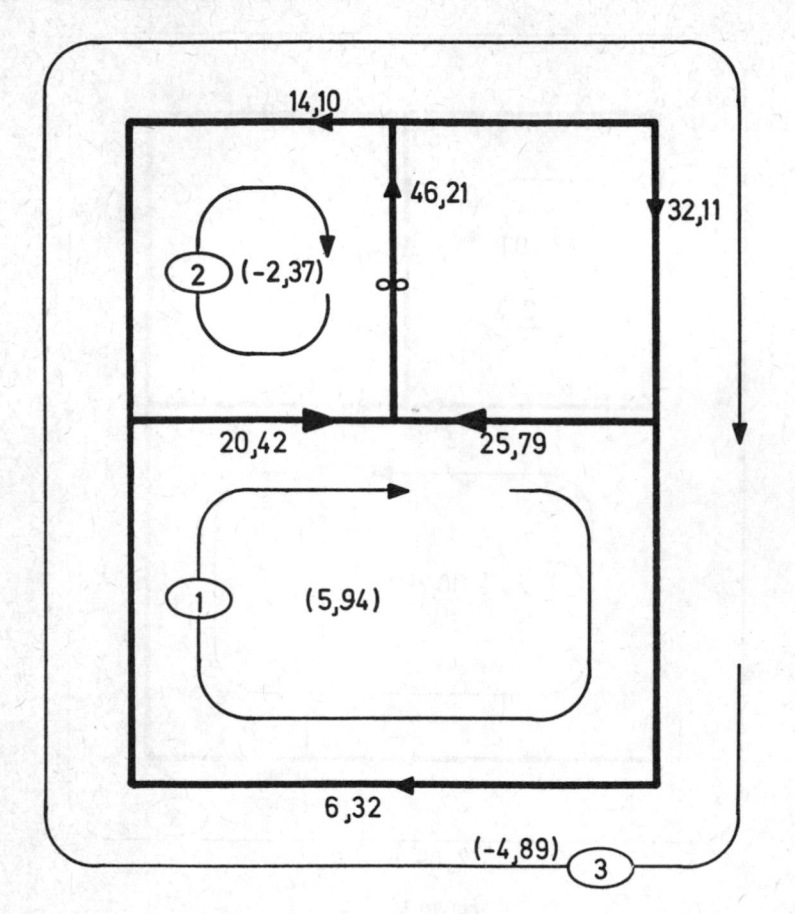

Figure 16:6 (c)

TABLE I   MESH CORRECTION FACTORS FOR EXAMPLE

Iteration	ΔQ_1	ΔQ_2	ΔQ_3
1	−10,79	+13,79	−7,89
2	+5,94	−2,37	−4,89
3	−0,45	+4,36	+0,37
4	+1,65	+0,05	−2,08
5	+0,16	+1,42	−0,32
6	+0,56	+0,21	−0,73
7	+0,13	+0,51	−0,20
8	+0,20	+0,13	−0,41

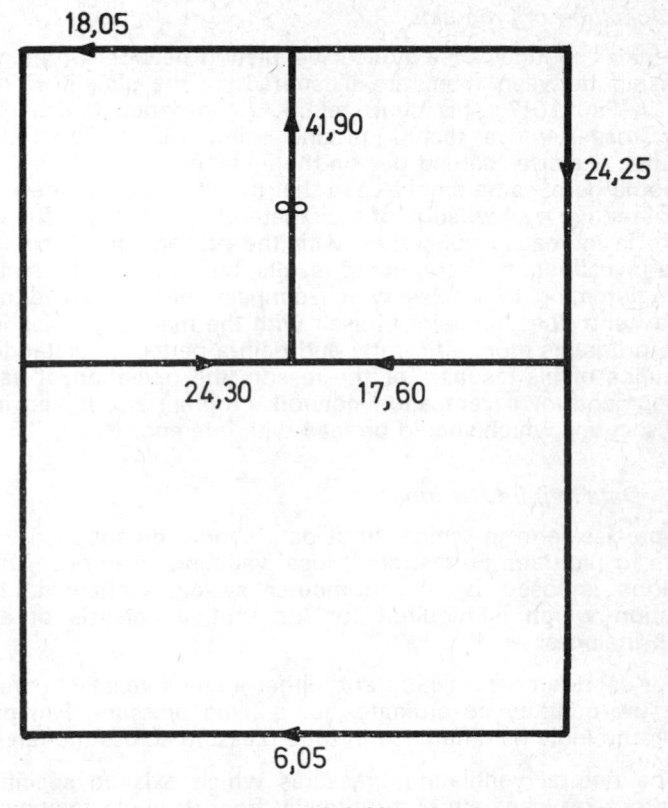

Figure 16 :6 (d)

4   VENTILATION NETWORK ANALYSIS BY DIGITAL COMPUTER

The application of iterative techniques to even simple ventilation networks involves a considerable amount of arithmetic. For practical mine systems, iterative methods become impractical if the repetitive calculations are to be carried out by manual means. Small desk-top computers assist in the calculation of mesh correction factors and the application of these to branch flows. However, the number of iterations which may be required, together with the organizational procedures of mesh selection and network updating, still involve a great amount of tedious work.

The modern approach is to automate the complete process fully by using the larger and faster computers. A number of computer programs have been developed for this purpose, requiring between 5 000 and 15 000 words of computer memory store, depending upon the complexity of the program, the language in which it is written and the size of the network to be analysed. The availability of such programs reduces the manual work to that of specifying the data which described the network.

4.1   *Operation of programs*

The major routines of a typical ventilation network program and the relationship between them are illustrated by the simplified flow chart shown in Fig. 16:7. This chart refers to a program which utilizes the Hardy Cross iterative technique and prints out a flow analysis for cumulative exercises carried out on the initial network.

It should perhaps be emphasized that the utilization of these programs does not require a knowledge of their method of operation. The ventilation engineer is intimately concerned with the preparation of his input data and the investigation of computed results, but not with the mathematical and programming intricacies which connect the two. Nevertheless, the engineer who does acquaint himself with the main principles is likely to use the programs more efficiently and gain a better understanding of the significance of his results. For the reason, the operation of each of the main segments of a ventilation network program is outlined in the following sections which should be read with reference to Fig. 16.7.

4.1.1   *Data required as input*

The precise form in which input data should be supplied varies from program to program. Furthermore, local variations may occur because of restrictions imposed by the computer system employed. The basic information which is required for the routine analysis of an airflow network includes:

(*a*)   For each fan, its position and either a characteristic curve specified as pressure-quantity co-ordinates, or a fixed pressure. Fan pressure is used here to indicate difference in total pressure across the fan.

(*b*)   The natural ventilating pressures which exist in specified loops. Some programs generate *nvp* internally from dry-bulb temperatures and junction levels relative to some datum. Other programs require the specification of *nvp* in the same way as fixed pressure fans and referred to definite branches. This latter method, although less exact, is the one which has been received most favourably by practicing ventilation engineers.

(*c*)   The geometry of the basic network and the resistance of each branch. The basic network is normally the ventilation system of a mine at the time of the last ventilation survey. For a newly-planned mine, the resistance values must be obtained from design data. Each junction is given an integer reference number. The basic network may then be specified by quoting each branch in terms of junction numbers, (from—to) followed by *either* the branch resistance and assumed air quantity, *or* an observed frictional pressure drop and air quantity. The latter alternative uses directly the results of ventilation surveys.

(*d*)   The specification of exercise data. Each exercise will consist of one or more modifications to be made to the network last analysed during that run of the computer. A flow pattern will be produced for each exercise. In modern programs, the modifications allow great flexibility and networks may be changed from exercise to exercise in any way which is likely to have practical significance. The modifications which are required

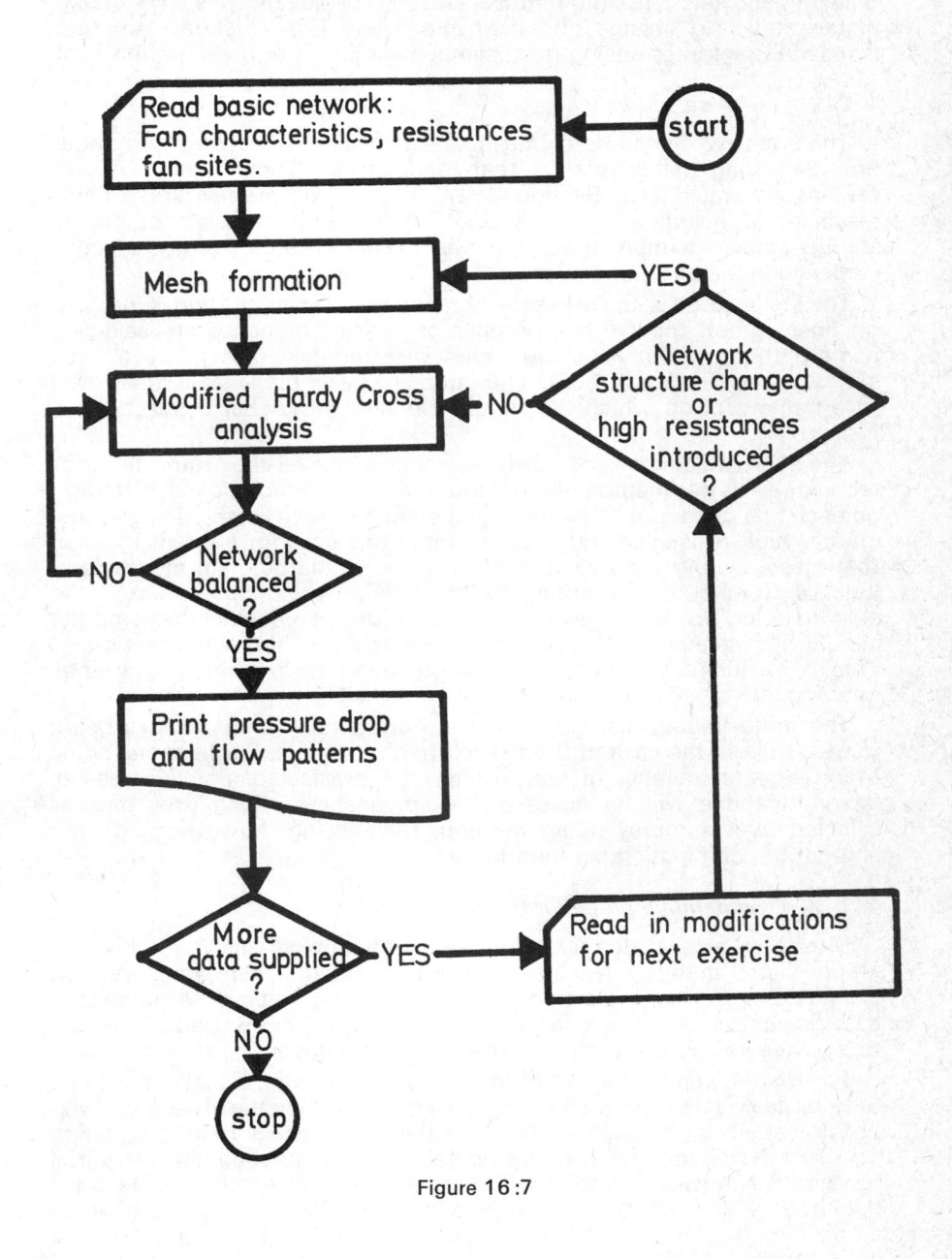

Figure 16:7

most often are (i) change of resistance values; (ii) introduction of new branches and junctions; (iii) removal (sealing) of old branches; (iv) change of fan duty; (v) change of fan position; and (vi) variations in natural ventilating pressures arising from climatic variations or underground fires.

4.1.2   *Mesh selection*

There are two methods of mesh selection used in network programs, both satisfying the criteria (i) that there are a minimum of $b - j + 1$ meshes generated (see Section 3.2), (ii) that the meshes are suitably dispersed to include all branches and (iii) that no high-resistance branch should appear in more than one mesh. This ensures rapidity of convergence in the ensuing analyses.

The first method is known as the "branch tree" technique and is founded on linear graph theory.[10] A number of "basic" branches are selected, namely, those which have high resistance, contain fans or have fixed airflows (see Section 4.1.5). The "tree" of basic branches is then used as a framework on which the required minimum number of meshes are formed.

The alternative means of mesh selection is named the "route-finding" technique.[9] In this method, the computer attempts to form a mesh starting on each branch in turn. After the initial branch of each mesh, the computer ignores high-resistance and fixed-quantity branches for the remainder of that mesh. During the selection of each mesh, the program moves from junction to junction, attempting to find a route which closes back to the starting point. Unsuccessful paths are memorized in order that the computer should not attempt to follow those routes again within the current mesh. This is an interesting example of a computer performing a "learning" process.

The route-finding method results in considerably more meshes being formed than in the case of the branch tree technique. Furthermore, some of this greater number of meshes may be duplicated. For this reason, fewer iterations will be necessary in an analysis which uses meshes selected by the route-finding method, there being, however, a greater amount of computation per iteration.

4.1.3   *The iterative procedure*

Most programs written for mine ventilation network analysis follow the Hardy Cross method. The iterative procedures are therefore based on the equations given in Section 3.4.1. There are, however, a number of modifications which have been made to the Hardy Cross procedure in order to improve its efficiency and the speed of computation.

For routine ventilation planning, it is usual to assume that the Square Law of flow is obeyed in all branches. Equation 20 is therefore employed in the majority of programs rather than the more general form of equation 19. This restriction reduced considerably the computing time required for a given network. Programs have been written which operate on a general law, $p = RQ^n$. These require data specifying the value of n for each branch. The practical difficulties involved in obtaining such data have resulted in the generalized programs being used for research purposes rather than in practical applications.

In the manual calculations of the Hardy Cross method, it is convenient to determine all mesh correction factors and then to apply these to the branch flows as the final step in each iteration. In modern programs, each mesh correction factor, ΔQ_m, is applied immediately to the branch flows around mesh m before moving on to the computation of the next mesh correction factor. The convergence towards a balanced flow pattern is thus continuous rather than a step by step process at the end of each iteration.

For any single loop, the mesh correction factor, ΔQ_m, may oscillate about zero for the first few iterations and then settle down into a relatively slow constant sign convergence towards zero. The program may instruct the computer to test for this condition and, if necessary, to generate magnified correction factors at appropriate stages during the iterative procedure. This device accelerates convergence of the whole network.

A modification made to a previously balanced network may result in significant airflow changes taking place within one localized area only. The program may instruct the computer to concentrate attention on those areas of the network where significant mesh correction factors are being generated. The effect of this is analogous to that of a stone being thrown into a calm pond. Ripples of mesh correction factors are propagated out from the centre of imbalance, dying away again as a new balance is approached. Secondary ripples may be set up around high-resistance branches. Ignoring those areas which have already reached balance can result in considerable saving of computing time when the more extensive networks are being analysed.

On completion of each iteration, the computer will check the current values of all mesh correction factors. If any one of them is above a level set by the input data then a further iteration is initiated. The output of results cannot occur until the network has been balanced to the specified level of accuracy.

4.1.4   *The treatment of fans*

When a fan having a fixed pressure, p_{ft}, is present in a branch, this fixed value is incorporated into equation 20 with the characteristic slope, S_{ft}, set to zero. More usually the fan characteristic curve is given, this being defined by a series of pressure-quantity co-ordinates specified by the ventilation engineer in his input data. The program may utilize a curve-fitting procedure to define an equation which represents the relevant characteristic curve.[11] This equation can then be used to determine the fan pressure and characteristic slope corresponding to the current value of airflow at any time during the analysis. Alternatively, the program may be made more efficient by using simple linear interpolation between specified co-ordinate points. The accuracy of both techniques relies upon the number of co-ordinate points used to define the fan characteristic curve.

4.1.5   *Fixed-quantity branches*

In any network exercise, the ventilation engineer may wish the airflows passing through specified branches to be fixed at definite values. For example, the air velocities along mineral transport roadways may have to be restricted to definite limits because of dust problems. Similarly, the airflows through working faces will be determined by consideration of such factors as temperature, humidity, dust, gas concentrations, and so on. In practice, local regulation of the airflow to a pre-determined value may be achieved by the erection of ventilation doors or brattice sheets and by the use of booster fans.

Network computer programs now in common use have the facility for allowing specified branch airflows to be "fixed" at values given by the ventilation engineer in his input data. The Hardy Cross analysis will then balance the airflows in all other branches in such a way that the fixed values of airflow will be maintained. Unfortunately, if the air quantity in any branch is to remain constant during an analysis then its resistance must be allowed to vary. This is, after all, what happens in the mine when ventilation regulators are adjusted. The result is that the output from the computer will indicate the values of resistance which are necessary in those branches in order to give the requested fixed values of airflow. The computed resistances may then be used to determine the degree of regulation required.

If an unreasonably high fixed quantity is requested, the computed resistance will fall below that value of resistance which can be realized in practice; it may even become negative. In such cases the specified fixed quantity can be obtained only by the installation of a booster fan.

A modern network program may test for this condition provided that the ventilation engineer specifies a minimum practical value of resistance for each fixed-quantity branch, that is, the resistance of the unrestricted airway. In the event of any resistance falling below the minimum value set for a fixed quantity branch, the program will print out the impractical flow pattern, followed by the initiation of an unrequested exercise in which the resistance of the relevant branch is fixed at the minimum value and the air quantity is allowed to vary. In such an event the computer will print out explanatory messages. In practical terms, a program with this facility will (i) give the flow pattern for any exercise, even if unrealistic fixed quantities have been specified; (ii) explain why it is impracticable and (iii) give an unrequested flow pattern which shows the air quantities which *would* be obtained if the scheme were attempted in practice. This very powerful addition to the fixed-quantity feature was first introduced into network programs during a series of user trials, when a number of ventilation engineers asked the question "If I cannot have q m³/s in branch a to b then what quantity *can* I obtain?" The use of such a program can give a subjective impression of the computer doing some ventilation engineering in addition to carrying out arithmetic operations.

4.1.6 *Output results*

The precise format of the output will again depend upon the particular program being used. The results from the initial network and each subsequent exercise will consist of at least the frictional pressure drop and airflow for each branch. Also included may be the branch resistances and the details of modifications made between exercises. The more sophisticated programs carry out checks for unlikely situations such as reversal of airflow or very low values of resistance and print out suitable messages to highlight these circumstances. It is also possible for a program to initiate unrequested exercises if a computed flow pattern is impracticable. (see Section 4.1.5).

The output results will normally be in the form of tables printed on paper by a high-speed line printer. However, programs are available which also produce output in the form of plotted networks.[12] For on-line interactive computing, plotted networks may be shown on the screens of visual display units. Autoplotting programs require the specification of junction co-ordinates in the input data.

4.1.7 *Network modifications*

After the analysis of the initial network, the modifications specified by each subsequent exercise in the input data will be read by the computer, the appropriate adjustments made to the network currently held in the machine memory and a further analysis initiated. The main types of modification are listed in Section 4.1.1 (*d*). Each flow pattern printed out represents the air quantities used in the first iteration of the following analysis. The exercise modifications are therefore cumulative. Any change made to the network during an exercise will remain in force until and unless it is explicitly cancelled in a later exercise. This allows ventilation plans to be built up stage by stage.

Straightforward changes of branch resistances, fan pressures or positions of fans are handled by the computer simply in terms of over-writing values held in the appropriate memory stores. If, however, an exercise involves a high-resistance branch or changes the geometry of the network in any way, then the pattern of meshes must be amended. The computer inter-rogates the meshes currently held in memory, adds new meshes where necessary, and re-selects those existing meshes which are affected by the change.

4.2 *Starting to use ventilation network programs*

The mine ventilation engineer who wishes to commence digital computer usage for network analysis must first establish the availability of time on a suitable machine. Most computers having a FORTRAN or ALGOL compiler and with a core store of 32K (37 768 words) or more, will suffice (some network programs will run on machines of considerably smaller capacity). Many mining companies now have their own computers or terminal links to machines of adequate size.

The next stage is to check that a ventilation network program is accessible. These programs have become available in a growing number of countries since the mid-nineteen-sixties. Central mining organizations or research institutes will often be able to provide information or direct help.

The ventilation engineer should familiarize himself with the scope of the program and the precise format required for the input of data. Proforma input sheets are normally supplied which facilitate the organization of data. As a variety of network programs have been developed, the venti-lation engineer may find that not all of the facilities described in this text are present in the program at his disposal.

Experience has shown that a mine ventilation engineer can be trained to use a network program within a day. Nevertheless, it is recommended that a few trial runs be carried out on simple but practical networks before embarking upon full scale investigations. Training in the use of programs is facilitated considerably if the computer can be used in conversation mode, thus allowing the engineer to see the result of a network exercise before deciding upon the next set of modifications. This, however, is expensive in computer time and is not practicable at the moment for large networks. An interesting side effect of using these programs is that a ventilation engineer can, within a few weeks, gain a "feel" for airflow distribution which has previously taken years of practical experience to build up. After a few network investigations, the ventilation engineer will find himself more able to choose exercises designed to give a desired airflow distribution.

The initial, or basic, network specified by the input data will normally represent the mine as it exists at that time, or at the time of the last ventilation survey. The computed flow pattern for the basic network should therefore agree with measured air quantities. The degree of correlation between the two will indicate the inherent consistency of the input data. Any major deviations will indicate either an error in the ventilation survey or a numerical mistake in the data submitted to the computer. Exercises built upon an unreliable basic network cannot be expected to give accurate forecasts of future air distributions. There is therefore little point in conducting network analyses unless the preceding ventilation surveys have been carried out in a manner which follows good practice.

Provided that the computer has sufficient storage capacity, it is convenient to retain the basic network of each mine permanently stored at the computer centre. This can be updated as the mine develops and routine data submission for subsequent network analyses is reduced to the specification of exercises. Such a facility can lead to a valuable saving of time in cases of sudden emergency, particularly if the mine has access to a computer terminal link.

The analysis of ventilation networks by computer invokes a change of the engineer's attitude towards this subject. The removal of all manual calculating procedures enables ventilation staff to concentrate their attention upon the collection of observed data and the significance of computed results. A large number of exercises can be built up in a single set of data input, each one an alternative possible solution to the particular problem under consideration. From the output results the most practicable solutions can be chosen or the network can be re-submitted with further exercises. The number of exercises which may be attempted is limited only by the availability of computing time and the work involved in preparing data and scrutinizing the output.

The computer never reduces the workload of a mine ventilation office but it does make that work much more rewarding.

5   THE PLACE OF NETWORK ANALYSIS IN VENTILATION PLANNING

While the techniques of network analysis are fundamental to the quantitative planning of underground airflow distributions, they should not be applied in isolation. Their dependence upon good ventilation surveys has already been stressed. The flow of information between the various facets of airflow planning is illustrated in Fig. 16:8.

The observations made during ventilation surveys are processed in order to produce accurate and up to date ventilation plans for the mine, showing the variation of all important environmental parameters around the airflow circuits. This processing may again be carried out by computer and will also give the basic data required by a network analysis program. The ventilation engineer will compile exercise data representing alternative means for ventilating future mine workings or possible emergency situations and include these as additional input to the network program. The output results provide a means for producing forecast ventilation plans.

As minerals are extracted and the mine continues to develop, further ventilation surveys become necessary. The time which elapses between surveys depends upon how rapidly branch resistances and the geometry of the mine change. After a basic network has been soundly established,

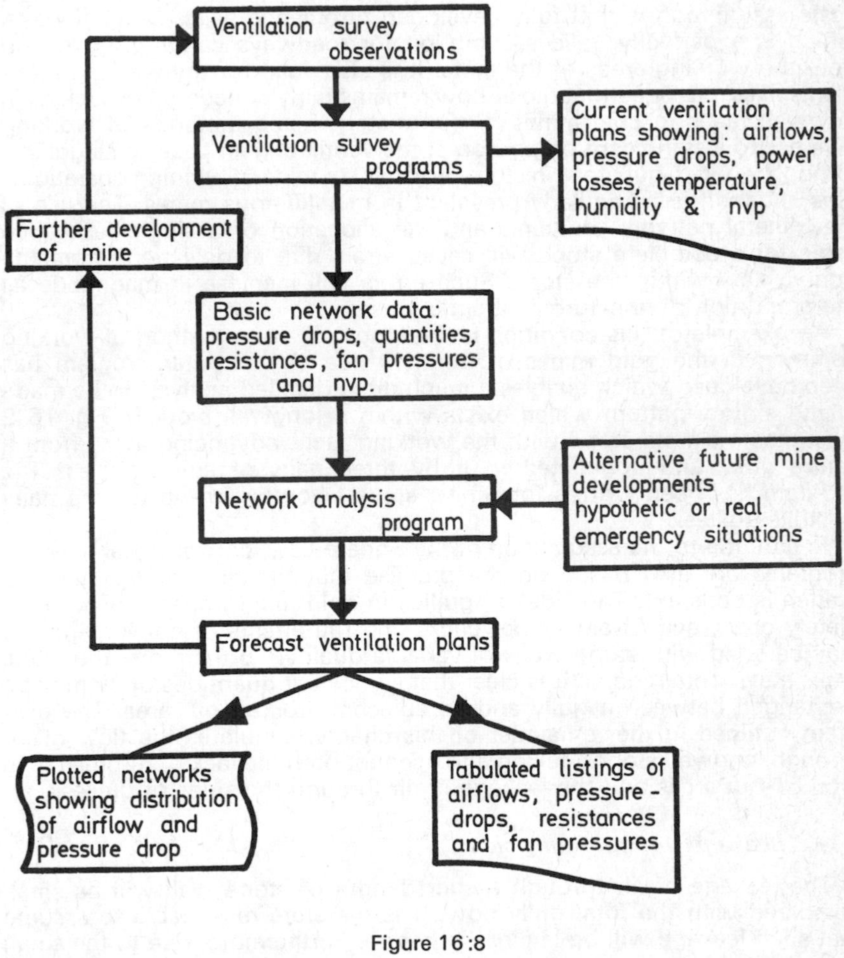

Figure 16 :8

localized surveys in the developing areas will often suffice for routine updating purposes. Full surveys will be required at relatively infrequent intervals or when major changes of ventilation are to be planned. The flow of information throughout airflow planning procedures becomes a continuous process as illustrated by the closed loop flow chart illustrated in Fig. 16:8. The implementation of this type of organized date flow can greatly enhance the efficiency and effectiveness of a mine ventilation department.

6   THE APPLICATION OF NETWORK ANALYSIS TO LONGWALL STOPES

The network programs used for normal ventilation planning purposes have been confined to the use of the Square Law, $p = RQ^2$. This restriction enables the programs to be efficient in computing time while giving an accuracy of forecast which is satisfactory for most practical purposes. The basic assumption is that fully developed turbulence exists in all airways, which is a perfectly valid assumption for roadways carrying air to and from the working areas of the mine. It is also valid for the working areas themselves, provided that the airflow remains fairly concentrated such as in longwall faces in coal mines. Unfortunately, some methods of working give rise to a significant proportion of the ventilating air passing sluggishly through worked-out areas in close proximity to mineral winning operations. This situation is particularly prevalent in metalliferous mines. The use of the general network programs and the allocation of a single resistance value for a complete stope will cause errors due to deviations from the Square Law within the stope. Such errors will increase in magnitude as the proportion of non-turbulent airflow rises.

An example of this condition is the longwall stope method of working common in the gold mines of South Africa. A computer program has been developed which enables a much more detailed analysis to be made of the airflow pattern which exists within a longwall stope.[13] Fig. 16:9 illustrates a simple stope with the working faces advancing away from a centre gully and connected to it by three pairs of strike gullies. The program has been written for similar stope layouts with up to nine pairs of strike gullies.

In addition to the assumption of the Square Law, conventional network programs are also based on the premise that the flow along any one branch is constant. The sides of gullies in gold mine stopes may be completely open, apart from timber packs and the effects of convergence or may be lined with stone walls of variable quality. Furthermore, the stone walls may contain gaps. It is clear that significant quantities of air may be exchanged between a gully and an adjacent worked-out area. The program outlined in the remainder of this chapter simulates the flow of air through longwall stopes, taking into account both the lack of turbulence in worked-out areas and the leakage of air through the sides of gullies.

6.1   Leakage through gully sides

The leakage of air through a short length of stone wall will be small compared with the total gully flow. It is therefore reasonable to assume that such leakage will be laminar in nature. Furthermore, due to the small pressure differential existing across a stone wall, the effects of compressibility are negligible.

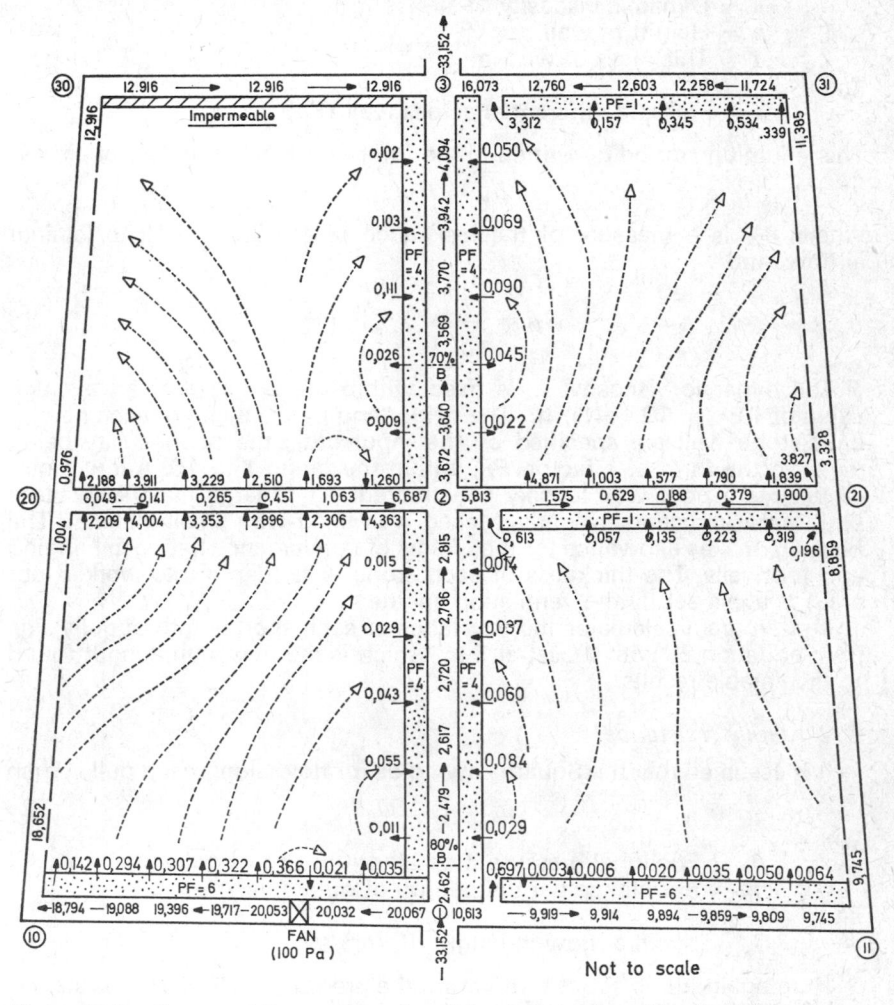

Figure 16:9   Computed flow patterns in a 3-level stope. Quantities (m³/s) are shown at 10 m intervals

For incompressible laminar flow through a permeable medium, Darcy's law applies:

that is

$$Q_w = -\frac{k}{\mu}\,\frac{h}{t}\,p_w \Delta L \qquad \qquad \ldots .21$$

where

$\quad Q_w =$ Leakage (m^3/s) through a short length of wall, ΔL, m
$\quad\quad k =$ Permeability of wall, m^2
$\quad\quad \mu =$ Dynamic viscosity of air, Ns/m^2
$\quad\quad h =$ Height of wall, m
$\quad\quad t =$ Thickness of wall, m

and

$\quad p_w =$ Pressure differential across wall (Pa)

This equation can be re-written in the form of a ventilation law of airflow

$$p_w = R_w Q_w \qquad \qquad \dots 22$$

where R_w is a measure of the resistance of the stone wall to laminar airflow, and

$$R_w = \frac{\mu t}{kh\Delta L} \quad \text{Ns/m}^5 \qquad \qquad \dots 23$$

The dynamic viscosity, μ, is fixed within the program at an average value of $1,84 \times 10^{-5}$ Ns/m^2. The height and permeability of each newly-built stone wall are specified by the input data, the permeability being given in the form of a factor, PF, within the range 1 to 10. A low factor represents a poor wall loosely constructed out of large material while a high factor indicates a tightly packed wall filled with small material. The program makes allowance for the effects of convergence between hanging and footwalls. The thickness of each stone wall (depth into worked-out area) is again set by the ventilation engineer.

The program calculates the resistance of each short length of gully side from equation 23 with ΔL set at 5 m, which is the maximum length found to give stable results.

6.2 Gully resistance

It is assumed that the Square Law holds for flow along each gully. Then

$$p_g = r_g \Delta L Q_g^2 \qquad \qquad \dots 24$$

where

$\quad p_g =$ Frictional pressure drop along ΔL (m) of gully (Pa)
$\quad r_g =$ Resistance per unit length of gully (Ns^2/m^9)

and

$\quad Q_g =$ Mean airflow in length ΔL (m^3/s)

Here again, ΔL is set at 5 m within the programme. The unit resistance, r_g is given by

$$r_g = \frac{KS}{A^3} \quad \text{Ns}^2/\text{m}^8 \text{ per m} \qquad \qquad \dots 25$$

The friction factor, K, is allocated a value of 0,015 Ns^2/m^4, which is a typical value for an unlined rectangular airway with uneven sides. The cross-sectional area, $A(m^2)$, and the rubbing surface, $S(m^2)$, are computed from the airway dimensions given by the ventilation engineer in his input data. Brattice cloths may be inserted into any number of gullies, the relevant resistance values being adjusted in the appropriate manner.

6.3 Mesh selection

The program divides the complete stope into a large number of meshes, treating each 5 m length of gully and each 5 m length of gully side as an individual branch. Unfortunately, the presence of stone walls leads necessarily to a larger proportion of very high resistances than normally occurs in the more general network analysis programs. Thus convergence to a balanced flow pattern is somewhat slower.

6.4 Hardy Cross analysis

An initial flow balance is carried out ignoring all leakage flows. This analysis commences at an assumed airflow of zero in each branch, the first set of mesh correction values, ΔQ_m, being set at 1. The purpose of this procedure is to establish a rapidly-computed starting point for the slower analysis involving the high-resistance leakage paths. The computation of mesh correction factors then continues using equation 19 with $n = 2$ for gully flows and $n = 1$ for leakage flows. Any gully fans are also taken into account.

6.5 Input/output

The data required by this program are as follows:

(a) Ventilating pressure applied across the stope.

(b) Length, height and width of each gully and face.

(c) Position of each brattice cloth and the percentage of gully cross section covered.

(d) Position and pressure of each gully fan.

(e) Position, permeability and thickness of each stone wall.

(f) Position and nature of any discontinuities in each stone wall (gaps or sudden variations in permeability).

The output results from the computer give the air quantities at 5-m intervals along each gully, the quantity entering and leaving each length of face and the air leakage at 5 m intervals along each gully side. The tabulated airflows given may be transferred to a plan of the stope. Fig. 16:9 shows an example where flows have been compounded into 10 m intervals for the purpose of clarity. The effects of brattice sheets, a fan, stone walls and gaps in walls are clearly illustrated by this example.

6.6 Updating

As in the case of the general network programs, exercise data may be appended to the information describing the original stope. Any changes not involving stope layout may be made in an exercise. This facility allows the ventilation engineer to investigate the effect of (i) changing the positions, standards and discontinuities of stone walls, (ii) positions and pressures of gully fans, (iii) positions and cover of brattice sheets and, (iv) ventilating pressure applied across the stope.

The effect of a set of exercise data is that the appropriate changes in resistance are made, meshes are re-formed when necessary and a further flow pattern is computed.

The availability of the longwall stope network program is of considerable assistance in quantifying the airflow patterns which exist in such stopes. The program is valuable in planning how the ventilation should be controlled in its passage through the stope and how best to provide acceptable airflows in those places where men are employed.

7   REFERENCES

1   McPherson, M. J. The metrication and rationalization of mine ventilation calculations. *Min. Eng.,* No. 131, 1971, p. 729–736.

2   Maas, W. An electrical analogue for mine ventilation and its application to ventilation planning. *Geologie en Mijnbouw,* 12, April 1950.

3   Scott, D. R., Hinsley, F. B. and Hudson, R. F. A. calculator for the solution of ventilation network problems. *Trans. Inst. Min. Eng.,* Vol. 112, 1953, p. 623.

4   McElroy, G. E. A network analyser for solving mine ventilation distribution problems. *U.S. Bur. Mines Inf. Cir.* 7704, 1954.

5   Williams, R. W. Mine ventilation analogues. *Min. Mag.,* Vol. 119, No. 1, 1968, p. 24–29.

6   Atkinson, J. J. On the theory of the ventilation of mines. *Trans. N. of England Inst. Min. Engrs.* No. 3, 1854, p. 118.

7   Cross, H. Analysis of flow in networks of conduits or conductors. *Bull. Illinois Univ. Eng. Exp. Station,* No. 286, 1936.

8   Scott, D. R. and Hinsley, F. B. Ventilation network theory. Parts 1 to 5. *Colliery Engng,* Vol. 28, 1951, p. 67–71; p. 159–169; p. 229–235; p. 497–500; Vol. 29, 1952, p. 137–143.

9   McPherson, M. J. Ventilation network analysis by digital computer. *Min. Eng.,* No. 73, 1966, p. 12–28.

10 Hartman, H. L. and Wang, Y. J. Computer solution of three dimensional mine ventilation networks with multiple fans and natural ventilation. *Int. J. Rock Mech. Min. Sci.,* Vol. 4, 1967.

11 Wang, Y. J. and Saperstein, L. W. Computer-aided solution of complex ventilation networks. *Soc. Min. Engrs. A.I.M.E.,* Vol. 247, 1970.

12 Colloquium on Mine Ventilation, Section 1. The application of computers in mine ventilation. *Min. Eng.,* Vol. 113, 1970, p. 297–302.

13 McPherson, M. J. The simulation of airflow distribution in Gold Mine Stopes. *Chamber of Mines of S. Africa, Research Report* No. 49/71, 1971.

17 Basic Fan Engineering

J. H. DE LA HARPE

Technical Director, James Howden & Safanco, Limited, Johannesburg

1 INTRODUCTION

Air-moving turbo-machines with compression ratios (discharge absolute pressure/inlet absolute pressure) of less than approximately 1,1 are called fans. Machines with higher compression ratios are referred to as blowers and compressors.

It is usually assumed that the volume of the air or gas moving through a fan remains constant between inlet and discharge. The actual decrease in volume due to compression is less than 7 per cent. When the compression ratio is higher than 1,1 the reduction in volume can be significant.

375

2   FAN TYPES AND SPECIFIC SPEED

When any particular fan is run at any speed, its performance at or near its peak efficiency lies within a relatively narrow range. It is, therefore, necessary to have fans of different designs to cover the whole pressure-volume spectrum. In order to avoid a haphazard selection of fan types it is advisable when designing new fans to make use of a specific speed chart as illustrated in Fig. 17:1.

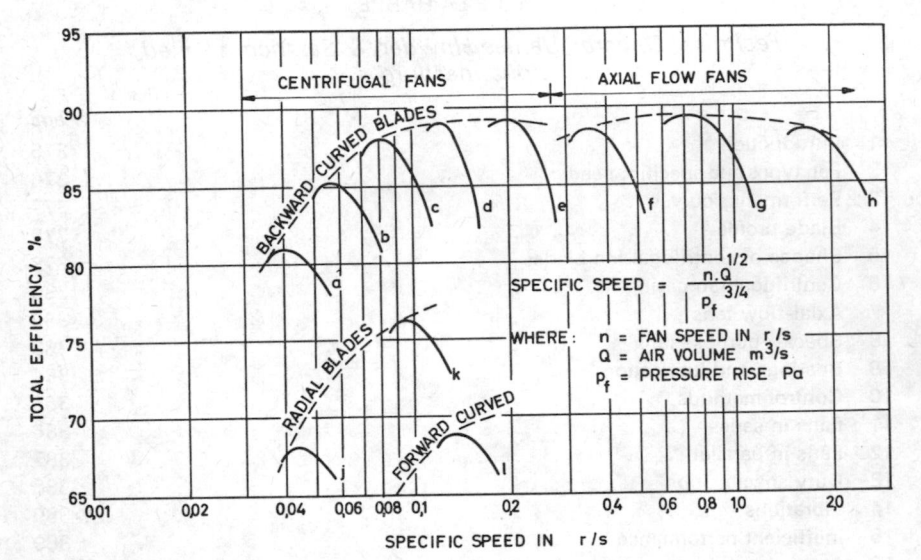

Figure 17:1

We can define specific speed as that speed at which a particular fan of unknown size would have to operate in order to develop a pressure of one pascal at a capacity of one cubic metre per second. It can be shown that

$$n_s = \frac{nQ^{1/2}}{p_f^{3/4}}$$

where

n_s = specific speed
n = fan speed in revolutions per second
Q = air volume in m³/s
p_f = pressure rise across fan in pascals.

A centrifugal fan which delivers a low volume at a high pressure has a low specific speed. The impeller is narrow and friction losses are high, so that its best efficiency is relatively low. A centrifugal fan which delivers a high volume at a low pressure has a high specific speed. Friction losses are low and its efficiency is relatively high.

In Fig. 17:1 curves *a* to *e* are efficiency curves for a set of centrifugal fans with backward-curved blades. Centrifugal fans with radial blades and those with forward-curved blades have lower efficiencies as shown by curves *j, k* and *l.*

If still higher volumes are required, the type of fan will range from double-inlet centrifugal fans through mixed-flow fans to axial-flow fans. Axial flow fans with the lowest specific speed have a large number of short blades on a large hub (large hub ratio), while those with the highest specific speed have a small number of long blades on a small hub (small hub ratio).

Curves *f*, *g* and *h* are efficiency curves for a set of axial-flow fans. Curve *f* represents a fan with a large hub ratio, curve *g* is for a fan with a medium hub ratio and curve *h* represents a fan with a small hub ratio.

At the extreme ends of the scale very low specific speed duties can be catered for by multistage blowers with narrow-width impellers, and very high specific speed duties can be obtained by using any number of centrifugal or axial-flow fans in parallel operation.

3   PERFORMANCE CURVES

The theoretical pressure-volume curve of an ideal fan, that is, one in which there are no losses, is a straight line between the points of zero volume and zero pressure as indicated by the line *AB* in Fig. 17:2.

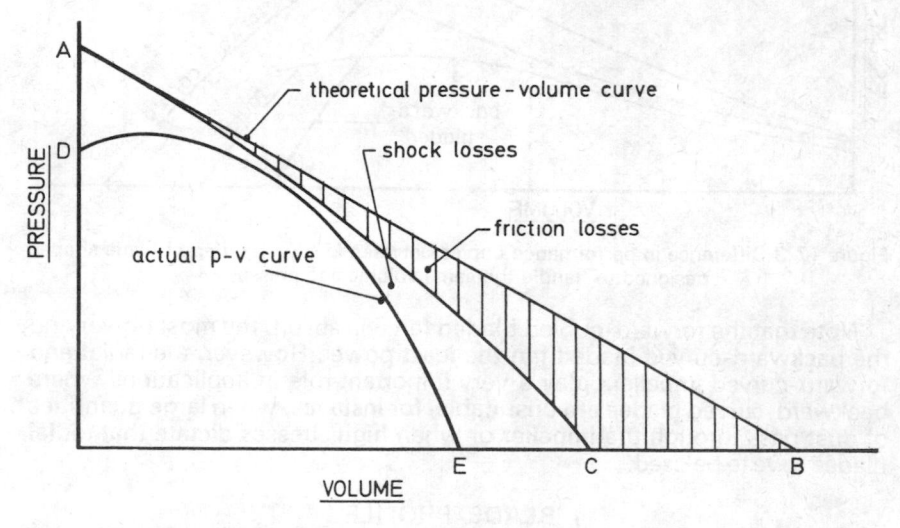

Figure 17:2 Theoretical and actual pressure. Volume curves of a centrifugal fan with backward-curved blades

The useful performance curve, *DE*, is obtained after the values of friction and shock losses have been deducted from the pressure values shown on the ideal or theoretical pressure-volume curve.

The most modern centrifugal fans with backward-curved blades, have efficiencies between impeller inlet and outlet as high as 94 to 96 per cent. Losses in the fan casing reduce the fan total efficiency to just under 90 per cent as measured in accordance with BS.848.

The shape of the performance curve is determined mainly by the configuration of the impeller blades at the discharge.

The pressure-volume curve for a fan with backward-curved blades is steeper than that for a fan with radial or forward-curved blades. The power curve for a fan with backward-curved blades reaches a maximum value at a volume just higher than that at which the peak efficiency occurs. The power curves for fans with radial and forward-curved blades increase with increasing volume.

The curves in Fig. 17:3 illustrate the difference in performance between fans with blades of different shapes designed to handle the same duty.

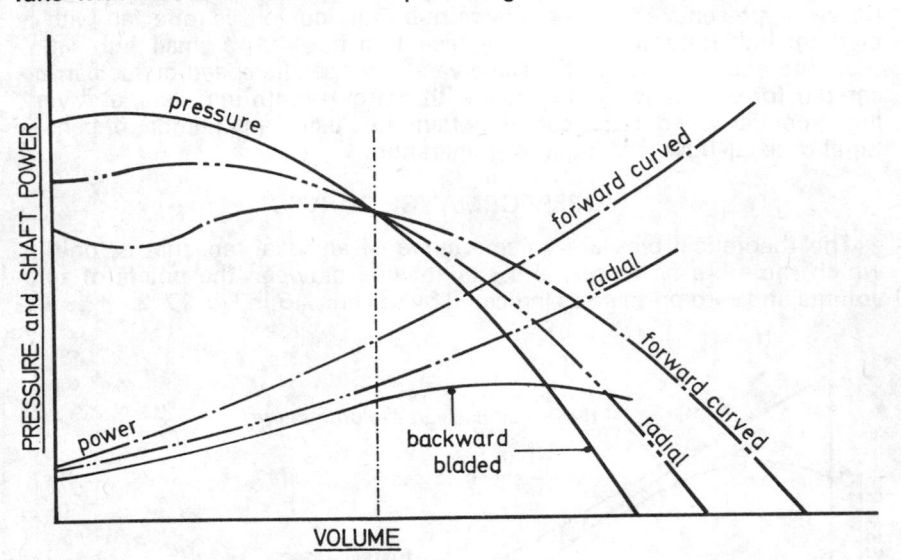

Figure 17:3 Difference in performance curves between fans with different blade shapes designed to handle the same volume and pressure

Note that the forward-curved bladed fan will absorb the most power and the backward-curved bladed fan the least power. However, the radial and forward-curved impellers play a very important role in applications where backward-curved blades are unsuitable, for instance, when large quantities of dust pass through the impeller or when high stresses dictate that radial blades have to be used.

4 BLADE PROFILE

For a number of years it was believed that high fan efficiencies could be obtained only with aerofoil-shaped blades. It is now known that this is not necessarily the case. With careful attention to inlet arrangements and manufacture, high efficiencies can be obtained if plate blades are used. Aerofoil blades are, however, still used freely, especially when blade stresses are high.

5 SHAPES OF CENTRIFUGAL FAN BLADES

A wide variety of centrifugal impeller designs is being manufactured today. The main blade shapes are illustrated in Fig. 17:4.

The multi-bladed forward-curved blades in Fig. 17:4 (a) deliver a large volume of air at a relatively low running speed. The fan efficiency is

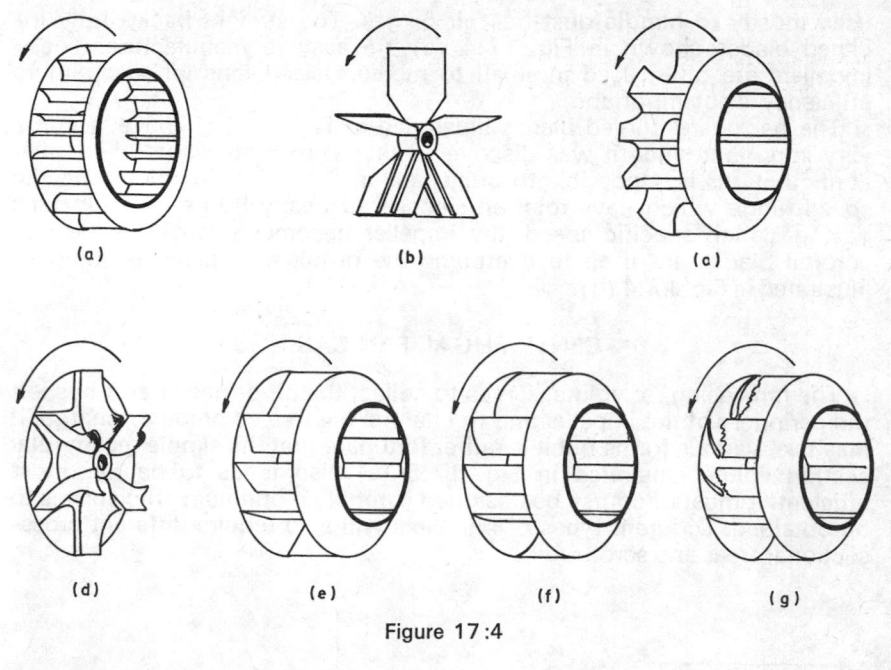

(a)   (b)   (c)

(d)   (e)   (f)   (g)

Figure 17:4

relatively low, but this type of fan is still used for ventilation and in air-conditioning units, portable heating units, etc.

The radial- or paddle-bladed impeller, Fig. 17:4 (b), is produced by almost every fan manufacturer. Its efficiency is relatively low but it is indispensable when air or gas containing high concentrations of dust is passed through the fan. Mill exhausters normally have this type of impeller with various refinements such as replaceable chequered plate liners, dust deflectors, etc.

A slightly higher efficiency is obtained by means of blades which are curved forward with only the tips ending radially. The back shroud can be cut out between the blades as shown in Fig. 17:4 (c) without any significant effect on the fan performance. These openings allow the heavier dust to pass through the impeller, as in the paddle-bladed fan, without causing wear in the back corners usually formed between the blades and the back shroud. The blades are usually lined with replaceable liners when heavy dust concentrations are handled.

The impeller illustrated in Fig. 17:4 (d) is used in high-speed blowers and compressors. The blades are unshrouded on the inlet side and the back shroud is cut away in order to reduce the axial thrust on the thrust bearing. Shock losses at the impeller inlet are reduced by the shape of the blades in the inlet eye section. Here the blades are curved in a forward direction relative to the direction of rotation in order to guide the air into the back part of the impeller where the straight radial blades turn the air towards the periphery. The construction is very robust and lends itself to being machined out of a solid forging in exceptional cases where very high tip speeds are encountered.

Impellers with blades which lie backward relative to the rotation are used mostly to handle dust-free air or gas. The straight backwardly in-clined blades shown in Fig. 17:4 (e) are easy to manufacture. These impellers are often used in small to medium-sized fans when optimum efficiency is not important.

The backward-curved blades illustrated in Fig. 17:4 (f) have become very important since it was discovered that with proper control of inlet configurations it is possible to build fans in the low to medium specific speed range which have total efficiencies of nearly 90 per cent. In fans having a high specific speed, the impeller becomes relatively wide and aerofoil blades are used to overcome the problem of blade bending as illustrated in Fig. 17:4 (g).

6   CENTRIFUGAL FAN CASINGS

The fan casing, or volute, serves to collect the air or gas after it has left the periphery of the impeller and to channel it into a common discharge. It may take various forms but it is rather fortunate that the simple rectangular section volute illustrated in Fig. 17:5 (a) also tends to be the most efficient. It must of course be designed carefully if optimum efficiency is to be obtained. Different types of impellers will also require different cross-sectional areas and scroll radii.

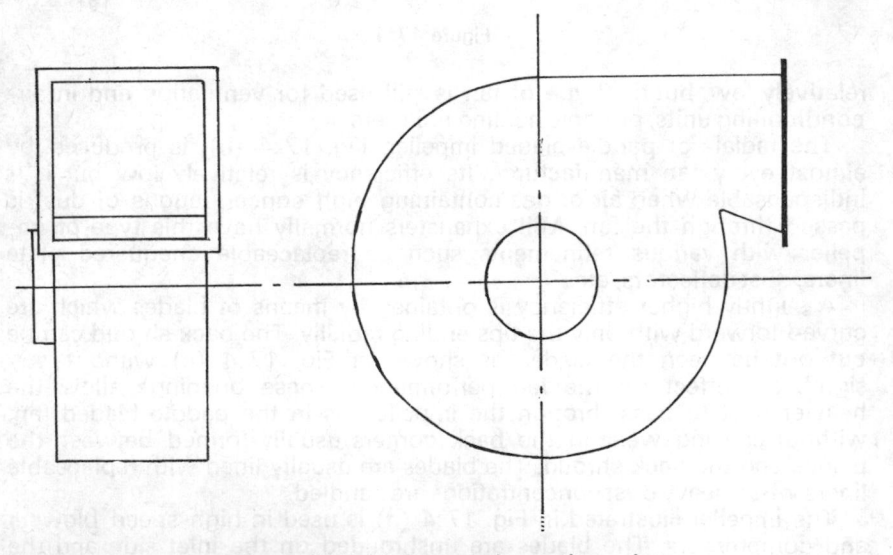

Figure 17:5 (a) Rectangular section volute

Diffuser vanes are sometimes installed around the impeller as shown in Fig. 17:5 (b). These vanes can raise the peak efficiency slightly but they also tend to narrow down the useful operating range of the fan so that operation of the fan is unstable outside this range. The construction is also more expensive. Such diffuser vanes are often used in the interstage passages of multistage blowers.

The vaneless diffuser, illustrated in Fig. 17:5 (c), is also often used in

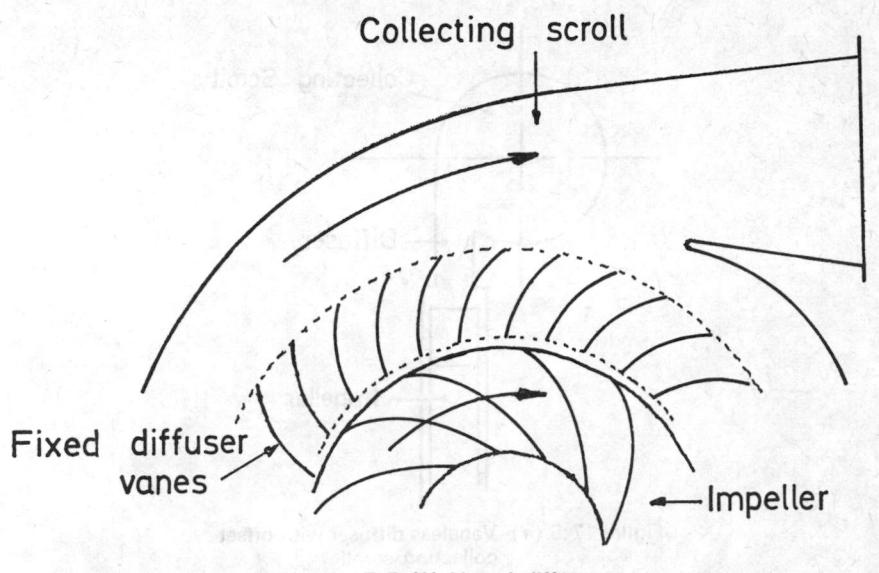

Figure 17:5 (*b*) Vaned diffuser

multistage blowers. In these blowers the air or gas is discharged into the narrow diffuser passage and finds its own path to the periphery. The efficiency curve for this type is slightly flat at the peak but the useful stable operating range is wider than that for the vaned diffuser.

The casing with the almost circular cross-section, illustrated in Fig. 17:5 (d), has a good efficiency but is expensive unless relatively large numbers of a particular size can be cast, or if the application warrants the extra expense.

The centrifugal fan diffuser which discharges in an axial direction, as illustrated in Fig. 17:5 (e), is used on the latest carbon dioxide circu-

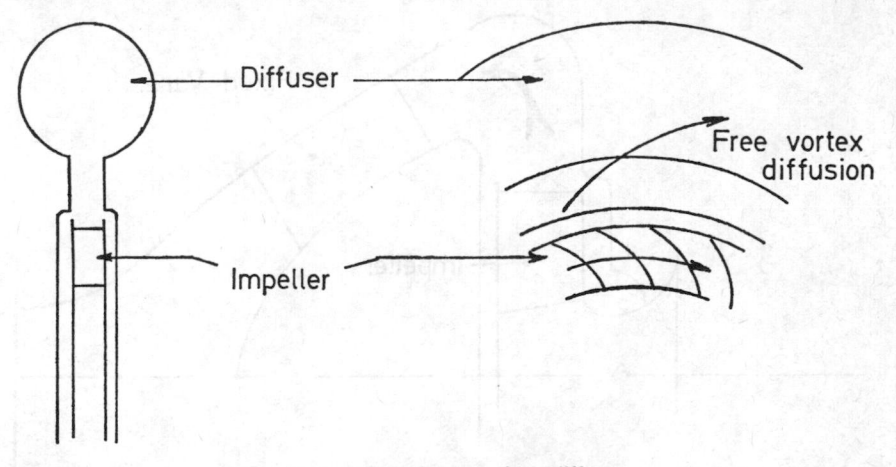

Figure 17:5 (*c*) Vaneless diffuser

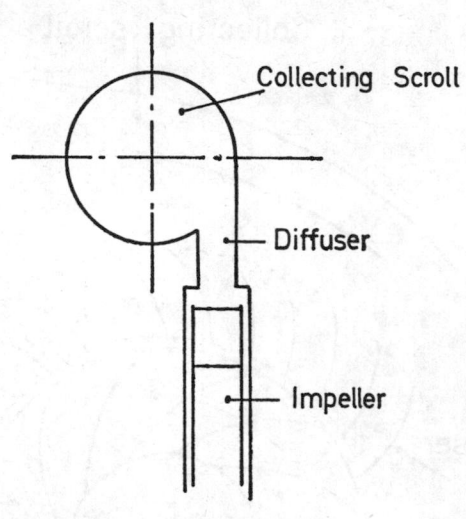

Figure 17:5 (*d*) Vaneless diffuser with offset
collecting scroll

lators in nuclear power stations in the United Kingdom. Here the shape is
dictated by the layout which includes a sealing dome and a totally sub-
merged motor.

7   AXIAL-FLOW FANS

Axial-flow fans have high specific speeds as can be seen in Fig. 17:1.
They can move large volumes of air or gas at relatively low pressures.

The axial-flow fan in its simplest form consists of an open impeller
mounted directly on a motor shaft as shown in Fig. 17:6 (a) Axial-flow
fans are used as desk and ceiling fans where the object is merely to put

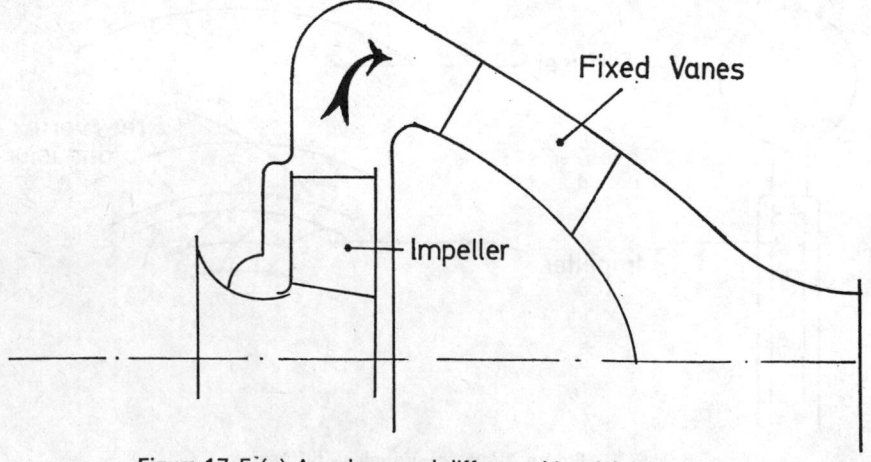

Figure 17:5 (*e*) Annular vaned diffuser with axial discharge

stagnant air in motion. Similar fans adapted for use at high temperatures are also used to circulate gas in kilns and furnaces.

A ring around the impeller, as illustrated in Fig. 17:6 (b), reduces the amount of air recirculated around the impeller and makes it suitable for use as a wall-mounted extraction or pressurizing fan, heater fan, etc.

A low-pressure fan comprises an impeller and motor installed inside a duct as shown in Fig. 17:6 (c). Gas is delivered at higher pressures when straightening vanes are provided to decrease or remove the extent of air swirl after the impeller as in Figure 17:6 (d).

When the air power becomes significant, axial-flow fans may be fitted with carefully shaped bell-mouth inlets and well designed diffusers and hub fairings as shown in Fig. 17:6 (e). Such fans can, in some instances, be mounted vertically, otherwise the air or gas can be caused to turn through 90° at the inlet and/or discharge as in some mine installations and also when used as forced-draught and induced-draught fans in boiler applications. Many such fans have blades which are adjustable while the fan is stationary. When used as boiler fans in power stations, particularly in Europe, the blade pitch can often be adjusted while the fan is in operation. Such a fan can operate efficiently over a very wide range of duties.

The largest axial-flow fans are mostly found in cooling tower installations. Such a fan is illustrated in Fig. 17:6 (f). The impeller is mounted on a vertical shaft and delivers a large volume at a low pressure, usually less than 250 Pa. Similar fans are used to move large volumes of air through dry heat exchangers.

8   SPECIAL-PURPOSE FANS

Fans are often required to perform duties that cannot be performed by fans of standard design. High-temperature gas requires special attention. Bearings are usually the first to receive special treatment i.e., in the low- to medium-temperature range a change of lubricant may be sufficient. The use, at higher temperatures, of cooling discs, hollow shafts, splined shafts or split shafts may enable standard bearings or water-cooled bearings to be used. Still higher temperatures may require the shaft to be water-cooled.

The material used in the construction of fan impellers must be carefully selected when temperatures are high. Mild steel, which is the most common material used in fan fabrication, loses its strength with an increase in temperature and will scale rapidly at temperatures above 450°C. Stainless steel may be used at higher temperatures than mild steel, but certain corrosive atmospheres could in fact cause etching of the normally hard surface and so lead to premature failure of an impeller. There are a number of different types of steel available, each one suited to a very limited range of conditions. However, when a particular type of steel is used for its heat-resistant properties, any fabrication, which requires the application of heat for welding, must be done under very strictly controlled conditions.

If the temperature is so high that putting the gas directly through the fan becomes impractical, it may be necessary to bleed cold air into the system ahead of the fan.

It is also essential to install expansion joints in the ducts near the inlet and discharge of the fan to avoid distortion of the casing.

Corrosive gases call for special treatment of the impeller and casing. In some instances mild steel can be covered with acid-resisting materials

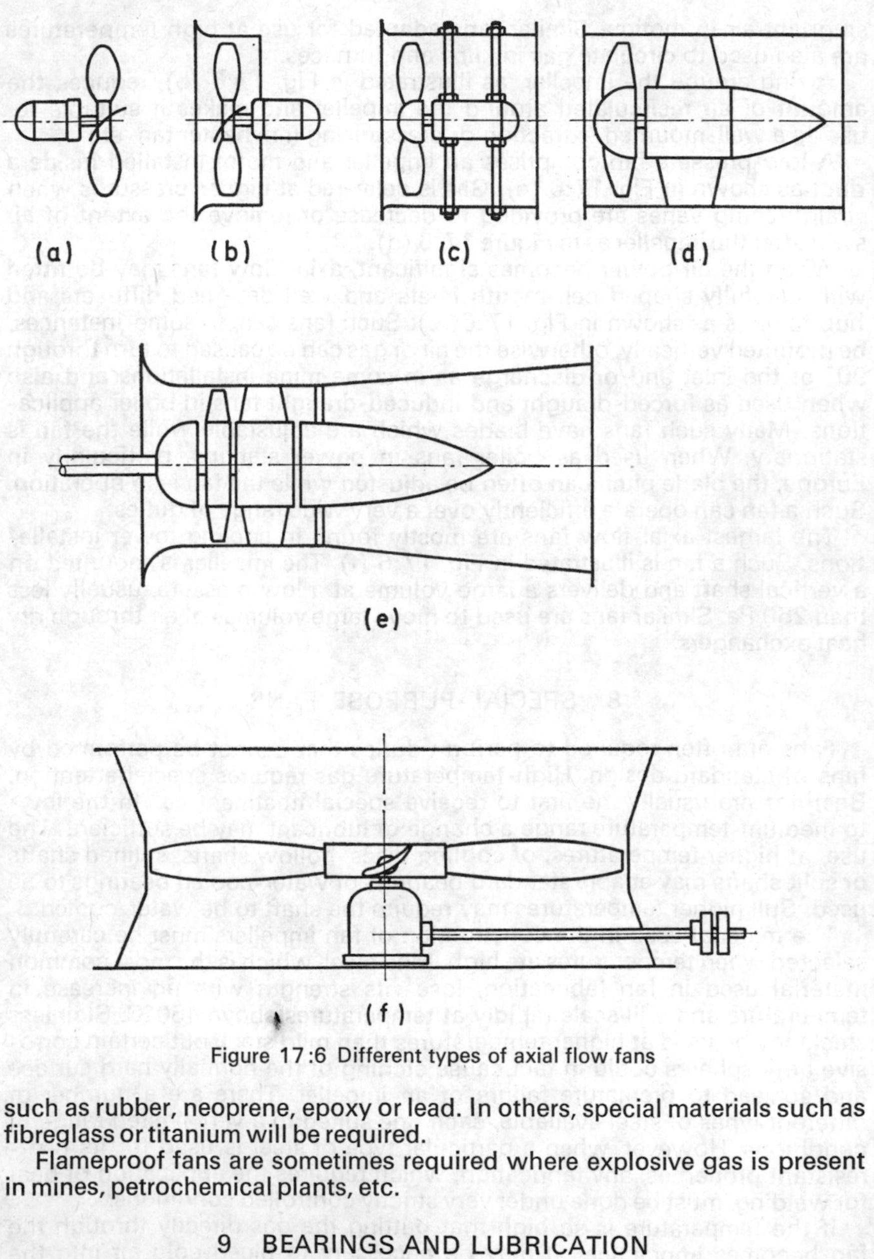

(a)   (b)   (c)   (d)

(e)

(f)

Figure 17:6 Different types of axial flow fans

such as rubber, neoprene, epoxy or lead. In others, special materials such as fibreglass or titanium will be required.

Flameproof fans are sometimes required where explosive gas is present in mines, petrochemical plants, etc.

9   BEARINGS AND LUBRICATION

By far the most popular bearings in use today are the frictionless ball and roller bearings and oil-lubricated sleeve bearings. In very special instances, plastic bearings and air bearings may be used. Grease-lubricated ball and roller bearings are very reliable and easy to maintain, but must be treated correctly. Too much grease can cause overheating. The wrong type of grease for the job can also lead to premature failure. It is best to use normal soda soap or lithium-soap grease. The use of special high-temperature or extreme-pressure grease must be avoided if possible. Many bearing failures are caused by the use of such sophisticated lubricants.

Oil-lubricated frictionless bearings are very reliable and can run at higher temperatures than grease-lubricated bearings. Under severe conditions mist lubrication may be required. This comprises atomizing the oil into a fine mist which is mixed with compressed air and then blown into the bearing. Apart from the cooling effect on the bearing the inside of the bearing is pressurized. This prevents the entry of dust and corrosive gas into the bearing and is an ideal arrangement in very dusty and corrosive surroundings, but it must be remembered that a continuous supply of a small quantity of compressed air must be provided.

Oil-lubricated sleeve bearings are often used, especially on large fans. These are ring-oiled when loadings are light, or force-lubricated when they are heavy. Care must be taken to ensure that the flow of oil will not stop while the fan is running and will continue until the fan shaft comes to rest when the fan is stopped or if a power failure occurs. Many lubrication systems and safety devices are available to ensure trouble-free operation of sleeve bearings.

10   CONTROL METHODS

A fan will operate at that point on its characteristic curve which is intersected by the characteristic curve of the system to which it is applied, and no other. However, it is often necessary to vary the output of a fan during operation while the system remains unchanged. In order to be able to do this, an artificial change must be made either to the system or to the fan characteristic.

(a)   The simplest method of altering a system is to provide an air damper in the system. Since any obstruction to the flow close to the fan inlet may cause poor performance, the best position for such a damper is in the discharge duct.

This is a low-cost method but should not be used where there is a danger of operating the fan in the stall zone. A damper uses up a certain amount of pressure which is consequently wasted. Power is required to provide this waste pressure and it can be appreciated that damper control must therefore be inefficient. (See Fig. 17 :7 (a)).

(b)   Inlet vane control (also known as either variable inlet vane or radial-vane control) can be installed. This method consists of fitting a number of blades or vanes to the inlet. These are arranged radially about the centre of the fan inlet eye, with provision for altering the setting, either individually or simultaneously.

The vanes impart a swirl to the stream of air entering the impeller.

Since the impeller of a centrifugal fan must, in addition to accelerating the air, give it the same rotational speed as the impeller itself, any pre-rotation, such as provided by inlet vane control, will reduce the amount of work which has to be done. Power is therefore saved, resulting in a reduced operating cost. The effect is illustrated in Fig. 17 :7 (b).

(c)   Speed control is very effective and provides the most efficient means of duty control. However, initial cost is normally very high.

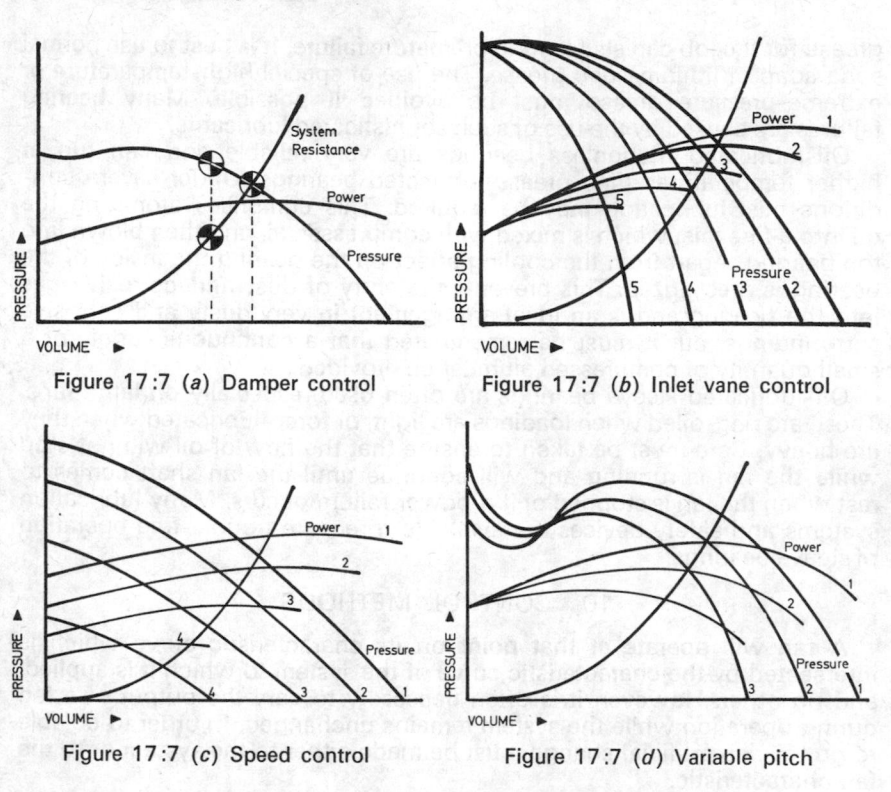

Figure 17:7 (*a*) Damper control

Figure 17:7 (*b*) Inlet vane control

Figure 17:7 (*c*) Speed control

Figure 17:7 (*d*) Variable pitch

Speed variation can be obtained by using a steam turbine or a variable-speed electric motor as the driving unit. Hydraulic and power couplings may also provide this facility, but operating efficiencies may not be consistently high. The effect of speed control is shown in Fig. 17:7 (c).

(*d*)   Axial-flow fans may be controlled by any of the methods mentioned previously. The basic design, however, allows the use of different blade angle settings to provide control of output. The most sophisticated type allows the angle to be altered while the fan is in operation. This method of output control is normally very efficient. The effect is illustrated in Fig. 17:7 (d).

11 FANS IN SERIES

When two fans with pressure-volume curves *AA* and *BB* (Fig. 17:8) are installed in series, the combined pressure at any volume *V* will be the sum of the individual pressures at that volume, giving curve *CC*, Fig. 17:8.

If the fans *AA* and *BB* are installed in a system with resistance curve *OR*, then each fan on its own will operate at point *X* for fan *AA* and point *Y* for fan *BB*, delivering volumes V_1 or V_2, respectively. The two fans in series will operate at point *Z* delivering volume V_3.

If the upstream fan delivers gas at a reasonably high pressure, then the density of the inlet of the second fan will be increased, resulting in a corresponding increase in its pressure and power.

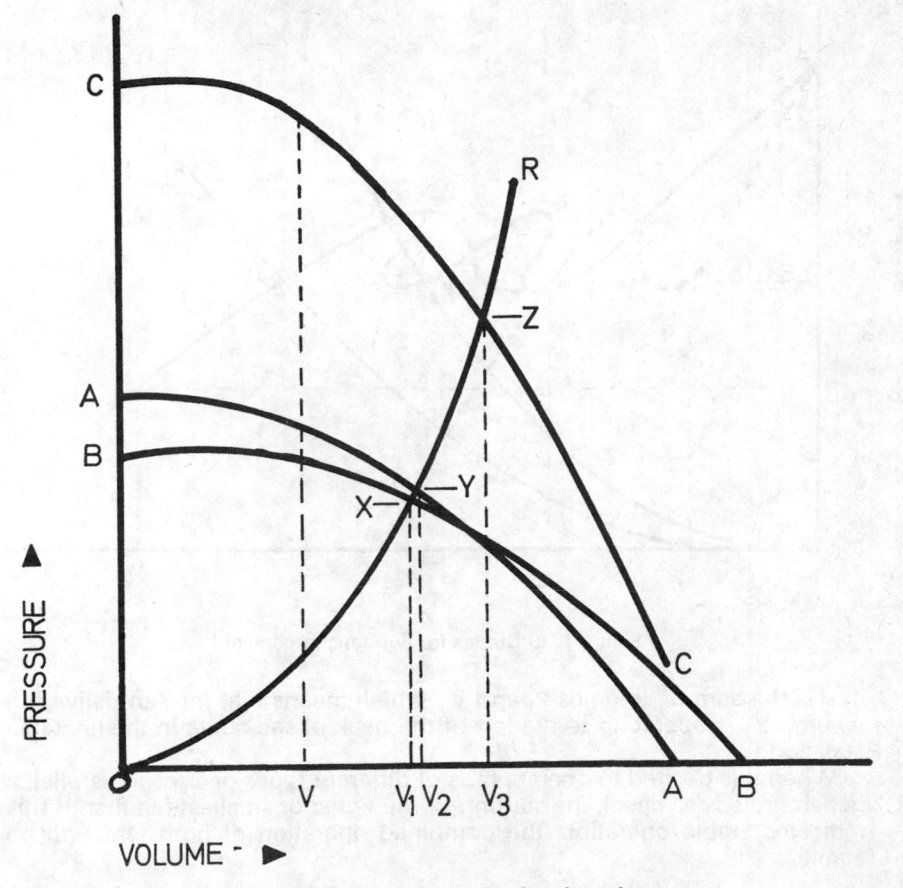

Figure 17:8 Curves for two fans in series

12   FANS IN PARALLEL

When two fans, which have pronounced stalls such as axial-flow or forward-curved fans, are installed to operate in parallel, particular care must be taken to ensure that the combined operation will not be unstable.

Assume that both fans are identical and that each fan has a pressure-volume curve AA, Fig. 17:9. At any pressure P the volume V will be the sum of the volumes delivered by the two fans. If the volumes are added at constant pressure lines for the full performance curve, a double loop is formed at the top of the combined curve as indicated. If the system has a resistance curve OR_1 then the operation will be stable whether one or both fans are running, as the points of intersection of the system resistance curve with both fan curves will be single points f and g. If the system has a resistance curve OR_2, however, then the operation of one fan only will be stable at point C, but the operation will be unstable when both fans are running, since the system resistance curve OR_2 will now intersect the combined curve at two points, namely, at d and e. The combined volume

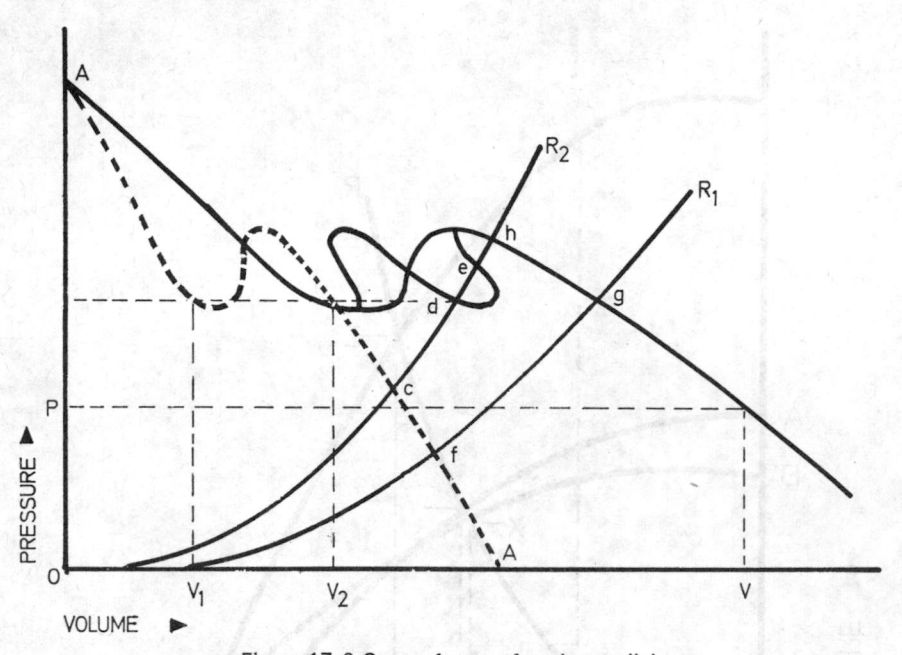

Figure 17:9 Curves for two fans in parallel

at *d* is the sum of volumes V_1 and V_2, which means that the fan delivering volume V_1 is operating to the left of the peak of the curve in the unstable stall zone.

When it is desired to operate fans of different types or sizes in parallel, a general rule is to check the starting of the *worst* or smallest fan first. If this indicates stable operation, the combined operation of both fans will be stable.

13   DUTY SPECIFICATION

The pressure-volume requirements specified for tender purposes should be calculated as accurately as possible. It is dangerous to add an arbitrary amount in order to be "on the safe side". Referring to Fig. 17:10, if the true system resistance is *OA* and a volume of V_1 against pressure P_1 is required, but volume V_2 is specified in the enquiry, then the fan supplier will select a fan that will be stable and operate efficiently on a system resistance curve *OB*. When it is installed, however, the fan will operate at the point of intersection of the fan curve and the system resistance curve *OA*. The operation will be unstable and inefficient and it will be difficult, if not impossible, to cure the problem unless some air can be short-circuited between the fan discharge and its inlet.

On the other hand, if a volume V_2 is required at a pressure P_2, but pressure P_1 is specified for that volume, then the fan will operate at the intersection of the fan curve and the system resistance curve *OC*, delivering a volume V_3 against pressure P_3. Again, the operation of the fan will be inefficient and possibly unstable. In addition, there would be a strong possibility of overloading the motor. The fan could be brought to operate stably at

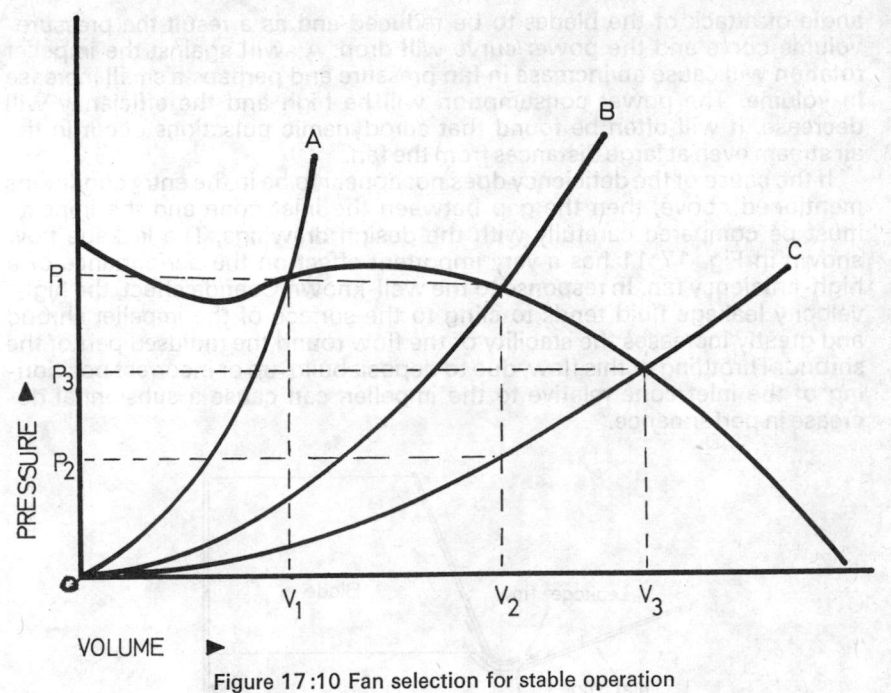

Figure 17:10 Fan selection for stable operation

volume V_2 by installing an extra resistance in the system but power will be wasted in overcoming this resistance.

14   VIBRATIONS

Aerodynamic vibrations and pulsations in the air or gas ducts are often the result of poor inlet conditions. A damper, or a short bend immediately upstream of the impeller eye, can cause such pulsations. Dangerous pulsations can be caused by any configuration of the inlet duct which can cause a swirl in the gas stream in a direction opposite to the direction of rotation of the impeller.

Rhythmic vibrations can have various causes such as out-of-balance, uneven deposits on blades, water in hollow blades, a loose impeller, a coupling which is out of alignment, etc. The cause should be found and rectified before damage occurs.

15   INEFFICIENT PERFORMANCE

A large amount of research work has been put into the development of a modern fan. If such a fan, after installation, does not operate according to its predicted performance curve, this can only mean that operating conditions are different from the laboratory conditions. In the vast majority of cases the cause can be found at the fan inlet. The air or gas distribution upstream of the impeller and in the immediate vicinity of the impeller eye must be examined carefully. Any uneven flow distribution can upset the performance. A swirl in the direction of the impeller rotation will cause the angle of attack of the blades to be reduced and as a result the pressure-volume curve and the power curve will drop. A swirl against the impeller rotation will cause an increase in fan pressure and perhaps a small increase in volume. The power consumption will be high and the efficiency will decrease. It will often be found that aerodynamic pulsations occur in the air stream even at large distances from the fan.

If the cause of the deficiency does not appear to be in the entry conditions mentioned above, then the gap between the inlet cone and the impeller must be compared carefully with the design drawings. The leakage flow shown in Fig. 17:11 has a very important effect on the performance of a high-efficiency fan. In response to the well-known Coanda effect, the high-velocity leakage fluid tends to cling to the surface of the impeller shroud and greatly increases the stability of the flow round the radiused part of the shroud. Throttling of this flow, due to deposit build-up or incorrect positioning of the inlet cone relative to the impeller, can cause a substantial decrease in performance.

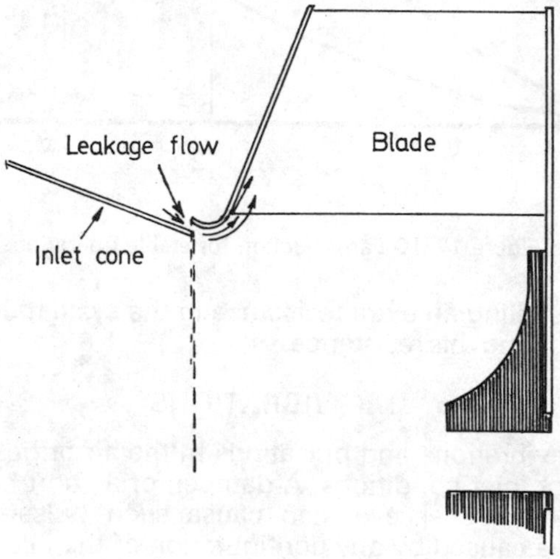

Figure 17:11 Flow lines at impeller throat showing importance of leakage flow

When complaints about poor performance are investigated, it is sometimes surprising to find that the fan is running in reverse. Sometimes motor and fan pulleys are interchanged, causing the fan speed to be too high or too low. Fan pressure is sometimes measured downstream of a partly closed damper and a complaint is lodged that the fan performance is low.

If an obvious cause cannot be found, it is best to ask the supplier to investigate.

16   FAN NOISE

Fans running at high tip speeds, particularly if they are of the axial-flow type, usually have a high noise level. Fan acoustics need careful study to be fully understood and cannot be explained in a few paragraphs.

The noise level can be reduced considerably by various methods. Properly designed silencers at the fan inlet and outlet are very effective. Lagging of the fan and ducting with sound-absorbing materials combined with flexible connections between fan and ducting will solve some noise problems.

High-speed motors sometimes have a high noise level. In such cases it may be advisable to enclose the whole unit in a soundproof room. In the case of auxiliary mine ventilation fans it may be advisable to use lower-speed two-stage fans rather than high-speed single-stage fans.

17   MOTORS AND DRIVES

Fans can be driven by various means :

(a)   Diesel engines

Diesel engines are not used very often to drive mine fans but are useful on standby fans which may be needed in case of a power failure, and also on remote locations where adequate electric power may not be available temporarily.

It is normally advisable to incorporate a clutch on the engine shaft. This is engaged after the engine has been started.

(b)   Steam turbines

Steam turbines are often used in installations where steam is generated for other purposes. A steam turbine drive has the advantage that it allows for a certain percentage of speed variation to cope with a fluctuating fan output requirement. A steam turbine is usually coupled onto the fan shaft through a speed-reducing gearbox.

(c)   Compressed air turbines

Small compressed air-driven axial-flow fans are still used on some mines. With these it is only necessary to connect an air hose to the fan. The compressed air drives a small turbine which is an integral part of the fan impeller.

Other air motors of the sliding-vane type or piston type are also available but are rarely used to drive mine fans.

(d)   Electric motors

The large majority of fans are driven by means of electric motors which are still the most practical drive units for fans of all sizes. Motor enclosures can be open-protected, totally enclosed fan-cooled, duct-ventilated or flame-proof, depending on the environment in which they operate.

Alternating current motors have the disadvantage of being basically fixed-speed units, whereas variable-duty fans will use the least amount of power if output control is achieved by variation of the speed. The capital cost of a fan drive is always higher for variable speed arrangements, irrespective of the method employed for varying the speed, but savings on power cost over the expected useful life of a particular fan might more than offset the initial capital expenditure on a variable speed drive which is therefore often worth considering.

Motors that are wound to run at two or more fixed speeds are available. Although such motors cost more than single-speed motors, their use can result in considerable savings in power on fans that have to cope with widely varying duties. A two-speed motor combined with an inlet vane control mechanism provides a very economical means for obtaining partial fan capacities.

A method which is used occasionally to obtain a two-speed drive is to couple two squirrel cage motors of different speeds, say, a six-pole and an eight-pole motor, in series by means of a flexible coupling.

Power is supplied to the motor of the required speed which drives the fan while the other motor runs idle. An improvement on this scheme is to couple the motors one at either end of the fan shaft through uni-directional couplings which disengage when the motor is not driving.

This arrangement is also used sometimes when, for instance, a turbine-driven fan has a stand-by electric motor coupled to the other end of the fan shaft.

The power required to drive a fan is proportional to the cube of the fan speed, and, the lower-speed motor therefore as a rule of considerably lower power than the motor of higher speed.

Of the different types of electric motors that are available, the three-phase squirrel cage type is the most popular. It is a simple and reliable machine. It is also suitable for simple direct on-line starting where permitted by local regulations and the power supply. The maximum starting current is normally of the order of seven times the full load current.

Slip-ring motors with liquid starters or auto-transformer starting equipment are used mostly on large main ventilation fans; an excessive surge in the starting current can thus be avoided.

Couplings

A fan shaft can be coupled directly to the shaft of the driving unit through any one of a fairly extensive variety of couplings. The most popular couplings are the simple "flexible" types of coupling which allow for a small amount of linear or angular misalignment. Numerous types and makes are available.

There are also centrifugal shoe-type friction couplings that will engage when the driving unit is started and disengage when the driving unit is stopped. These couplings are very useful on dual-drive systems. They have the further advantage that the shoes will slip with overload, which allows for a gradual increase in fan speed during starting.

Starting shock loads can be reduced considerably by installing slipping couplings such as fluid-, powder- or magnetic-type couplings. Some of these couplings can also be used to provide a certain measure of speed control, usually with a small loss of power in the form of heat. Provision must then be made for dissipation of this heat, necessitating some form of cooling.

Belt drives

Belt drives are very popular, particularly on smaller fans. They provide a means for selecting the most economical speed for any fan for a particular duty. V-belts are by far the most popular, although flat belts and timing-gear belts are used occasionally in certain circumstances.

An additional advantage of a belt drive is that it allows the fan speed to be increased or decreased by changing the pulleys. This can be a useful feature if a user is uncertain of his air requirements when ordering a fan.

Gearboxes

The average ventilation and dust-extraction type of fan is very rarely driven through a gearbox.

Speed-reducing gearboxes, such as wormgear reducers, are often installed on very low-speed fans such as those used in cooling towers, and speed-increasing gearboxes are used with high-speed blowers and compressors.

18 MEASUREMENT OF FAN PRESSURES

Much has been said and written on the subject of the measurement of fan pressures. Briefly, it is sufficient to remember that resistance on the downstream side of a fan is measured by means of a side tube. On the upstream side, resistance is measured by means of a facing tube. The suction for a surface exhaust fan with free discharge is, therefore, usually specified as the facing tube pressure at the shaft collar.

If a fan is not mounted at either the inlet end or the exhaust end of an airway but somewhere in between, then the pressure that will correspond to the "static" pressure on the fan manufacturer's curve will be the summation of the facing tube pressure measured immediately ahead of the fan on the upstream side and the side tube pressure measured just after the fan discharge.

If the velocity pressure at the fan discharge end is added to this "static" pressure, then this value will correspond to the "total" pressure on the fan manufacturer's curve.

19 FAN TESTING

In South Africa fans are normally tested in accordance with the methods laid down in British Standard 848:1963. Various test methods are described and every ventilation engineer should have access to a copy of the Standard.

The test method used must suit the type of fan to be tested. Normally, a fan will develop enough pressure to overcome the resistance of the test duct and the volume measurement station. The pressure loss can be relatively high if, for instance, an orifice plate is used for volume measurement. This can lead to problems when a low-pressure fan is tested, because, as the volume flow increases, the resistance of the test column may become greater than the pressure that the fan can develop, sometimes even before the peak pressure point on the fan performance curve is reached. This means that a full performance test cannot be carried out.

Other lower loss methods of volume measurement can be used to overcome the problem. A Pitot tube or anemometer traverse will not cause any pressure loss but is time-consuming because of the large number of readings that have to be taken. A nozzle or venturi will be preferable for volume measurements on medium-pressure fans, whereas a conical inlet can be used down to reasonably low pressures (see Chapter 13).

When high specific-speed fans developing very low pressures are tested, a booster fan must be used to overcome the resistance of the test column. This makes it possible to obtain a full performance curve down to zero static pressure on any fan. It is necessary only to ensure that the booster fan does not create an uneven air flow pattern in the test column.

Shaft power can be determined in various ways. One is to measure the power input into a calibrated electric motor by means of precision-grade instruments. The motor output power is then calculated.

A more positive method is to use a swinging cradle dynamometer which has an arm pressing down on a scale, or, alternatively, a scale pan which can be loaded until it reaches equilibrium. This is a very convenient and accurate way of measuring relatively low shaft powers.

Large shaft powers can be measured quite accurately with a calibrated torquemeter. The optical type torquemeter is simple and reliable and easy to calibrate and use.

In South Africa, test facilities exist by means of which quite large fans can be given a full-scale performance test in the manufacturer's work-shops before delivery. Large mine fans are often tested only after installa-tion at site. British Standard 848 :1963, Section 3, describes clearly the site testing of fans for mines and tunnels. The paragraph dealing with the measurement of fan static pressure on extract fans warrants careful reading. It implies correctly that a facing tube pressure reading on the inlet side of an exhaust fan corresponds to the system resistance or the fan static pressure.

If mine fans are to be tested with reasonable accuracy after installation, it is important to ensure that an adequate length of straight and smooth airway is incorporated in the fan layout. Volume measurements should be made on the inlet side of a fan whenever possible because uniform flow conditions seldom exist on the discharge side in the immediate vicinity of the fan.

Finally, it can be mentioned that it is possible to calculate the efficiency of a fan by making use of the measured temperature rise across the fan.[1] In practice, the measurement of the temperature difference across the fan presents problems, due principally to the temperature variations at the fan inlet and discharge. A further complication arises when the fan handles air containing free moisture. [2,3] (see Chapter 9.)

20   EFFECTS OF DIFFUSERS

In a fan and duct system the total pressure generated by the fan is made up of the fan static pressure which is available to overcome the resistance of the system and the velocity pressure which sustains the air flow along the duct. If the cross-sectional area of the duct is enlarged gradually at a certain point in the system, and if the volume flow remains constant, the velocity and hence the velocity pressure will be reduced in the enlarged section. Depending upon the efficiency of the enlargement or diffuser, a fraction of the velocity pressure will be lost irretrievably, but the balance will be converted into static pressure which then becomes available to overcome the system resistance without an increase in the power input into the fan.

It is therefore always advisable to add a diffuser to an air system. A diffuser or evasee is normally mounted directly on to the fan discharge, but it should be remembered that the system will also benefit if a diffuser is added to the end of an airway which may be a considerable distance away from the discharge end of the fan.

The effect of an evasee is demonstrated clearly by a surface fan ex-hausting air from a mine shaft. If a hole should be drilled or an inspection cover opened at the base of the fan evasee, air will be drawn into the evasee from outside, thus proving that a negative pressure exists at this point. This negative pressure assists the fan in overcoming resistance on the inlet side of the fan.

21   ECONOMICS OF FAN EFFICIENCY

If the average cost of electricity on a South African gold mine at present is taken to be in the region of R40 per kW per annum, the saving on, say, a 2 per cent increase in fan efficiency on a small fan with a 5 or 10 kW motor will be negligible. The same 2 per cent increase in efficiency on a fan absorbing 3 000 kW, however, will amount to a saving of approximately R2 400 per annum. A mine may be using a number of large fans in its ventilation system. If all the power used for ventilation is added together, it becomes quite clear how important it is that fan efficiency should be considered very carefully when fans are purchased. It is, however, also important to consider the capital cost of a fan installation at the purchase stage. The total cost of the installation over the useful life of the fan will be made up of the initial cost of the installation plus running costs plus maintenance costs. (see Chapter 21).

It might thus well be that a higher-priced fan running at a slightly higher efficiency will in the long run be more economical to purchase than a lower efficiency fan at a lower purchase price.

22   SELECTION, INSTALLATION AND MAINTENANCE

As stated in Section 13, it is important that the purchaser of a fan should stipulate the volume and pressure requirements as accurately as possible. The fan supplier usually has available a large number of fans of various designs and will offer a fan with the most suitable type of impeller for the specified requirement (see Section 4).

The installation of a fan, particularly if it is a large fan delivered to the site in a completely knocked-down condition, should be entrusted to a person who is thoroughly conversant with fan erection work. It is most important that the manufacturer's drawings be adhered to. Deviations from specified dimensions, particularly in the vicinity of the impeller eye, can cause a serious shortfall in performance (see Section 15).

After erection of the fan, it is important to enforce a regular maintenance programme. Small fans usually require very little maintenance and will often run for years without much attention. Large main ventilation fans, however, are very important for the proper functioning of mining operations, and a sudden breakdown can have serious repercussions. Such fans should be examined at least once a week. Particular attention should be paid to bearing lubrication systems. Safety devices should also be checked for proper functioning. Impellers and volume control equipment, such as inlet-vane controls, should be cleaned thoroughly and checked at three-to six-monthly intervals, and repainted with a good quality paint when necessary. Other parts such as flexible couplings, brakes and motor sliprings should also be checked regularly. Bearings should be opened and checked at six-monthly intervals.

With proper care, such a fan should give many years of trouble-free service.

23   FAN FAILURES

Fan failures are very often caused by misuse. Auxiliary ventilation fans that are used near areas where blasting is carried out are often found to contain rocks, bars and other foreign material that has been blown through the protecting screen. Dust deposits on fan blades can give rise to serious vibration problems. Centrifugal fans may be thrown out of balance by rags and other foreign material collecting on blade noses. If such a fan is allowed to continue running with an out-of-balance impeller for too long, bearing failure and possibly fatigue cracking of the impeller or casing can occur. Excessive vibration is a condition that should be corrected without delay.

Impellers of fans handling gases containing high concentrations of dust should be examined occasionally for wear, and the impeller should be replaced or repaired when necessary. As a rule, large main ventilation fans receive more attention than smaller fans and failures do not occur very frequently. Bearings may fail because of a fault in the lubrication system which can happen occasionally even though sophisticated safety devices may be installed.

A good regular maintenance programme is the best safeguard against fan failures.

24   SAFETY DEVICES

Safety devices on large ventilation fans are usually centred around the bearings.

Vibration cut-outs will trip the fan motor if the vibration of the fan shaft exceeds a pre-set value. A stand-by oil pump will continue to keep the oil supply going in case the main pump should fail.

Temperature sensing thermostats are fitted to each bearing. These can be pre-set to two temperature values. Should the bearing temperature increase above the first pre-set value, an alarm will be switched on automatically. If the temperature should reach the higher value, the fan motor will be tripped.

A pressurestat will trip the motor if the oil pressure should fall below the design pressure. Similarly, an oil flowmeter is often installed to trip the motor if a blockage in the oil system should result in a reduced oil supply to the bearings, in spite of the oil pressure remaining normal.

In all cases, the oil supply should be designed so that sufficient oil will be available in a header tank or a pressure tank to lubricate the bearings during the time it takes the fan to come to a standstill after the motor has been tripped.

It is possible for a fan to continue running after the power supply has been cut due to the flow of the upcast air through the impeller. It is then possible for the bearings to run dry with disastrous results. The answer to this is to install a brake on the fan shaft. The brake is released hydraulically and held in this position while the fan is running. As soon as the motor is tripped the brake will be applied gradually and the fan will be stopped before the oil supply ceases.

Strange as it might seem, bearing failures still occur. It has happened, for instance, that an electrician has tried unsuccessfully to start a fan before starting up the oil pump. He thought that there was a defect in one of the safety devices and therefore shorted these out and started the fan. Without oil the bearings and shaft were damaged beyond repair within minutes.

25 TENDERS

A fan enquiry should state clearly the purpose for which the fan is to be used. The volume and pressure required should be stated, indicating what part of the resistance will be on the suction side of the fan as this will affect the air density at the fan inlet. The altitude and air temperature will also be required to be known as well as the condition of the air to be handled. Dust-laden air on a dust extraction plant, for instance, may require a fan different from that required for clean air. Severe conditions may also require special attention. Furthermore, rotation and direction of discharge should be specified in the case of centrifugal fans.

With all the above information available the tenderer will be able to select the most economical and best type of fan for the purpose.

Acknowledgement

The author wishes to thank the management of James Howden and Safanco, Limited, for permission to publish this chapter.

26 REFERENCES

1   Whillier, A., *et al.* Fan efficiency determination from air temperature measurements. *S. Afr. mech. eng.* Vol. 18, 1969, p. 125–32.
2   McPherson, M. J. The isentropic compression of moist air in fans. *J. Mine Vent. Soc. S. Afr.* Vol. 24, 1971, p. 74–89.
3   Drummond, J. A. Fan efficiency investigation on mines of Union Corporation Ltd. *J. Mine Vent. Soc. S. Afr.* Vol. 25. 1972, p. 180–95.

BIBLIOGRAPHY

Wallis, R. A. *Axial-flow fans: design and practice.* New York. Academic Press, 1961.

Stepanoff, A. J. Ph.D. *Turboblowers: Theory, design and application of centrifugal and axial-flow compressors and fans.* John Wiley & Sons, Inc., New York. Chapman and Hall, Limited, London.

Jorgensen, Robert. *Fan engineering,* Buffalo Forge Company, Buffalo, New York. 6th Ed., 1961.

White, W. W. and De La Harpe, J. H. Recent developments in the design of heavy duty fans. *S. Afr. mech. eng.* Vol 20, 1970, p. 406–17.

British Standard 848. Part 1 : 1963 : *Methods of testing fans for general purposes.*

18 Main and Auxiliary Ventilation Practice in South African Gold Mines

D. F. H. GRAVE

Group Ventilation Engineer,
Anglo American Corporation of South Africa, Limited

1 INTRODUCTION

Underground ventilation practice is intimately bound up with mining conditions, and it is thus important to present in outline the main features of the South African gold mines.

The gold-bearing reef varies in width from about 75 mm to about 2 m with the dip varying from 0 to 90 °. The stoping width is commonly about 1,2 m with little variation. Massive ore deposits simply do not exist, although in a few mines some stopes are 2,5 to 3 m wide. This large tabular deposit extends for a distance of about 240 km, frcm Evander on the East Rand through the old Witwatersrand, Carletonville and Klerksdorp to the Orange Free State goldfields at Welkom, Odendaalsrus and Virginia.

While there are large differences in grade, ranging often from highly payable to unpay over short distances, the whole deposit is sufficiently consistent to make widespread exploitation practical and profitable, as indeed it has proved to be over the past eighty-five years. Although the outcrop workings and the shallower mines are by now largely worked out, the reef can, in many instances, be mined to great depth. Future exploitation in even deeper areas is feasible. Among the many factors which affect the viability of any new mine at depth — or the survival of an existing deep mine — the cost of ventilation is of increasing importance, and the devising of a practical ventilating technique is a *sine qua non*.

Some forty-four mines are operating on the goldfields of the greater Witwatersrand at present. Although a few of these are near the end of their life, exploration of potential mining areas is continuing and it is likely that one or two new mines will be opened within the next few years, with the possibility of others to follow. Needless to say, these new mines are likely to be at greater depth than most if not all of the mines presently in operation, and ventilation will be one of the major engineering problems in the operation of these mines.

There are, of course, numerous differences between one gold mine and another even within a system as homogeneous as the gold mines of the greater Witwatersrand.

These differences, as far as the ventilation system is concerned, are associated mainly with whether the mine is deep or shallow, whether it works to an outcrop or not, and whether stoping is "longwall" or "scattered".[1]

Shallow mines, which in this country have few ventilation problems, do not highlight the aspects that are of interest in this study and will thus not be considered here. The same applies to outcrop mines, the exception being one of the world's deepest mines (East Rand Proprietary Mines Ltd.) which is an outcrop mine; a few other deep mines on the Witwatersrand that started from the outcrop are still working at depths of over 3 000 metres. The effect of outcrop workings on a mine that has long gone to far greater depth is to provide a convenient upcast air route on the plane of the reef (provided that the old workings have been kept open to an adequate extent) and at the same time to make it impracticable to site the main fans on top of the upcast shaft system because of the numerous holings to surface. In the case of old outcrop mines such as East Rand Proprietary Mines, Durban Roodepoort Deep, City Deep, Crown Mines, etc., the main ventilation fans have to be sited underground, usually in the downcast. This has some disadvantages as regards heat input but is unavoidable. This condition applies to relatively few mines, virtually all of them of the older generation. In most new deep-level mines the orebody does not outcrop to surface.

On these new mines the depth of the deepest workings ranges from 1 000 to over 3 400 m, the corresponding natural rock temperatures being 31 °C and 52 °C, respectively. The mean rock-breaking depths are, of course, somewhat less, namely, 500 to 2 800 m, at rock temperatures ranging from 20 °C to 46 °C. The shallower depths apply to not more than eight of the forty-four mines.

Table 1 shows the number of mines in various ranges of operating depths.

TABLE 1

Depth below surface Range m	Number of mines
0 — 1 000	1
1 000 — 2 000	18
2 000 — 3 000	20
3 000 — 3 500	5

On the deep sub-outcrop mines, the mine is served by one or more shaft systems, each with an upcast and a downcast shaft. In some cases the shaft system consists of a single shaft with a dividing wall.

At depths greater than 1 500 m the shaft system is often extended to depth by a sub-vertical shaft system, usually identical in dimensions and capacity with the shafts from surface.

The air quantities handled range from 200 to 550 m^3/s per shaft system.

The shafts are mostly circular and concrete-lined. The maximum diameter is 10 m. The circular shafts are sometimes modified in size by the use of a "flat", 1 to 2 metres long, joining the two semicircles of the curve section. This has the effect of increasing the shaft area while permitting the use of smaller shuttering for the concrete lining and of making a near-elliptical shaft. Some rectangular shafts are still in use, though few have been sunk on the mines in recent years. These are in some instances concrete-lined, and in others rough excavations in the rock. Square timber setts (in rectangular shafts) or "I"-section buntons are used. Modern shafts on these mines are almost without exception circular or near-elliptical concrete-lined with streamlined buntons. The "squashed pipe" and hexagonal "Air-save" sections are common and have an air resistance less than half that of "I"-section buntons.[2] (Fig. 18:1)

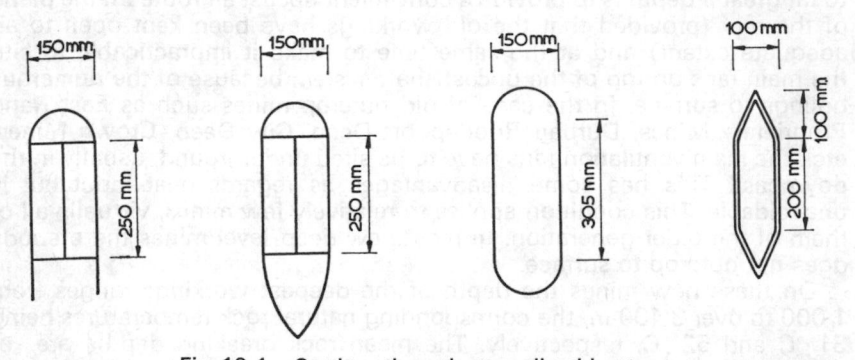

Fig. 18:1   Sections through streamlined buntons

Upcast shafts (and the upcast portions of divided shafts) are normally clear and concrete-lined with no buntons. Except in a few instances no hoisting is done in upcast shafts. One reason for this is the corrosion caused by the saturated air in an upcast shaft. Most upcast shafts are provided with a large, high-pressure fan at the top, and there are great practical difficulties in the handling of high tonnages of rock through an airlock.

Most upcast shafts are over 1 000 m deep, some up to 2 000 m. The air entering the bottom of an upcast shaft is normally saturated at a temperature in the region of 32 °C. In some cases the temperature is higher because of the use of the upcast air for heat rejection from underground refrigeration plants. As this saturated air rises in the shaft, the temperature falls as a result of auto-decompression and much of the water vapour content of the air condenses. The resulting water droplets are either carried up with the air stream or fall down the shaft, depending on air velocity and droplet size. Within a certain velocity range (7,5 to 12,5 m/s) the droplets remain in suspension in the shaft, being constantly added to by condensation from the upcast air until a substantial water blanket is built up in the shaft. This has the effect of throttling the air flow and frequently stalls the fan. After the resulting drop in air velocity and a cascade of water down the shaft, normal air flow is restored and the process repeats itself, at intervals sometimes as short as two hours. This phenomenon was first reported by Lambrechts (1956).[3] As a result of his research upcast shafts are now designed so that velocities of between 7,5 and 12,5 m/s are avoided. Further, arrangements are made at the top of every shaft to trap water carried in the air stream and to channel it away.

Air velocities in downcast shafts are normally in the range 10 m/s to 13 m/s though higher velocities are not uncommon. For upcast shafts the velocity ranges up to 20 m/s, velocities around 10 m/s being avoided as noted above. While considerations of power cost must be in favour of low velocities, high velocities are sometimes accepted in order to provide extra production over and above the original designed capacity of the shaft.

Air velocities in intake airways are generally of the order of 5 m/s and seldom go above 10 m/s. In return airways a somewhat higher velocity can be accepted, but even there velocities of over 7 m/s are uncommon. As far as possible airways are kept free of timber and roof bolting is used where necessary. On occasion, however, heavy support is needed and the resistance to air flow is therefore high.

2   STOPE VENTILATION

In stopes, which are the main production areas in a mine, ventilation air is caused, as far as practicable, to concentrate along the face. Most stopes have a centre gully which is used for the transport of men, material and ore, with strike gullies connecting to the faces. Obviously leakage via the centre gully will rob the working face of much of its air; over 50 per cent of the air reaching a stope will travel that way if not prevented.[4] However, the use of brattices and doors in centre gullies, combined with the use of adequate strike walls, is successful in coursing the bulk of the air to the face. This applies equally to scattered and to longwall stoping, although in the case of longwall stoping strike walls and centre gully brattices and/or doors are of a more permanent nature and consequently of much better quality than is the case in scattered stoping where a stope might be worked out in under a year. For example, in longwall stopes at E.R.P.M., the strike walls (ribs) are six metres thick and consist of waste rock blasted from the hanging. At a dip of $\pm 26°$ and a stoping width of $\pm 1,1$ m these ribs form an impassable barrier to air flow and all the air is forced to the face. Three ribs are constructed per 80-metre panel and they play an important part in supporting the worked-out area. In other longwalls use is made of wooden mat-packs treated with a vermiculite-gypsum mixture which seals the packs and provides a fireproof cover. Here again the natural settling of the worked-out area consolidates the seal and helps course the available air to the face.

In the case of "scattered" stopes, which form the great majority of stopes on these mines, air is coursed to the face by means of strike walls made of waste rock (with or without plaster) brick walls (vermiculite-cement bricks are often used) or curtains made of plastic materials (PVC, polythene, plastic-covered cloth, etc.). Curtains are widely used at present. They are suspended either from wires stretching between mat-packs in the stope, are glued to the hanging wall or supported internally by spring-wire sewn into the curtain. Although curtains are not as intrinsically airtight as brick walls, they have the advantage of being constructed

TABLE 2 VENTILATION PIPE CONSUMPTION 1971

Diam. mm	Galvanised iron		Flexible		Plywood		Total m
	Metres/ annum	Highest individual consumption	Metres/ annum	Highest individual consumption	Metres/ annum	Highest individual consumption	
325	734	734					734
380	58 374	5 480					58 374
405	24 469	4 422	280	220			24 749
430			2 661	1 005			2 661
570	104 561	10 520					104 561
580			3 554	2 290			3 554
600					1 012	1 012	1 012
610			11 739	3 400			11 739
740					4 570	4 570	4 570
760	47 902	7 493	2 394	1 370			50 296
915	424	424					424
Totals	236 464		22 128		5 582		264 174

easily and rapidly, are not labour-intensive and are relatively cheap. Quickness and ease of erection are particularly important where face advance is rapid and the pressures of production are high.

3   DEVELOPMENT VENTILATION

Development ends or headings are ventilated by means of electric fans, usually of the axial-flow type (see below), and rigid ventilation piping. Piping is normally made of galvanized iron 1 mm to 1,2 mm thick, with loose ring flanges. Fixed-angle iron flanges are being used to an increasing extent as their use results in a better condition of the pipe ends which are frequently damaged in transit. Such damage leads to poor joint connections and loss of air.

Plywood piping is used to a limited extent, as is flexible ducting. The latter is made of PVC-covered nylon and has distinct advantages, notably ease of transport and of erection. As it is commonly used in lengths of 15 m as opposed to 4 m for the galvanized iron piping, the number of joints is much less and leakage is minimal.

Pipe diameters are usually 380 mm, 570 mm, 610 mm and 760 mm. The 570 mm diameter is the most useful size. For special applications, such as in shaft sinking, larger sizes are used.

TABLE 3   AMOUNT SPENT ON VENTILATION PIPING
BY THE GOLD MINES

Year	Total costs Rands
1960	1 455 000
1970	1 725 000
1971	1 917 000

The systems used in development ventilation are mainly the forcing system (Fig. 18:2) and the exhaust overlap system (Fig. 18:3). The forcing system is the most popular as only one ventilation duct is necessary and because it permits the air to be directed onto the working face. By regulation a minimum amount of air of 0,15 m³/s per square metre of face must be blown in. This minimum is exceeded substantially in all

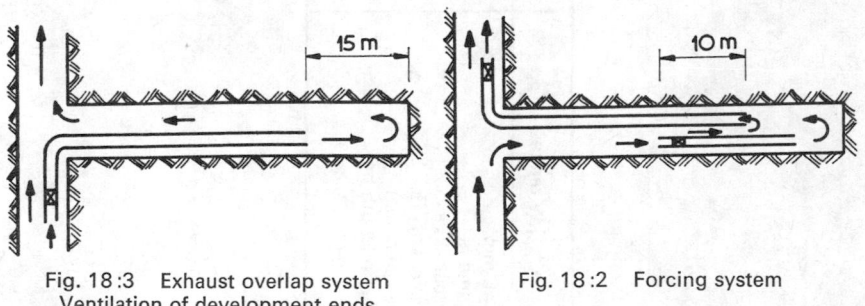

Fig. 18:3   Exhaust overlap system
Ventilation of development ends

Fig. 18:2   Forcing system

TABLE 4 DEVELOPMENT END FANS

kW ranges	0–2,9	3,0–5,9	6,0–10,9	11,0–18,9	19,0–33,9	34,0–41,9
Diam. mm	305–610	305–760	480–760	570–910	570–910	660–910
Volume m³/s	0,5–2,4	0,71–3,78	2,8–5,3	3,3–10,4	5,0–12,0	7,0–14,0
Pressure kPa	0,25–1,0	0,25–1,31	0,58–1,5	0,5–2,13	1,12–2,99	1,5–2,7
Density kg/m³	1,03–1,37	1,06–1,37	1,03–1,37	1,06–1,37	1,15–1,24	1,06–1,2
Pipe diam. mm	325–570	380–760	380–760	405–760	570–760	760–1 020
Column length m	15–100	50–200	30–400	50–500	55–335	130–700
No. of fans	1 901	3 366	2 778	2 909	256	596

Grand total 11 806 fans   Smallest fan 0,37 kW
Biggest fan 41,1 kW   Cost of repairs (1971) R1 029 700

cases. In the forcing system the air is discharged at a distance of less than 15 m from the face. In the exhaust overlap system the exhaust column is carried to a point about 30 m from the face. A smaller diameter forcing column picks up air about 30 m from the intake of the exhaust column and conveys it to the face. In order to avoid recirculation the air quantity blown to the face must be not more than one third of the air quantity exhausted, and the length of the overlap must be at least 10 m. For very rapid clearance of blasting fumes from a development end the exhaust column is extended to within 4 m of the face. A small-diameter (250 mm) pipe of construction heavier than normal is used, a special shield being provided to protect the extension piece from blast damage.

These two ventilation systems are shown clearly in the sketch.

There are about 4 000 development ends being worked on the mines. About 80 per cent of these are ventilated by the forcing system, $17\frac{1}{2}$ per cent by the exhaust overlap. The remainder are ventilated by such methods as exhaust only and compressed air only.

The advantage of the exhaust overlap system is that the blasting fumes are removed rapidly from the development end, making earlier re-entry possible. This system is generally used when long single ends need to be developed at high speed.

"Twin haulages" (or "twin ends") are commonly developed when an area is to be opened which is confidently expected to be payable and where exploitation is to follow closely upon the opening-up of the area.

In twin haulage development (Fig. 18:4) one haulage is used as a return, the other as an intake. The haulages are commonly developed about 15 to 30 m apart, with connecting crosscuts at intervals of 150 to 200 m. This makes it possible to establish through-ventilation up to a point at a maximum distance of 200 m from the advancing faces and renders lengthy ventilation pipe columns unnecessary. When the area to be mined has been reached, the twin haulages are used for the development, and later the stoping, of the area, one haulage being used for intake air and for access and transport of men, materials and ore, the other functioning as a return airway and sometimes used for drainage. Usually the return airway is unequipped.[5]

A barricade is used to prevent unauthorized access to the return airway which is frequently filled with blasting fumes.

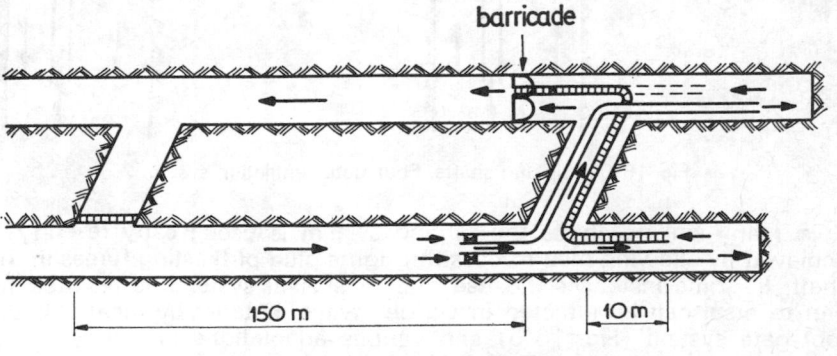

Figure 18.4   Ventilation of twin development ends

It is obviously uneconomical to use a twin system for development only, where the second airway can have no useful function after holing. Such a case would be long development for the purpose of effecting a holing into an area of doubtful payability, where the likelihood of extensive exploration and exploitation of the area concerned is remote. In these circumstances single-end development is preferable, and the ventilation of single ends of lengths of up to 2 000 m from through ventilation is practicable even in areas of high rock temperature.

Where the area to be developed is known or expected to be payable, the twin haulage method of development is highly advantageous as it facilitates development and makes available sufficient intake and return airways for the speedy exploitation of the mining block. This method has become standard practice on many large, deep mines.

For sinking shaft ventilation the exhaust overlap system is used frequently, air being exhausted to the shaft bank through large-diameter pipes and a smaller air quantity being forced to the face by means of fans on the Galloway stage. This method ensures a rapid clearance of blasting fumes from the face and the minimum danger of exposure to blasting fumes. However, it has the disadvantages that power supply and maintenance are required for fan units on the stage, and that a small air quantity reaches the actual working face.

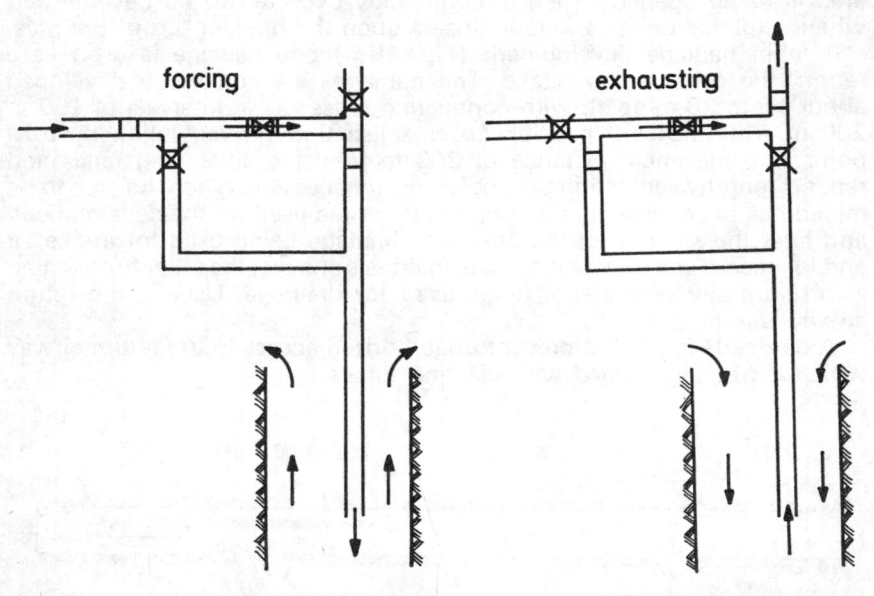

Fig. 18 :5   Sinking shafts. Four-gate ventilation system

In many sinking shafts the forcing system is used; early re-entry is achieved by allowing men to pass through a plug of blasting fumes in the shaft. In some instances the use of fan reversal systems is resorted to. Fan reversal can be effected in various ways, notably by means of the four-gate system (Fig. 18:5) and various adaptations of the four-gate system whereby the direction of the air in the ventilation column can be reversed by the operation of a single lever. This method is not popular, however, as dust deposited in the pipes after the blast can be dislodged when the air direction is reversed at the start of the new cycle and the face area contaminated.

TABLE 5   VENTILATION OF SINKING SHAFTS 1971

No. of shafts forcing	5	11,8 m³/s to 37,0 m³/s
force/exhaust	4	*Force* *Exhaust*
		2,3 to 22,6 m³/s 6,8 to 56,6 m³/s
exhaust only	2	5,0 m³/s to 19,0 m³/s

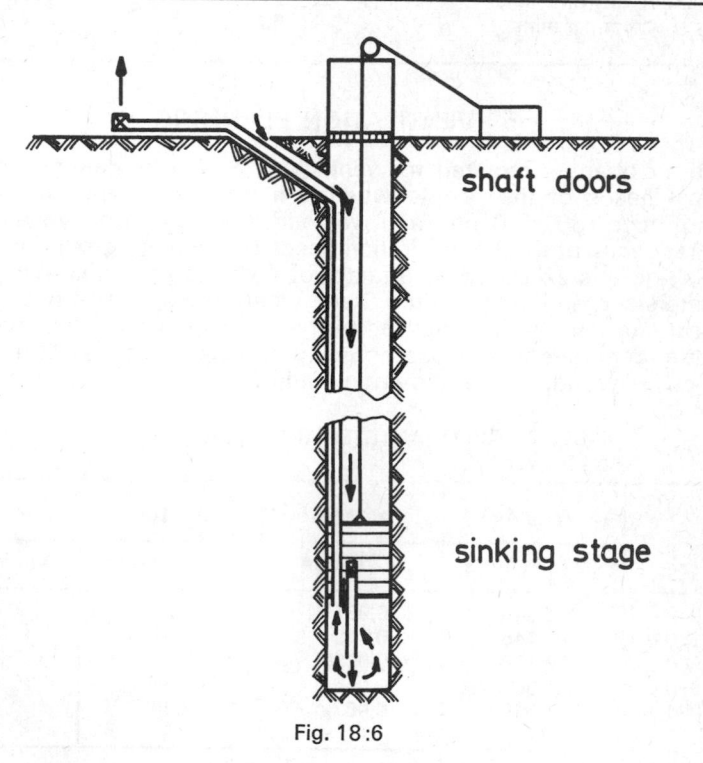

shaft doors

sinking stage

Fig. 18 :6

4   DIESEL ENGINES

While electric locomotives either trolley-wire or battery-operated, are in use on some mines, diesel engines are used widely and in some mines there are as many as 200. The diesel engines used are mainly of small size. The diesel engine is the only form of internal combustion engine permitted underground.

Legal requirements for the underground use of diesel engines include monthly tests of the air in the areas in which they are working and quarterly tests of the exhaust fumes. The maximum permissible concentration of carbon monoxide in the exhaust fumes is 2 000 parts per million and of oxides of nitrogen 1 000 parts per million. In the general air the corresponding maxima are 100 parts per million carbon monoxide and 5 parts per million oxides of nitrogen. The normal practice is to provide some 0,063 m³/s of ventilating air per kW of diesel engine power; this permits the legal requirements to be met easily.

TABLE 6   DIESEL LOCOS UNDERGROUND

Largest loco	60 kW
Total number	2 639 (1 490 in range 15 – 30 kW)
Maximum on any one mine	217
Average number per mine	63

5   VENTILATION PLANNING

The air quantity required for ventilating a mine is determined by the physical needs of the people working in the mine. Thus a volume of 0,014 2 m³/s (30 cfm) per man was laid down at an early stage as the basic requirement for the respiration needs of the underground workers.

This figure is exceeded by a factor of 4 or 5 on the gold mines of the Witwatersrand and Orange Free State, where the air quantity dictated by the heat and dust hazards has led to the provision of air quantities which are more generous than those normally provided in mines in most other parts of the world. This is shown in Table 7.

TABLE 7   AIR QUANTITIES AND TONNAGES 1940–71

	Total Air	Air/Man	Air/Ton	
Year	Quantity m³/s	m³/s/Man	m³/s/1 000 t	No. of Mines
1940	8 348	0,031 4	1,27	41
1950	11 145	0,049	1,87	46
1960	17 158	0,059	2,18	52
1970	24 307	0,085	2,91	46
1971	24 548	0,087	2,985	44

For the purposes of ventilation planning the factor of air quantity per ton broken has considerable significance. This has an obvious application in predicting the air requirements of a new mine. Based on experience on many mines in which rock temperatures were high, Lambrechts and Barcza devised an empirical relationship which has proved its worth over many years.[1] Recent advances in the use of the computer in heat-flow calculations have resulted in the introduction of quantitative methods which largely confirm the accuracy of the empirical air quantity-tonnage graph (Fig. 17:7) and will assist greatly in its extrapolation into zones of higher rock temperature.

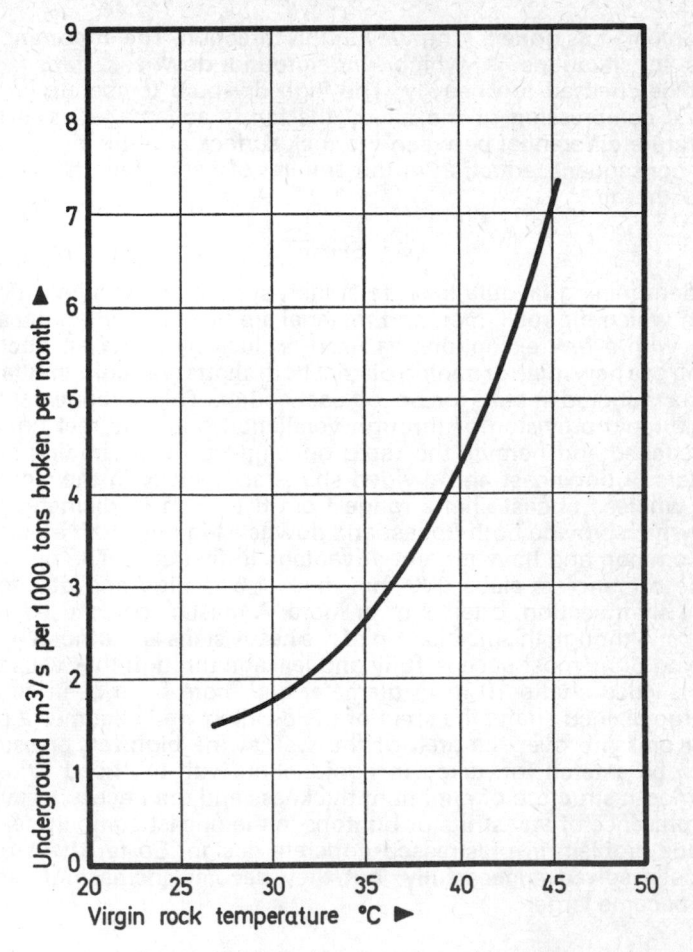

Figure 18.7   Air tonnage ratio (after Lambrechts)

Auto-compression raises the temperature of air by about 1 °C for every 100 m the air travels vertically down a shaft. The wet-bulb temperature rises by half this amount, that is, 0,5 °C per 100 m. This temperature increase is obviously unavoidable and has to be taken into account in the ventilation of deep mines. It is a fortunate coincidence that the geothermal gradient in the Witwatersrand quartzites is of the same order, which means in effect that the natural rock temperature and the air temperature in a dry shaft are much the same. Because of this, if a shaft and airways can be kept completely dry, little heat will flow from the rock to the air, and this will minimize the effect of the high rock temperatures prevalent in the gold mines. Indeed, the maintenance of dry conditions throughout the workings would be a tremendous advantage. However, the use of water in the working places for dust suppression is mandatory and the ideal of a completely dry mine, as has been achieved in places like the Kolar Gold Field in India, is virtually unattainable here, though one mine in particular

(Vlakfontein) has gone a long way in this direction. The importance of dry intakes in situations in which underground downcast fans are used cannot be stressed too heavily. The high dry-bulb temperature resulting from the compression of the air by the fan is advantageous in that the temperature differential between the rock surface and the air is minimized with a consequent reduction in the amount of heat which flows from the rock to the air.[6]

6   SHAFTS

Modern mining layouts include a shaft system comprising a downcast shaft in which the rock, men and material are hoisted and an upcast shaft which, with a few exceptions, is used exclusively as an air duct. In the opening of a new mine or mining district both shafts are sunk simultaneously within a hundred metres or so of each other. This arrangement makes possible rapid provision of through ventilation once the reef horizon has been reached and permits the rapid opening-up of the mining area. The diameters of downcast and divided shafts are usually in the range of 8 to 10 m, whereas upcast shafts range from 6 to 7 m in diameter. Divided shafts which provide both upcast and downcast in one shaft are becoming more common and have a great advantage in first cost. The dividing wall is made of concrete slabs 300 mm thick, 1,5 m high and of a length to suit the shaft section, often 9 m or more. A mastic seal is used between the slabs. Although the installation of the heavy slabs is a difficult operation, it is being done most successfully and leakage through the wall is usually small. Divided shafts 10 m in diameter and more have been sunk. With very large divided shafts the span of the dividing wall becomes a problem. The air pressure over the area of the wall at the high fan pressures that have to be catered for, taken in conjunction with the need to provide a light smooth structure of minimum thickness and the necessary avoidance of the presence of any struts or buntons in the upcast compartment, poses a serious problem in prestressed concrete design. So far these problems have been solved successfully, but they become increasingly severe as shafts become larger.

TABLE 8   SINKING SHAFTS (1971)

Circular	6
Near-elliptical	5

Diameters range from 4,9 m to 9,5 m

The usefulness of a mine shaft system is limited by the capacity of the hoists installed, the quantity of ore that can be handled and the ventilation it can provide. In other words, a shaft, to be of maximum use in the exploitation of a mining area, must be able to handle the maximum amount of ore to be hoisted and at the same time handle the men, material and services (which include ventilation) to permit mining of the ore. The very high cost of shaft sinking and equipping, and of all the ancillary equipment such as hoists, offices, accommodation for workmen, ore handling, etc., make it essential that any given shaft system should be capable of serving the largest possible area. The shaft system must thus allow of a high mining and hoisting rate and must also cover as wide an area as practicable.

7   REFRIGERATION

With rock temperatures below the critical (32 °C) some sort of balance has been achieved between the amount of ore that can be mined and hoisted in a shaft and the quantity of air that can be handled in the shaft system for the ventilation of the workings. With the relatively generous air quantities provided, the build-up of dust and gases is negligible and there is nothing to prevent re-use of air in successive working places.

At higher rock temperatures, however, this condition no longer applies. At rock temperatures of over 32 °C (in some cases the VRT reaches 50 °C) air heats up very rapidly as it travels through the stopes and soon the wet-bulb temperatures rise to over 32 °C at which temperature work is impractical and, in fact, dangerous. It is essential that air should be cooled if it is to be used in successive workings. In many instances the air has to be cooled before it is first used in a stope.

Refrigeration is thus essential on the deeper mines if maximum production from a shaft system is to be attained.

The determination of the refrigeration requirements of a deep mine is very much bound up with the details of the production pattern. While an

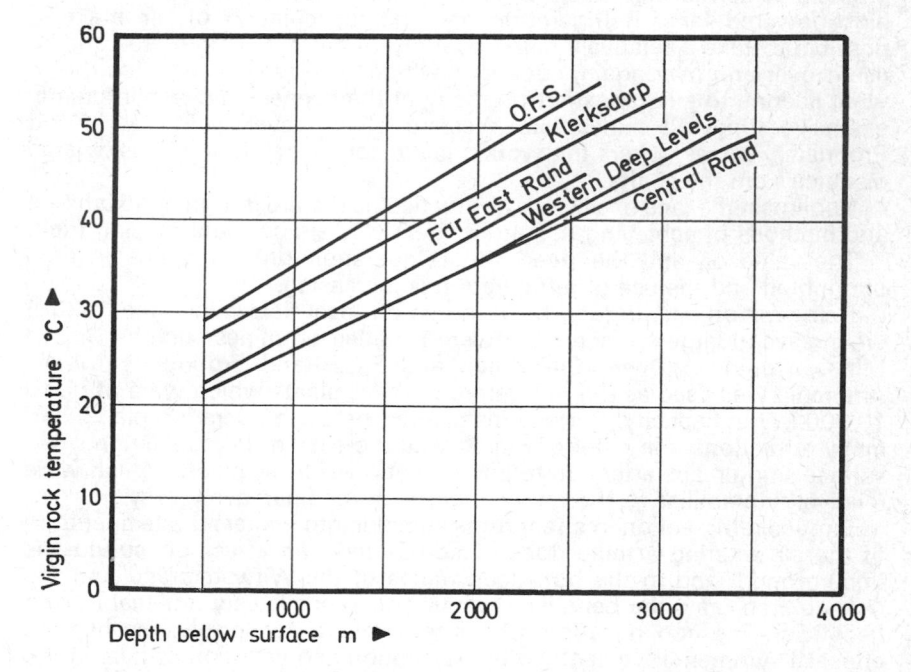

Figure 18.8   Rock temperature graphs (after Lambrechts)

empirical assessment is possible at long range, more accurate methods are available which give a far better assessment once the mining programme is decided upon. Computer methods are very useful in this respect.

Some degree of optimization between the amounts of air and refrigeration required for a given mining programme is desirable. While it might be thought possible to calculate theoretically the proportions of air and cooling that will best serve a given mining area, so many of the factors involved are variable and in many cases not capable of measurement, that the engineer has, to a very great extent, to be guided by experience. In particular, control of air movement in a stoping area is affected by such factors as ground movement, type of support, effectiveness of the ventilation controls and the thoroughness with which they are installed, the effectiveness of supervision, mishaps such as rock falls and the bursting of ventilation walls. These two latter mishaps often occur in inaccessible areas and repair may be impossible. All of this means that some over-design as regards air quantity is essential if the operation is to be practicable and production is not to be interrupted by ventilation failures.

The area that a mine shaft system can serve is affected by the details of the ore transportation system, by travelling time for workmen and by the distance that air can be moved practically and economically underground between the shaft and the workings. As noted above, the cost of shaft sinking has widened considerably previously applied limits and has brought about a reassessment of the factors involved. The use of high-speed haulages has made it possible for a shaft to serve a wide area underground. Transfer of large air quantities underground remains a problem which is met to some extent by the use of large airways and high-powered fans. Refrigeration and the recirculation of air make it possible to take a relatively small quantity of air to a remote area and to use it over and over again, cooling it where necessary. In practice this is what is done to a large extent on many of the deepest mines, particularly extensive longwall mines like Western Deep Levels and East Rand Proprietary Mines, where the workings are concentrated at a considerable distance from the shafts.

Cooling in the face or as close as practicable thereto is a great advantage and methods of achieving this more effectively are constantly being tried.

The value of, and the need for, refrigeration on hot mines is thus undoubted and the use of refrigeration is increasing.

Refrigeration has, in fact, been in use on local fields since the 1930's, when several large surface units were installed on mines such as Crown Mines, Robinson Deep, City Deep and East Rand Proprietary Mines. Ammonia was used as the refrigerant in these plants which were of up to 10 000 kW in capacity. Surface installation of the refrigeration plants had many attractions, the chief of which was the ease of heat rejection. Also surface siting made attention to and operation of these plants, which were relatively unfamiliar to the engineering staff, comparatively easy.

Surface refrigeration in effect turns summer into winter; the temperature of the air entering a mine does of course have an effect on conditions underground, and in the hot, deep mines of the Witwatersrand and the Orange Free State the benefit of winter conditions is very noticeable, and beneficial. The cooling effect of winter air and, conversely, the heating effect of summer air, is damped by absorption and emission of heat in the shaft walls, with the result that the peaks and troughs are flattened. In deep mines the damping effect cancels out to some extent the cooling effect of winter.

The beneficial effect of the "twelve-month winter" brought about by surface refrigeration eventually began to be lost, and it was realized that many of the benefits of the cooling effect were being lost in shafts, shaft stations, intake haulages, shallow workings and other points where refrigeration was not needed, and that the deepest and most remote workings which were at the end of the line received the least benefit. Some means of concentrating the cooling effect at the deepest points was needed. Because the hottest workings were 2 000 m and more underground and the static pressure on a chilled water pipe system would be excessive, the idea of siting the cooling plants on surface and piping chilled water underground proved impracticable. The only practical solution was to site the refrigeration plant underground.

Underground installation has many associated difficulties, the main one being heat rejection. This has been overcome by the use of upcast air for carrying away the rejected heat. Water has been used as a vehicle for the heat extracted underground, but its use has not been found practicable except in one or two instances.

Availability of upcast air to carry away the rejected heat obviously places a limit on the amount of refrigeration that can be installed underground. This has been overcome to a large extent by the use of high condensing pressures and temperatures. Condensing temperatures of up to 60 °C are now accepted as being generally usable underground. This leads to greater stress on the machine and higher power consumption, and there is obviously a limit to how far one can go in this direction. Again, the site of a cooling plant underground must be chosen with regard to the availability of upcast air. For this reason a centrally located plant, close to the upcast shaft, is often preferred (Fig. 18.9). Transfer of heat from the condenser water to the upcast air is usually effected in vertical cooling towers. These are underground excavations some 20 to 25 m high and 8 m or more in diameter and normally unpacked. The use of screens and egg crate-type packing has been found to improve performance. Air velocities in the tower are about 4 m/s and water loadings up to 19 1/s m². Temperatures of the upcast air are about 32°C rising to 37°C after leaving the tower. Sprays arranged in horizontal airways are also used.

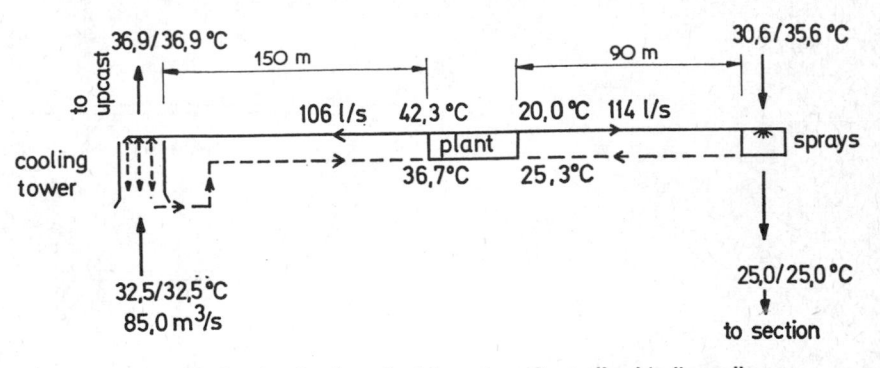

Figure 18.9   Application of refrigeration. Centralized bulk cooling

TABLE 9   REFRIGERATION ON MINES

Year	Surface		Underground		No. of mines using refrigeration
	Units	kW	Units	kW	
1960	3	24 267	26	30 246	9
1970	2	14 315	90	120 936	15
1971	2	14 315	106	153 583	17

Table 9 shows the distribution of surface as against underground refrigeration plants and the increase in the use of refrigeration on these mines in recent years. (Fig. 18:12).

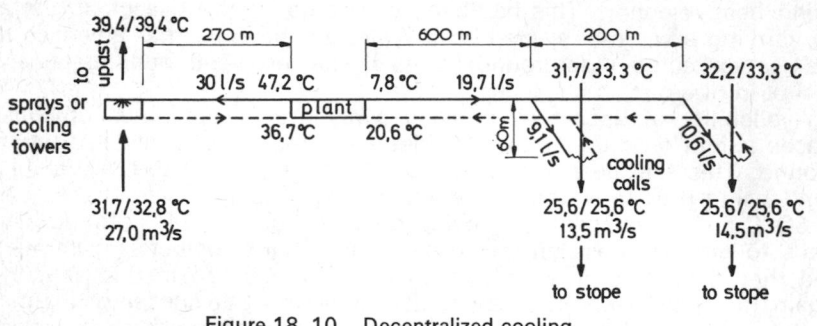

Figure 18.10   Decentralized cooling

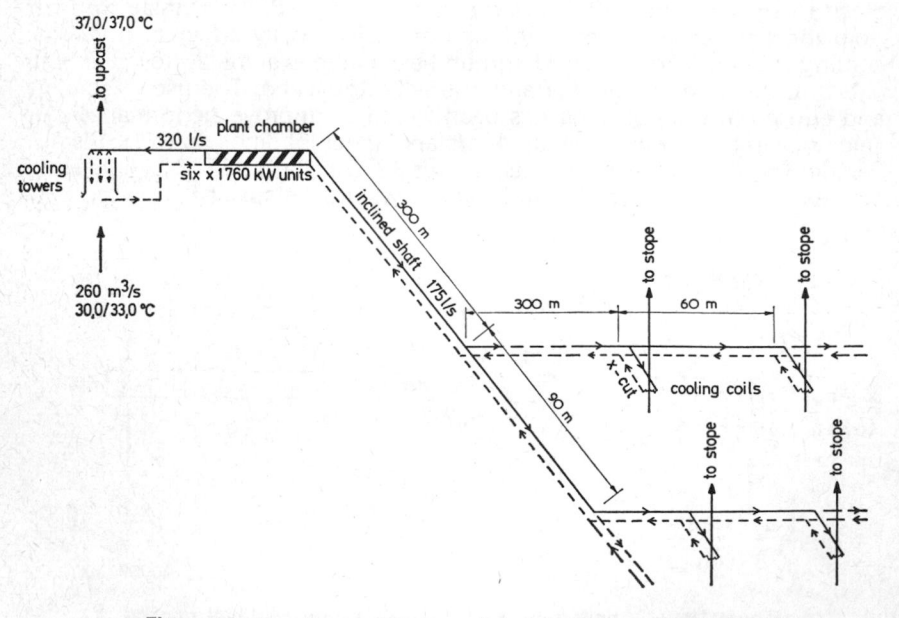

Figure 18.11   Decentralized cooling (a typical installation)

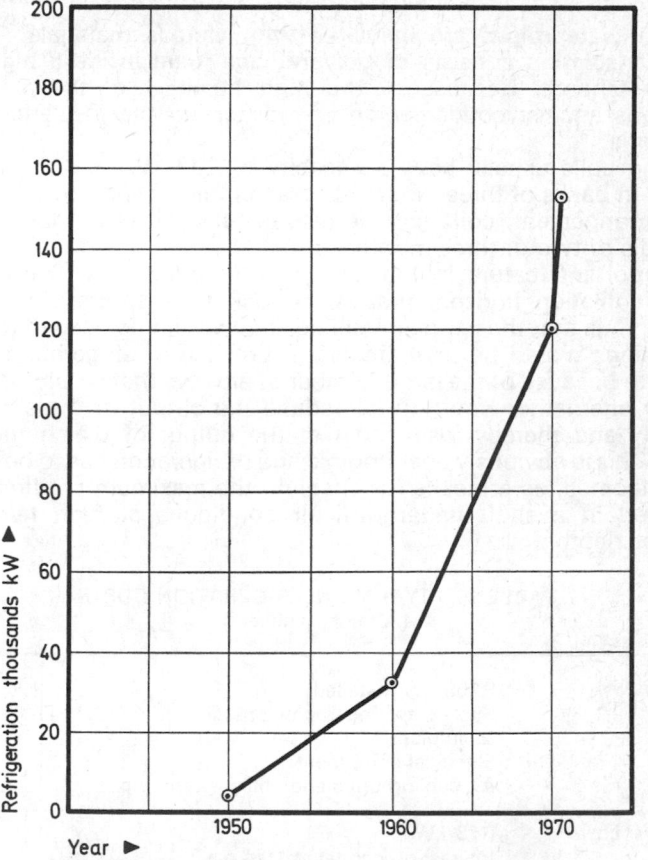

Figure 18.12   Build-up of underground refrigeration

One of the main advantages of underground refrigeration is that the "coolth" generated can be supplied to the air in the working place and not dissipated in unnecessary ways.

The most modern refrigeration installations cool water which is piped to the working place. Air is cooled at a site as close to the working face as possible (Figs. 18:10 and 18:11). In this way the maximum cooling is obtained from the cooling plant and the greatest amount of cooling is produced in the air in the working area. Ideally, air on leaving one working place is cooled before passing on to the next. In practice it is sometimes necessary to cool air in the working face, because of the rapidity with which air heats up in areas of high rock temperature, particularly where water is used liberally. Because of the daily blast it is obviously impracticable to have water-to-air heat exchangers (cooling coils) in the working face, as is the practice on some of the collieries in Germany. Cooling coils are installed in crosscuts or gullies some 100 m behind the face, or in the footwall, and the cooled air is piped to the face through ventilation pipes. In some instances a special boxhole is needed to bring the chilled air to the stope horizon.

Chilled water pipes are insulated with various materials. The most effective insulation consists of polyurethane foam inside a high-density polythene sheath. Because of the high humidity of the ambient air, precautions against condensation of moisture in the insulation material are essential.

Cooling coils usually have a capacity of 100 kW, and are frequently arranged in banks of three mounted on a car for transport by rail. With this mobile arrangement, coils can be moved forward as the face advances at intervals of two or three months.

An important feature in the use of refrigeration in mines below the critical ventilation horizon, that is, at rock temperatures in the range 32 to 52 °C, is that the large air volumes that would be needed to ventilate the workings would be unattainable in practice if refrigeration were not resorted to because of the large number of airways that would be required. The only alternative would be to reduce the output of the shaft system drastically and thereby lose much of the output of which the shaft is capable. This is obviously uneconomic and refrigeration has to be accepted, even welcomed, as a means for enabling the maximum production to be maintained in a shaft under difficult conditions at high temperatures and great depth.

TABLE 10   TYPICAL REFRIGERATION COSTS
(After A. Whillier [7])

A.	*Initial costs* R168/kW installed	
	Site excavating & concreting	13%
	Main plant	35%
	Electrical equipment	10%
	Air cooling units and chilled water pipes	42%
B.	*Annual costs* R48/kW	
	Interest on capital at 10% p.a.	R17
	Amortization of capital 20 years 10% interest	R3
	Electric power	
	Capacity at R40 p.a. per electric kW	R17
	Operating & Maintenance attendants	
	Servicing & maintenance of plant	R11
	Servicing & maintenance of chilled water pipes & stope coolers	
C.	*Money spent on cooling plants in* 1971	
	Complete plants	R1 830 700
	Spares & repairs	R498 500
D.	*Power consumption of refrigeration plant* (1971)	
	19×10^6 kW h per month	
	$(26 \times 10^3$ kW)	

8   MAIN VENTILATION ARRANGEMENTS

The gold mines of the Witwatersrand and extensions, Klerksdorp and the Orange Free State, downcast a total of 24 600 m³/s of fresh air measured at an air density of 1,2 kg/m³, that is, 30 tons of air per second. This represents an average of almost 560 m³/s per mine, ranging from a maximum of 1,270 m³/s to a minimum of 34 m³/s. To this can be added a total of some 1 500 m³/s of compressed air (±30 m³/s per mine on the average) at the same reference density.

The forty-four mines in the industry which together produce 1 000 tons of gold per year, are manned by about 314 000 underground workers. The number of men working underground at one mine ranges from 1 000 to 14 000, the average being 7 500.

In order to achieve this production about 8 500 000 metric tons of ore are broken per month — the monthly tonnage per mine ranging from over 8 200 to 440 000.

The air ventilating the mines is supplemented by considerable amounts of refrigeration. As noted above, some 90 large refrigeration plants and 16 small units, totalling 153 600 kW were in operation underground during 1971. In addition, two surface refrigeration plants totalling 14 300 kW were working as well. The number and capacity of underground refrigeration plants are expected to increase considerably in the future. So far refrigeration is being used by two-fifths of the mines, generally high production mines at great depth, and it is expected that more and more mines will find it imperative to use refrigeration in order to achieve maximum production.

Mechanical equipment for rockbreaking and ore transport includes over 18 000 rockdrills, 1 400 mechanical loaders, 23 500 scraper shovels and over 2 600 diesel locomotives. The diesel locomotives range in power from 15 kW to over 60 kW. Up to 220 diesels are used on one mine.

Of the air downcasting in the mines almost one third, that is 7 000 m³/s, is filtered to extract dust. This is because of the ore transport system in general use, which results in the handling of large quantities of dry ore in tips and loading boxes close to the downcast shaft. The dust produced would contaminate the whole mine if it were not removed. Practically all of the dust filters used underground are of the fabric type, mostly vertical bag — with a few sawdust beds and electrostatic filters.

The average rockbreaking depth below surface of the mines is almost 1 600 m (Table II). The average virgin rock temperature is 37 °C, that is, blood temperature. For individual mines the weighted mean rockbreaking depth below surface ranges from 120 m to over 2 800 m, the corresponding virgin rock temperatures being 19 °C and 46 °C, respectively. The deepest workings are over 3 400 m below surface, at a VRT of 52 °C. It must be

TABLE 11   WEIGHTED MEAN ROCKBREAKING DEPTHS

Year	Depth m	VRT °C
1964	1 318	33,9
1965	1 347	33,9
1966	1 380	35,0
1967	1 426	35,1
1968	1 456	35,4
1969	1 483	36,1
1970	1 545	36,8
1971	1 587	37,0

mentioned that most of the newer mines are at the greater depths and that the mines are generally going deeper and into hotter areas.

The environmental conditions prevailing underground are summarized in the tables below.

TABLE 12   ATMOSPHERIC ENVIRONMENT
44 GOLD MINES (1971)

A   TEMPERATURES

Development ends (excluding sinking vertical shafts)

Wet-bulb temp. °C	Total number		Av. wet-bulb temperature °C		Av. volume of ventilating air m³/s	
	Qtr. ending March	Qtr. ending Sept.	Qtr. ending March	Qtr. ending Sept.	Qtr. ending March	Qtr. ending Sept.
Below 27,5	499	926	25,3	24,8	2,9	3,1
27,5–29,0	460	555	28,4	28,4	3,2	2,9
29,1–31,0	885	820	30,1	30,0	3,2	2,9
31,1–33,0	735	358	32,0	31,9	3,0	2,7
Above 33,0	116	54	33,8	33,8	2,9	2,6
Grand total and averages	2 695	2 713	29,6	28,2	3,1	2,9

Stopes

Wet-bulb temp. °C	Total number		Av. wet-bulb temperature °C		Av. volume of ventilating air m³/s	
	Qtr. ending March	Qtr. ending Sept.	Qtr. ending March	Qtr. ending Sept.	Qtr. ending March	Qtr. ending Sept.
Below 27,5	762	281	24,5	24,4	0,58	0,66
27,5–29,0	525	726	28,3	28,3	0,69	0,83
29,1–31,0	1 190	929	30,1	30,0	0,92	1,02
31,1–33,0	813	385	31,8	31,7	1,23	1,36
33,1 and over	82	13	33,4	33,7	1,35	1,16
Grand total and averages	3 372	3 334	29,0	27,7	0,89	0,88

B   KATA THERMOMETER READINGS

Development ends (*excluding sinking shafts*)

Wet kata	Total number		Average kata	
	Qtr. ending March	Qtr. ending Sept.	Qtr. ending March	Qtr. ending Sept.
0,0–5,9	209	132	4,7	4,8
6,0–9,9	756	597	8,1	8,3
10,0 and over	1 722	1 988	14,8	16,1
Grand totals and averages	2 687	2 717	12,1	13,7

Stopes

Wet kata	Total number		Average kata	
	Qtr. ending March	Qtr. ending Sept.	Qtr. ending March	Qtr. ending Sept.
0,0–5,9	149	72	5,1	5,1
6,0–9,9	1 231	824	8,2	8,5
10,0 and over	1 979	2 447	14,0	15,0
Grand totals and averages	3 359	3 343	11,5	13,2

9   MAIN FANS

Most of the ventilating air is drawn from the surface down vertical or inclined shafts to depths averaging nearly 2 km below surface, for considerable distances through underground tunnels and workings before reaching the surface again.

The power to produce this air flow is provided by 235 main fans, of which 184 are installed on surface and 51 underground. Of these, 211 operate in upcast air, while 24 are downcast fans. 168 are centrifugal fans and 67 axial-flow. The largest motor is 2 460 kW and the smallest 37 kW. Most of these fans were installed during the past twenty years, though some have been working since 1938.

All the fans over 1 000 kW are centrifugal, and all but two of these are installed on surface at the upcast shaft. Pressures are up to 7 kPa. A detailed analysis is given in Table 13.

Air quantities handled by fans range from 15 to 322 m³/s. Of the 172 main underground booster fans 98 are of the axial-flow type and 74 centrifugal. Powers range from 50 to 1 000 kW, while pressures handling air volumes up to 150 m³/s are 0,5 to 6,0 kPa, respectively. Details are given in Table 14.

TABLE 13 MAIN FANS

kW	Surf-ace	Ugd.	Up-cast	Down-cast	Cen-tri-fugal	Axial	Diam. mm	Volume m³/s	Pressure kPa	Speed r/s	Type of fan
0–500	89	24	103	10	66	47	1 372–3 660	25,0–180,0	0,36–5,7	4,22–24,6	Cent.
							1 020–3 048	15,4–135,0	0,45–3,74	9,59–23,3	Axial
500–1 000	26	25	39	12	31	20	1 543–4 470	56,0–230,0	2,89–6,8	6,43–25,0	Cent.
							2 160–3 810	88,0–240,0	1,0–4,48	6,83–12,5	Axial
1 000–1 500	25	2	25	2	27		2 717–5 200	115,0–283,0	2,99–6,48	7,1–24,1	Cent.
1 500–2 000	22		22		22		2 921–5 200	219,0–284,0	3,99–6,74	10,0–12,5	Cent.
2 000–2 500	22		22		22		3 430–4 013	242,0–321,7	2,83–7,0	9,88–12,5	Cent.
Totals	184	51	211	24	168	67					

TABLE 14   BOOSTER FANS

kW	Centri-fugal	Axial	Diam. mm	Volume m³/s	Pressure kPa	Speed r/s	Type of fan
45–150	15	23	1 131–1 730	12,0–50,0	0,5–4,0	7,67–24,3	Cent.
			1 524–2 740	20,0–84,0	0,65–1,64	10,0–20,0	Axial
150–300	26	42	1 270–1 940	28,0–89,0	0,72–4,35	12,2–24,5	Cent.
			1 170–2 743	37,4–103,0	0,65–2,99	9,7–24,2	Axial
300–450	11	17	1 530–2 235	46,3–104,4	1,86–3,5	9,8–17,3	Cent.
			1 460–2 540	45,0–147,0	1,41–4,98	8,42–24,0	Axial
450–600	8	8	2 060–2 450	71,0–110,0	3,85–4,98	12,5–16,4	Cent.
			1 566–2 420	54,8–150,0	1,74–4,93	12,5–24,2	Axial
600+	14	7	1 430–2 500	90,0–142,0	3,74–6,0	12,2–25,0	Cent.
			2 300–2 490	48,0–94,4	2,06–5,48	12,3–12,5	Axial
Totals	74	98					

The total amount of power used on the mines for driving main and booster fans is 122 million kWh per month (167×10^3 kW) of which 100 million (137×10^3 kW) are used by surface fans and the balance by underground fans.

Efficiency is an important parameter in the process of fan selection. Most modern large fan installations operate at high static efficiencies, many at over 80 per cent. Because of the uncertainties of mining, it is never possible to lay out accurately the circuit that the air is to follow as one can in the case of a duct system in a factory, for example. It is, therefore, seldom practicable to plan to operate a backward aerofoil bladed fan at its peak efficiency, which may be 84 per cent or more, because of the need for "top cover" above the duty point.

In most mines twin main fans are used in parallel. Sometimes three or even four main fans are used in parallel. Multiple-fan installations have many advantages, among which are security and the fact that individual components are kept down to a reasonable size. With one fan in a twin installation stopped, the air quantity handled drops to about 70 per cent of the full volume. This is often acceptable for short periods. In three- and four-fan installations the effect of stopping one fan is correspondingly less. There are cases where, say, three fans are provided for ultimate use although only two will be needed for some years before the full duty is reached. This situation makes routine maintenance easy and also means that a lengthy breakdown of one unit can be accepted without difficulty. However, because of the capital cost involved, the installation of the third fan is often deferred until the full volume of air is required.

Where main fans are installed underground the installation should be so designed that there is no short-circuit between the fan intake and delivery. Such conditions would arise if the fan were installed close to an ore bin discharging in the shaft and accepting rock at a point on the discharge side of the fan. This situation can cause a great deal of trouble from upcasting of the orepass with consequent loss of fan capacity and contamination of the main downcast with dust. Such techniques as leaving a plug of ore in the ore bin are seldom successful, and it is worthwhile going to great lengths to avoid the use of any fan installation that can be complicated in this way.

In underground fan installations, particularly in the upcast, advantage has to be taken of natural barriers, such as dykes or faults, or unpay areas.

While refrigeration either by bulk cooling, whether on surface or underground, or by providing chilled water cooling close to the face, is the accepted and effective technique for dealing with high rock temperatures and great depths, other methods are being investigated.

Acclimatization has been in use on these mines for upwards of thirty-five years. By its use the dangers resulting from the exposure of men unaccustomed to hard work in very hot conditions have been largely avoided, and manual labour is safely and efficiently done in conditions where it would otherwise be virtually impossible.[8, 9] However, environmental engineering has to a large extent kept up with the greater depths of mining over the years so that conditions are in fact considerably better now at depths of 3 km than they were 20 or 30 years ago when the mines were much shallower.

A new development that shows great promise is the use of cool suits. These are jackets containing some 5 kg of ice arranged in pockets around the body. The jacket is worn over a light woollen vest. A foam-lined plastic over-jacket protects the wearer and prevents heat from outside from melting the ice prematurely.

For obvious reasons this device can be used only in very hot working places, that is, at 33 °C WB and over. However, once that condition is met the cool suit or ice jacket is acceptable, indeed, welcome, and the worker feels a sense of comfort and energy that is normally absent at such temperatures.

The ice jackets are worn for about $2\frac{1}{2}$ hours, after which time the ice has melted. A fresh ice jacket is then put on and the melted jacket is returned to the ice chamber for re-freezing. Two jackets normally see a workman through the shift, the last hour being spent on light tasks.

While it is doubtful at this stage whether cool suits will ever replace refrigeration as a full-scale method of ventilating, or rather cooling, very hot working places, there is no doubt that this method will have considerable value in protecting workers in awkward hot places, and that at the least it will save the industry a lot of money.

Finally, it may be said that mining engineers are very much aware of the problems posed by the increasing depths and the associated high temperatures. As stated by Mudd (1970)[10] "possibly the most important factor in underground mining is the efficient use of labour. It is becoming increasingly difficult to find men prepared to undertake heavy manual labour in hot and uncomfortable conditions. It may become imperative to mechanize, not because it is cheaper but because it is the only way to get the work done at all."

Mechanization as it may be applicable to the South African gold mines will certainly make fundamental changes to the whole structure of mining on these fields. However, when this comes about, ventilation techniques although possibly applied in different ways and to smaller numbers of workers, will still need to be advanced and sophisticated. There will always be much of interest to ventilation engineers in the methods used for ventilating these mines.

10   REFERENCES

1   Barcza, M. and Lambrechts, J. de V. Ventilation and air conditioning practice in S.A. gold mines. *Trans. Seventh Commonwealth Mining and Metallurgical Congress*, 1961.

2   Grave, D. F. H. Airflow resistance in downcast shafts equipped with streamlined buntons. *J. S. Afr. Inst. Min. Metall.*, Vol. 62, 1962, p. 604–11.

3   Lambrechts, J. de V. The value of water drainage in upcast mine shafts and fan drifts. *J. chem. Metall. Min. Soc. S. Afr.*, Vol. 56, 1956, p. 307–24.

4   Whillier, A. and Harrison, M. Private communication.

5   Forrest, H. M. Ventilation of development ends by the twin haulage method. *Bull. Mine Vent. Soc. S. Afr.*, Vol. 2, 1949, p. 3–7.

6   Jacobs, J. and Loubser, D. Development of twin haulages at depth to a distance of 12 500 ft. without artificial cooling. *Pap. D. Ass. Mine Mgrs. S. Afr.*, 1964–5, p. 229.

7   Whillier, A. and Louw, J. H. The cost of underground refrigeration. Chamber of Mines Research Report, No. 55/70, 1970.

8   Wyndham, C. H. and Strydom, N. B. Acclimatizing men to heat in climatic rooms on mines. *J. S. Afr. Inst. Min. Metall.*, Vol. 70, 1969, p. 60–4.

9   Kok, R. and Strydom, N. B. A guide to climatic room acclimatization. Chamber of Mines of South Africa Research Report No. 41/70, 1970.

10   Mudd, J. B. Mining technology in the future, Special Centenary paper. American Institute of Mining Engineers, 1970.

19   Underground Fires

H. M. W. ESCHENBURG

Chief Ventilation Officer, Harmony Gold Mining Company, Ltd.

1   INTRODUCTION

An underground fire is a major catastrophe since it endangers human life and interrupts productive mining operations. If fires occur in normal buildings on surface there are usually escape routes open to the people affected; in an underground fire it can very easily happen that escape routes are cut off either by the fire itself, by heat, or alternatively by gases. For these reasons alone it is of vital importance that in any underground situation all necessary precautions be taken to avoid the outbreak of a fire, and if a fire has in fact occurred, that the outbreak of the fire be reported immediately, the fire be located as quickly as possible, and that fire-fighting operations be started as quickly as possible.

It is essential that every man involved in a mine fire knows exactly what his functions are. It is important that all facilities, such as material and labour are provided as quickly as possible for the fighting of fires. Detailed fire-fighting manuals should be prepared on every mine. A brief resumé of what such a manual should contain will be given later on in the chapter.

2   FIRE PREVENTION

The basic rules for fire prevention are covered by the Mines and Works Act and Regulations, which provide for the establishment of a Fire Prevention and Control Organization, the provision of fire-fighting equipment, the storage and handling of explosives and the accumulation of combustible materials underground.

One of the needs in fire prevention is to obtain the co-operation of all mine employees in complying with the mining regulations. New employees, European as well as Bantu, should attend induction courses at the mine training centre and be lectured on the hazards of fires, the causes of fires and the precautions to be taken against the outbreak of fires.

These lectures must include an explanation of the Manager's code in connection with fires wherever they are necessary, and must include instructions on the use of igniter cord and other combustible materials. The course should include a short session on fire-fighting equipment and how it is to be used.

Mine employees should be kept aware of the dangers of underground fires and of the causes of underground fires. Regular meetings of officials and union men should therefore be held and all aspects of the causes of fires, particularly of recent fires, and their prevention and control discussed.

Reports of underground fires in the period 1970–1 have indicated the following to be the main causes: faulty electric equipment, oxy-acetylene cutting and welding apparatus, explosives, friction, accumulations of rubbish, methane gas, conveyor belts.

In 23 per cent of the occurrences the cause of a fire was given as unknown, but it is more likely that it originated from one of the causes listed.

2.1   *Electrical equipment*

Electric cables which are damaged could short-circuit and result in a fire, and if the cables are covered with PVC the burning of this material may produce poisonous phosgene gas and hydrochloric acid gas.

To prevent damage by sagging of timber support, cables should not be attached to such supports or installed between timber sets, and the side or hanging walls, but should be suspended by catenary wires.

In areas where machinery is being used, electric cables should be supported in such a way as to avoid damage by scraper ropes or trucks and hoppers. If it is unavoidable to have cables close to, or in contact with, timber sets, the latter should be made fire-proof. In areas where blasting takes place cables should be well protected and examined regularly to ascertain whether they are being crushed or over-tensioned. Cables leading into abandoned areas should be removed. Ideally, the power into stoping areas or working areas should be switched off in the off-shift periods, especially during blasting and at any time period during which there are no persons underground.

Electric sub-stations and battery charging stations should be located in positions where they are well ventilated. The floors should be of flame-proof material such as concrete, and should be kept scrupulously clean. Switchgear should be installed away from any supports constructed of combustible materials. In addition, such stations should be furnished with fire extinguishers. These should be placed on the intake side of the station in such a way that they can be reached in case of fire, without the person having to enter the gaseous atmosphere generated by the fire. Electric winches should be sited so that the timber supports are kept as far away from the winches as possible. Preferably, the timber supports around winches should be fire-proofed. A method of fire-proofing these supports is to coat the timbers with a vermiculite mixture, or a fire-proof paint. Winch chambers should be kept scrupulously clean. All old oil, grease and cleaning material should be removed daily. Earth leakage, over-load and thermal over-load protection should be tested regularly.

There are recorded instances of winches being started accidently, possibly by a fall of hanging which operated the switch, so that the motor ran unattended. Slipping of clutch bands on the clutches caused the clutches to become over-heated so that a fire was started. This is a good example of why electric power to stoping or working areas should be switched off in the off-shift period.

2.2 Oxy-acetylene cutting and welding

Hot metal or slag from welding operations can cause fires. It is therefore important that welding operations be conducted as far away as possible from inflammable material. Whenever welding or cutting operations are carried out, fire extinguishers should be close at hand. Before any welding or cutting is done in close proximity to inflammable material, the inflammable material should be wetted down thoroughly.

When cutting and welding are conducted in timbered shafts or haulages, buckets of sand should be used to catch any molten slag and hot pieces of metal so that they do not fall onto timber.

If burning or welding has been carried out in a timbered shaft, a special check for smoke should be carried out for an hour after these operations have ceased.

The operator of oxy-acetylene cutting equipment or electric welding equipment should, before leaving the place, make absolutely certain that all hot materials or hot pieces of metal, etc., are doused with water.

It is sometimes advantageous to use wet sacks as a protection over inflammable material in close proximity to welding and cutting operations.

When oxy-acetylene welding equipment is used, the bottles should always be kept in a vertical position and secured in such a way that they cannot fall over accidentally. It is particularly important that acetylene bottles should never be laid horizontally or with the neck down when they are being used. The regulators and valves must always be above the general level of the body of the cylinder.

A specific managerial instruction covering the use of oxy-acetylene cylinders should be available on every mine. A list of safety precautions can be obtained from the suppliers of oxygen and acetylene gas.

No welding, burning or cutting should be permitted anywhere near explosives or stocks of dieselene, oil or paint.

2.3 Explosives

Boxes of explosives should not be stored close to timber or in any areas in which timber is stored in large quantities. Mud blasting is an operation which is particularly liable to create fires and should be avoided wherever possible.

If timber supports have to be blasted out the explosives should be charged into a hole drilled into the footwall below the support or into the hanging wall above it. It is more than likely that if explosives are tied to the timber, the timber will be set alight.

Igniter cord should never be strung from pack to pack but should be kept well away from timber. The temperature of the burning igniter cord is more than sufficient to ignite the timber.

Managerial instructions should be issued on every mine, detailing exactly how igniter cord should be handled. These instructions should be comprehensive and should be issued in both official languages.

Where fuse igniters or cheesa sticks are used, they should be extinguished and not thrown away after use. It should be a standard rule that all cheesa sticks be returned to surface in their holders and that the remains of the cheesa sticks should still be in their holders. Where starters or timing candles are used they must be kept well away from combustible material.

The destruction of old explosives underground constitutes a fire hazard. Where it is standard practice to destroy old explosives underground in the form of mud blasts, all the surrounding areas must be well watered down. The maximum number of sticks of explosive should never exceed four in a single mud blast, and each blast should be set off by a separate detonator and fuse.

Old detonators should always be taken to surface for destruction. Old fuses and igniter cord, if they have to be destroyed underground, should be burnt only in places where it is impossible to create a fire such as inside an empty car. ANBA and ANFEX can be destroyed by dissolving them in water.

2.4   *Friction*

Fires may be caused by friction which results from the fouling of scraper ropes on sticks or packs and by the rubbing of moving machinery against timber. Heat generated by dragging clutches and brakes on electric winches may be sufficient to ignite oil, grease and other material. Jammed conveyor belts may ignite because of the friction caused by rubbing of the driving pulley against the conveyor belt.

Conveyor belt fires are usually extremely dangerous and serious, as conveyor belts are invariably installed in intake airways. It is therefore extremely important to ensure that conveyor belts are well protected. Conveyor belts should be safeguarded by the use of special devices which automatically switch the conveyor belt off, if the belt becomes stationary with the driving head still operating. Conveyor belts can be fitted with temperature sensing devices at the driving heads. If the temperature exceeds a pre-set value the installation is automatically tripped out. Proper installation and maintenance of equipment and frequent and regular inspection by responsible persons can avoid fires caused by friction.

2.5   *Accumulation of rubbish*

Fires in accumulations of rubbish may occur spontaneously. Any accumulation of combustible rubbish is a potential fire hazard and all rubbish should be removed to surface. Good "housekeeping" will prevent this type of hazard. All workshops should be equipped with bins for oil-soaked waste, etc.

Old workings should be cleared of all loose timber and then securely barricaded off. Ideally, old areas or access cross-cuts to old areas should, wherever possible, be walled off.

In those mines in which smoking is permitted underground, regular propaganda should indicate to smokers that cigarette ends and discarded matches are fire hazards. Smoking should never be permitted in a timber store, fuel store or any other place where inflammable materials are stored.

2.6 *Methane*

Burning methane or explosions of methane can ignite combustible material in the vicinity. Methane explosions in collieries can lead to coal dust explosions. Fortunately this type of explosion cannot occur in metal mines, but pure methane explosions have frequently occurred.

Methane burns at a temperature of 700°C. Timber ignites at well below this temperature, and it is, therefore, obvious that a methane ignition will ignite timber. Timber should not be placed under a methane fissure. A blast may ignite the methane at the fissure and the burning methane will then ignite any timber in the near vicinity.

3   DETECTION OF UNDERGROUND FIRES

3.1 *Fire patrols*

The most commonly used fire detector in mines is still the human nose. If any person smells burning, he should immediately report this fact to his superior and every effort should then immediately be made to locate the fire and to extinguish it.

The most common method of checking for fires after the blast is to use a fire patrol. Fire patrols should consist of two men, so that the patrollers travel in pairs in case of accident. Members of fire patrols must be in possession of valid first-aid certificates, as these men are usually underground when there is no other shift in the mine. The mine should be patrolled for fire as soon after the blast as possible, and before the normal night shift is allowed to enter. If this is done, the danger of sending a shift into a smoke-filled mine is reduced.

Bantu workers are usually used to patrol for fires. They should be selected from experienced, reliable, sober holders of first-aid certificates, who are physically fit, have a good sense of smell, are not colour blind, have a reasonable standard of literacy and are utterly reliable. These men are given a course of training and instruction in smoke detection, the dangers of carbon monoxide, and are given detailed instructions on what to do in case they detect a fire. The patrols normally fall under the ventilation department, whose duty it is to lay out the routes in consultation with the mining department in such a way that all working places underground are covered.

Ideally the fire patrol routes should be laid out in such a way that the detection of a fire at any specific point immediately localizes the area in which the fire is.

It is an advantage to make the fire patrol travel in the same direction as the ventilation air wherever possible. In doing so the patrol will pass the point or location of a fire and thus be able to pin-point a fire accurately. This method of patrolling is relatively easy in flat-dip mines.

It is of very little use to have, say, a single fire point at the top of the upcast shaft. Although this would make the detection of a fire simple, the fire would have to be relatively large before it could be detected, and it would then be a major task to locate the fire underground.

Fire patrol routes should be checked and reviewed at least quarterly. A plan showing all fire points and fire patrol routes should be kept at each shaft, preferably in the banksman's cabin.

The safety of fire patrol routes underground should be checked daily. A simple method of achieving this is to work on the double token system. If the double token system is used, the patrol men, before they proceed underground, collect a specific type of token, for instance, a triangular disc bearing the fire point numbers. They hang the discs at the individual fire points underground and remove a differently shaped disc, which they return to surface. In this way the supervisor has only to check the shape of the disc returned to the office in the morning to know that the fire patrol men in fact had been at that specific point. If these discs are then changed during the normal day shift by the normal mining personnel, the whole route is then automatically checked twice daily by different people, first by the fire patrol on their route, and then by the mining personnel during the day shift. Unfortunately this is not a standard procedure.

On some mines the fire patrol use alternating tokens. They use triangles on the first day exchanging them for squares, and then take the squares down on the second day, exchanging them for the triangles again. This system can lead to misuse by the fire patrol, unless a very tight check is kept and the patrol are extremely reliable.

A system with watchman's clocks has been used with varying degrees of success. In this system station keys are located underground at the individual fire points, and the fire patrol carries a clock into which the key carrying the station number is inserted. The clock contains a paper tape or recording chart, which makes it possible for the man in charge to check the following day whether every fire point underground has been visited. This system is expensive because of the cost of the clocks and the station keys. It is usual for the time as well as the station number to be printed onto the tape or chart. Care has to be taken that the fire patrol does, in fact, pause long enough at individual fire points to detect smoke if it is present. A method for ensuring this is to instruct the fire patrol to "key" every point twice, that is, to "clock in", wait for a pre-determined time period, for example, three minutes, and then to "clock out" from the same point again.

Fire patrols should be organized in such a way that the men leave surface as soon as possible after the blast, without being exposed to blasting fumes and high dust concentrations. This time interval can be determined by the ventilation department relatively easily. A simple method for determining how long it takes for smoke to clear is to do a physical check underground using a gas detector to determine whether noxious fumes are still present or, alternatively, to use tracer gases for determining how long it takes air to travel from the remotest point in the mine to the upcast shaft.

In some instances fire patrols report their progress underground by telephoning to a centralized point, such as the shaft bank. Standard procedures should be laid down for fire patrols to report back to such points at specific times and if no report is received a search party must be sent down to locate them. The mine overseer, through whose section the patrol travels, is normally responsible for the safety of the route through his section.

Where Bantu are used to patrol for fire they should not be permitted to cross newly-blasted points, and routes should therefore be laid out in such a way as to avoid this.

On mines where normal night-shift work is not conducted, it is desirable to do a second fire patrol some hours later. There have been numerous instances when the first patrol did not detect a fire as it was too small, but which in due course developed into a major conflagration.

It is useful occasionally to build a test fire underground to determine whether a fire patrol will in fact detect the fire and whether the fire patrol route is adequate.

3.2   Electronic fire detectors

A number of electronic fire-detecting devices have recently been placed on the market. These can be divided into two types, namely, ionization-type detectors and gas detectors.

The operation of the ionization-type detector depends on the principle of alteration by combustion products of the degree of ionization of air between two charged plates. This type of detector is relatively effective, provided that it is sufficiently close to the fire. Experience has indicated that a "smoke travelling-time" from the fire to the detector of less than ten minutes is desirable. If the detector is situated at a distance greater than this the products of combustion will usually have been precipitated from the air stream by the time the air reaches the detector so that the detector will be ineffective.

Other types of electronic detectors include carbon monoxide gas detectors. These units have the advantage that their operation is not affected by distance from the fire, but have the disadvantage that their efficiency is affected by dilution of the gas. They are sensitive enough to detect carbon monoxide at concentrations of 500 parts per million or less. These detectors are, however, expensive, intricate electronic devices and need fairly extensive maintenance.

Various methods of transmitting signals from the fire detectors to surface are used. The simplest system is to transmit the signals direct via one pair of wires to a suitable point in the mine or on surface. More complex systems operating on several different principles are available.

The efficiencies of all electronic detecting systems depend upon the amount of maintenance which they receive.

3.3   Fire masters

Some mines have appointed Fire Masters whose specific duties are to assist Mine Management in the prevention and detection of fires. Their duties normally include checking for underground fire hazards and mal-practices, checking fire detection installations and maintaining equipment, keeping fire plans up to date, assisting with training of personnel and routine control of fire patrols.

3.4   Fire meetings

Regular fire meetings attended by ventilation, mining and engineering personnel are held on some mines. At these meetings recent fires, fire prevention and protection methods are discussed. Experimental work being carried out in connection with fires is discussed. In this way a continual review can be made of improvements in fire-fighting equipment and techniques.

Mines should be divided into areas, and each area should have a risk

index. In this way high-risk areas and high-danger areas can be pin-
pointed. High-risk areas could be those in which a large number of people
work. Risk indices can be calculated by examining the hazards in each
area and allocating a point rating system as determined by the potential
danger involved.

(a) *Presence of combustible material.* Five points each for intake
airways, workings and probable extrent of fire.

(b) *Risk to lives.* Five points each for number of people in the zone,
alternative escape routes, complication of withdrawal procedures,
severity of exposure.

(c) *Source of ignition.* Three points each for electrical equipment,
fuel oil, methane, blasting operations, old explosives, smoking,
burning, cutting or welding operations, possibility of spontaneous
combustion.

(d) *Risk to essential services.* Five points each for damage to, or
operation of fans, damage to, or operation of water pumps, damage
to electric supply to essential services, lack of services essential
for fire fighting.

(e) *Loss of production.* Number of mine overseers' sections affected,
20 points.

If individual zones of the mine are assessed according to these risk
indices, and if a risk value is determined for each area, it will then immediately be apparent which areas are high-risk zones and which areas are
low-risk zones. The necessary improvements can then be made, or the
necessary precautions taken.

Each element of risk should be assessed in turn and the necessary
precautions taken to reduce the high ones. Installation of automatic fire
alarms and automatic sprinkler systems for individual items of equipment
in high-risk zones reduce the degree of risk. Fire doors reduce the size of
the area affected.

4   FIRE CONTROL

4.1   *Fire exercises*

Useful conclusions can be reached if individual ventilation departments
carry out fire exercises. The ventilation staff is called together in front of a
plan and a point is indicated as being the possible source of fire. Staff
members then express their views and ideas on how this fire could be
controlled and contained.

4.2   *Fire-fighting equipment*

Mines and Works Regulations require every mine to provide and maintain
suitable fire-fighting equipment. It is usually the duty of the Fire Master to
ensure that fire-fighting equipment is always in working order. When there is
no official Fire Master, it is essential that some other person be responsible
for the maintenance of the equipment.

4.3   *Water plans and reticulation*

Plans showing the water reticulation system should exist for every
underground manager's section or, better still, for every mine overseer's

section. These plans should show the locations of the pipes and of the main valves and their sizes. It is part of the duty of the ventilation officer on every mine to report to the manager on the water supply, its quality, distribution and use. High-risk areas, such as stores and underground timber stores should be equipped with water hoses connected to a good water supply.

4 . 4   Fire boxes and fire cars

On some mines it has been found useful to have fire boxes at the first-aid stations. These boxes should contain fire hoses and nozzles, as well as the necessary equipment by means of which the hose can be connected rapidly to underground mine water valves.

In many mines fire cars are held ready at all times on the shaft bank. These cars are loaded with fire-fighting equipment which should include portable fire extinguishers, lengths of perforated spray pipe, fire hoses together with adaptors and fittings, spray nozzles, the necessary tools for connecting fire hoses to standard piping, bags of vermiculite, vermiculite bricks, fire resistant brattice cloth, portable telephone, pumps, foam generators, light-weight ventilation doors and pre-cut shuttering.

4 . 5   Fire-fighting foam

Fires require oxygen, fuel and heat to propagate. Foam reduces oxygen content by generating water vapour which in turn removes heat and this prevents combustion. Foam can be a useful tool for reaching inaccessible fires. It must, however, be borne in mind that if foam is to be effective it must reach the fire.

The use of foam to fight fires means that air is in fact used to carry water to the fire. The fire control team must be absolutely certain that the foam can and will reach the fire and smother it. The amount of foam used must be such that it will reach the fire in sufficient volume to extinguish it.

If the foam breaks down before it has actually reached the fire, the oxygen present in the air inside the foam bubble will feed the fire.

4 . 6   Fire-fighting procedures

Once a fire has started, it is necessary that reporting of the outbreak of the fire, the exact location, and the provision of material and men for fighting the fire be done speedily.

A good fire-fighting manual will provide the information necessary for avoiding unnecessary confusion. Heads of departments must know exactly what they have to do and what their individual duties are.

The following sequence of events usually occurs if a fire breaks out between shifts :

(a)   the fire patrol detects the fire and reports to the banksman ;

(b)   the banksman reports to the shaft mine overseer, who reports to the underground manager, who in turn notifies the mine manager.

At the same time the underground manager notifies the ventilation officer, the resident engineer and the electrical and mechanical engineers. The personnel officer is involved in organizing labour, the manager of mining services or the chief of study are involved in organizing stores and material and this automatically involves the mine store.

Fire patrols must have clear instructions as to how to report and to whom to report. The banksman must have clear instructions as to what to do when he receives a fire report from a fire patrol, and the shaft mine overseer must have clear instructions as to what to do when he receives a report of a fire from the banksman.

At each shaft an office must be allocated which will automatically become the control office in the event of a fire, and all persons involved in fire-fighting operations must know which office it is. It is important that office space be allocated to each individual department involved.

A manual of the fire-fighting drill should be complete and precise.[1] The first section of the manual should specify precisely the duties of every senior man. Succeeding sections of the manual should then give in detail the duties of each individual control or departmental head.

Immediately after the fire has been detected all persons should be removed from the affected areas. During this period ventilation flows and volumes must be maintained in the same direction as they flow normally, particularly if the fire occurs during a shift. Mining personnel are aware of the air directions and flows in their individual sections. In most cases they know exactly which way to go to reach fresh air if they find themselves in a smoky atmosphere. If ventilation flows are altered in any way during the time when there is a maximum number of persons underground, the consequences could be serious.

Any alteration to the direction and volume of the ventilating current in any part of the mine may be undertaken only if the exact position and extent of the fire are known, and if the consequences of the alteration can be predicted exactly. Under no circumstances should any change in ventilation be undertaken without specific authorization from the Central Fire Control.

During any fire the progress of the fire can very often be gauged by monitoring critical parameters, such as carbon monoxide level, carbon dioxide level and air temperatures at specific points. By an intelligent evaluation of these three parameters, one can determine accurately what effect fire-fighting procedures and certain methods of attack have on the fire. It is indeed fortunate that with modern technology it has become possible to remotely and accurately monitor all three parameters.

At one stage monitoring of the return gases from a fire could only be done by persons equipped with self-contained breathing apparatus. This is no longer the case. Temperature monitoring equipment is available where readings can either be taken visually from a point in fresh air, or continuously recorded on a strip recorder. The same applies to the products of combustion. Infra-red analysers for continuously monitoring carbon monoxide and/or carbon dioxide levels on the return side of the fire are available. One such instrument is the Lira (Luft infra-red analyser) which is part of the Proto equipment of the Central Rescue Station of the Chamber of Mines.

Under monitoring, one should also consider search parties sent out to locate a fire. It is essential that search parties are accompanied by a ventilation official equipped with a canary and carbon monoxide detecting tubes, to enable monitoring of the air to be carried out.

During fire-fighting operations, "fresh air" crews are often used to transport material into the fire areas, to construct brattices and barricades, or to install water pipe columns. All "fresh air" parties in the fire areas should be continually monitored by persons equipped with canaries to guard against a sudden inrush of carbon monoxide gas. Detector tubes should also be used, as it is a well-known fact that canaries are not affected by low levels of carbon monoxide which can be lethal to man.

5   REFERENCE

1   Procedures in Case of Fire at Harmony Gold Mine. Association of Mine Managers of South Africa, Papers and Discussions 1966–7, p. 39–67.

20   Compressed Air Control

W. L. LE ROUX

Productivity Manager, Buffelsfontein Gold Mining Company, Limited.

1   INTRODUCTION

Compressed air is a very useful and safe source of energy for many mining applications, especially for operating percussion rockdrills. Unlike steam, it can be transported over long distances and, unlike electricity, the air and the machines which it is used to drive are hardly affected by the moisture which is usually present in mine workings. Machines driven by compressed air can stand up to rougher handling than electrical machinery. Furthermore, unskilled labour can be used to connect up air-driven machines to the mains and to run the machinery at any required speed without danger of electrocution or of causing electrical short-circuits which would immobilize other machinery in the same section of the mine.

For these reasons, compressed air is used extensively in the South African gold mines, and as a result of these very same useful characteristics of safety and availability, it is also very extensively abused.

2   SOURCES OF COMPRESSED AIR

Some mines buy compressed air from a central compressor station and pay for it at an agreed price for each unit passing through a meter on the mine property. Most mines, however, have one or more compressor stations of their own and calculate the cost of an air unit by dividing the total cost of air production by the number of air units metered on the discharge side of the compressors.

The performance of compressors is in many respects comparable with that of fans. A centrifugal compressor has a stall point, its efficiencies vary from very low at free delivery to a maximum near the stall point, and generally the fan laws apply when allowance is made for the compressibility of air.

While a centrifugal compressor is capable of delivering a large range of air volumes over a large range of pressures, it can supply only a particular volume at a particular pressure and at a definite efficiency, unless its running speed is variable or unless some other type of control is incorporated. The speed of an electrically driven compressor is seldom variable. If, during part of the day, more air is required from it than it was primarily designed for, it can supply this increased air quantity only at a reduced pressure and with loss of efficiency. If, on the other hand, less than the design quantity is required temporarily, the compressor is likely to stall and a by-pass valve has to be opened to blow off some of the air to the atmosphere, unless the compressor has inlet vane control. By partially closing the vanes a smaller quantity can be obtained at the desired pressure, but with a considerable reduction in efficiency.

The speed of a steam-driven compressor is easily altered by adjusting the supply of steam, but the production of steam in the boilers is not as easily adjusted and therefore every variation in steam requirement must affect the efficiency of the boilers.

The aim should thus be to ensure as constant a load as possible. It may, for example, be possible to arrange that air-consuming processes such as sand-blasting, agitation of mud sumps and the use of air winches and loaders are not conducted during the drilling shift, but considerable variation in air requirements will still be found unavoidable and these variations must be catered for in at least two of the following three ways:

(a)   Several compressors of different capacities must be provided so that judicious combination of these will give approximately the required load at all times of the day.

(b)   Some compressors with variable speed or inlet vane control must be provided to give the desired flexibility when run alone or in conjunction with other compressors.

(c)   Ample storage capacity should be provided to smooth out momentary fluctuations in load. For this reason air receivers are usually installed at the compressor stations and at strategic points along the routes of the air mains. In large mines money is often wasted in this way because the capacity of the receivers is negligible in comparison with the capacity of the great length of large-diameter mains. In a few South African mines, however, benefits have been derived from the provision of very large receivers in the form of isolated rock tunnels with capacities of some thousands of cubic metres.

3   METERING OF COMPRESSED AIR

All gold mines need a continuous supply of compressed air. The continuous process of gold extraction needs air for agitation of the contents of certain tanks. Air is needed for operating the brakes of hoists. In some instances fans and pumps driven by compressed air are also required to run continuously.

Other processes are intermittent. On a producing mine most of the rockdrills work for only a limited period during the morning shift, during which period all air fans and pumps are also working. Air-driven loaders and scrapers are operated mostly during the morning and night shifts, while water blasts consume a large quantity of air at the end of the morning shift and at the beginning of the night shift.

Some of these processes require high air pressures whereas others require only relatively low air pressures. Each mine has its own pattern of consumption which again changes as the mine reaches different stages of development.

It is essential, in order to be able to study and control the flow of air to different parts of a mine at all times of the day, to have recording metering devices operating at strategic points.

Most flow meters record the pressure difference across an orifice plate in an air column (see Chapter 13). This pressure difference is proportional to the square of the air volume flowing through the orifice and is usually recorded on a chart which is graduated to give readings directly proportional to the volume flowing.

Other meters, such as the F.M.L., have swinging gates which measure the mass of air flowing through them and at the same time act as non-return valves.

Recording pressure gauges can be either independent or combined with flow meters.

Orifice-type meters offer some resistance to the flow of air and care should therefore be taken not to install too many of them in series. In some cases the installation of venturi tubes or Dall tubes, which are much more expensive than orifice plates, but which cause a much smaller pressure loss, can be justified economically.

4   UNITS OF COMPRESSED AIR

In most instances it is not the amount of air which is available that is of importance, but the amount of energy which is stored in that air and which can be used for driving machinery. It is therefore basically correct that, in costing, a figure should be arrived at for the cost per unit of energy in the air and not a cost per unit mass or volume of air. Such a unit was defined in a Power Agreement arrived at between various parties on the Witwatersrand in 1909. The *Air Unit* represents the amount of air power which one kilowatt-hour of electricity would generate under certain accepted conditions, assuming an overall isothermal compressor efficiency of 64,1 per cent.

Thus one air unit comprises:

15,7 cubic metres of free air compressed to 400 kPa gauge pressure
or 14,2 cubic metres of free air compressed to 500 kPa gauge pressure
or 13,2 cubic metres of free air compressed to 600 kPa gauge pressure
or 12,4 cubic metres of free air compressed to 700 kPa gauge pressure.

Mines which produce their own compressed air, however, find it more convenient to use a unit of volume. The electric power which is required to compress 1 000 m^3 of air costs about 35 cents, while the power required to compress 1 m^3 of air per second costs about R1,25 per hour or R30 per 24-hour day. When capital and maintenance costs are added, these figures are increased appreciably.

5   AIR CONSUMPTION OF VARIOUS APPLIANCES

Table I gives the approximate amount of air consumed by some commonly used appliances and wasted by leakage. These figures, of course, vary with the type and condition of the appliance and with the air pressure. In the last column the annual cost is given of running these appliances continuously, assuming an air pressure of 500 kPa and the cost of air as given above.

TABLE I

Appliance	m³/s free air	Cost per annum for continuous running
Jackhammer	0,060	R 660
Drifter	0,066	730
Venturi	0,024	260
400 mm air fans	0,070	770
25 mm water blast	0,230	2 530
Cameron pump 4 × 2	0,028	310
Cameron pump 6 × 3	0,066	730
Cameron pump 8 × 4	0,123	1 350
Cameron pump 10 × 5	0,165	1 820
Cameron pump 12 × 7	0,198	2 200
Quimby pump	0,076	840
Turbine motor 11 kW	0,151	1 660
Turbine motor 15 kW	0,203	2 230
Mechanical loader	0,137	1 500
Diamond drill	0,090	1 000
5 mm leak	0,030	330
10 mm leak	0,120	1 300
25 mm leak	0,750	8 250

6   OPTIMUM AIR PRESSURE

The rate of production of a gold mine depends to a very large extent on the number and depth of blasting holes drilled daily into the hard rock. For this a large number of rockdrill machines are required, each machine being handled by two persons. Thus an appreciable percentage of under-ground productive labour is employed on drilling. The speed of penetration of a rockdrill is dependent to a very large extent on the air pressure supplied to the machine. In fairly hard ground a typical machine on these fields could, for example, drill:

> 50 mm per minute with air at 300 kPa pressure
> *or* 150 mm per minute with air at 400 kPa pressure
> *or* 220 mm per minute with air at 500 kPa pressure.

Specially designed machines can attain still greater rates of penetration if supplied with air at pressures of over 700 kPa, and these machines are also lighter.

High drilling pressures can thus result in an increased number of holes being drilled by a smaller labour force. At the same time less air is used for drilling the same length of hole with high pressures than with low pressures.

In practice, the maximum available drilling pressure is determined by the capacities of the compressors, the pressures that can be withstood safely by the air pipes and hoses, and the loss of pressure due to friction in the pipes connecting the compressors and the machines.

In some equipment, such as mechanical loaders, pumps, winches, riveters and fans, a certain minimum pressure is required for efficient working, but it is usually found that the safety of either the machine itself or of the work being done by it also limits the practical maximum working pressure. For this reason these appliances are often throttled down during the drilling shift. In nearly all cases, with mechanical loaders the possible exception, a pressure of 400 kPa at these appliances is ample.

A pressure of 300 kPa is usually sufficient for all other applications such as Browns tanks, Oliver filters, water blasts, hoists, brakes, mud sump agitation, blowing-out of electric motors and assay crushers, etc.

Based on his knowledge of the requirements of his mine, the Compressed Air Supervisor should prepare a timetable for the guidance of the compressor station operators, showing the limits between which pressures may be allowed to vary at different times of the day.

In drawing up this timetable, it must be recognized that there is a natural increase in the gauge pressure of air travelling down a deep mine. This is due to the difference between the density of the air inside the air column and that of the air outside it. The following tabulation shows how the pressure increases with depth.

TABLE II

Depth in metres	Air pressures (kPa)			
0	400	500	600	700
500	430	524	640	750
1 000	460	580	690	800
1 500	490	610	730	850
2 000	530	650	780	900
2 500	560	690	820	950
3 000	590	730	870	1 010
3 500	620	770	910	1 060
4 000	650	800	960	1 110

From this tabulation it can be seen that on afternoon shift and on Sundays when the consumption of air and consequently also the friction loss in the mains are very low, a pressure of 400 kPa at the compressors can be sufficient for the efficient working of Cameron pumps underground, and a night shift pressure of 400 kPa might be sufficient for the operation of a mechanical loader in a deep development end.

7   LOSS OF PRESSURE IN PIPES AND HOSES

When air flows in a pipe or hose, frictional and shock losses occur just as happens with ventilation currents, and these cause a drop in pressure. D'Arcy's formula for calculating the pressure drop in an air column is very similar to Atkinson's equation which is used in ventilation calculations. The most significant factor is that the pressure drop is proportional to the *square* of the air volume flowing. Thus, doubling the amount of air flowing results in a four-fold increase in the pressure loss, and trebling the air flow increases the pressure loss by a factor of nine. (This subject is dealt with in detail by Hemp.[1])

The following tabulations are useful for calculating the pressure losses in pipes and hoses with various rates of air flow.

TABLE III   LOSS OF PRESSURE IN AIR HOSES AT 500 kPa GAUGE PRESSURE
(For old hoses with many menders these figures may be doubled)

m³/s free air	Pressure drop in kPa			
	25-mm hose		32-mm hose	
	30 m	60 m	30 m	60 m
0,05	22	44	5,5	11,0
0,06	37	74	10,0	20,0
0,07	65	130	17,5	35,0

TABLE IV

Pipe diameter		Cubic metres per second of free air that would give a pressure drop of 2 kPa per 100 metres			
mm	inches	at 400 kPa gauge	at 500 kPa gauge	at 600 kPa gauge	at 700 kPa gauge
25	1	0,005 8	0,006 4	0,006 9	0,007 4
51	2	0,037	0,041	0,044	0,047
102	4	0,24	0,26	0,28	0,31
152	6	0,71	0,79	0,85	0,91
203	8	1,50	1,67	1,80	1,92
254	10	2,79	3,10	3,35	3,59
305	12	4,58	5,07	5,49	5,89
356	14	6,82	7,56	8,17	8,76
406	16	9,90	11,0	11,86	12,7
457	18	13,5	15,0	16,2	17,4
508	20	17,8	19,7	21,3	22,8
559	22	23,4	25,9	28,1	30,0
610	24	28,6	31,6	34,2	36,8
660	26	36,5	40,4	43,6	46,8
711	28	44,2	48,9	53,0	56,7

Assumptions: (1)   Used pipes in good condition.   (2)   1 m³ of free air = 1 kg.

The advantages of using 32-mm hoses rather than 25-mm hoses on drilling machines, especially when the hoses are long and the machines consume large quantities of air, are illustrated in Table III.

It is often found in practice that the hoses supplying certain equipment with air are much too small. The result is that this equipment does not work efficiently. Table V gives an indication of the size of hose which should be used for various items of equipment.

An anachronism from the past is the old rule-of-thumb that the number of machines that can be supplied by an air column is equivalent to the square of the pipe diameter in inches. Thus a 102-mm (4-inch) pipe would

TABLE V

Equipment	Minimum size of pipe or hose	
	mm	inches
Cameron pump	38	$1\frac{1}{2}$
Larger Cameron pumps	51	2
Quimby pump	38	$1\frac{1}{2}$
Reciprocating winch 5 × 7	38	$1\frac{1}{2}$
Reciprocating winch 6 × 8	51	2
Turbine motor 11 kW	51	2
Turbine motor 15 kW	51	2
Mechanical loader (small)	51	2
Diamond drill	38	$1\frac{1}{2}$

be able to feed sixteen machines and a 254-mm (10-inch) pipe a hundred machines, etc. This is a fallacy which is probably the root cause of many existing ineffective reticulation systems, and the sooner it is forgotten, the better. In its stead, Table VI should be used. The values in this table are based on a pressure drop of 2 kPa per 100 m of piping and are therefore suitable for calculating the number of machines that may be used on long columns. For short columns the load may be increased by 50 per cent if necessary. In determining the number of machines to be supplied from a pipe, other equipment must be taken into account, each fan being counted as one machine, each scraper winch as three machines, and pumps according to their sizes.

TABLE VI

A 51 mm (2 inch) pipe can supply 1 machine
A 102 mm (4 inch) pipe can supply 5 machines
A 152 mm (6 inch) pipe can supply 15 machines
A 203 mm (8 inch) pipe can supply 30 machines
A 254 mm (10 inch) pipe can supply 55 machines
A 305 mm (12 inch) pipe can supply 85 machines

8   THE RETICULATION SYSTEM

The basic facts that have to be known before the optimum size of a new air pipe can be determined are the final length of the column and the maximum quantity of air that will be required during the drilling shift. This latter is seldom predictable to any degree of accuracy, but a fair estimate can usually be made on the basis of the number of appliances which will be used during the drilling shift and a reasonable allowance for leakage and wastage. As a first estimate of the compressed air requirements of a gold mine, a useful empirical rule is that one cubic metre of compressed air is required per second during the peak period of the shift for each 6 000 tons of rock broken per month. This estimate has to be adjusted in the light of conditions applying at the particular mine.

In practice the reticulation system can be divided into three main parts. First, there are the mains which lead from the compressor stations to the shafts, down the vertical and incline shafts and along the main haulages. The total length of any such column is often of the order of 5 000 to 10 000 metres. Second, there are branch pipes which lead from the shafts or haulages to the working areas, stopes or development ends as the case may be. These are seldom more than about 2 000 metres long. Third, there are the service pipes or hoses which lead from the branches to the appliances. These are seldom longer than 200 metres.

Air main installations are permanent installations with a life of 20 to 40 years. Branch pipe installations are semi-permanent with a life of 5 to 10 years, and service pipe installations are temporary.

Large pipes are usually of sizes of 51 mm (2 inches) different in diameter, such as 254, 305, 356 and 406 mm, and the problem is to decide when the use of the next larger size becomes justified. By balancing the cost of the loss in energy due to friction against the capital cost of larger columns, it can be shown that this is the case when the pressure drop is of the order of 2 kPa per 100 metres length of column, but because of the permanency of the mains and the fact that future air requirements cannot be predicted accurately, it is suggested that the following maxima be used for design purposes:

1 kPa pressure drop per 100 m for mains
2 kPa pressure drop per 100 m for branches
40 kPa pressure drop per 100 m for service pipes.

Thus, when the air requirements have been decided on, the required size of pipe for branch lines can be read off directly from Table IV. For mains, the quantity must not exceed 70 per cent of the values given in Table IV. For service pipes the load should not be more than four times the value given in Table IV.

The tables given here can be used for solving all kinds of problems relating to the reticulation of compressed air, such as the three examples below.

PROBLEM 1

A new section of a mine is expected to use twenty machines, three fans, one large pump and two air winches. What size of pipe is required?

ANSWER

Count the pump as two units, each winch as three units. The total is 31 units. From Table VI, a 203-mm (8-inch) pipe can cope with 30 machines. If the section is near the shaft and not likely to expand, 203-mm pipe should be used. Otherwise 254-mm should be used. This accommodates 55 machines but does not cost very much more.

PROBLEM 2

The pressure drop over 1 500 m of 305 mm air main is 90 kPa. The mean pressure is 600 kPa approximately. What quantity of air is flowing?

ANSWER

From Table IV it can be found that for a pressure drop of 2 kPa per 100 m of 305-mm (12-inch) pipe, at a pressure of 600 kPa, the air quantity flowing is 5,49 m³/s.

The actual pressure drop per 100 m length of pipe is

$$\frac{90}{15} = 6 \text{ kPa per } 100 \text{ m}$$

The air quantity flowing is thus

$$5,49 \times \sqrt{\frac{6}{2}} = 9,50 \text{ m}^3/\text{s}$$

PROBLEM 3

A large section of a mine served by a 305-mm (12-inch) main uses 4,8 m³/s during the peak period. Extension of work on this section is expected to treble the air consumption. The main is 1 600 m long and the average pressure at the beginning of the main is 500 kPa. The supervisor is asked for his recommendations.

ANSWER

From Table IV, at a gauge pressure of 500 kPa, a 305–mm main can carry 5,07 m³/s for a pressure drop of 2 kPa per 100 m or 32 kPa per 1 600 m.

∴ The pressure drop at present is approximately equal to

$$\left(\frac{4,8}{5,07}\right)^2 \times 32 = 28,7 \text{ kPa}$$

If the quantity is trebled to 14,4 m³/s without adding to the 305-mm main, the pressure drop will become

$$28,7 \times \left(\frac{14,4}{4,8}\right)^2 = 258,3 \text{ kPa}$$

Two alternatives present themselves, namely, replacing the main by a pipe of larger diameter or by installing another column parallel to it. In each case the aim should be to reduce the pressure drop to 1 kPa per 100 m or 16 kPa for the 1 600 m. The quantities shown in Table IV correspond to a pressure drop of 2 kPa per 100 m and for half this pressure drop these quantities therefore have to be divided by $\sqrt{2}$ or multiplied by 0,7 which is the simpler method. Table IV at 500 kPa pressure then becomes:

Pipe diameter		Capacity for 1 kPa
mm	inches	loss per 100 m
305	12	3,5
356	14	5,3
406	16	7,7
457	18	10,5
508	20	13,8
559	22	18,1

From these figures it is obvious that in order to convey 14,4 m³/s the 305-mm pipe would either have to be replaced by a 508-mm (20-inch) pipe, or it would have to be supplemented by a 457-mm (18-inch) pipe in parallel with it (3,5 + 10,5 = 14,0), although in each case using the next smaller size would not cause a very serious pressure loss. In practice it would probably be found that the difference in cost between a 457-mm pipe and a 508-mm pipe would be less than a quarter of the cost of a 305-mm pipe and consequently a 508-mm would be installed and the 305-mm pipe reclaimed for use elsewhere.

Ring-feeds have both advantages and disadvantages. If the air column feeding one section or level is overloaded while that in a nearby section or level has spare capacity, pressure in the former area can often be improved considerably by cross-connecting the two columns. A further advantage is that, when one of the columns becomes damaged, neither section is completely starved of air. In practice, however, the pressures in both sections usually become so low while the one feed is out of commission, that neither can do any effective drilling. Other disadvantages are that a burst pipe in one section immediately affects both sections, and that an inadvertently closed valve in the one feed can result in low pressures in both sections which may persist for several days before the cause is discovered. Except in isolated cases, ring-feeding should therefore be used only between major sections of a mine.

9   COMPRESSED AIR CONTROL

On most mines a Compressed Air Supervisor controls the production and distribution of compressed air. Such an official must have, in addition to a thorough understanding of the principles controlling the production, distribution and use of compressed air, a clear knowledge of mining, engineering and ventilation practices on his mine and, of course, he must know his mine intimately.

It is essential that there should be only one supervisor for the control of all compressed air — both surface and underground — and that he should be independent of all consumer departments so as to be in a position to report without bias on all matters deserving attention.

The Supervisor's first duty is to guard against wastage of air. In order to be able to do so he should make regular inspections of all air columns, more especially those in isolated parts of the mine. Any leaks found must be reported and repairs checked. Where a branch pipe or service pipe leads to an area which no longer requires a supply of air, closing the valve is not sufficient. The pipe must be disconnected and blanked. Many instances can be quoted where such a valve had been left open inadvertently and where the pipe inside the working place was later broken by a fall of hanging, resulting in a considerable loss of air before it was discovered. In one instance on record a 51-mm (2-inch) pipe was left blowing freely for several years under a surface rock dump.

No buried air pipes should be permitted anywhere except when a leak from the pipe would be detected immediately by a permanent meter. The practice of burying air pipes at workshops and reduction works is, in particular, much too prevalent. The ground above buried pipes, where they exist, must be inspected during rainy weather when leaks will be indicated by bubbles issuing from the wet ground.

The branch lines and, where possible, the mains serving working areas, must be shut off during the off-shifts in these areas. In developing areas this cannot be done till twenty minutes after the blast, but in stoping areas it can be done at least thirty minutes before the blast. Practical experience has shown that the only way of ensuring that all these valves are closed off daily at the correct time is to have this work done by a person directly responsible to the Compressed Air Supervisor. In many situations branch valves must be opened during the night shift because one isolated place in the area requires air. This will necessitate one of the Supervisor's assistants checking that the subsidiary branches to all other parts of the area concerned are closed off.

On the basis of his knowledge of the requirements of his mine, the Supervisor has to prepare an ideal pressure chart for the guidance of the compressor station operators.

When complaints regarding low pressures at any isolated working place are received the Supervisor should, rather than increase the pressure at the main station, consider the economics of either enlarging the sizes of pipes serving such a working place or supplying a booster compressor to serve it.

Recording flow-meters and pressure recorders must be installed at strategic points. These must be maintained and calibrated regularly by the Supervisor. A careful study of the charts will show where air wastages and unusual pressure losses are occurring.

The study of these charts and the distribution of daily lists of figures to all concerned, can easily be overdone. Highlighting malpractices is much more effective than lists of figures.

The leakage from an inaccessible pipe system, such as buried pipes on surface or mains down a vertical shaft, should be checked occasionally by closing valves to isolate all the legitimate consumers for a period of five to ten minutes. Any flow of air during this period indicates either a leak or a faulty valve. A positive check can be made of valves by closing them and opening taps on the discharge sides and observing whether the flow stops after a few minutes.

Pressure recorders, which are much cheaper and more easily installed than recording flow meters, are very useful in that they indicate any serious leakage and also act as a check on the times at which the different valves are closed.

A large amount of compressed air is wasted when it is used to cool men or machinery. Such cooling can be achieved much more effectively and cheaply by means of fans, but unfortunately it is so much easier to use compressed air. A very strict attitude has to be adopted by the mine management if this kind of abuse is to be avoided and no exceptions must be allowed.

An audible leak from a joint or a valve spindle on a shaft bank may account for a wastage of as little as 0,01 cubic metres of air per second, costing little more than one cent per hour, but it constitutes an indirect cost in the form of negative propaganda value.

To some extent the wastage of air during the drilling shift can be counteracted by propaganda, such as by quoting examples which show how the wastage of air in one miner's section can reduce drilling speeds in another miner's section.

With Cameron pumps, the same principle holds good as with drilling machines, namely, that any set amount of work can be done more cheaply when using the highest available air pressures than when using reduced air pressures. Often large pumps are seen to be working sluggishly off a 25-mm (1-inch) air feed. When it is pointed out that the pump would work much faster if supplied with a 51-mm feed, the reply might be made that there is not enough water to permit faster pumping so that the pump has to be throttled down in any case. Obviously such a pump is too big for the job and should either be replaced by a smaller pump or a sufficiently large sump should be provided which will permit intermittent pumping; a sump large enough to eliminate pumping during the drilling shift would be ideal.

Air is used for agitation in mud sumps, Brown's tanks and lime-mixing tanks. In each of these situations it is so easy to use more air than is required. The minimum effective quantity must be determined experimentally and consumption must be limited to this quantity by metering or by baffling the feed. In some cases it may be expedient to use high-pressure water jets instead of air jets for agitating mud sumps.

The air pressures at drilling machines should be checked regularly and, when these are not satisfactory, the cause must be investigated. If the columns serving the section are not too small, the reason for low pressure is usually leakage or other wastage of air, or faulty valves. Two persons equipped with reliable pressure gauges are required for checking the pressure losses along a line. The two gauges are fitted to the column about 300 m apart and several readings are taken simultaneously at pre-arranged times. The first gauge is then moved a few hundred metres beyond the second, and the process repeated. By this "leap-frog" method long distances can be checked during the course of a few hours. Speed is essential because this kind of work should be done only during the peak drilling period which is of short duration. Very often such a survey will reveal considerable losses of pressure over faulty valves.

All unnecessary valves should be removed. It is not advisable to provide a large number of valves for use in all emergencies, because it is better that drilling in a whole section should have to be stopped occasionally because of a burst air main, than to have a whole section permanently suffer low pressure, because even good valves cause a pressure loss and there is always the danger that one of the valves will be out of order or partly closed.

A rapid method of determining whether the hose serving an appliance is large enough is to insert a hypodermic needle gauge in the hose near the appliance and to observe the difference in pressure when the appliance is working and when it is stopped. If there is a big difference the test should be repeated near the other end of the hose. If there is also a big difference at that end, then there is a restriction in the branch pipe — otherwise it is in the hose.

10   REFERENCE

1   Hemp, R. The calculation of pressure drops in compressed air columns. *J. Mine Vent. Soc. S. Afr.*, Vol. 23, 1970, p 191–6.

BIBLIOGRAPHY

Compressed Air Handbook, Application Equipment,
Engineering Data and Test Procedure, Compressed Air and Gas Institute,
   New York.
The Compressed Air Unit, Rand Mines Compressed Air Department.
   Unpublished Report 16th April 1953.
Le Roux, W. L. Compressed air control, *J. Mine Vent. Soc. S. Afr.,* Vol. 9,
   1956, p 426–45.
Leimer, L. O. W. and McKechnie, R. M. K. The installation and operation
   of an underground compressed air receiver at Welkom No. 2 Shaft,
   Association of Mine Managers of South Africa. *Papers and Dis-
   cussions* 1970/71, p 27–47.

21 Mine Ventilation Economics

J. DE V. LAMBRECHTS

Professor of Mining Engineering, University of Pretoria

1 INTRODUCTION

This chapter is an attempt to state in simple language those fundamentals and commonsense "money" rules with which the mine ventilation engineer should be acquainted when giving practical advice on the planning and execution of mine ventilation schemes.

Sections 2 to 6 deal with general economic and money principles, the points being illustrated by simple arithmetic examples with a ventilation flavour.

Sections 7 to 11 deal with the application of these principles to mine ventilation problems.

2 THE ECONOMICS OF ALTERNATIVES

The principles of ventilation economics do not differ from those of general engineering economics. In contrast to the economist's broad approach to financial matters, the engineer's function is usually limited to a choice between alternatives; he has to state the alternatives and help to make a selection. The selection which the ventilation engineer makes may or may not be ideal from a design engineer's point of view, and a compromise frequently proves to be the most economical. For example, a perfect and expensive aerodynamical design for the bend at the top of an upcast shaft may prove to be less economical than a compromise design. Conversely, the cheapest fan or other layout may also not be the most economical.

The ventilation engineer does not have to decide whether his company should open up a new mine, but he has to consider alternative shaft shapes, sizes and equipment for that mine shaft. The decision to drive certain airways frequently requires no particular engineering or management skill but the ventilation engineer should consider the alternatives of different sizes or perhaps even different methods of support. It requires no ingenuity to decide that a mine must be ventilated by main fans but the ventilation engineer should be capable of selecting the most economical (not necessarily the cheapest) fans for the purpose.

The above are just a few examples to illustrate the statement that the ventilation engineer's application of economic principles is usually concerned only with a choice between alternatives and not with the more basic question of whether the job should be done at all.

At the same time it should be noted that these choices cannot always be based on economic considerations alone but must often be tempered with other practical considerations because "ventilation" is frequently not the sole purpose of doing or not doing a certain thing in mining.

3   MONEY, INTEREST AND TIME

3.1   *Capital* can have various definitions, but in the context of this chapter on mine ventilation economics it is regarded as money spent on buying or acquiring fixed assets such as large fans, mine shafts, airways, cooling plants, etc. This definition can, however, be extended to smaller items of equipment, for example, small fans or a microscope or a spotcooler, in which case such items may actually be included under working costs in the company's costing system, although for purposes of an economics study the ventilation engineer may treat them as items of capital expenditure. In fact, it matters little where the money comes from; this is the financiers' business. The point is that whether the money has to be borrowed, or whether it already lies idle in the bank, or whether it is deducted from working profits all amounts to the same thing in the ventilation engineer's approach to economics.

It is outside the scope of this chapter to delve deeply into subtle distinctions between capital and working costs and the practising ventilation official will be well advised to acquaint himself with his company's internal policy by discussing the problem with a cost accountant or other financial adviser.

3.2   *Interest* is the payment which one makes for the use of money for buying things. This could be money borrowed from someone else or it could be one's own or company money. The argument in the latter case is simply that if the money were not spent on, say, a fan or an airway, it could be invested elsewhere and be earning interest, and money *not* earned in this way is the same as spending that money. Interest is invariably expressed as per cent per year and calculation of interest for periods of less than a year seldom enters into engineering economics. Interest rates vary from time to time, depending on the money market and whatever figure is used should be in keeping with the mining company's internal policy. A figure of 9 per cent is typical under present-day conditions.

There should be no confusion between "simple" and "compound" interest; there is in fact only one kind of interest. What is meant by compound interest is really that interest earned in one year is compounded with or added to the capital in the following and successive years so that the capital increases gradually. It is better to think of "compounding of interest" when talking about "compound" interest, bearing in mind that the interest itself does not differ at all from simple interest. Compound interest is always implied in economics studies.

3.3   The *time* value of money is an important concept which should be clearly grasped. R100 today, at 6 per cent interest will be worth R106 in one year's time and R112,36 in two years' time (R106 + 6 per cent of R106= R112,36), and in 15 years' time it will be worth R239,66. The important thing to remember is that the value of money is never static, but must be judged in relation to time and, of course, in relation to the interest rate. Money doubles itself in about 18 years at 4 per cent, in 14 years at 5 per cent and in 12 years at 6 per cent.

That the purchasing power or the *real* worth of money should depreciate or "devalue" with time as a result of inflation is another matter which will not normally be taken into account in the study of ventilation economics.

3.4   *Interest formula*

The basic formula for compound interest is:

$$A = P(1 + i)^n \qquad \qquad ...1$$

where
A = amount after n years
n = number of years
P = principal (or capital, or money spent *now* on purchasing something)
i = interest rate as a decimal (for example, 6 per cent = 0,06)

Other important formulae can be derived from this basic formula, as will be shown later.

Tables are available from which the solutions can be read off quickly for a large range of interest rates and times, and such a table is reproduced in the Appendix, along with other tables frequently used in economics calculations. Alternatively, mini-computers have recently become available for the same purpose.

EXAMPLE 1

What will R1 130 amount to in 11 years at 5 per cent interest?
Reading off from Table I in the 5 per cent column at 11 years gives a figure of 1,710 34 so that the answer is 1 130 × 1,710 34 = R1 930 (by slide rule).

Applying the formula $A = P(1 + i)^n = 1\ 130(1 + 0,05)^{11}$ will give the same answer but will take more time.

3.5 *Present value*

Present value is a very useful concept in many economics studies. It is the lump sum cost of current or future expenditures or the lump sum value of current or future incomes at the *present time*, bearing in mind what has already been said about interest rates and the time value of money. It provides a ready means for comparing the cost of different schemes where each scheme comprises different kinds of cost or income such as capital expenditure, running cost, and, possibly some secondhand resale value at some future date.

For example, in a number of tenders for large ventilation fans, the prices of the fans would vary; there may be alternative offers for motors; efficiencies, and therefore power costs, would be different, and the prospects of re-selling the fans or motors in perhaps 15 years' time would vary. One simply cannot add up all the items in order to make a price comparison. The items have to be reduced to a common denominator, as it were, and this can be achieved by calculating the *present value* of all the separate items and then adding these up. The total present value for each fan installation, for example, provides a direct means for deciding which fan installation will be the most economical, bearing in mind that there may be other over-riding considerations such as the reputation (good or bad) of the supplier, the fear that certain imported items may become unavailable during war-time or that a component part may be too large to transport down a shaft.

Present value of $1\,(v^n)$

From the basic formula $A = P(1 + i)^n$ one can derive $P = \dfrac{A}{(1 + i)^n}$

which simply means that the present value can be found easily if the sum or amount A in n years' time is known as well as the interest rate i.

Thus, present value of a sum of A units of money $= P = \dfrac{A}{(1 + i)^n}$

(it is immaterial whether the unit is a rand, pound, dollar, cent or any other unit).

For the purpose of simplifying the printing (in tables) of the somewhat awkward expression $\dfrac{A}{(1 + i)^n}$ most publishers write this as Av^n where, of course, $v^n = \dfrac{1}{(1 + i)^n}$. Most published tables of present value (see Table II) are therefore headed simply by v^n, meaning the present value which *one* unit of money in n years would have at the *present time,* and A units would thus have the value of Av^n.

$$\text{Present value of } 1 = v^n = \frac{1}{(1 + i)^n} \qquad \ldots 2$$

EXAMPLE 2

What is the present value of R1 930 due in eleven years' time at 5 per cent compound interest?

SOLUTION

Reading off from the v^n Table II in the 5 per cent column at eleven years gives a figure of 0,584 68, so that the answer is 1 930 × 0,584 68 = R1 130. (Compare this with Example 1 where R1 130 amounted to R1 930 in eleven years at 5 per cent).

Present value of 1 per year ($a_{\overline{n}|}$)

This should be clearly distinguished from the "present value of 1" For example, the "present value of 1" would be used in the case of a fan which has just been bought or its resale value in, say, fifteen years' time. But the yearly power cost for running the fan would involve the concept of "present value of 1 per year".

Again starting with $P = \dfrac{A}{(1 + i)^n}$ we have $P = \dfrac{1}{(1 + i)^n} = v^n$

in the case of *one* unit of money. Here one has to deal over a period of n years with n separate payments of which the present values are, respectively, $v, v^2, v^3 \ldots v^n$. This is a geometric progression, the summation of which is $\dfrac{1 - v^n}{^1/v - 1}$, and replacing v^n by its value $\dfrac{1}{(1 + i)^n}$ one finds:

$$\text{Sum} = \frac{1 - (1 + i)^{-n}}{i} = \frac{1 - v^n}{i} \qquad \ldots 3$$

Again, to simplify the printing, most publications use the convention

$a_{\overline{n}|} = \dfrac{1 - v^n}{i}$, the expression $a_{\overline{n}|}$ being read as "a angle n" and meaning the

present value of 1 per year for n years at an interest rate of i. Again the required values can be read off from Table III.

EXAMPLE 3

The power cost of running a fan is R1 900 per year. What is the present value of this expenditure over fifteen years at 6 per cent interest?

SOLUTION

Reading off from the $a_{\overline{n}|}$ table in the 6 per cent column at fifteen years gives a figure of 9,712 2 so that the answer is 1 900 × 9,712 2 = R18 450. (An accountant who may have to account for every cent would give the answer as R18 453, 18 but this degree of accuracy is not needed in ventilation economics or engineering economics generally).

Amount of 1 *per year:* $s_{\bar{n}|}$

This is the accumulated amount of one unit of money per year for a given number of yearly payments at a given interest rate. It is customary to designate this amount by $s_{\bar{n}|}$, read "*s* angle *n*", and is the accumulated amount after the last payment has been made. The last or end payment draws no interest, the second last for 1 year and the first payment draws interest for $(n - 1)$ years.

Introducing the interest rate *i* one finds that the sum of all payments

$$= s_{\bar{n}|} = 1 + (1 + i) + (1 + i)^2 + \ldots (1 + i)^{n-1}.$$

This is a geometric progression which adds up to :

$$s_{\bar{n}|} = \frac{(1 + i)^n - 1}{i} \qquad \ldots 4$$

Table IV gives values of $s_{\bar{n}|}$.

EXAMPLE 4 (Similar to Example 3)

The power cost of running a fan is R1 900 per year. What is the total cost of running the fan for fifteen years at 6 per cent interest ?

SOLUTION

Reading off from the $s_{\bar{n}|}$ table in the 6 per cent column at fifteen years gives a figure of 23,276 0 so that the answer is 1 900 $\times$ 23, 276 0 = R44 200.

EXAMPLE 5

To check from Example 4 back to Example 3 one might ask : "What is the present value of R44 200 payable in 15 years at 6 per cent ?"

SOLUTION

It should be noted that the question now no longer deals with yearly payments but simply with the lump sum present value of some future lump sum ; and the v^n table applies, from which 44 200 $\times$ 0,417 27 = R18 450 which latter figure was also the present value found in Example 3.

EXAMPLE 6

This is a variation of Examples 3, 4 and 5. What sum of money must be banked today at 6 per cent interest to enable the bank to pay the yearly power bill of R1 900 for running a fan during the next fifteen years? Here the $a_{\bar{n}|}$ table is used and 9,712 2 $\times$ 1 900 = R18 450, which is the same answer as found in Example 3. In other words, R18 450 has to be banked at the present time to enable the bank to pay the power bill over the next fifteen years. At the end of this period both capital and accrued interest will be exhausted.

There are also other derivations of the basic formula $A = P(1 + i)^n$, but the four formulae already given will serve most purposes in ventilation or engineering economics. They are summarized here in convenient form and should be read in conjunction with the Tables I to IV.

$$\text{Amount of } 1 = (1 + i)^n \ldots 1 \quad \text{(Table I)}$$
$$\text{Present value of } 1 = v^n \qquad \ldots 2 \quad \text{(Table II)}$$
$$\text{Present value of 1 per year} = a_{\overline{n}|} \qquad \ldots 3 \quad \text{(Table III)}$$
$$\text{Amount of 1 per year} = s_{\overline{n}|} \qquad \ldots 4 \quad \text{(Table IV)}$$

3.6   *Annuity and sinking fund*

It should be added that the terms "annuity" and "sinking fund" are frequently used in insurance, pension fund and banking matters, and are closely related to the matters discussed above, but these terms are best avoided in a study of ventilation economics.

For the sake of completeness, it is sufficient to state that

$\dfrac{1}{s_{\overline{n}|}}$ is the annuity that in n payments will amount to 1

$\dfrac{1}{a_{\overline{n}|}}$ is the annuity that 1 will buy, and

$$\frac{1}{s_{\overline{n}|}} = \frac{1}{a_{\overline{n}|}} - 1$$

$\dfrac{1}{s_{\overline{n}|}}$ is also the sinking fund deposit factor and therefore the same as the

annuity that in n payments will amount to 1.

4   ANNUAL COST

The use of the "present value" concept is a popular method of making cost comparisons. Another method which has much appeal is the "annual cost" method which, as its name implies, means that all costs are expressed in terms of what the system or machine will cost, on average, in one year over its life at a suitable rate of interest. Both the "present value" and "annual cost" methods (and there are others) will give the correct and, therefore, the same answers when it comes to making the most economical choice from a number of alternatives.

The "annual cost" method has the advantage of being a more direct and apparently less artifical concept than "present value". It also lends itself to a straightforward calculation of its contribution towards cost per ton mined or milled, because the answer is found directly by dividing the annual cost by annual tons. For example, if the anual cost of a ventilation machine or system comes to R50 000 for a mine milling 100 000 tons per

month, this machine or system is costing $\dfrac{50\ 000 \times 100}{100\ 000 \times 12} = 4{,}2$ cents per ton milled.

Two methods of calculating annual cost will be dealt with, namely,

(a)   An accurate method requiring the use of interest tables.

(b)   An approximate one which requires no tables.

4.1   Accurate method for annual cost

Under "present value of 1 per year" an explanation was given of the use of the $a_{\overline{n}|}$ table.

Now if $a_{\overline{n}|}$ is the present value of 1 per year, it can be shown that 1 is the present value of $1/a_{\overline{n}|}$ or $(a_{\overline{n}|})^{-1}$ per year. Thus if R is the annual payment, then present value $= R \cdot a_{\overline{n}|}$ and if we substitute principal or starting capital or cost for present value and call this *one* unit of money, then $1 = R \cdot a_{\overline{n}|}$ and $R = 1/a_{\overline{n}|}$.

In other words, if the capital outlay is 1 unit, the equal annual payment or the annual cost of the capital outlay plus interest will be $(a_{\overline{n}|})^{-1}$, or the reciprocal of $a_{\overline{n}|}$. This is in fact a repetition of what was mentioned previously, namely, that $(a_{\overline{n}|})^{-1}$ is the annuity that 1 will buy, but as mentioned in the same context, the word "annuity" is seldom used in engineering economics, although it has virtually the same meaning as "annual cost".

EXAMPLE 7

A machine is bought for R50 000 and costs R30 000 per year in electrical power and maintenance. The estimated life is fifteen years, and interest is reckoned at 6 per cent compound. What is the overall cost of this machine?

SOLUTION

In the 6 per cent column at 15 years in the $a_{\overline{n}|}$ table the figure is 9,712 2 so that the annual cost of the R50 000 spread out over

15 years = 50 000 ÷ 9,712 2	=	R5 150
plus power and maintenance per year	=	30 000
Total annual cost	=	R35 150

4.2   Approximate method for annual cost

An approximate method involving no interest tables is frequently quite adequate, especially where one is not interested in absolute values but merely in making the most economical choice from a number of alternatives. It involves the assumption of a straight-line redemption of the capital with the addition of *average* interest, plus, of course, such annual charges as for power, maintenance, etc.

Straight-line redemption simply means paying off or writing off the original capital in equal amounts each year so that nothing is left at the end of the life period. For example, R20 000 paid off over 10 years would mean redeeming by R2 000 per year.

Interest is calculated on the assumption that the interest is paid the first year on the full amount, but as the amount gets less each year the interest decreases.

The average interest payments form an arithmetic progression, the first term being Pi and the last term $(P/n)i$. The average interest is the average

of the first and last terms namely, $\dfrac{Pi(n+1)}{2(n)}$.

EXAMPLE 8   (The same as the previous Example 7)

SOLUTION

$$\text{Annual redemption} = \frac{50\,000}{15} = \text{R } 3\,330$$

$$\text{Annual interest} = \frac{50\,000 \times 0{,}06(16)}{2 \quad (15)} = 1\,600$$

$$\text{Annual power and maintenance} = 30\,000$$

$$\text{Total annual cost} = \text{R}34\,930$$

This should be compared with R35 150 in Example 7.

An even simpler but rough and ready solution to the above problem is to ignore the arithmetic progression and to assume an average annual interest payment of the full rate times half the capital. In the above example this would be 6 per cent of R25 000 = R1 500 instead of R1 600.

4.3 *Break-up value*

In making comparisons between the costs of different machines or systems it frequently happens that one has to show some break-up or resale or scrap value at some future date. The expected break-up value will depend on the number of years, quality of the machine purchased, standard or non-standard components, etc.

It may be easier to find a buyer for a relatively small secondhand fan in twenty years' time than for a very large "tailor made" fan. An all-steel secondhand fan assembly may find a buyer in time to come whereas a concrete-housed one may be worthless except for the motor and a few spare parts. There are many items to consider and in a ventilation or engineering economics study it is best to obtain an estimate from an engineer qualified in his particular field.

The break-up or resale value, it might be added, is seldom of material importance in economics studies where periods of say fifteen or twenty years are concerned, but it should be considered for the sake of completeness.

In dealing with this item in money terms it is a simple matter to introduce it in the "present value" method, remembering that it appears as a credit and should be subtracted and not added.

EXAMPLE 9

The secondhand value of a machine bought now is estimated at R5 000 in sixteen years' time. How can this be allowed for in an economic study, with interest at 7 per cent?

SOLUTION

The v^n table applies (present value of 1) and in the 7 per cent column at sixteen years the figure is 0,338 73 so that the present value of R5 000 = 5 000 × 0,338 73 = R1 690. This simple problem again illustrates the very important *time value* of money: R5 000 in sixteen years' time is worth only R1 690 today at 7 per cent interest.

5   REDEMPTION, AMORTIZATION AND DEPRECIATION

These terms are sometimes used synonymously but the subtle difference between them should be understood. Company policies in these matters can involve quite complicated arguments as far as the professional economist is concerned, but it is not necessary in a short chapter on economics for the mine ventilation engineer to go into these arguments, and a simple treatment will suffice.

Redemption means simply to redeem or pay off or write off the money invested in, say, a machine or airway.

Amortization involves redemption of the capital or the money invested plus payment of interest. Usually, but not necessarily, amortization takes place by means of a *uniform* monthly or yearly payment to cover capital redemption plus interest. Clearly with such a uniform repayment, more and more of the sum paid as time goes by is used for the redemption of capital and less and less is paid in interest on the diminishing capital. Money borrowed from a building society for a housing loan is usually repaid in this way.

Calculation of amortization is the same as in the case of calculating an annual cost, mentioned earlier. Amortization rate of annual payment = capital $\div a_{\overline{n}|}$ (from Table III in Appendix).

The ventilation engineer is not normally concerned with where the money comes from for buying a fan or refrigeration plant or for paying for a ventilation shaft or airway; nor is he concerned with how the money is going to be repaid. In fact, there is seldom any question of repaying the debt on such items in the same methodical way as a houseowner would repay his debts to a building society. Nevertheless, for purposes of an economics study one should assume that an orderly system of amortization applies, even if it is only on paper or in one's mind. The reasoning behind this is beyond the scope of this chapter, and has to do with various and sometimes complicated schemes for financing mining ventures.

Depreciation

All machinery suffers wear and tear and may ultimately break down, or it may be economical in due course to scrap the old machine and buy a more efficient one. A ventilation shaft or airway will usually become worthless when the mine closes down. These are examples of depreciation.

Mining companies follow certain policies in depreciating their assets, but these need not be gone into. The ventilation engineer should, however, appreciate that such depreciation is an essential argument in an economics study and it is customary to place, on any piece of equipment, a certain "life", at the end of which the value of the equipment is usually reckoned as zero. That there might actually be a secondhand market for an item of equipment does not necessarily affect the assumption of complete depreciation or a limited life in an economics study.

The life of an asset varies greatly and may vary from, say, 2 years for a ventilation pipe, 5 years for a small fan, 15 years for a large fan to perhaps 100 years for a water conservation dam. Economics studies made by a ventilation engineer should include a life figure in keeping with his company's policy.

It may be said, in concluding this section, that redemption, amortization and depreciation all involve the same "life" of whatever equipment or ventilation system is involved.

6   OWNING AND OPERATING COST

In economics studies it is not enough to know what a machine or a system costs in the first instance, in other words, what it will cost to buy and thus to own. Similarly, what it will cost to run or operate that machine or system does not give any complete answer. What is most important is that the sum of owning and operating costs should be a minimum.

Fig. 21:1 shows the classical example illustrating this important criterion. The example is that of finding the lowest "owning and operating" cost for an airway, where there is a choice of different sizes.

Obviously the first cost of excavating the airway will increase as the size increases, but the power cost of circulating air through it will decrease with increase in size. At a certain size the sum of the two costs will be a minimum and the procedure illustrated in Figure 21:1 provides a useful graphical means for finding this minimum.

The rules given previously for reducing different kinds of cost to some common denominator such as present value or annual cost apply here also. One cannot simply add the first cost to the power cost for one year. Both have to be calculated in terms of present value or average annual cost or total cost over the life of the scheme before drawing the curves and summating. All three of these methods will establish the minimum at the same airway size, although the minimum will, of course, be different if a different life or interest rate were used.

This type of curve will usually be fairly flat where it passes through the absolute minimum, which means that one can allow some tolerance on either side. If, for example, the "total" curve has an absolute minimum at, say, 2,8 m × 2,8 m but is relatively flat from 2,6 m × 2,6 m to 3,0 m × 3,0 m, one need not argue too much about a size of exactly 2,8 m × 2,8 m. Other considerations may sway the choice. For example, the need for a larger haulage for larger locos may make the final choice 3 m × 3 m. On the other hand, at great mining depths and rock pressure a small size may be desirable and yet be within the economical tolerance limits.

7   ECONOMIC SIZE OF AIRWAY

Looked at purely from the point of view of ventilation economics, the problem of finding the optimum size of any airway resolves itself simply into finding that size which makes the sum of owning and operating cost a minimum. In its simplest and most adequate form this in turn amounts to finding the minimum value of the sum of the initial cost of the airway and the present value of power costs over an assumed life.

Refinements which can be introduced in the case of major projects are:

(a)   the first cost of the ventilating machinery (added to the initial cost of the airway);

(*b*)   the maintenance cost of the ventilating plant (added to the power cost) ; and

(*c*)   fixed or overhead costs, but since these are usually constant (within limits) they do not normally affect the issue.

Two methods will be dealt with, the one graphical and the other mathematical and, by way of example, the case of a vertical shaft will be worked through in detail. The refinements referred to above will be omitted.

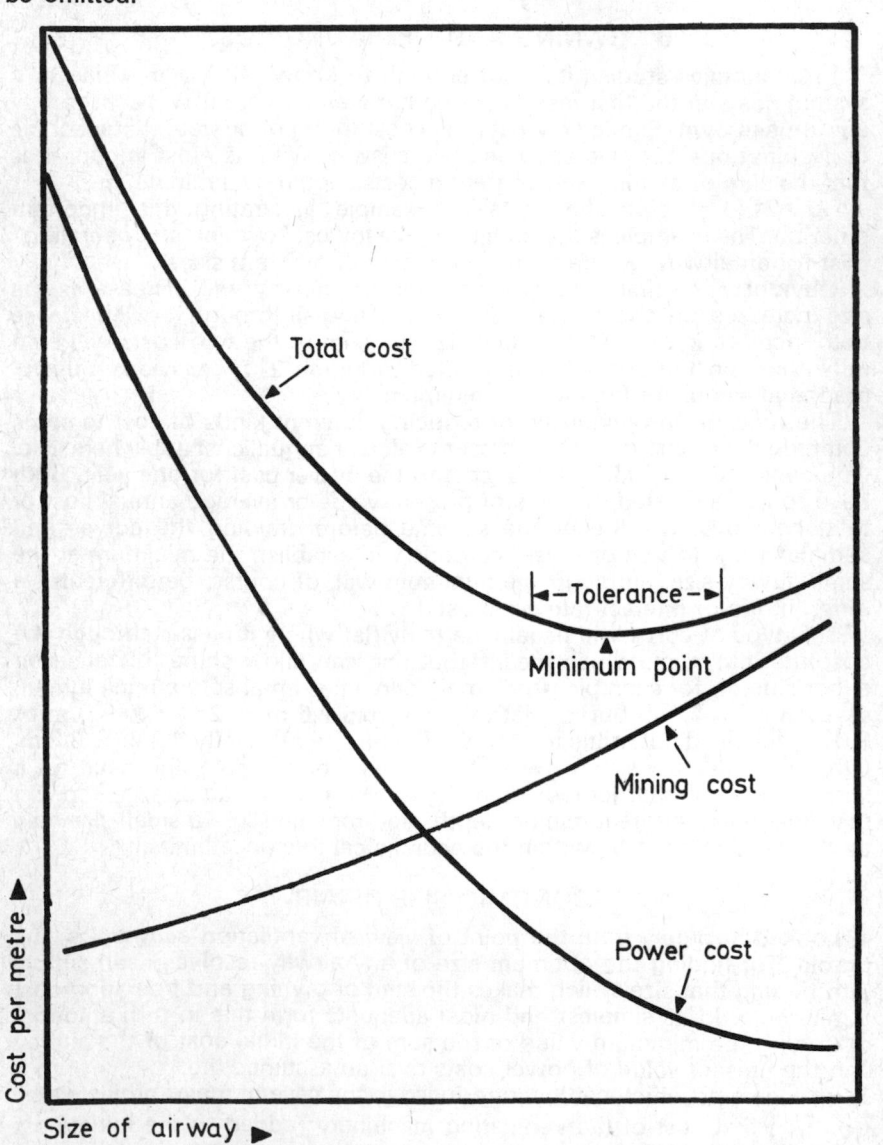

Fig. 21 : 1   Illustrating total cost as the sum of owning and operating cost.

Cost functions

Before one can proceed to find the most economical size of an airway, it is essential that certain cost functions be established in an orderly fashion so as to avoid the pitfall of comparing different things on dissimilar bases. For example, the cost of shaft sinking must be firmly related to size, say diameter, and one cannot use isolated cost figures obtained from different mines for different shaft sizes. One such cost function has been suggested by Barenbrug[1] namely: Cost = $130d$ to $260d$ Rand per metre, where d is the circular shaft diameter in metres, depending on whether the shaft is lined or unlined, equipped or unequipped, sinking conditions difficult or easy, etc.

Other cost functions which must be predetermined are:

(*a*)   The cost of electrical power, say per kW per year.

(*b*)   The interest rate on money (say 6 per cent or 7 per cent per annum).
Physical factors which have to be predetermined are:

(*a*)   Atkinson's friction factor.

(*b*)   The life of the airway.

(*c*)   Mean volume of air flowing.

(*d*)   Mean density.

(*e*)   The height-width ratio for non-circular airways.

(*f*)   Note that the length or depth of airway is *not* required to be known and one can use one unit of length or 1 000 units or L units, whichever happens to be the most convenient.

EXAMPLE 10

Calculate the most economical size of a circular equipped downcast shaft to handle a mean air quantity of 400 m³/s at mean density 1,1 kg/m³. Shaft sinking and equipping costs are to be taken at R200d per metre (excluding overheads or fixed charges which are assumed to remain constant). Power costs average R55 per kilowatt per year and Atkinson's friction factor K = 0,025 Ns²/m⁴.
Assume a life of 20 years and interest at 6 per cent per annum.

(i) GRAPHICAL SOLUTION

An arbitrary depth of 1 000 m will be considered.

$$p = \frac{KSQ^2}{A^3} \times \text{density correction}$$

$$= \frac{K \times \text{length} \times \text{perimeter} \times (\text{quantity})^2}{\text{Area}^3} \times \frac{\text{density}}{1,2}$$

$$= \frac{0,025 \times 1\,000 \times \text{perimeter} \times 400^2}{A^3} \times \frac{1,1}{1,2} \text{ Pa}$$

$$= 3\,667\,000 \times \text{perimeter} \times A^{-3} \text{ Pa}$$

Using some commonsense knowledge or experience one can start at 6 m diameter and calculate pressure losses at 0,5 m diameter intervals to, say, 8 m. (Actually the calculation has been taken a little further for the sake of illustration.) The power costs per annum are then easily derived for each shaft size and similarly the shaft sinking and equipping costs are derived from the information given, namely, cost = R200d/ metre. Thereafter the annual power cost over twenty years at 6 per cent interest is reduced to present value by using the $a_{\overline{n}|}$ table, as explained previously. The cost of shaft sinking and equipping does not need any further adjustment because it is already an expenditure at the start or at the "present" time. That shaft sinking would actually be spread out over perhaps a year or two is another refinement which is ignored in the present case for the sake of simplicity.

The results of these calculations are tabulated in Table V and graphed in Fig. 21 :2, showing the economical shaft size to be about 7,3 m (the slide-rule has been used throughout for these calculations).

TABLE V   EXAMPLE 10: DATA FOR 1 000 m OF SHAFT

Diam. m	Press. loss kPa	Air power kW	Power cost R1 000/ year	PV of power cost (Factor 11,47) R1 000	Shaft cost 200d/m R1 000	Total present value R1 000
5,0	8,02	3 200	176	2 040	1 000	3 040
5,5	4,70	1 880	103	1 180	1 100	2 280
6,0	3,01	1 205	66	755	1 200	1 955
6,5	2,02	805	44,2	506	1 300	1 806
7,0	1,42	570	31,2	358	1 400	1 758
7,5	1,02	405	22,3	255	1 500	1 755
8,0	0,73	290	15,9	182	1 600	1 782
8,5	0,53	210	11,5	132	1 700	1 832
9,0	0,40	150	8,2	94	1 800	1 894

(ii) MATHEMATICAL SOLUTION

The much shorter and neater mathematical solution will probably appeal to those readers with a knowledge of calculus, although it is not as illustrative as the graphical method.

The basis of the calculation is simply that the differentiation of cost with respect to shaft diameter must be zero. This method has been used by West[2] and Hinsley[3].

Using the same basic data as before and Atkinson's formula, it can be shown, for *one* metre of shaft depth, that

$$\text{pressure loss } p = 23\ 800 \times d^{-5}$$

$$PV \text{ of power cost} = 23\ 800 \times d^{-5} \times \frac{400}{1\ 000} \times 55 \times 11,47$$

$$= 6 \times 10^6 \times d^{-5} \text{ (Rand)}$$

$$\text{Present value of shaft sinking cost} = 200d \text{ (Rand)}$$

$$\text{Total present value} = R\ (6 \times 10^6 \times d^{-5}) + 200d$$

Differentiating :

$$\frac{dR}{dd} = (-5 \times 6 \times 10^6 \times d^{-6}) + 200 = 0$$

from which $d = 7{,}29$ m which agrees with the graphical answer of about 7,3 m.

Exactly the same method, either graphical or mathematical, can be used for calculating the economic size of any airway for a given air quantity, be it a horizontal tunnel or ventilation pipe.

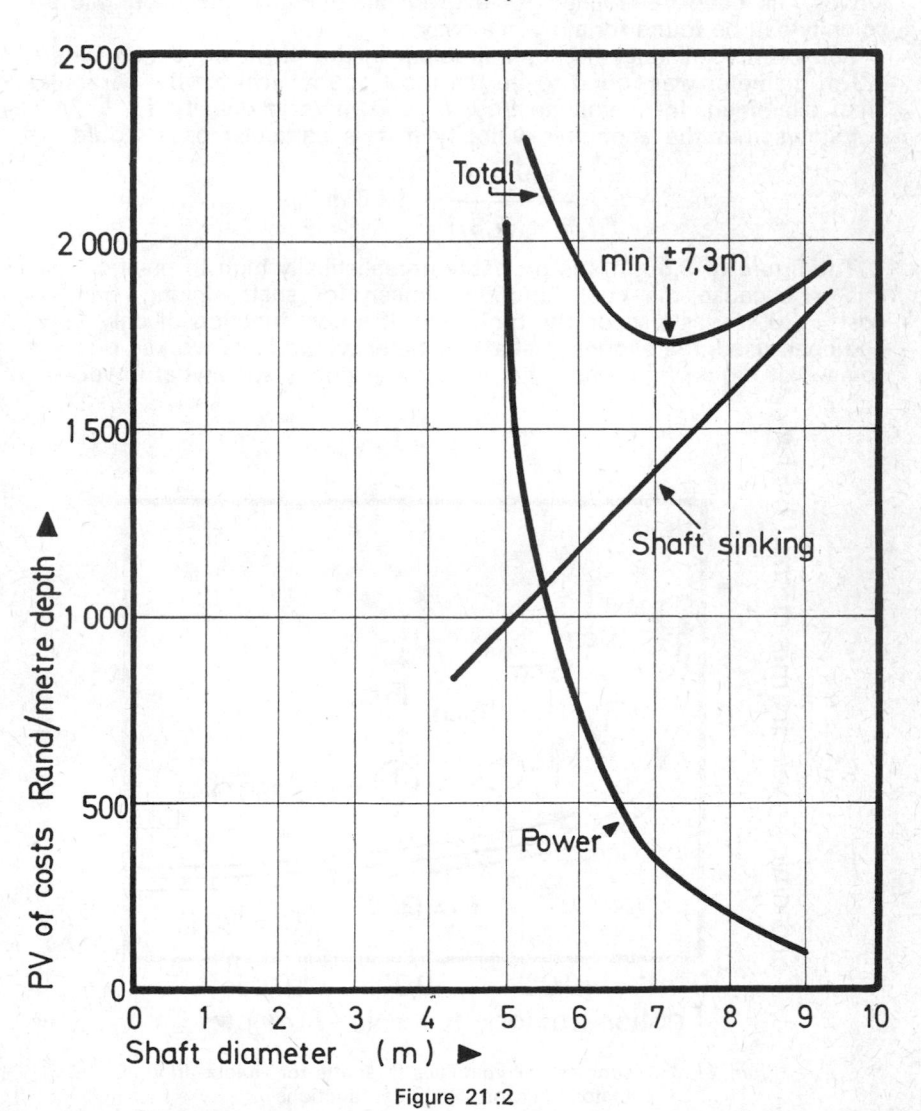

Figure 21 :2

In the case of normal development ends underground, West[2] has suggested a cost function which takes the form:

Cost per metre $= a + (b \times$ area$)$

where $a =$ a constant cost per metre advance

$b =$ cost per cubic metre mined.

8   ECONOMIC AIR VELOCITY

A corollary to the previous section is that once the economic size of an airway has been determined for a given air quantity, the economic air velocity can be found for a given airway.

For example, taking the shaft problem in the previous section where 7,3 m diameter was found to be the most economical for the particular shaft examined, for a volume flow of 400 m³/s at density 1,1 kg/m³, it follows that the economic velocity in this particular case would be

$$\frac{400 \times 4}{\pi \times (7,3)^2} = 9,55 \text{ m/s.}$$

The figure of 9,55 m/s is probably unrealistically high in practice, but this is because the cost function chosen for shaft sinking, namely, cost $= 200d$ was also on the high side. If a cost function of only $130d$ had been used, the economic shaft diameter would have worked out at a somewhat higher figure and the economic velocity somewhat lower.

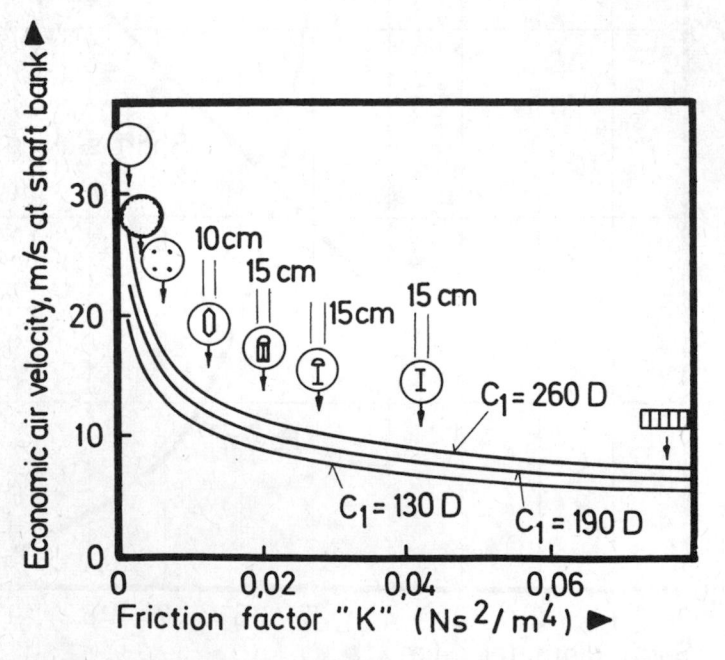

Figure 21 :3   Economic air velocities in shafts for various friction factors, buntons and cost functions

The above remarks at the same time illustrate what should be self-evident, namely, that a very expensive airway should not be utilized uneconomically by circulating too little air through it if ventilation is to be the main function of that airway.

Fig. 21:3 is a reproduction of Barenbrug's[1] curves of economic air velocities in vertical shafts for various bunton configurations and cost functions.

The indications which have been given above about economic air velocities may serve as a rough guide, but should be used with discretion and should not be used in major project studies as a "lazy" substitute for detailed calculation.

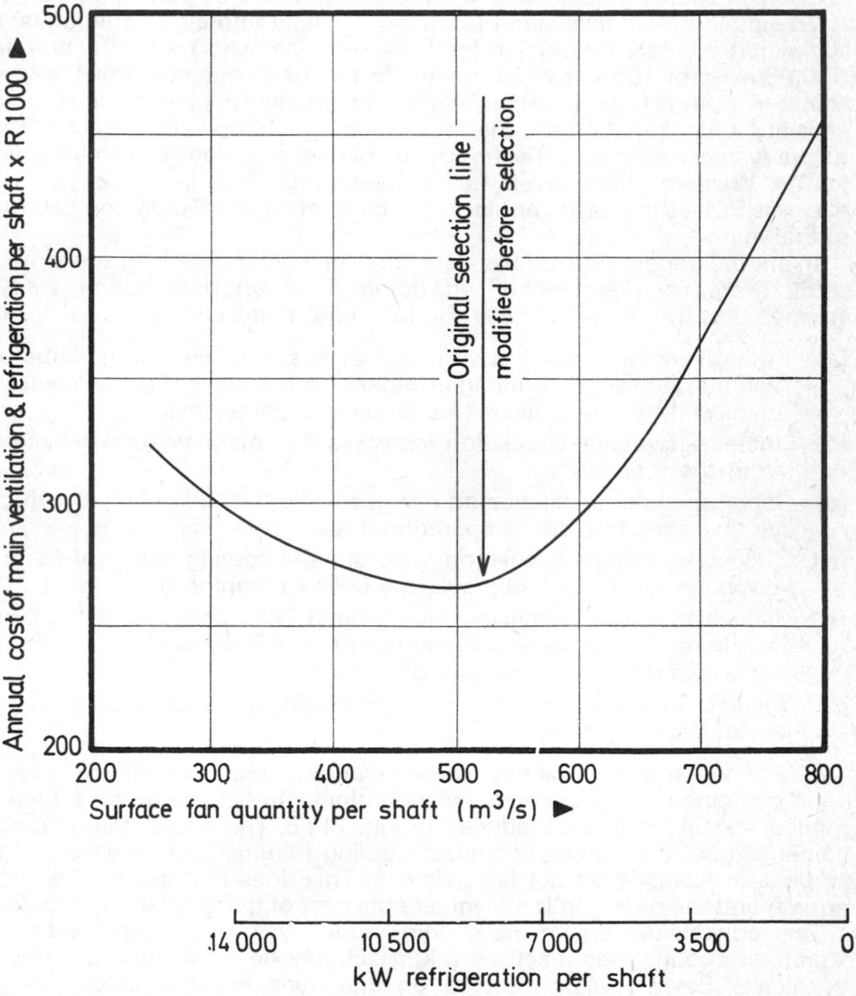

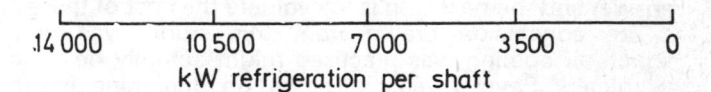

Figure 21:4   Ventilation and refrigeration economics for planning at Western Deep Levels Mine

9 ECONOMICS OF VENTILATION VERSUS AIR COOLING

In many deep South African gold mines air cooling (mainly underground) has been practised to supplement straight ventilation. The total volume circulation (1971)[4] in 44 large mines amounted to about 25 000 m^3/s, and on 16 mines the installed cooling plant capacity was about 168 000 kW refrigeration. (3,517 kW = 1 American ice ton).

In some instances cooling is a once-through process and in others stage cooling is combined with re-use of the cooled air. The arguments of the past had the merit of simplicity, namely, that the volume of air cooled and re-used is almost the same as additional fresh air being made available and that if a mine required a total of Q_1 m^3/s with Q_2 m^3/s being cooled and re-used, then the actual volume circulation would be $(Q_1 - Q_2)$ m^3/s.

To simplify the conversion of cooling capacity into air-volume units, a somewhat arbitrary conversion factor is used, namely, 1 kW refrigeration = 0,03 m^3/s or 100 kW = 3,0 m^3/s. On this basis one could then do an economics study to find the combination of volume circulation and cooling capacity which would make the total "owning and operating" cost of the whole system a minimum. The final result of one such study by Lambrechts[5] for the Western Deep Levels Ltd is reproduced here in Fig. 21 : 4, and this was in fact the basis for planning the original ventilation and cooling of that mine.

In another report, Barcza[6] has described the basis for such an economics study. However, Lambrechts[7] in doing a partial optimization study, attempted to introduce *inter alia* the following factors:

(a) In a given ventilation network, power costs increase as the cube of volume circulation, resulting in either greatly increased power costs or increased capital requirements for more or larger shafts.

(b) Increased volume circulation *increases* the total heat load extracted from the rock.

(c) Increased volume circulation *decreases* the heat addition per unit of air and, therefore, the temperature rise.

(d) Increased volume circulation *increases* the cooling power of the air but not as much as had previously been thought to be the case.

(e) Increased cooling capacity underground with limited air circulation would result in a *decreased* coefficient of performance and therefore *increased* power cost per unit of cooling.

(f) Increased volume circulation through stoping areas leads to *decreased* air utilization.

The above and other factors, some favourable and some unfavourable, were combined into one computer programme and the result for a hypothetical model mine is reproduced in Fig. 21 : 5. This shows the different combinations of air quantity against cooling requirements to ensure that stope kata readings do not fall below 8. This does not provide the final answer and the next step is to evaluate the cost of these different schemes.

The conclusion drawn from this study was that deep mines in which air cooling was practised might actually be uneconomically over-ventilated. Several years research on one mine has not succeeded in resolving the issue one way or the other, and this is where the controversy rests at present.

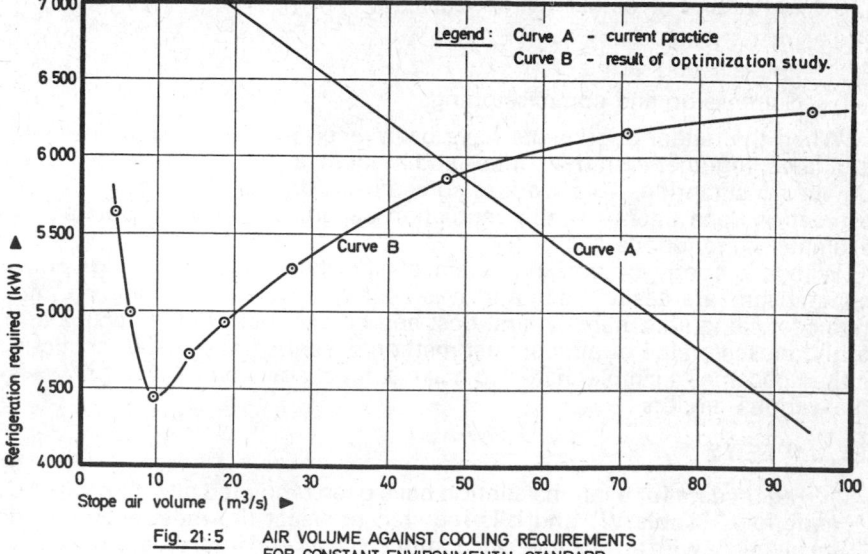

<u>Fig. 21:5</u>   AIR VOLUME AGAINST COOLING REQUIREMENTS
FOR CONSTANT ENVIRONMENTAL STANDARD

Figure 21:5

10   EXAMINATION OF TENDER DOCUMENTS

An essential prerequisite to the honest and objective appraisal of tenders for fans, refrigeration plant or other ventilation machinery, is that there should be careful prior specification of what is wanted. The tenderers have the right to know what the buyer requires and vague specifications invariably lead to unnecessary alternatives being offered and quotations which are not on the same basis and frequently not comparable.

The ventilation engineer's part in drawing up a specification may frequently go no further than a basic duty specification, for example, volume, pressure and density in the case of a fan; or volume, density, temperature range and refrigeration duty in the case of a cooling plant. Frequently he should also express himself on other matters such as axial flow or backward-bladed centrifugal fans, all-steel or concrete-cased fans, bearing in mind that his ventilation plans may call for shifting of the fan to a new location in a few years' time. He may require two or three fans to share the duty in parallel and he should indicate the variation in duty that may be foreseen.

These and other matters should be discussed with other engineers in the organization (mining, mechanical, electrical, civil), who will no doubt wish to include other requirements and more detailed specifications. Frequently it is advisable to break down the overall specification into definite brackets and to call for lump-sum quotations for all items within each bracket, for example:

(i)   Fan only.
(ii)   Connections between shaft and fan, fan evase, motor house, airlock, including complete erection.

(iii)   Motor and electrical switchgear.
(iv)   Instrumentation.
(v)   Extras.
(vi)   Supervision and commissioning.

When the tender documents have been received, the items are usually tabulated, together with their prices and other data such as efficiencies and power consumption. This work is sometimes done by the organization's estimating department but the ventilation department may be required to examine the tender details.

With a properly organized system of specifying and tendering, price comparisons are easily made and it is usually a case of splitting up into two cost categories, namely, first cost and power cost. By the application of the present value or annual cost method described in previous sections it then becomes a simple matter to make a direct cost comparison between the various tenders.

EXAMPLE 12

Tender data for a fan installation have been tabulated and summarized as follows (Table VI) and it is required to select the most economical installation, with an assumed life of fifteen years and interest at 6 per cent. Power is assumed to cost R40/kW/year.

TABLE VI

Tender	Total first cost. Rand	Power required kW	Power cost per year. Rand
A	272 000	2 820	112 500
B	222 000	3 300	132 000
C	232 000	3 080	123 500
D	230 000	2 970	118 500

SOLUTION

The "first cost" is already tantamount to a present value and needs no further adjustment. The power bill has to be paid regularly over a period of fifteen years and this recurring cost must be reduced to a "present value" by multiplying by the appropriate $a_{\overline{n}|}$ factor $= 9,712\,2$ from tables. The results are tabulated in Table VII.

TABLE VII

Tender	First cost Rand	Present value of power cost Rand	Total present value Rand
A	272 000	1 095 000	1 367 000
B	222 000	1 282 000	1 504 000
C	232 000	1 195 000	1 427 000
D	230 000	1 153 000	1 383 000

Tender A would appear to be the most economical, although the most expensive in first cost.

Alternatively, by the "annual cost" method, the $a_{\overline{n}|}$ division factor is 9,712 2 and the results can in this case be tabulated as follows:

TABLE VIII

Tender	Annual cost of installation Rand	Annual power cost Rand	Total annual cost Rand
A	28 000	112 500	140 500
B	22 900	132 000	154 900
C	23 900	123 500	147 400
D	23 700	118 500	142 500

Again tender A is shown to be the most economical with the others following in the same order as before.

11   GENERAL PLANNING

A mistake which has probably frequently been made is to try to super-impose ventilation planning on the completed mine planning of the mining engineer. Especially in deep-level mining it is essential that ventilation planning should be closely integrated into mine planning from start to finish. Only in this way can all aspects of planning be the best and most economical.

There are many things to consider other than those already mentioned, such as geographical distribution of mineral values and ore reserves, future expansion, siting of shafts, availability of return air for condenser water cooling for cooling plants, hoisting and transport capacities of shafts and haulages.

Only by teamwork and close co-operation between ventilation and other engineers can the best results be achieved. Finally, from management's point of view, the ventilation engineer should be given every opportunity to become an active member of the planning team, fully in the picture at all times and not simply left with the impossible task of "ventilating" a poorly planned mine.

12   REFERENCES

1   Barenbrug, A. W. T. The economic aspect of reducing shaft resistance. *J. S. Afr., Inst. Min. Metall.,* Vol. 62, 1961, p 111–19.

2   West, M. J. Economic factors in the design and operation of underground ventilation circuits. *Trans. Inst. Min. Metall.,* Vol. 68, 1959, p 561.

3   Hinsley, F. B. Airway resistance and ventilation planning. *Proc. S. Wales Inst. Engrs.* Vol. 61, 1945, p 211.

4   Chamber of Mines of South Africa, *Annual ventilation report,* Research Report 24/72, June 1972.

5   Lambrechts, J. de V. Ventilation planning for Western Deep Levels Limited. *Assoc. Mine Managers S. Afr., Papers and Discussions,* 1958/59, p 1017.
6   Barcza, M. The relative cost of cooling and re-using air as opposed to the provision of more downcast air. Unpublished Rand Mines Vent. Dept. Research Rep. No. 7, Aug. 1960.
7   Lambrechts, J. de V. Optimization of ventilation and refrigeration in deep mines. 8th Commonwealth Min. Metall. Congress Australia, 1965.

BIBLIOGRAPHY

Quilliam, J. H. Engineering economics. *J. Mine Vent. Soc. S. Afr.* Vol. 15, 1962, p 173.
De Garmo, Paul E. *Engineering economy.* The Macmillan Co., New York, 1967.
Smith, G. W. *Engineering economy.* Iowa State University Press, 1968.
Williams, K. P. *The mathematical theory of finance.* The Macmillan Co., New York, 1949.

TABLE I $(1 + i)^n$

n	4%	5%	6%	7%	8%	9%	10%	11%	12%
1	1,04000	1,05000	1,06000	1,07000	1,08000	1,09000	1,10000	1,11000	1,12000
2	1,08160	1,10250	1,12360	1,14490	1,16640	1,18810	1,21000	1,23210	1,25440
3	1,12486	1,15763	1,19102	1,22504	1,25971	1,29503	1,33100	1,36763	1,40493
4	1,16986	1,21551	1,26248	1,31080	1,36049	1,41158	1,46410	1,51807	1,57352
5	1,21665	1,27628	1,33823	1,40255	1,46933	1,53862	1,61051	1,68506	1,76234
6	1,26532	1,34010	1,41852	1,50073	1,58687	1,67710	1,77156	1,87041	1,97382
7	1,31593	1,40710	1,50363	1,60578	1,71382	1,82804	1,94872	2,07616	2,21068
8	1,36857	1,47746	1,59385	1,71819	1,85093	1,99256	2,14359	2,30454	2,47596
9	1,42331	1,55133	1,68948	1,83846	1,99900	2,17189	2,35794	2,55804	2,77308
10	1,48024	1,62889	1,79085	1,96715	2,15892	2,36736	2,59374	2,83942	3,10585
11	1,53945	1,71034	1,89830	2,10485	2,33164	2,58043	2,85312	3,15176	3,47855
12	1,60103	1,79586	2,01220	2,25219	2,51817	2,81266	3,13843	3,49845	3,89598
13	1,66507	1,88565	2,13293	2,40985	2,71962	3,06580	3,45227	3,88328	4,36349
14	1,73168	1,97993	2,26090	2,57853	2,93719	3,34173	3,79750	4,31044	4,88711
15	1,80094	2,07893	2,39656	2,75903	3,17217	3,64248	4,17725	4,78459	5,47357
16	1,87298	2,18287	2,54035	2,95216	3,42594	3,97031	4,59497	5,31089	6,13039
17	1,94790	2,29202	2,69277	3,15882	3,70002	4,32763	5,05447	5,89509	6,86604
18	2,02582	2,40662	2,85434	3,37993	3,99602	4,71712	5,55992	6,54355	7,68997
19	2,10685	2,52695	3,02560	3,61653	4,31570	5,14166	6,11591	7,26334	8,61276
20	2,19112	2,65330	3,20714	3,86968	4,66096	5,60441	6,72750	8,06231	9,64629
21	2,27877	2,78596	3,39956	4,14056	5,03383	6,10881	7,40025	8,94917	10,80385
22	2,36992	2,92526	3,60354	4,43040	5,43654	6,65860	8,14027	9,93357	12,10031
23	2,46472	3,07152	3,81975	4,74053	5,87146	7,25787	8,95430	11,02627	13,55235
24	2,56330	3,22510	4,04893	5,07237	6,34118	7,91108	9,84973	12,23916	15,17863
25	2,66584	3,38635	4,29187	5,42743	6,84848	8,62308	10,83471	13,58546	17,00006

$$\text{TABLE II } v^n = \frac{1}{(1 + i)^n}$$

n	4%	5%	6%	7%	8%	9%	10%	11%	12%
1	0,96154	0,95238	0,94340	0,93458	0,92593	0,91706	0,90872	0,90054	0,89250
2	0,92456	0,90703	0,89000	0,87344	0,85734	0,84137	0,82615	0,81134	0,79692
3	0,88900	0,86384	0,83962	0,81630	0,79383	0,77193	0,75108	0,73097	0,71157
4	0,85480	0,82270	0,79209	0,76290	0,73503	0,70822	0,68283	0,65856	0,63536
5	0,82193	0,78353	0,74726	0,71299	0,68058	0,64977	0,62077	0,59332	0,56731
6	0,79031	0,74622	0,70496	0,66634	0,63017	0,59614	0,56436	0,53454	0,50655
7	0,75992	0,71068	0,66506	0,62275	0,58349	0,54693	0,51307	0,48159	0,45229
8	0,73069	0,67684	0,62741	0,58201	0,54027	0,50179	0,46644	0,43388	0,40385
9	0,70259	0,64461	0,59190	0,54393	0,50025	0,46037	0,42405	0,39089	0,36059
10	0,67556	0,61391	0,55839	0,50835	0,46319	0,42237	0,38551	0,35217	0,32197
11	0,64958	0,58468	0,52679	0,47509	0,42888	0,38750	0,35043	0,31728	0,28748
12	0,62460	0,55684	0,49697	0,44401	0,39711	0,35552	0,31863	0,28585	0,25669
13	0,60057	0,53032	0,46884	0,41496	0,36770	0,32617	0,28967	0,25753	0,22919
14	0,57748	0,50507	0,44230	0,38782	0,34046	0,29925	0,26334	0,23201	0,20464
15	0,55526	0,48102	0,41727	0,36245	0,31524	0,27455	0,23941	0,20903	0,18273
16	0,53391	0,45811	0,39365	0,33873	0,29189	0,25188	0,21765	0,18832	0,16315
17	0,51337	0,43630	0,37136	0,31657	0,27027	0,23109	0,19787	0,16966	0,14568
18	0,49363	0,41552	0,35034	0,29586	0,25025	0,21202	0,17989	0,15286	0,13008
19	0,47464	0,39573	0,33051	0,27651	0,23171	0,19452	0,16354	0,13771	0,11615
20	0,45639	0,37689	0,31180	0,25842	0,21455	0,17846	0,14868	0,12407	0,10371
21	0,43883	0,35894	0,29416	0,24151	0,19866	0,16373	0,13517	0,11178	0,09260
22	0,42196	0,34185	0,27751	0,22571	0,18394	0,15022	0,12288	0,10071	0,08268
23	0,40573	0,32557	0,26180	0,21095	0,17031	0,13782	0,11172	0,09073	0,07383
24	0,39012	0,31007	0,24698	0,19715	0,15770	0,12644	0,10157	0,08175	0,06593
25	0,37512	0,29530	0,23300	0,18425	0,14602	0,11601	0,09234	0,07365	0,05887

TABLE III $a_{\overline{n}|} = \dfrac{1 - v^n}{i}$

n	4%	5%	6%	7%	8%	9%	10%	11%	12%
1	0,9615	0,9524	0,9434	0,9346	0,9259	0,9174	0,9090	0,9009	0,8928
2	1,8861	1,8594	1,8334	1,8080	1,7833	1,7591	1,7355	1,7125	1,6900
3	2,7751	2,7232	2,6730	2,6243	2,5771	2,5312	2,4868	2,4437	2,4018
4	3,6299	3,5460	3,4651	3,3872	3,3121	3,2397	3,1698	3,1024	3,0373
5	4,4518	4,3295	4,2124	4,1002	3,9927	3,8896	3,7907	3,6958	3,6047
6	5,2421	5,0757	4,9173	4,7665	4,6229	4,4859	4,3552	4,2305	4,1114
7	6,0021	5,7864	5,5824	5,3893	5,2064	5,0329	4,8684	4,7121	4,5637
8	6,7327	6,4632	6,2098	5,9713	5,7466	5,5348	5,3349	5,1461	4,9676
9	7,4353	7,1078	6,8017	6,5152	6,2469	5,9952	5,7590	5,5370	5,3282
10	8,1109	7,7217	7,3601	7,0236	6,7101	6,4176	6,1445	5,8892	5,6502
11	8,7605	8,3064	7,8869	7,4987	7,1390	6,8051	6,4950	6,2065	5,9376
12	9,3851	8,8633	8,3838	7,9427	7,5361	7,1607	6,8136	6,4923	6,1943
13	9,9856	9,3636	8,8527	8,3577	7,9038	7,4866	7,1033	6,7498	6,4235
14	10,5631	9,8986	9,2950	8,7455	8,2444	7,7861	7,3666	6,9818	6,6281
15	11,1184	10,3797	9,7122	9,1079	8,5595	8,0606	7,6060	7,1908	6,8108
16	11,6523	10,8378	10,1059	9,4466	8,8514	8,3125	7,8237	7,3791	6,9739
17	12,1657	11,2741	10,4773	9,7632	9,1216	8,5436	8,0215	7,5487	7,1196
18	12,6593	11,6896	10,8276	10,0591	9,3719	8,7556	8,2014	7,7016	7,2496
19	13,1339	12,0853	11,1581	10,3356	9,6036	8,9501	8,3649	7,8392	7,3657
20	13,5903	12,4622	11,4699	10,5940	9,8181	9,1285	8,5135	7,9633	7,4694
21	14,0292	12,8212	11,7641	10,8355	10,0168	9,2922	8,6486	8,0750	7,5620
22	14,4511	13,1630	12,0416	11,0612	10,2007	9,4424	8,7715	8,1757	7,6446
23	14,8568	13,4886	12,3034	11,2722	10,3711	9,5802	8,8832	8,2664	7,7184
24	15,2470	13,7986	12,5504	11,4693	10,5288	9,7066	8,9847	8,3481	7,7843
25	15,6221	14,0939	12,7834	11,6536	10,6748	9,8225	9,0770	8,4217	7,8431

TABLE IV $S_{\overline{n}|} = \dfrac{(1+i)^{n}-1}{i}$

n	4%	5%	6%	7%	8%	9%	10%	11%	12%
1	1,0000	1,0000	1,0000	1,0000	1,0000	1,0000	1,0000	1,0000	1,0000
2	2,0400	2,0500	2,0600	2,0700	2,0800	2,0900	2,1000	2,1100	2,1200
3	3,1216	3,1525	3,1826	3,2149	3,2464	3,2781	3,3100	3,3421	3,3744
4	4,2465	4,3101	4,3746	4,4399	4,5061	4,5731	4,6410	4,7097	4,7793
5	5,4163	5,5256	5,6371	5,7507	5,8666	5,9847	6,1051	6,2278	6,3528
6	6,6330	6,8019	6,9753	7,1533	7,3359	7,5233	7,7156	7,9129	8,1152
7	7,8983	8,1420	8,3938	8,6540	8,9228	9,2004	9,4872	9,7833	10,0890
8	9,2142	9,5491	9,8975	10,2598	10,6366	11,0285	11,4359	11,8594	12,2997
9	10,5828	11,0266	11,4913	11,9780	12,4876	13,0210	13,5795	14,1640	14,7757
10	12,0061	12,5779	13,1808	13,8164	14,4866	15,1929	15,9374	16,7220	17,5487
11	13,4864	14,2068	14,9716	15,7836	16,6455	17,5603	18,5312	19,5614	20,6546
12	15,0258	15,9171	16,8699	17,8885	18,9771	20,1407	21,3843	22,7132	24,1331
13	16,6268	17,7130	18,8821	20,1406	21,4953	22,9534	24,5227	26,2116	28,0291
14	18,2919	19,5986	21,0151	22,5505	24,2149	26,0192	27,9750	30,0949	32,3926
15	20,0236	21,5786	23,2760	25,1290	27,1521	29,3609	31,7725	34,4054	37,2797
16	21,8245	23,6575	25,6725	27,8881	30,3243	33,0034	35,9497	39,1899	42,7533
17	23,6975	25,8404	28,2129	30,8402	33,7502	36,9737	40,5447	44,5008	48,8837
18	25,6454	28,1324	30,9057	33,9990	37,4502	41,3013	45,5992	50,3959	55,7497
19	27,6712	30,5390	33,7600	37,3790	41,4463	46,0185	51,1591	56,9395	63,4397
20	29,7781	33,0660	36,7856	40,9955	45,7620	51,1601	57,2750	64,2028	72,0524
21	31,9692	35,7193	39,9927	44,8652	50,4229	56,7645	64,0025	72,2651	81,6987
22	34,2480	38,5052	43,3923	49,0057	55,4568	62,8733	71,4027	81,2143	92,5026
23	36,6179	41,5305	46,9958	53,4361	60,8933	69,5319	79,5430	91,1479	104,6029
24	39,0826	44,5020	50,8156	58,1767	66,7648	76,7898	88,4973	102,1742	118,1552
25	41,6459	47,7271	54,8645	63,2490	73,1059	84,7009	98,3471	114,4133	133,3339

INDEX